SOCIOLOGY AND THE HEALTH SCIENCES

SOCIOLOGY
and the Health Sciences

PAUL B. HORTON, Ph.D.

Professor of Sociology
Western Michigan University

•

In Consultation with
Dorothy N. Bowers, R.N., B.S.

•

Illustrated by
Frederick J. Ashby

The Blakiston Division
McGRAW-HILL BOOK COMPANY
NEW YORK   LONDON   SYDNEY   TORONTO

SOCIOLOGY AND THE HEALTH SCIENCES

Library of Congress Catalog Card Number: 64-24999

ISBN 07-030421-1

10 11 12 13 14 – M P – 7 6 5 4 3 2

Preface

What should a sociology text intended for use in nursing education try to cover? If it presents material for an introductory sociology course together with a survey of social problems, it becomes either very long or very superficial. This textbook gives only brief attention to sound problems, being largely confined to introductory sociology.

This is not a text in the sociology of medicine or the sociology of nursing. It is my belief that a "sociology for nurses" text should not differ greatly from an introductory sociology text for any other group of students. The principal justification for a separate text lies in the popularity of the two-hour sociology course in nursing education, for which most standard textbooks are too long.

I have found that my own nursing students, crammed with health and illness from morning till night, find a welcome respite in a course dealing with other subjects. Only to a limited extent have I looked to the fields of health and medicine for illustrations of the application of sociological principles. Instructor and students will inevitably explore these areas together. Although each chapter makes only limited reference to the healing arts, the questions following each chapter call upon the student to apply sociological principles to nursing practice.

This volume is a condensed and partially rewritten version of my *Sociology*, of which Chester L. Hunt was co-author (McGraw-Hill Book Company, New York, 1964), that text being written for the college course in introductory sociology. Many paragraphs and sections are identical; others have been condensed, rewritten, or omitted.

Paul B. Horton

Contents

SOCIOLOGY AND THE HEALTH SCIENCES

CHAPTER
1

Fields and Methods
of Sociology

What are the social scientists up to today?

A television camera could show a number of professors lecturing to more or less eager students in more or less stuffy classrooms; experiments being performed in psychological laboratories; two-way communication systems between men and management being installed in large corporations; teams of investigators taking notes in communities like Middletown; social workers making case reports on their rounds; a battery of electronic computers clicking away while they sort cards for public opinion polls; interviewers taking a sample of the unemployment situation in Illinois; sunburned persons in pith helmets asking questions of puzzled natives in New Guinea. Finally, the camera would focus on shelf after shelf of books. . . .

Here in America, 165 million people, scattered over three million square miles of plain, valley, and hillside, form and re-form into numberless groups and organizations, with loyalties and sentiments woven around each. . . . The camera might go on to indicate the many curious methods by which Americans earn their living, or try to offset the boredom of earning a living under machine-age conditions. . . .

This is the field of the social scientists: watching people behave, and searching out the laws which govern their behavior.

Stuart Chase with Edmund de S. Brunner, *The Proper Study of Mankind*, Harper & Row, Publishers, Incorporated, New York, 1956, pp. 19–20.

What will you say when you go home next weekend and your grandmother asks, 'Sociology? Well, what *is* sociology?" If you reply, "Sociology
is the scientific study of human social relationships with special emphasis
on groups and institutions," she may say, "Oh," and you will guess that
she is as confused as you are. If you tell her, "Sociology is the scientific
study of social problems, like race, crime, divorce, et cetera," your definition will give her *some idea* of what sociology is about, and may be
a pretty good answer to give to someone who is unfamiliar with sociology.
But your answer will not be entirely correct, for sociology is much more
than the study of social problems. As a student of sociology, you need
a better definition.

The Field of Sociology

First of all, *forget whatever you have read about sociology in popular
magazines and newspapers,* for most of it is ludicrously inaccurate. When
a magazine writer wishes to make some of his offhand guesswork sound
more impressive, he may preface it with the phrase, "Sociologists fear
that . . . ," "Sociologists are alarmed by . . . ," or "Sociologists are
wringing their hands over. . . ." This journalistic device helps a writer
to speak authoritatively without knowing very much about the subject.
Often a writer sets up his "straw man" by attributing to sociologists the
viewpoints he is about to demolish. For example, one magazine writer
[Bliven, 1960] [1] lists nine developments over which, he says, "the sociologists, of course, are wringing their hands. . . ." Of these nine propositions, six would be flatly rejected by most sociologists, two are marginal,
and only one bears much resemblance to what most sociologists believe.
Such writing makes for colorful journalism, but it caricatures the sociologist as a frustrated do-gooder in a perpetual state of shock over the
mess we are in.

Careless use of the term *sociologist* is also confusing. Magazine and
newspaper writers, social workers, labor leaders, government officials, or
anyone else who is interested in social relations may be described as
sociologist. This is incorrect. A sociologist is one who has earned advanced degrees or pursued other advanced studies in sociology (not in
psychology, theology, social work, or some other field) and is engaged
in teaching, research, or other professional work as a sociologist. No
formal definition of sociology is very satisfactory. Short definitions do
not really define, but long, explicit definitions are usually cumbersome.
Yet a definition of some sort is needed, and sociology is often defined
as *the scientific study of man's social life.* Man behaves differently from

[1] Bracketed references in the text are to sources described in full in the Bibliography at the end
of the book.

Sociology is interested in the way groups interact with one another.

other animals. Man has unique forms of group life, pursues customs, develops institutions, creates values. Sociology applies scientific methods to the study of these phenomena in the search for scientific knowledge. It may be helpful to give some definitions in reverse—to state what sociology is *not*.

Sociology is science, not social philosophy. A science is a body of knowledge, whereas a philosophy is a system of ideas and values. A social philosophy is a set of ideas about how men *ought* to behave and treat one another; a social science studies how they actually *do* behave, without trying to say what they *ought* to do. There are many social philosophies—Christian, Marxian, Buddhist, existentialist, and many others, but there cannot be a "Christian" sociology just as there cannot be a "Christian" biochemistry, astronomy, or mathematics. Many sociologists are Christians, just as many physicists and botanists are Christians. A program of "Christian social action" may make use of sociological knowledge, along with knowledge from medicine, psychology, and other fields. There is a field of "sociology of religion," in which sociological methods are used in studying religious behavior and religious institutions, without either supporting or condemning them. For sociology seeks to be a science, not a set of values or an outline for living.

Sociology seeks knowledge, not social reform. Sociological research sometimes develops knowledge that is useful to social reformers, and some sociologists occasionally change hats and become part-time reformers. But sociology as a field of knowledge is interested in *studying* the society, not in preserving, reforming, or overthrowing it.

Sociology is social science, not socialism. Socialism is a social philosophy with a political program, whereas sociology is a search for scientific knowledge. Socialists sometimes find in sociological research some material they can use in their propaganda; so do Republicans and Democrats. A few sociologists have been socialists; many more have been Republicans or Democrats.

Sociology concentrates its study upon man's group life and the products of his group living. The sociologist is especially interested in the customs, traditions, and values that emerge from group living, and in the way group living is in turn affected by these customs, traditions, and values.

Sociology is interested in the way groups interact with one another and in the processes and institutions they develop. Sociology is subdivided into many specialized fields, of which a partial list includes:

Communication and public opinion	Social disorganization
Criminology	Social psychology
Demography (population)	Social stratification
The family	Sociological theory
Industrial sociology	Sociology of the arts
Medical sociology	Sociology of complex organizations
Methodology of social research	Sociology of education
Occupational sociology	Sociology of law
Political sociology	Sociology of religion
Race and ethnic relations	Sociology of small groups
Rural sociology	

These topics are not the exclusive property of sociology, for other fields share our interest in them. For example, our interest in communication and public opinion is shared by psychology and political science; criminology is shared with psychology, political science, law, and police science, and so on. No science can fence itself off from other sciences, least of all sociology. We are especially close to psychology and anthropology, with which we overlap so constantly that any firm boundaries would be arbitrary and unrealistic. The more we learn about man's behavior, the more we realize that no one field of knowledge can fully explain him.

Observation—the Basic Technique of Scientific Method

All science is based upon verifiable evidence. What is evidence and where is it found? Evidence consists of verifiable facts of all kinds and is found through scientific observation. But "scientific observation" is not the same as "looking at things." Each of us has been looking at things all his life, but this does not make him a scientific observer, any more than a lifetime of swatting flies makes one an entomologist. Wherein does scientific observation differ from looking at things?

Accuracy. Scientific observation is accurate. The scientific observer is extremely careful to make certain that things are as he describes them. The statement, "My back yard is full of dead trees," is of uncertain accuracy unless the trees have been examined by an expert to be sure they are dead and not merely dormant. Or the statement, "Families are larger than they used to be," is of low accuracy. *What* size families, and *where*, are more numerous than they were *when?* If we say, "The proportion of American families with four or more children has grown substantially in the past decade," the statement is more accurate. Painstaking checking, rechecking, and cross-checking to produce carefully stated propositions are the price of scientific accuracy.

Precision. Scientific observation is precise. The statement, "My back yard is full of dead trees," is not precise, even though it may be accurate. What is meant by "full of" dead trees? If the sentence reads, "All the trees in my yard are dead," or, "There are twenty dead trees in my yard," the statement gains in precision. Accuracy refers to the truth or correctness of a statement; precision refers to degree or measurement. If the above statement about family size is revised to read, "The proportion of American families with four or more children increased from 6.6 per cent of all families in 1948 to 11.0 per cent in 1963," it becomes more precise.

In a laboratory experiment the scientist weighs, measures, counts, or times each development with great care. A report that says, "I took some hot salt water, added a pinch of copper sulfate and a little nitric acid, let it cool for a while . . ." would be almost useless. How much water? How hot? How much salt, copper sulfate, and acid? Cooled for how long and to what temperature? Unless quite precise, an observation is of limited value to science.

Since scientific writing seeks precision, science avoids colorful or extravagant language. Whereas literature aims to arouse the feelings of the reader, science aims to convey accurate information. Literary writing may be intentionally vague, imprecise, and fanciful, stimulating the reader to wonder what is meant (e.g., whether Hamlet was really insane). The dramatic sweep of the novelist and the provocative imagery of the poet have no place in scientific writing. Yet good scientific writing need not be dull, and should never plod through an insufferable mass of ill-arranged detail. Good scientific writing is clear, is easily understood by a qualified reader, and derives its suspense from a readable procession of significant facts and interpretations.

How much precision is needed depends on what we are studying. In measuring atoms, for instance, a millionth of an inch may be too large an error, whereas at an agricultural experiment station a variation of several feet may be unimportant. A social scientist might observe the behavior of a mob of "several hundred" persons without counting them, just as an entomologist can describe a "large" swarm of bees without counting them. Science, however, always seeks as much precision as the particular problem requires. If the conditions of observation make this degree of precision impossible, the scientist must suspend judgment until more precise observations can be collected.

System. Scientific observation is systematic. A scientific investigation defines a problem, then draws up an organized plan for collecting facts about it. Suppose the question is, "How does the drop-out rate of college students who marry while in college compare with the drop-out rate of unmarried students?" One might try to answer the question by simply recalling the students he has known; but this sample would be small, it might not be typical, and one's memory is imperfect. Conclusions based on casual recollections are not very reliable. If our research plan calls for a systematic check on the college records of several thousand students, then our drop-out rates for single and married students are based on dependable factual data, not on chance recollection and guesswork. Unless these data have been collected as part of an organized systematic program of scientific observation, they are likely to be spotty and incomplete. Anecdotes, personal recollections, offhand opinions, and impressions gained while traveling may suggest a hypothesis that is worth testing; but no scientist would base a conclusion upon such data.

Records. Scientific observation is *recorded*. Man's memory is notoriously fallible. Data that are not recorded are not dependable. No laboratory scientist would attempt to memorize a detailed experiment. He writes it out completely, recording each operation and reaction, so that his procedures and findings can be accurately known and verified by other scientists.

In the field of human behavior, the need for recorded observation is less fully realized. Suppose a professor were to say, "A number of women students have majored in this field, and although some do excellent work, on the average they don't quite measure up to the men students in this field." What, exactly, is the professor saying? Unless he has actually recorded and computed average scores for both groups, he is in effect saying, "I have mentally recalled the grades of hundreds of my students, have mentally added the scores and mentally computed averages for male and female students, and have found the female average to be lower." Obviously his feat of memory would be impossible. All conclusions based on the recollection of a mass of unrecorded data are untrustworthy.

In fact, such conclusions based on informal recollection may be worse than useless, for they generally are the observer's prejudices masquerading as scientific conclusions. Since memory is imperfect, we often "remember" things the way we prefer them to have been, rather than as they actually were. Prejudice, wishful thinking, and habitual attitude all operate to twist our observations to fit our preferences. It is important, therefore, that evidence be recorded as quickly as possible, before our prejudices, preferences, and afterthoughts have had time to distort it. The following accounts of a disaster as reported by one of the survivors show the progressive changes made by time.

Men's memories of themselves aren't accurate. One month after the sinking of the Litch I questioned the survivors for a second time. The stories had altered— in some cases radically. When the ship blew up it was honorable and acceptable to save one's own skin. Later, as we got closer to civilization and normal society, many men remembered something new, how they had struggled to save others at the risk of their own lives.

My notes on a signalman, made ten minutes after he was rescued, read, "After I jumped over, I swam as fast as I could, I swam upwind like you always told us. I had no life jacket and got scared. I saw someone floating with his head under water. It was Mr.———. His back was broken; I could tell by the funny way it angled just below the neck. I said to myself if he's dead there's no use in his wasting the life jacket. I took the jacket from him and held on to it. I don't know what happened to Mr. ———'s body."

When I interviewed the same man a month later he told me this: "I swam from the ship as fast as I could. I swam upwind just like you always told us. I saw someone floating with his head under water. It was Mr. ———. Although his back was broken and his head had been submerged, I figured maybe the doctor could do something for him. I pulled his head out of the water and tied the jacket tie under his chin so that his head'd stay in the air. I trod water for about an hour, just holding onto Mr. ———'s life jacket for a rest occasionally. I saw a raft about five hundred yards away. I thought maybe the doctor or a hospital corpsman might be on it. I swam over to it. The doctor wasn't there. We paddled over to where Mr. ——— had been, but there was no sign of him."

I met the signalman on the street in Washington a couple of months ago— five years after the Litch sank. His story had changed more. Now it was he, the signalman, who had the life jacket. When he saw that Mr. ——— had a broken back, the signalman removed his life jacket and gave it to the injured officer. "I knew he was dead, but figured maybe there was a chance in a thousand he might be saved. It was my duty to try to help him, so I gave him my jacket."

William J. Lederer, *All the Ships at Sea,* William Morrow and Company, Inc., New York, 1950, pp. 203–204. Reprinted by permission of William Sloane Associates.

Objectivity. Scientific observation is *objective.* This means that, in so far as is humanly possible, the observation is unaffected by the observer's own beliefs, preferences, wishes, or values. In other words, *objectivity means the ability to see and accept facts as they are, not as one might wish them to be.* It is fairly easy to be objective when observing something about which we have no preferences or values. It is fairly easy to study objectively the mating practices of the fruit fly, but less easy to view the mating practices of the human being with objective detachment. On any matter where our emotions, beliefs, habits, and values are involved, we are likely to "see" whatever agrees with our emotional needs and values. Few Americans, for example, could record a detailed description of the workings of the polygamous family system without including many words and phrases that would betray their disapproval. If a set of scientific observations is reported objectively, the reader will be unable to know whether the observer likes or dislikes what he has reported.

Yet many experiments have shown that even our simplest observations are affected by our feelings and expectations. For example, in one investigation [Harvey, 1953] most observers judged a white disk imprinted with the name "Eisenhower" to be larger than disks of the same size with random names from the phone book; poor children generally estimated the size of coins to be larger than children from prosperous homes; and a leaf-shaped piece of green cloth was judged to be greener than a donkey-shaped piece of the same cloth.

Many questions that should be clear-cut scientific questions arouse violent controversy because we find it hard to be objective or even to be sure *when we are* being objective. The question, "Does cigarette smoking cause lung cancer?" is not an impossibly difficult scientific question, yet each new study provokes bitter emotional reaction. The data are not yet entirely conclusive, leaving a free field for the biases of every interested party. The tobacco industry, which can draw a mountain of conclusion from a molehill of scientific evidence when preparing advertising claims, persistently reminds us that we need more evidence before drawing conclusions on *this* question. Cigarette smokers with an appetite to defend are also practicing their newly discovered habit of withholding judgment until more data are available. Some ardent battlers against the cigarette hail each new study as final proof of what they have known all along. On this question, few are disinterested and few can be fully objective.

To be objective is perhaps the most taxing of all scientific obligations. It is not enough to be willing to see facts as they are. One must also know what his biases are if he is to guard against them. A bias is simply a tendency, usually unconscious, to see facts in a certain way because of our wishes, interests, and values. Thus in a racial incident one observer "sees" a white person insulting or abusing a Negro, while another observer "sees" a Negro acting presumptuously and provocatively. One observer sees American Negroes courageously asserting their democratic rights, while another sees them foolishly "asking for trouble."

Seldom are "the facts" so undebatable that bias does not distort them. Our perception is selective; we see and remember those facts which support our beliefs and overlook the others. Many experiments have shown that most people who observe a social situation will see and hear only what they expect to see and hear. If what we expect to see is not there, we see it anyway! This is dramatically shown in a famous experiment [Allport and Postman, 1945] in which observers were shown a picture of a roughly dressed white man holding an open razor and arguing violently with a well-dressed Negro who was shown in an apologetic, conciliatory posture; then the observers were asked to describe the scene. Some of them "saw" the razor in the Negro's hand, where they expected it to be.

Then, in passing on a description of the scene (A described it to B, who described it to C, and so on), the account soon had the razor in the Negro's hand, where it "belonged." Even though they were not emotionally involved in the situation, had ample time to study it, and were making a conscious effort to be accurate in what they saw and reported or heard, the observers' unconscious biases still led many of them to "see" or "hear" a fact that wasn't there.

If the student is inclined to doubt that people often see and hear what they expect to see and hear, let him try a simple experiment. At a party, greet each arriving guest with a broad smile, a hearty handshake, and a murmured, "Pity to see you here this evening," and speed each departing guest with, "Glad you must leave so early!" Many will hear what they expect to hear, not what was actually spoken. This is why, if one's biases tell him that Negroes are lazy, Jews are pushy, businessmen are crooked, and musicians are temperamental, he will seldom see anything that disagrees with these expectations. Bias is like a sieve that allows to pass through it only what is supposed to pass through. Bias screens out our perceptions, generally admitting to our consciousness only those perceptions that agree with the biases.

Some common threats, then, to objectivity are vested interest, habit, and bias. Objectivity does not come easily, but it can be learned. One can become more objective as he becomes aware of his biases and makes allowance for them. Through rigorous training in scientific methodology, through studying many experiments and noting many examples of objective and nonobjective uses of data, an observer may eventually develop some ability to cut through many layers of self-deception and to perceive facts with a greater degree of scientific objectivity. The scientist also has another powerful ally—the criticism of his fellows. The scientist publishes his work so that it may be checked by other scientists who may not share his biases and who come to the problem with a different point of view. This process of publication and criticism means that shoddy work is soon exposed, and the scientist who lets his bias dictate his uses of data is pilloried by his fellows.

Trained Observation. Scientific observations are made by *trained observers*. A billion people watch the sun and the moon sweep across the sky, but more sophisticated observers possess certain knowledge that tells them that is not exactly what happens. The untrained observer does not know what to look for or how to interpret it. He does not know the pitfalls that lead to inaccurate observation; nor is he fully aware of the tricks his own limitations and biases may play on him. Startling reports of weird phenomena generally come from uneducated, unsophisticated persons, and are discounted by the experts. When some remarkable observations are reported, the scientist will want to know: (1) What is the observer's general level of education and sophistication? Is he a member of a superstition-ridden folk group, or of a well-informed and somewhat skeptical population? Ghosts, spells, magic, and other supernatural happenings are very real to some groups but an amusing absurdity to others. (2) What is his special knowledge or training in this particular field? Does he have the knowledge to know whether this event has a perfectly natural explanation? Thus the biologist among the ship's passengers is less likely to see a sea monster than are the members of the crew, and the meteorologist sees fewer flying saucers than do people with no special knowledge of atmospheric phenomena.

The recent Bridey Murphy case shows the fruits of amateur investigation. A Colorado businessman who dabbled in hypnotism drew from a hypnotized housewife a fascinating account of her earlier life as Bridey Murphy in Ireland over a hundred years ago. This tale aroused great interest, became a best-selling book [Bernstein, 1956] syndicated in over forty newspapers, and stimulated a rash of books and articles on hypnotism, reincarnation, and occult topics. If this businessman had been a trained psychologist, he would have known that almost any hypnotized subject in a deep trance will babble freely about earlier incarnations (or future incarnations) if asked about them. A trained observer would have checked the childhood experiences and associations of this housewife to see whether she might be dredging up childhood recollections while in a trance. When the checking was done by less gullible observers, the Bridey Murphy affair promptly collapsed [Gardner, 1957, chap. 26]. Most sensational tales of weird phenomena would promptly be spiked by natural explanations if a scientifically trained observer were present.

Many events happen without any scientific observer on the sidelines. If each sea monster broke water before a panel of ichthyologists, each ghost materialized before the searching gaze of psychologists, and each revolution were staged before a team of visiting sociologists, our knowledge would be far more complete. But for many phenomena, the only reports we have are the casual impressions of untrained observers who happen to be there; these reports may be interesting and possibly useful, but they must be interpreted most cautiously by scientists.

Controlled Conditions. Scientific observation is conducted under *controlled conditions*. Laboratories are popular with scientists because they are handy places to control heat, light, pressure, time intervals, or whatever is important. We have a scientific experiment when we *control all variables except one*, then see what happens when that one is varied. Unless all variables except one have been controlled, we cannot be sure which variable has produced the results. For example, if we wish to study the effects of phosphates on plant growth, all other factors—seed, soil, water, sunlight, temperature, humidity—must be the same for all the sample plots; then the varying amounts of phosphates on different test plots can be held responsible for different growth rates. This is the basic technique in all scientific experimentation—allow one variable to vary while holding all other variables constant.

Failure to control all variables is a common error in scientific method and accounts for most false conclusions. For example, the promotion of antihistamines as a cold cure a few years ago was based on several experiments in which half the patients reporting with cold symptoms were given an antihistamine pill, while the other half were given a blank pill that contained no medicine. This latter half were the "control group," used as a base for measuring the effectiveness of the new pill upon the test group. The findings were encouraging, with many more of the test group reporting that their colds had gone away. These findings were enthusiastically and uncritically reported in popular magazines, and dozens of "cold-stopper" manufacturers climbed on the gold-filled bandwagon.

These experiments were honestly conducted, but further research disclosed a serious error in method. Although the men reporting for treatment believed they were all getting the same pill, the physician knew which pill each man received. Thus when the man made his before-and-after reports to the physician, the unconscious bias of the physician apparently led him to shade the reports in the direction that would support the findings he hoped to get. When a national test of the Salk polio vaccine was arranged some time later, safeguards were erected to guard against the unconscious bias of the persons conducting the experiment. Identical-looking doses of vaccine and of placebos were numbered and recorded in a secret code book, so that neither the patients nor the physicians giving the injections and reporting each case had any way of knowing which way to shade their reports. This meant that we could *know* that the findings were due to the vaccine and not to unconscious bias. Deliberate dishonesty is exceedingly rare among serious scientists, but unconscious bias is a constant hazard, requiring research controls that make it more difficult for bias to operate.

Since laboratories are such convenient places to control the conditions of observation, scientists use them whenever possible. But much that is important cannot be dragged into a laboratory. Volcanic eruptions and earthquakes cannot be staged in a test tube; nor can we study the courtship process very realistically by herding some couples into a laboratory. Both the physical and the social scientists frequently must observe phenomena in their natural setting. Techniques may range from lowering a bathysphere to the ocean floor to giving a questionnaire to a group of army recruits. If we remember that the basic scientific procedure is the conducting of accurate observations, while laboratories, instruments, and

IBM cards are merely *tools* of observation, this difference in technique will not confuse us.

Since many phenomena must be observed in their natural setting, and often are reported by untrained observers, the scientist is especially interested in knowing the conditions under which the event was observed. Was the observer an interested bystander or an emotionally involved participant? Was he calm, relaxed, and comfortable, or was he excited, terrified, exhausted, hunger-crazed, or otherwise incapable of accurate observation? What were the lighting conditions and other visual circumstances? It is not surprising that sailors, traditionally a highly superstitious group who often suffered prolonged isolation, danger, hunger, thirst, and exhaustion, should have peered through ocean spray or evening haze and seen enticing mermaids and terrifying monsters that other observers have been unable to verify.

The scientific critic will trust a reported observation only in so far as the conditions of observation have been controlled. On this basis, science is skeptical of the claims of spiritualism and mind reading. A spiritualist can conduct a very convincing seance in his own stage setting, but spiritualists are loath to attempt a seance where the room, furnishings, and lighting are controlled by the scientists. The professional mind reader is very convincing in a theater setting, but unwilling to attempt a reading under scientifically controlled conditions. Until spiritualists and mind readers are willing to make demonstrations under conditions that preclude the possibility of deception, scientists will dismiss the one as a fraud and the other as entertainment.

In these several respects, then, scientific observation differs from looking at things. We spend our lives looking at things, and doing so brings us much information, many impressions, and numerous conclusions. But these conclusions are clouded by accident of coincidence, by selective memory, and by personal bias. Therefore, before accepting any generalization as true, the critical observer wants to know upon what it is based. Is the conclusion based on a systematically collected body of scientific evidence, or is it an offhand reaction to haphazard observation?

Steps in Scientific Research

The scientific method (some would prefer to say scientific methods) includes a great deal. The scientist must accumulate all the background information he can find on the problem. After much study and observation, he formulates a *hypothesis.* This is a carefully considered theoretical statement that seeks to relate all the known facts in a logical manner. The hypothesis is then tested by scientific research. For example, the hypothesis that cancer is a virus disease is based upon a great deal of observation; it relates known facts in a logical manner and is now being tested through many research projects. Eventually a hypothesis is confirmed, rejected, or revised, and in this manner a science grows.

There are several steps in scientific research. They are easy to list but not always easy to follow.

1. _Formulate the problem,_ that is, finds a problem of some apparent scientific importance and define it so that it can be studied scientifically. Suppose the question arises whether fraternity membership is a hindrance to academic success. Our hypothesis might be, "Fraternity members receive lower average grades than otherwise comparable nonmembers."

2. _Plan the research design,_ outlining just what is to be studied, what data will be sought, and where and how they will be collected, processed and analyzed. In the above example we would need to decide how to select and match the samples of fraternity members and nonmembers, where to secure data on the grades, and what mechanical and statistical procedures to use in analyzing these data and in arriving at conclusions.

3. _Collect the data_ in accordance with the research design. Often it will be necessary to change the design to meet some unforeseen difficulty.

4. _Analyze the data._ Tabulate, classify, compare, and process the data, making whatever tests and computations are necessary to help find the results.

5. _Draw conclusions._ Was the original hypothesis confirmed or rejected? Or were the results inconclusive? What has this research added to our knowledge? What implications has it for sociological theory? What new questions and suggestions for further research have arisen from this investigation?

Sociology as a Science

Science may be defined in at least two ways: (1) as a body of organized, verified knowledge secured through scientific investigation; (2) as a method of study whereby a body of organized, verified knowledge is discovered. These are, of course, two ways of saying much the same thing.

If this first definition is accepted, then sociology is a science _to the extent that it develops a body of organized, verified knowledge_ based on scientific investigation. To the extent that sociology forsakes myth, folklore, and wishful thinking and bases its conclusions on scientific evidence, it is a science. If science is defined as a method of study, then sociology is a science _to the extent that it uses scientific methods of study._ All natural phenomena can be studied scientifically if one is willing to use scientific methods. Any kind of behavior—whether of atoms, animals, or adolescents—is a proper field for scientific study.

During most of man's history, few of his actions were based on verified knowledge, for man through the ages has been guided mainly by folklore, habit, and guesswork. Until a few centuries ago, very few accepted the idea that man should find out about the natural world by systematically observing the natural world itself, rather than by consulting his oracles, ancestors, or intuition. This new idea created the modern world. A few decades ago, man began acting on the idea that this same approach might also give useful knowledge about his social life. Just how far he has replaced folklore with knowledge in this area will be explored in the chapters that follow.

The Methods of Sociological Research

The methods of sociological research are basically those used by all scientists. As the great Karl Pearson [1900, p. 12] has remarked, "The unity of all science consists alone in its method, not in its material. The man who classifies facts of any kind whatever, who sees their mutual relation and describes their sequences, is applying the scientific method and is a man of science."

While scientific methods are basically alike for all sciences, scientific *techniques* differ, for techniques are the particular ways in which scientific methods are applied to a particular problem. Each science must, therefore, develop a series of techniques to fit the body of material it studies. What are some of the techniques of sociological research?

Cross-sectional, Longitudinal, and Ex Post Facto Studies. Every study has some sort of time setting. A study that limits its observations to a single point in time is called a *cross-sectional* study. For example, Bossard and Sanger [1952] made an intensive study of one hundred large families to see how they differed from small families at that time in the United States. If the study extends over time, describing a trend or making a before-and-after set of observations, it is called a *longitudinal* study. Thus Campbell and McCormack [1957] sought to find out whether military training develops authoritarian attitudes. They gave an authoritarian scale (a questionnaire designed to measure authoritarian attitudes) to Air Force cadets at the beginning of Air Force training and repeated the test a year later. Contrary to expectation, the retest showed authoritarian attitudes to be lower than the original test. While a single study on a rather small sample is not conclusive, this study points up the danger of simply assuming that military training produces authoritarian personalities.

An *ex post facto* study seeks to trace a present situation back to some earlier factors that may have been involved. For example Glick [1957, p. 112] compared divorcees with married persons as to their age at marriage and found divorce among those married before the age of eighteen to be almost three times as common as among those marrying between the ages of twenty-two and twenty-four. A great deal of sociological research is of the ex post facto sort.

Planned Experiments. All sciences use planned experiments. The concept of the experiment is simple: hold all variables constant except one; cause it to vary and see what happens. Do we want to know whether vitamin X will prevent colds? We need two groups, a test group and a control group, who are alike in all other significant respects—income, education, occupation, diet, health habits, general health level, or anything else suspected of being related to colds. The test group takes vitamin X while the control group takes placebos (dummy pills), without knowing which they are getting; then any differences in cold incidence must be due to vitamin X.

There are two common ways of setting up test and control groups. One is the matched-pair technique. For each person in the test group, another person like him in all important variables (such as age, religion, education, occupation, or anything important to this research) is found and placed in the control group. Another technique is to make statistically random assignments of persons to test and control groups—such as assigning the first person to the test group, the next to the control group, and so on. Suppose we wish to measure the effectiveness of an experimental treatment program for delinquents in a reformatory. Using one technique, we would match each delinquent who received the experimental treatment (test group) with another delinquent, matched for all other variables thought important, who received only the usual treatment (control group). Using the other technique, every second (or third, or tenth) delinquent would be assigned to the experimental group upon arrival at the reformatory, with the others becoming the control group. Wherever the researcher is permitted to make assignments in this way, the random-assignment technique is far easier and at least as accurate; but often when the research situation precludes this technique, the matched-pair technique may be used.

Sometimes the research situation provides ready-made test and control groups. For example, during World War II there was some debate over whether it was more efficient to use Negro troops in segregated or in mixed units. A few experimental units were organized with Negro platoons within white infantry companies. Some time later a sample of servicemen were asked how they would feel about serving in such a mixed outfit. As shown in Figure 1, it was found that the servicemen who actually served in mixed companies offered the least objection, while those in divisions with no mixed companies were the most unfavorable. In other words those who were nearest to the mixed companies were the most

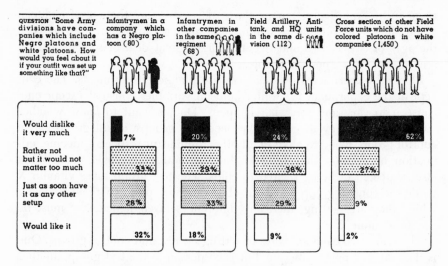

FIGURE 1 Attitudes toward Serving in a Company Containing Negro and White Platoons among Men Who Have Done So and Men Who Have Not (*Europe, June, 1945*).

SOURCE: Reproduced from Samuel A. Stouffer et al., *Studies in Social Psychology in World War II,* vol. 1, *The American Soldier: Adjustment during Army Life,* Princeton University Press, Princeton, N.J., 1949, p. 594.

favorable. And while most of those in mixed companies had objected strongly *before* their organization, they offered the least objection after having actual experience in a mixed company. This experiment clearly showed that a great change in attitudes took place as a result of enforced contacts.

These research findings formed the basis for the decision to end segregation in the armed services. As a result, the armed services now have much less racial "trouble," and are making far more efficient use of Negro troops [Nichols, 1954]. We see from this example that a planned experiment in the social sciences can provide knowledge that is useful in the making of practical social policy.

Planned experiments in sociology face certain difficulties. An experiment involving thousands of people may be prohibitively expensive. It may take many years to complete an experiment. Our values prohibit using people for any experiments that might injure them. When people are unwilling to cooperate in an experiment, we cannot force them to do so (although we may occasionally trick them into unconscious cooperation). Furthermore, when people realize they are experimental subjects, they begin to act differently, and the experiment may be spoiled. Almost any kind of experiment upon people *who know they are being studied* will give some interesting findings that may vanish soon after the experiment is ended. This illustrates how the findings of many experiments are due to the attention the subjects are getting, not to the factor being tested.

Planned experiments on human subjects are most reliable when these subjects do not know the true object of the experiment. They may be given a rationale, a reasonable explanation of what the experimenter is doing, and this rationale may be a harmless but necessary deception concealing the true purpose of the experiment. For example, an experiment to determine the effect of background music on work output in a factory might be explained as a trial to see whether workers *like* the music.

Because of all these limitations, social sciences (excepting psychology) make limited use of planned experiments. We use them wherever practical, but depend more heavily on other techniques.

Observational Studies. Observational studies are like planned experiments in all respects except one: in the planned experiment the scientist arranges for something to happen so that he can observe what follows, whereas in the observational study the scientist observes something that happens, or that has already happened, by itself. Both rely on systematic observation under controlled conditions in a search for verifiable sequences and relationships. Both are used in all of the sciences, but the procedures for using them vary according to the material being studied. The types of studies that follow are not mutually exclusive, for a study may use several different techniques.

Impressionistic Studies. These are informal descriptive and analytic accounts based on observations that are less fully controlled than in more formal studies. Suppose a sociologist with a special interest in the family makes a tour of Russia. He is eager for information on the Russian family, asks questions about family life of most of the people he meets, scans the papers and magazines for their pictures of family life. He returns home with some very definite impressions of Russian family life, but they are not based on a systematic, scientifically controlled investigation—on an orderly search of the published literature, on scientifically constructed sample of informants, and so on. If he is a responsible scholar, he will state his impressions as *impressions,* not as scientifically established conclusions.

No matter how elaborate, carefully planned, and systematically conducted a study may be, if the recorded data consist of the impressions of the observer, it is classed as an impressionistic study. Thus the Lynds [1929, 1937] spent many months in "Middletown" (Muncie, Indiana); they systematically searched the newspaper files, interviewed virtually everyone who held a position of authority or was locally said to be important, and participated in community life. They ended up with a large mass of highly perceptive impressions—probably accurate but largely unverifiable except through long and costly research.

Impressionistic studies are highly useful in social science. They provide many hypotheses and research leads and suggest many insights that might be overlooked by other methods. The best of the impressionistic studies hold an honored place in sociological literature.

Statistical Comparative Studies. If everything that can be found through an experiment is already written down somewhere, it is sensible to look up the record. Much sociological research consists of looking up recorded statistical facts and comparing and interpreting them. For a simple example consider the question "Now that women have greater freedom to lead an interesting and independent life without marriage, are more women remaining single?" The answer is easily derived from census data, which show the proportion of single women dropping from 24.3 per cent in 1890 to 18.2 per cent in 1963. (These figures give the percentage of all American women fourteen years or older who had never been married at the moment of survey, with correction for changes in the age distribution of the population.) Many such questions can be answered quickly by checking data in the annual *Statistical Abstract of the United States,* which summarizes statistics collected by many governmental and other agencies and is available in nearly any library. Other questions may require study of more specialized statistical sources, such as the many *Special Reports* issued by the Bureau of the Census.

Many research questions involve a comparison of several kinds of statistical data from several sources. For example, Lander [1954] was concerned about the relation between juvenile delinquency and overcrowded, substandard housing. From court records he compiled delinquency rates for 155 census districts in Baltimore, and from census data he found the average number of persons per room and the percentage of officially substandard housing units for each census district. He found that delinquency rates closely followed rates of overcrowding and substandard housing, but that this association disappeared when he controlled the other variables such as race, income, education, and occupation. However, he found one variable—home ownership—which remained highly associated when all others were controlled. He concluded that home ownership was an index of family stability and that this connection helped explain the lower delinquency rates in areas of high home ownership.

Sometimes the research scholar must go out and collect the raw statistical data to clarify a problem. For example, consider the question "Why are some marriages happier than others?" Research studies of many kinds have sought the answer to this question. In each of two especially interesting studies, a sample of several hundred married couples was divided into several groups of differing degrees of marital happiness or unhappiness; then these groups were compared with one another on dozens of points. One of these studies centered on the circumstances preceding the marriage of the couple—age at marriage, length of courtship and engagement, education completed, approval or disapproval of marriage by parents, employment history, and dozens more. This study [Burgess and Cottrell, 1939] found that the happily and unhappily married groups differed strikingly in many of these background circumstances. The other study [Terman, 1938] compared the personality characteristics of happily and unhappily married informants and found marked personality differences between the two groups.

Many people "have no use for statistics." But often it is because they don't understand them. Statistics, like shotguns, are dangerous when handled by the ignorant, as is shown in Huff's entertaining little book *How to Lie with Statistics* [1954]. Those who know the uses and abuses of statistics realize that statistics are nothing more and nothing less than *organized measured facts*. They are as trustworthy or untrustworthy as the scientific method of the person who compiles them. To reject statistics is but a way of rejecting facts.

Sociologists make a great many comparative statistical studies. Since almost any kind of research is likely to involve statistical organization and comparison of facts at some point or other, the sociologist must be something of a statistician, and the citizen who hopes to be intelligently aware of the world he lives in must have some understanding of statistical interpretation.

Questionnaire and Interview Studies. Sometimes the facts we need are not recorded anywhere, and we can find them only by asking people. For example, what is the "ideal-size family" in the eyes of American young people? This question has some importance for population prediction, business planning, educational planning, and many other purposes. We can find the answer only by asking people what they think is the ideal size for a family. Questionnaire and interview studies are systematic ways of asking questions under scientific controls. A questionnaire is filled out by the informant himself; an interview schedule is filled out by a trained interviewer who asks the questions of the informant. Both methods have their pitfalls, which the trained sociologist should be able to avoid. It is fairly easy to get purely factual information quite accurately (e.g., "Do you own or rent your home?" "Have you a car?"), but surveys of attitudes and opinions have greater margins of error. The informants may not understand the question; they may pick an answer even though they do not have a firm opinion on the matter; they may give an "acceptable" answer rather than the real one; or they may be swayed by the way the question is worded. A survey may also give false conclusions because the sample of persons surveyed is not a representative cross section of the population. Questionnaire and interview studies, like other research, methods, must be used by trained scholars who are aware of their pit-falls.

Even though questionnaire and interview studies have a margin of error, they may still be useful, for they are more reliable than guesswork. For example, after victory over Germany in 1944, the Army had more men in uniform than were needed. *Which* men should be demobilized? This was an explosive question, with grave morale consequences. The Army made a questionnaire study [Stouffer, 1949, chap. 11] in which several thousand servicemen were asked:

> After the war when the Army starts releasing soldiers back to civilian life, which of these two groups of men do you think should be released first? (Check only one.)
> —— Men with dependents
> or
> —— Men over 30 years of age

This question was repeated several times with various pairings of over-seas service, combat experience, length of time in service, age, and num-ber dependents. Responses showed that the largest number of servicemen would give first priority to men who had seen combat, next priority to married men with children, and so on. Using these responses, the Army developed a point system for determining eligibility for discharge. That this approach was a highly practical one is shown by the fact that the discharge policy of the Army proceeded with very little criticism or re-sentment, either from servicemen or from civilians.

Participant-Observer Studies. No man can ever fully know what it feels like to be a mother; nor can any civilian completely understand army life. Some things can be fully understood only by experiencing them. The *participant-observer* seeks insight by taking part himself in whatever he is studying. If he wishes to understand labor unions, he will join one, work in the shop, attend the union meetings, and possibly become a minor union official or a union organizer. If he wishes to study a religious

The participant-observer seeks insight by taking part himself.

sect, he will join it and seek to share in its worship. Through his own participation, together with the opportunity for very intimate observation, he may gain insights that no amount of external observation would provide.

At the height of the flying-saucer craze an interesting cult arose in a Midwestern American city. A small group of believers received certain "revelations" that the earth would soon be destroyed and that only a faithful few would be rescued by flying saucers and carried to a friendly planet. Several participant-observers joined the group, concealing their professional identities, and took part in its activities until it dissolved some months later [Festinger, 1956]. In another instance a white novelist [Griffin, 1961] was commissioned by a Negro magazine to make a participant-observer study of Negro life. With his hair trimmed short and his skin darkened by a drug, he traveled about the South, where everyone identified him as a Negro. Although he was a native Southerner, he found that his view of Negro life from the inside carried many surprising revelations.

There are pitfalls in this technique. The participant-observer may become so emotionally involved that he loses his objectivity. Or he may overgeneralize; that is, he may assume that what he finds in the group he studies is also true of all other groups. Since his data are largely impressionistic, his conclusions are not easily verified. Yet the participant-observer studies have given us many insights and have also suggested many hypotheses for further study.

The *eyewitness account* is an amateur, small-scale participant-observer study. How do people act after a disaster such as a tornado or an explosion? What happens at a religious revival, a riot, a picket-line disturbance? Rarely is there a visiting sociologist, pencil in hand, ready to record the event. Social scientists often seek eyewitness accounts from persons who were there. A detailed eyewitness account, collected as soon as possible after the event, is a useful source of information. Such accounts must be used with care, for the eyewitness is usually an untrained observer, and his own excitement or involvement may have impaired his accuracy and objectivity. Yet the eyewitness account is a priceless source of data for the social scientist.

Case Studies. The case study is a complete, detailed account of some phenomenon. It may be a life history of a person, or a complete account of a brief event. The case history of a group—a family, a clique, a union, a religious movement—may suggest some insights into group behavior. An accurate, detailed account of a riot, a panic, an orgy, a disaster, or any social event may have scientific value. An unhappy family, a happy family, a community, an organization—almost any phenomenon can be studied by the case-study technique.

Perhaps the greatest value of the case study is in the suggestion of hypotheses that can then be tested by other methods. Most of our reliable knowledge about juvenile delinquency, for instance, has developed through the testing of hypotheses that were suggested by early case studies of delinquents [Thomas, 1923; Shaw, 1931]. Much of our present knowledge of personality disorganization stems from hypotheses suggested by a classic collection of case studies in Thomas and Znaniecki's *The Polish Peasant in Europe and America* [1927]. These hypotheses are not often *tested* by the case-study method.

A generalization cannot be based on a single case, for a case can be found to "prove" almost anything. Generalizations must be based on a large mass of carefully processed data, and the collection of a great many case studies is expensive. Also, it is difficult to "add up" a number of case studies or to compute averages or apply other statistical measures. Therefore we seldom use case studies when seeking to test a hypothesis. But after the hypothesis has been tested and we have arrived at some sound generalizations, a good case study may give a beautiful illustration of these generalizations. For example, there is conclusive evidence that juvenile delinquency is closely associated with unsatisfactory family life [Glueck and Glueck, 1959]. A case study showing how unsastisfactory family life has apparently encouraged delinquency in a particular family makes a vivid illustration of this generalization [Shaw, 1938].

Pure and Applied Sociology

A distinction between pure and applied science is drawn in every scientific field. *Pure science* is the search for knowledge, without much concern for its practical use. *Applied science* is the search for ways of using scientific knowledge to solve practical problems. A biochemist who seeks to learn how a cell absorbs food or how a cell ages and grows old is working as a pure scientist. If he then tries to find some substance or procedure that will control the aging process, he is working as an applied scientist. A sociologist making a study of "the social structure of a slum neighborhood" is working as a pure scientist; if he then follows with a study of "how to prevent delinquency in a slum neighborhood," he is working as an applied scientist. Many people view sociology entirely as an applied science—as an attempt to solve social problems. Properly viewed, it is both a pure and an applied science, for unless a science is constantly searching for more basic knowledge, its "practical applications of knowledge" are not likely to be very practical.

Practical applications of sociological knowledge are not widely appreciated. Sociologists are sometimes employed by corporations, government bureaus, and social agencies, usually as research scholars, and are sometimes consulted by legislative committees that are planning new legislation. But the private citizen rarely bases his social decisions on sociological knowledge. If a man wants to know how to fertilize artichokes, he generally collects some scientific data before deciding. But how are social-policy decisions made? Each year dozens of communities vote on whether to allow liquor to be sold by the glass in taverns and restaurants. Arguments about automobile accidents, crime, drunkenness, and other evils are hurled around with abandon. But has any *comprehensive, carefully controlled* comparison of communities with and without liquor sale by the glass ever been conducted? The author knows of none. Local groups in hundreds of communities are promoting a crusade against pornography, yet there is virtually *no scientific evidence* on the question of whether pornography is a dangerous stimulant or a harmless outlet for salacious impulses. This decision, like many others, is being made by people who are happily indifferent to the fact that their decision is based upon ignorance and emotion, not upon knowledge.

On many other social questions, such as the causes and treatment of crime and delinquency, drug and alcohol addiction, sex offenses, the causes and consequences of racial discrimination, or the adjustment of the family to a changing society, there *is* considerable scientific knowledge, but this knowledge is rejected by many persons who prefer their prejudices. As a nation, we have only begun to apply scientific methods to our thinking about social issues.

Popular Sociology. A great deal of sociological material is printed that has not been written by sociologists. The popular magazines are studded with articles on crime, family life, sex, education, suburbia, social class— practically every sociological topic imaginable. This is popular sociology —treatment of sociological topics, often by writers with little formal sociological training, for a popular audience. Popular sociology at its worst is seen in articles like the "sex-and-sin" exposés on which certain men's magazines dwell so sensationally. Such articles are generally descriptively inaccurate, with a total lack of the interpretive analysis that would fit such facts into a relevant social context. At the opposite pole are many writers who do a fairly creditable job of popularizing sociological findings. Their writings may exhibit occasional inaccuracies and instances of misplaced emphasis, doubtful interpretation, oversimplification, and too sweeping generalization. Yet it is likely that popular understanding of sociological topics has been greatly increased by such writers.

Why isn't popular sociology written by professional sociologists? For the same reason that popular medicine and popular science are usually written by journalists rather than by physicians and scientists. Popular writing is a special skill that few scientists or professors have mastered. The scientist's passion for accuracy and for a careful qualification of his statements is a positive handicap in popular writing. His unwillingness to oversimplify, overdramatize, or indulge in the grandly sweeping generalization all make his writing more accurate but less exciting. Sociologists write for the scholarly audience, while journalists popularize sociology, more or less accurately, for the public.

The Roles of the Sociologist

What is the proper task of the sociologist? Should he merely observe human action with the calm, detached curiosity of the ecologist who counts the lemmings as they dive into the sea? Or should he plunge into social action to avert the dangers he sees so clearly? Should the professor of sociology encourage students to develop a detached understanding of social phenomena, or should he inspire them to man the barricades for social reform? What is the sociologist's proper role in a changing society?

The Sociologist as a Social Scientist. The sociologist has both a professional role as a social scientist or technician and a citizen role as a member of his society. These roles are quite different and must be considered separately.

Correcting Popular Nonsense. One task of the sociologist as scientist is to clear away the intellectual rubbish of misinformation and superstition that clutters so much of our social thinking. Sociologists have helped to bury a great deal of nonsense about heredity, race, class, sex differences, deviation, and nearly every other aspect of behavior. Partly because of sociology, it is today rare to hear an educated person argue that the white race is innately superior, that women are intellectually inferior to men, that behavior traits are inherited, that punishment reforms criminals, or that rural people are less "immoral" than urbanites, ideas that nearly every educated person accepted a half century ago. By helping replace superstition and misinformation with accurate knowledge about human behavior, sociologists are perhaps performing their most important function.

Making Sociological Predictions. Sociological prediction should be of interest to legislators and others concerned with social policy, for every major policy decision makes certain assumptions about the present and future structure of the society. When a legislator says "Schools must operate within their present income," he is assuming that present school funds are adequate to prepare children for the society in which they will be living for another seventy-five years, while the legislator who says "We must raise more funds for schools" makes an opposite assumption. Unavoidably, every policy pronouncement makes assumptions about the kind of society we shall have in the future. What sort of predictions do sociologists offer? Here are a few samples, offered without explanation or documentation at this point, as examples of the kind of predictions sociologists can make.

Urban sprawl will spread rapidly along the superhighways and will result in the creation of regional planning and administrative authorities.

The trend toward child marriage is likely to continue, and an abnormally high proportion of these very early marriages will be unsuccessful.

The trend toward the employment of working mothers will continue until most women are working for a substantial portion of their married lives.

The present trend toward racial desegregation will continue until all or nearly all forms of institutionalized segregation or discrimination are destroyed.

Birth rates will, sooner or later, fall to approach death rates, or death rates must rise to approach birth rates.

Farm organizations and labor unions have passed the peak of their power; both will suffer a relative decline in membership and power.

There is no certainty that any one of these predictions will be fulfilled, only a strong likelihood that most of them will come true. Such predictions help to clarify the kind of social setting in which we must function for the next generation or two.

Sociological prediction can also help to estimate the probable effects of specific proposals. Every social policy decision *is* a prediction. A policy (e.g., Federal grants for urban renewal) is begun in the hope that it will produce a desired effect (e.g., halt the spread of urban blight). Policies have failed often because they embodied unsound assumptions and predictions. Sociologists can help predict the effects of a policy, and thus contribute to the selection of policies that achieve the intended purposes. For example:

What effect would the removal or the addition of the death penalty have on the murder rate? (Practically none.)

What effects do brotherhood propaganda and "education for brotherhood" efforts have on race prejudices? (Practically none.)

What effects do attempts at enforced desegregation have on race prejudices? (Momentary tension, followed by substantial reduction in prejudices.)

If welfare payments were withheld from unwed mothers, what effect would this withdrawal have on illegitimacy rates? (Little or none.)

Would publishing the names of juvenile delinquents help to reduce delinquency? (No; would more likely increase it.)

Would the suppression of obscene literature help to reduce sex crimes and sex immorality? (Nobody knows, for there is no dependable scientific evidence on this question.)

These are a few of the many social-policy questions that sociologists could help to settle. So far, our society has not generally accorded the sociologist the status of technical expert on social-policy matters. The image of the sociologist as a professional bleeding heart, so often reflected in the popular press, does not help the public to visualize the sociologist as a technical expert. Congressional committees, however, often consult sociologists and other social scientists when holding hearings on proposed legislation. In some areas, notably in criminology and race relations, the conclusions of sociologists (and other social scientists) have had considerable influence. It was largely the findings of sociologists and psychologists that led the United States Supreme Court to rule that "segregated schools are inherently unequal." The present strategy of the desegregation movement is based squarely on sociologists' prediction that such efforts are likely to be successful.

One of the greatest services any scholarly group can offer is to show the society what policies are most likely to work in achieving its objectives. This is a service sociologists are qualified to perform.

The Sociologist as a Person. Should the sociologist evaluate both the *workability* and the *desirability* of a social policy? This old question of science and values is most easily answered by distinguishing the different roles of the sociologist—as scientist and as private citizen. The majority opinion of sociologists is that, *as a scientist,* the sociologist can make only one sort of commitment—to the values of science, that is, objectivity and the search for truth. *As a person,* he has a value system that is as real and important to him as anybody else's is to them. Thus the sociologist *as a scientist* does not know whether TV violence is harmful to children, and he avoids making any positive public statements on the matter; as a

As a citizen, he is perfectly justified in supporting causes.

parent, he makes a decision according to his own opinions and values. *As a sociologist* he may analyze the policies and sacrifice of values necessary to lower the divorce rate, and may contrast those with the policies and sacrifice of values that accompany a high divorce rate. He does not, *as a scientist*, state which the society should choose, for this is not a scientific question. As a citizen, he may have strong convictions which he freely states and defends.

There are some social-policy questions on which the society is in so nearly complete agreement that no one is likely to question the social scientist's involvement. For example, nearly everyone agrees that drug addiction and alcoholism are undesirable. On such matters, where the society has an overwhelming consensus about value, some would say that the sociologist has a duty to make policy recommendations [Lindesmith, 1960]. No one is likely to question the propriety of a sociologist's publishing a semipopular article on the reduction of crime or the achievement of a happy family life. But where there is no general value agreement in the society (e.g., "Should gambling be legalized or forbidden?"), most sociologists agree that the sociologist should carefully separate his roles as objective social scientist and as interested citizen.

As a citizen he is perfectly justified in supporting causes, joining reform movements, signing petitions, and trying to realize his values like any other citizen. Many sociologists have been active in reform movements, community agencies, and causes of various sorts. Practically all sociologists have some firm opinions on what policies they prefer the society to follow, and sociologists are in considerable agreement with one another on many of these policies. Possibly the time may come when the social policies that seem best to sociologists will also seem best to the rest of the community. As persons who cannot and would not divorce themselves from the society in which they live, most sociologists hope so.

The Sociologist as a Technician. Today sociologists are increasingly finding employment with government departments, corporations, hospitals, large welfare agencies, and other large organizations. Sometimes they are engaged in research, sometimes in other activities: planning and conducting community action programs; advising on public relations, employee relations, problems of morale or of "intergroup relations" within the organization; working on human relations problems of many sorts. The "staff sociologist" is becoming more familiar in all kinds of large organizations.[2] Often he has specialized in social psychology, industrial sociology, urban or rural sociology, or the sociology of complex organizations.

In such positions the sociologist is working as an applied scientist. His employer has engaged him to use his scientific knowledge in pursuing certain values, such as a harmonious and efficient working force, an attractive public image of the industry, or an effective community action program. This role raises a question of ethics. When a sociologist accepts

[2] See "Sociologists Invade the Plant," *Business Week*, Mar. 21, 1959, pp. 95ff., for examples.

employment as a technician, pursuing values chosen by his employer, has he compromised his scientific integrity? To take an extreme example, there is evidence [Monroe, 1962] that gambling operators have recently engaged social scientists to find out why people do or do not gamble, so that the operators will know how to lure more customers. (We do not know whether any sociologists gave advice!) Would this be a form of scientific prostitution?

One answer to this question is that neither the profession nor the public expects the same neutrality from a General Motors economist or sociologist that they expect from a university professor. The university professor is expected to search for and teach the truth; the technician is expected to serve the interests of his employer *within certain limits*. He must not betray the values of accuracy to which science is dedicated or the values of decency which his fellow sociologists, as persons, feel to be acceptable. Thus a corporation's sociologist might seek to locate and remove some unnecessary sources of friction within the organization, or a hospital staff sociologist might advise on internal organization, fund raising, community relations, or outpatient operations. All these would be viewed by his fellows as legitimate professional activities. The author knows of no sociologists who have accepted positions that involve them in unionbusting or strikebreaking, in serving antidemocratic causes or movements, or in campaigns to deceive or misinform the American people. If any were so to commit themselves, they would become sociological outcasts for serving values that most sociologists privately despise and that in some cases are a betrayal of truth.

The Study of Sociology

Some students will learn little in a sociology course because they feel they already know everything worth knowing about social life. Having prowled the same haunts in a dozen towns and pursued the same encounters in a dozen or a hundred bars, they know all about Life. Those who feel this way will learn very little, here or anywhere.

A lifetime of eating food does not make one a dietitian; nor does surviving a number of traffic jams make one a traffic engineer. Each student, true enough, has been having social experiences all his life, and from these he has learned many things, some true and some false. To separate truth from falsehood is one of the tasks of sociology. Only those students who are willing to learn—who are willing and able to subject their beliefs, assumptions, and practices to objective scientific scrutiny—will gain much from the study of any of the social sciences.

The Use of Concepts in Sociology. Every field of study requires that the student memorize many words to which that field attaches special meanings. This pursuit is not an idle ritual; it is done because precise concepts are necessary. First, *we need concepts to carry on a scientific discussion.* How would you explain machinery to a person who had no concept of "wheel"? How useful to a specialist would a patient's medical history be if his physician had recorded it in the language of the layman? The several dozen concepts that will harass the student in this book are necessary for a clear discussion of social phenomena. Second, *the formulation of concepts leads to increased knowledge.* Some accurate descriptive knowledge must be organized before a concept can be framed. Then the analysis and criticism of this new concept point up the gaps and errors in present knowledge. The *use* of the concept often calls attention to facts and relationships that may have been overlooked. Years ago, while studying the mulatto, Stonequist [1937] framed the concept of the marginal man who is on the fringe of two groups or two ways of life while fully belonging to neither. The use of this concept quickly led to the recognition that there were many kinds of marginal persons—the foreman, who is not clearly either "management" or "labor"; the immigrant, partly adapted to two ways of life while fully adapted to neither; the ambitious climber, no longer working class, yet not securely middle class; and many others. Sound concepts like that of the marginal man lead to increased knowledge.

Most of the concepts of sociology are expressed in words that also have a popular meaning, just as the term "order" has one meaning in zoology and another at the restaurant table. Every science appropriates some common words and makes them into scientific concepts by giving them a specific definition. Sociology is no exception.

Sociology and the Health Sciences. Why should the student nurse study sociology? Partly because, as an educated person, she should have some contact with each of the liberal arts and sciences [Russell, 1960]. But even more, because a nurse cannot be fully effective in her field without some knowledge of the social sciences, especially sociology and psychology.

For the past few decades, medical science has been shifting its focus from the study of *disease* to the study of the *person.* Medical science, as distinct from guesswork and folklore, is little more than a century old, and for most of this period, its research has been based on the hypothesis that *disease is caused by bacteria.* This hypothesis led to success in controlling the great mass killers such as smallpox, typhus, and diphtheria. Later the hypothesis was expanded to state that *disease is also caused by viruses,* which led to more successes. But diseases such as ulcers and heart disease called for still another hypothesis: *disease is also caused by emotional stress* [Dunbar, 1955; Selye, 1956]. We know that from 50 to 75 per cent of all illness today is at least partly *psychosomatic,* that is, caused by emotional stress. To understand many illnesses today we must consider not only the patient's physiology but also his family life, work experience, cultural background, mental outlook, and many other social characteristics. Each patient is not only a "case"; he is also a person, as the following anecdote reveals.

> Understanding a little bit about Italian culture made me understand why droves of relatives flocked to Mrs. S's bedside every day, crying and displaying outward grief and emotion over a relatively innocuous disease (innocuous to me because I am not a part of the Italian culture and therefore don't react to illness and hospitalization in the same way she does). Certainly, to understand a patient entails knowing about him as a person with [a] culture.

Frances Cooke Macgregor, "Social Sciences and Nursing Education," *American Journal of Nursing,* 57:899–902, 1957.

Furthermore, medical knowledge has expanded so enormously that specialization and large-scale organization are necessary in medical practice. A dozen or more separate professions interact in that remarkable institution, the hospital. Sociologists are interested in observing how these professions interact with one another [Lortie, 1958; Stern, 1945; Wilson, 1954] and with patients and the public [Kutner, 1958; Deutscher, 1955]. They study the social structure of the hospital [H. Smith, 1949; 1955]; the operation of health-care plans [Brewester et al., 1963]; comparative illness and death rates for different groups, classes, or nations [Anderson, 1958; Stern, 1951]. Wherever social and cultural factors touch upon health—and they do at many points—sociologists are interested observers.

Summary

Sociology attempts to study society scientifically. Sociology is science, not social philosophy; it is knowledge, not social reform; it is social science, not socialism. Each social science has its own focus, and sociology's is upon man's group life and the social products of this group life.

The basic technique of scientific investigation is *observation.* Scientific observation differs from just looking at things in that scientific observation is (1) *accurate,* seeking to describe what really exists; (2) as *precise* and exact as is necessary; (3) *systematic,* in an effort to find all the relevant data; (4) *recorded* in complete detail as quickly as possible; (5) *objective,* in being as free from distortion by vested interest, bias, or wishful thinking as is humanly possible; (6) *conducted by trained observers* who know what to look for and how to recognize it; (7) *conducted under controlled conditions* that reduce the danger of fraud, self-deception, or mistaken interpretation.

The several steps in a scientific research project are to (1) formulate the problem, (2) plan the research design, (3) collect the data, (4) analyze the data, and (5) draw conclusions.

Whether the study of man's social relationships is a science is often debated. To the extent that man's social life is studied through scientific methods so that a body of verified knowledge is developed—to that extent these studies become social sciences.

The methods of sociological research include studies that are cross-sectional, longitudinal, or ex post facto. They may be planned experiments, or they may be observational studies of several kinds—impressionistic studies, statistical comparative studies, questionnaire and interview studies, participant-observer studies, and case studies. Some difficulties in sociological research pose a challenge to our methodology—the complexity of social phenomena and the limitations of prediction when working with many variables. Sociology, like all sciences, may be either pure or applied. Pure sociology searches for new knowledge; applied sociology seeks to apply sociological knowledge to practical problems. A good deal of more or less accurate sociology is popularized by professional journalists, who are sometimes incorrectly called sociologists.

The sociologist in his professional role as a social scientist tends to be a pure scientist devoted to searching out and teaching truth and occasionally making sociological predictions. He may function as an applied scientist when employed as a technician or when he fills his private role as a citizen.

The study of sociology will be successful only if the student is willing to learn about matters he may think he is already familiar with. He must learn some concepts that are needed for a precise scientific discussion.

Questions and Projects

1. How would you define sociology to an uneducated person with no understanding of the fields of knowledge? How would you define it to a well-educated person whose education had included no sociology?

2. What is a sociologist? How is the term often misused?

3. What is the difference between social science and social philosophy? Which do you think is more important?

4. Are sociologists interested in social reform?

5. Suppose a foreman says, "I've supervised all kinds of workers, and Negro workers just don't measure up to white standards." What will be necessary for this statement to be a scientifically justified conclusion?

6. What difficulties in being objective would confront a scholar writing a biography of Martin Luther if the scholar were a devout Catholic? A devout Protestant? A convinced atheist?

7. How do you "control" a variable? If the effects of student marriage

on college or nursing-school achievement were to be studied, what variables would need to be controlled? How could they be controlled?

8. Negroes have higher death rates from tuberculosis and venereal disease than whites, but lower death rates from cancer and heart disease. Why? What variables would have to be controlled to decide whether race were a factor?

9. Why are planned experiments rather rare in sociology?

10. What precautions are needed in using eyewitness accounts as sources of scientific evidence?

11. How does the participant-observer technique differ from merely looking at things? Isn't everyone a participant-observer?

12. Do you think the scientific training of nurses and physicians makes them more objective observers in other fields such as social problems, political affairs, and other social phenomena?

13. What are some things a sociologist may do as a private citizen that he may not do as a scientist?

Are there any other professions in which a person may do, as a citizen, things that he may not do in his professional capacity?

14. When you are in an informal student bull session, listen to each statement with these questions in mind: How scientifically sound is this statement? Is it based on scientific evidence or on guesswork, folklore, and wishful thinking? Could it be documented with adequate scientific support? At the conclusion, try to estimate what proportion of the statements could be scientifically substantiated.

15. Write a brief impressionistic account of some group or community which you have observed. Then list several of your generalizations about the group and outline a research project for collecting the empirical data that would make it possible to test the accuracy of these statements.

16. Read Sinclair Lewis's novel *Arrowsmith*. What are some of the difficulties Martin had to meet in becoming rigorously scientific?

Suggested Readings

ADAMS, SAMUEL HOPKINS: "The Jukes Myth," *Saturday Review*, Apr. 2, 1955, pp. 13ff.; reprinted in Edgar A. Schuler et al. (eds.), *Readings in Sociology*, 2d ed., Thomas Y. Crowell Company, New York, 1960, pp. 40–46. An amusing account of the method whereby the author of a famous study arrived at some highly dubious conclusions about heredity and crime.

ALLPORT, GORDON W., J. S. BRUNER, AND E. M. JANDORF: "Personality

under Social Catastrophe: Ninety Life-histories of the Nazi Revolution," *Character and Personality*, 10:1–22, 1941; reprinted in Clyde Kluckhohn and Henry A. Murray (eds.), *Personality in Nature, Society, and Culture*, Alfred A. Knopf, Inc., New York, 1949, pp. 347–366. Shows how a collection of life histories can be used in arriving at scientific generalizations.

CHASE, STUART, WITH EDMUND DE S. BRUNNER: *The Proper Study of*

Mankind, Harper & Row, Publishers, Incorporated, New York, 1948, 1956. A highly readable treatment of the contribution of social science to the solution of human problems.

DUNHAM, BARROWS: *Man against Myth,* Little, Brown and Company, Boston, 1947. A critical examination of some of the major myths of our time.

EVANS, BERGEN: *The Natural History of Nonsense,* Alfred A. Knopf, Inc., New York, 1946. An entertaining examination of many popular myths and superstitions, demolished with a rare blend of wit and learning.

GARDNER, MARTIN: *Fads and Fallacies in the Name of Science,* Dover Publications, Inc., New York, 1957. Earlier edition under title, *In the Name of Science,* G. P. Putnam's Sons, New York, 1952. An interesting account of many unscientific and pseudoscientific theories and the cults that promote them.

GRAHAM, AARON: "Social Factors in Relation to the Chronic Illnesses," in Howard E. Freeman, Sol Levine, and Leo G. Reader, *Handbook of Medical Sociology,* Prentice-Hall, Inc., Englewood Cliffs, N.J., 1963, pp. 65–98. Reviews and analyzes many studies relating illness to social class, race, religion, and other social factors.

LANTZ, HERMAN R.: *People of Coal Town,* Columbia University Press, New York, 1958. A largely impressionistic case history of a community.

LEVINE, EUGENE: "The ABC's of Statistics," *American Journal of Nursing,* 59:70–75, 1959. A brief explanation of how simple statistical procedures are used in nursing research.

MAC DOUGALL, CURTIS D.: *Hoaxes,* Dover Publications, Inc., New York, 1958. An entertaining survey of frauds in art, literature, science, history, politics, and journalism.

MACGREGOR, FRANCES COOKE: "Social Sciences and Nursing Education," *American Journal of Nursing,* 57:899–902, 1957. A brief discussion of how the social sciences are helpful in nursing practice.

MC CORMICK, THOMAS C., AND ROY G. FRANCES: *Methods of Research in the Behavioral Sciences,* Harper & Row, Publishers, Incorporated, New York, 1958. A brief handbook on planning and conducting a social research project.

SCHLOTFELDT, ROZELLA M.: "Reflections on Nursing Research," *American Journal of Nursing,* 60:492–494, 1960. A brief discussion of scientific research in the development of a science of nursing.

Statistical Abstract of the United States (published annually by the Bureau of the Census) and *The World Almanac and Book of Facts* (published annually by the *New York World-Telegram and Sun*). Two useful sources of statistical and factual information on nearly any subject, available in every library. Every student should be familiar with them.

The Nature of Culture

The cars of the migrant people crawled out of the side roads onto the great cross-country highway, and they took the migrant way to the West. In the daylight they scuttled like bugs to the westward; and as the dark caught them, they clustered like bugs near to shelter and to water. And because they were lonely and perplexed, because they had all come from a place of sadness and worry and defeat, and because they were all going to a new mysterious place, they huddled together; they talked together, they shared their lives, their food, and the things they hoped for in the new country. Thus it might be that one family camped near a spring, and another camped for the spring and for company, and a third because two families had pioneered the place and found it good. And when the sun went down, perhaps twenty families and twenty cars were there. . . .

Every night a world created, complete with furniture—friends made and enemies established; a world complete with braggarts and with cowards, with quiet men, with humble men, with kindly men. Every night relationships that make a world, established; and every morning the world torn down like a circus.

At first the families were timid in the building and tumbling worlds, but gradually the technique of building worlds became their technique. Then leaders emerged, then laws were made, then codes came into being. And as the worlds moved westward they were more complete and better furnished, for their builders were more experienced in building them.

The families learned what rights must be observed—the right of privacy in the tent; the right to keep the past black hidden in the heart; the right to talk and to listen; the right to refuse help or to accept, to offer help or to decline it; the right of son to court and daughter to be courted; the right of the hungry to be fed; the rights of the pregnant and the sick to transcend all other rights.

And the families learned, although no one told them, what rights are monstrous and must be destroyed: the right to intrude upon privacy, the right to be noisy while the camp slept, the right of seduction or rape, the right of adultery and theft and murder. These rights were crushed, because the little worlds could not exist for even a night with such rights alive.

And as the worlds moved westward, rules became laws, although no one told the families. It is unlawful to foul near the camp; it is unlawful to eat good rich food near one who is hungry, unless he is asked to share.

And with the laws, the punishments—and there were only two—

a quick and murderous fight or ostracism; and ostracism was the worst. For if one broke the laws his name and face went with him, and he had no place in any world, no matter where created.

In the worlds, social conduct became fixed and rigid, so that a man must say "Good morning" when asked for it, so that a man might have a willing girl if he stayed with her, if he fathered her children and protected them. But a man might not have one girl one night and another the next, for this would endanger the worlds.

The families moved westward, and the technique of building the worlds improved so that the people could be safe in their worlds; and the form was so fixed that a family acting in the rules knew it was safe in the rules.

From their life experiences a group develops a set of rules and procedures for meeting their needs. This set of rules and procedures, together with a supporting set of ideas and values, is called a *culture*.

We commonly say that a person is cultured if he can identify operatic arias, read a French menu, and select the right fork. But people who are bored by the classics, eat peas with their knives, and speak in four-letter words also have a culture. "Culture" is a word with both a popular and a sociological meaning.

The classic definition of culture framed by Sir Edward Tylor [1871, p. 1] reads, "Culture . . . is that complex whole which includes knowledge, belief, art, morals, law, custom and any other capabilities and habits acquired by man as a member of society." Stated more simply, *culture is everything that is socially learned and shared by the members of a society.* It is the entire social heritage the individual receives from the group.

This social heritage may be divided into *material* and *nonmaterial culture*. Nonmaterial culture consists of the words people use, the ideas, customs, and beliefs they hold, and the habits they follow. Material culture consists of man-made objects such as tools, furniture, automobiles, buildings, irrigation ditches, cultivated farms, roads, bridges, and in fact any physical substance that has been changed and used by man. In the game of baseball, for instance, the gloves, bats, uniforms, and grandstands are a few elements of material culture. The nonmaterial culture would include the rules of the game, the skills of the players, the concepts of strategy, and the traditional behavior of players and spectators. In every case the material culture is the outgrowth of the nonmaterial culture. Without the nonmaterial culture the material culture is meaningless. If the *game* of baseball is forgotten, a ball bat becomes just a stick of wood.

We also make a distinction between culture and society. A *culture* is a *system of behavior* shared by the members of a society; a *society* is a *group of people* who share a common culture. A society is made up of people who are interacting on the basis of shared beliefs, customs, values, and activities. The common patterns governing their interaction make up the culture of the society. As Gillin and Gillin state [1948, pp. 188, 189], "Culture is the cement binding together into a society its component individuals. . . . Human society is *people* interacting; culture is the *patterning* of their behavior." The two terms may be used almost interchangeably in places; yet we must remember that society refers to people and culture to behavior patterns.

The Development of Culture

Subhuman Societies. Let us begin by looking at a form of life in which culture is largely absent—the subhuman world. Many subhuman species have an orderly system of social life. Many bird species mate for a lifetime and (in contrast to human behavior) are absolutely loyal to their mates. Many species of insects, such as ants and bees, have an elaborate pattern of social life complete with specialized occupations, lines of authority, and detailed distribution of duties and privileges. But the *subhuman social life is based on instinct, not on social learning*. Within a given species of ants, all anthills are very much alike, whereas human dwellings vary tremendously. For man's instincts, unlike those of the subhumans, do not give him any inborn patterns of behavior, but only a set of needs, urges, and hungers that he must satisfy in some way or other. In his trial-and-error efforts to satisfy his urges, man creates his culture, with its tremendous variations from society to society. Unable to rely upon instinct, man must build culture in order to survive.

Man's Learning Capacity. Man's great advantage over the other animals is his greater learning capacity. Other animals do of course think, reason, and learn; this has been shown by many experiments. In some experiments a chimpanzee must figure out that he can get a banana, placed beyond reach, only by fitting together two sticks to make a longer one. In other experiments, where slugs must be put into a slot machine in order to get food, the chimpanzees quickly learn which size or color slugs are valuable, and sort out, hoard, hide, and steal these from one another in a quite human manner. Many such experiments with many species have clearly established that animals *do* learn, and apparently they learn *in the same way* that human beings learn; they just don't learn as fast or as much. A famous experiment [Kellogg and Kellogg, 1933] in which a human infant and a chimpanzee infant were raised together and treated alike showed that they behaved alike in many ways, but that before long the child greatly outdistanced the chimpanzee in learning.

Communication. Animals can learn; they can form interacting groups and have a social life; they can even communicate with one another at a very simple level. These facts have led a few scholars to conclude that some animals have a culture. Several experiments have shown that animal learning is affected by their social setting. For example Kuo [1931] found that when kittens could watch the mother cat catching rats, 85 per cent of them were catching rats themselves by the time they were four months old. Other kittens were raised with rats as companions; none of them killed the type of rats they grew up with and only 16 per cent killed any kind of rats. This suggests that animals can learn through example and that it may be a form of social learning. But if cats have a "rat-killing culture," it is far removed from the hunting complex of the Plains Indians or the English gentry.

The idea of animal culture becomes rather farfetched if we try to imagine Leo the Lion acting in a manner governed by custom, tradition, or sacred ideal. As Myerson observes:

> We cannot imagine him, for example, stopping in palpitating pursuit of a tawny female because some Leo the Saint, a hundred lion generations ago, reached the conclusion that burning desire might be satisfied only under very special circumstances. Nor can we visualize this same Leo aching for food yet withholding his mighty paw from a delicacy because that delicacy has been staked off for another lion or because old lions in a congress a hundred years before decreed private ownership in delicacies and forbade even ravenous hunger to satisfy itself except under strict rule and regulation.
>
> We cannot imagine the young lion contemplating the life of some past Leo the Great and planning his entire career in emulation of the dead hero. . . . We cannot imagine him in agonies of self-condemnation because he has fallen short of an ideal which has been incorporated within him by the teaching and preaching of a thousand years and of countless lions. . . .
>
> He does not foresee his own death, and knows nothing of his own birth. Sex means to him only the satisfaction that an individual of the opposite sex can bring him. It does not mean parenthood, domesticity, respectability, the fulfilling of an ideal, a responsibility, and the becoming part of a great racial sweep.

Abraham Myerson, *Social Psychology*, Prentice-Hall, Inc., Englewood Cliffs, N.J., 1934, pp. 3–6. Adapted by permission.

It is fashionable to believe a great deal of nonsense about animal behavior. A faithful dog, gazing intently at his master, inspires all sorts of fanciful notions as to what he is thinking. Dogs are often credited with remarkable "homing" instincts; yet for every dog that finds its way

Only man uses symbols.

home across a continent, the lost-and-found ads list a hundred dogs that cannot find their way home from the next block. Mama Bear is pictured as patiently "teaching" her cubs how to fish, yet we have no evidence that she is consciously trying to teach them anything. Perhaps she is just hungry. Only for man is there conclusive evidence of deliberate teaching and intentional communication of ideas.

This may be mankind's greatest advantage—*his ability to communicate what he has learned to others.* The chimpanzee might learn how to get the banana, but he has no effective way of communicating this insight to others; each must get the idea for himself, either through imitation or through his own imagination. Each chimpanzee stands, or rather crouches, on his own feet and must face the world starting from scratch. Man stands on the shoulders of his ancestors and brings to his problems a great heritage of accumulated wisdom.

Language and Symbolic Communication. Many animals can exchange feelings through growls, purrs, mating calls, and other sounds. Some animals give off odors or make bodily movements that convey meanings to others. These sounds and motions are not language, for each is largely or entirely an inborn, instinctive response rather than an acquired, symbolic response. There is no evidence that a dog growls or barks because he wants to tell another dog something; perhaps he barks just because he feels like barking. As far as we know, no dog has yet developed a barking code (e.g., one short bark for "let's eat," two yips for "after you," etc.). A language is just such a code—*a set of sounds with a particular meaning attached to each sound.* A largely emotional or instinctive set of yips and yells is not a language, even though these sounds do serve to carry some accurate meanings to others of the species. Only when an *artificial* meaning is attached to each sound—so that the sound becomes a symbol of that idea—do we have a language.

Only man uses symbols; therefore only man's communication reaches beyond the level of exchanging very simple feelings and intentions. With symbolic communication men can exchange detailed directions, share discoveries, and organize elaborate activities. Without it they would quickly revert to the caves and treetops.

Somewhat as speech separates man from the animals, the written language is a dividing line between primitive and civilized cultures. The man in the preliterate culture must memorize the traditional lore, and the man with a fine memory is valued as a walking library. Old people are useful in a society that must rely on human memory to preserve its culture. But the human memory is not limitless. A culture dependent upon human memory and oral tradition must remain fairly simple. The use of writing allows an almost limitless expansion of the culture, since endless bits of lore can be stored away until needed. Techniques and processes of infinite complexity can be recorded in precise detail and endless variety. Even the illiterate person is affected by living in a literate culture, since his entire life is colored by the fact that others can draw upon the storehouse of the written word. The dictum of Pharaoh's court, "Thus it is written; thus it shall be done," is the basis of every civilized society.

Language is so intimately tied up with culture that every new addition to the group's cultural heritage involves additions to the language. In order to know a group one must learn to speak its language. Even special groups within a society such as hoboes, soldiers, railroad men, or teen-agers have their own vocabularies. College students are painfully aware that each new field of study forces them to learn many new words and to learn new meanings for many of the old ones.

Language is related to the rest of culture in other ways. Not only does culture produce language, but language helps or hinders the spread of culture. It is difficult to think without language, for one's thoughts are likely to be vague and unclear until put into words. One can perhaps visualize objects or actions without using words, but ideas require language. Try visualizing ideas such as "goodness," "never," or "necessary" without using words! Sometimes an idea or concept is hard to translate because the language has no words with which to express it. The translation of papal encyclicals into classical Latin is complicated by the lack of Latin terms for modern words like "automation" and "atomic reactor." India's effort to limit the use of English and to employ the traditional Hindustani as the national language is facing similar difficulties. Since Hindustani developed before the dawn of modern science and industry, either a whole new set of expressions must be hastily coined or Hindustani must absorb words borrowed at a tremendous rate from other languages. Hence the zealous Indian attempt to support Hindustani is being followed by a reluctant admission that English might have to be the language of university instruction for the indefinite future [Rao, 1956, pp. 1–12]. An adequate language is the indispensable means of communication through which culture is shared, transmitted, and accumulated.

The Accumulation of Culture. A look at prehistory shows that man once lived very much like his animal cousins. Our earliest human ancestors lived in caves, wore no clothes, raised no crops, domesticated no animals, and used no fire. Archeological reports indicate that hundreds of thousands of years passed before man learned to cook his food, plant crops or build shelters. We who have come to expect a "new model" every year find it hard to visualize an era when man made no great change in his habits for perhaps a thousand generations and, like the animals, lived at the mercy of an unfriendly nature.

Man spent ages in making his early discoveries and inventions, but these became the *cultural base* for more rapid discovery and invention in the future. It took him several hundred thousand years to invent the wheel; once invented, the wheel might then be used in thousands of other inventions. For this and other reasons, man's culture accumulated exceedingly slowly in prehistoric times, more rapidly in historic times,

Table 1   IF A MILLION YEARS* OF HUMAN HISTORY WERE COMPRESSED INTO THE LIFETIME OF ONE 70-YEAR-OLD MAN

1,000,000 years of history	Compressed into one 70-year lifetime
1,000,000 years ago	Pithecanthropus erectus is born.
500,000 years ago	He spends half his lifetime learning to make and use crude stone axes and knives.
50,000 years ago	And most of the next half in improving them.
40,000 years ago	Three years ago, he began to use bone and horn tools.
10,000 years ago	Nine months ago, the last ice age ended, and he left his cave dwellings.
7,000 years ago	Six or eight months ago, he began to make pottery, weave cloth, grow crops, and domesticate animals.
5,000 years ago	About three months ago, he began to cast and use metals, and built the Pyramids.
3,000 years ago	Ten weeks ago, he invented the spoked wheel and began making glass.
2,000 years ago	Seven weeks ago, Christ was born.
700 years ago	Two weeks ago, he finished the Crusades.
185 years ago	Five days ago, he crossed the Delaware with Washington.
60 years ago	Yesterday he invented the airplane.
15–20 years ago	This morning he fought World War II.
In the year A.D. 2000	Tomorrow he will celebrate the arrival of the twenty-first century!

* Plus or minus a few hundred thousand years, about which we shall not quibble.

and with breakneck speed in modern times. Man's greatest problem today is how to adjust himself and his social arrangements to the speed with which his culture is changing.

Culture as a System of Norms

For shaking hands we extend the right hand; our culture defines this gesture as proper. For scratching our heads we may use either hand; our culture has no norm for head scratching. The term "norm" has two possible meanings. A *statistical norm* is a measure of what actually exists; a *cultural norm* is a concept of what is *expected* to exist. The famous Kinsey studies sought to find some statistical norms of sexual behavior in the United States. The effort infuriated many people who confused statistical with cultural norms. A cultural norm is a set of behavior *expectations*, a cultural image of how people are supposed to act. A culture is an elaborate system of such norms—of standardized, expected ways of feeling and acting—which the members of a society follow more or less perfectly. Except where otherwise indicated, it is the cultural norms to which the sociologist refers. These norms are of several kinds and several degrees of compulsion.

Folkways. Social life everywhere is full of problems—how to wrest a living from nature, how to divide up the fruits of toil or good fortune, how to relate ourselves agreeably to one another, and so on. Man seems to have tried every possible way of dealing with such problems. Different societies have found a wide variety of patterns to be workable. A group may eat once, twice, or several times each day; they may eat while standing, seated in chairs, or squatting on the ground; they may eat together or each may eat in privacy; they may eat with their fingers or use some kind of utensils; they may start with wine and end with fish, start with fish and end with wine, or they may reject both fish and wine as inedible. And so it goes for thousands of items of behavior. Each trait is a selection from a number of possibilities, all of which are more or less workable. Through trial and error, sheer accident, or some unknown influence a group arrives at one of these possibilities, repeats it, and accepts it as the normal way of meeting a particular need. It is passed on to succeeding generations and becomes one of the ways of the folk—hence a folkway. *Folkways are simply the customary, normal, habitual ways a group does things.* Shaking hands, eating with knives and forks, wearing neckties on some occasions and sport shirts on others, driving on the right-hand side of the street, and eating toast for breakfast are a few of our many folkways.

New generations absorb the folkways partly by deliberate teaching but mainly by observing and taking part in the life about them. The

Folkways are simply the customary ways a group does things.

child is surrounded by folkways. Since he constantly sees these ways of doing things, they become to him the only real ways. If he chances to hear of the customs of other groups, they appear as quaint oddities and not as practical, realistic ways of getting things done. Even the most primitive society will have a few thousand folkways; in modern, industrialized societies they become even more numerous and involved. Sorting out the proper folkway becomes so difficult that Emily Post was able to earn a fortune as an interpreter of our folkways, even though her fat volume does not catalogue all American folkways but lists only some of the nonoccupational folkways of the urban upper class.

Mores. Some of the folkways are more important than others. In our society if one uses the wrong fork for one's salad, there is momentary embarrassment but no great injury. But if one uses the wrong man to sire one's child, many aspects of financial obligation, property inheritance rights, family relationships, and sentimental linkage become disrupted. We therefore recognize two classes of folkways: (1) those which should be followed as a matter of good manners and polite behavior and (2) those which *must* be followed because they are believed essential to group welfare. These ideas of right and wrong which attach to certain of the folkways are then called *mores*. By the mores we mean those strong ideas of right and wrong that require certain acts and forbid others.

The members of a group normally share a sublime faith that violation of their mores will bring disaster upon the group. Outsiders, however, often see that at least some of the group's mores are irrational. The mores may include food taboos that make cattle, hogs, or horses unfit to be eaten; modesty taboos that forbid exposure of the face, ankle, wrist, breast, or whatever is considered "immodest"; language taboos that forbid misuse of certain sacred or obscene words; and many others. Such taboos seem very important to their believers but may be entirely unknown in other cultures and seem to have no necessary connection with group welfare. The act forbidden by the mores need not actually be injurious. If a society *believes* that the act is injurious, it is condemned by the mores. Mores are *beliefs* in the rightness or wrongness of acts.

Mores are not deliberately invented or thought up or worked out because someone decides they would be a good idea. They emerge gradually out of the customary practices of the people, largely without conscious choice or intention. Mores arise from a group decision that a particular act seems to be harmful and must be forbidden (or, conversely, that a particular act is so beneficial that it must be required). Originally, then, mores are a practical group judgment about group welfare. For example, suppose through some coincidence several members of a tribe have nasty accidents after swimming in a certain pool. The tribe draws the logical conclusion that there is something dangerous about the pool. As soon as they firmly agree that people should stay away from the pool, the mores have defined this act as wrong. Persons who swim in the pool thereafter are likely to expect misfortune, and others who know of their act will wait to see how they are punished. Thus any misfortune will be interpreted as a punishment and will reinforce these mores. Before long, their origin is forgotten, and people think of a dip in this pool as being wrong *in and of itself*, not just because it seems to have been followed by misfortune. In this way mores, which originate as practical group judgments of the effects of actions, become transformed into absolutes—into things that are right because they are right and wrong because they are wrong. In other words *mores become self-validating and self-perpetuating*. They become sacred. To question them is indecent and to violate them is intolerable. Every society punishes those who violate its mores.

Mores are taught to the young, not as a set of practical expedients but as a set of sacred absolutes. Wherever the mores are firmly established, obedience is automatic. When fully internalized by the individual, the mores control behavior by making it psychologically very difficult for him to commit the forbidden act. For example, we do not refrain from eating our children or our enemies because of an intellectual decision that cannibalism is impractical or wasteful but because the idea of cannibalism is so repellent to us that the thought of eating human flesh never seriously occurs to us. Most of us would be unable to eat human flesh even if we tried to do so. Mores function by making it emotionally impossible, or nearly so, for one to violate them. In a society with a clearly defined, firmly implanted set of mores, there is very little personal misconduct.

Some people claim that mores are just group opinions and not the same as "real" right and wrong. They argue for absolute standards of morality, claiming that the nature of the universe makes certain actions definitely wrong and others definitely right, regardless of time, place, or circumstances. This is an important ethical issue but one which has had meaning for only a small minority of the populace. As far as the behavior of most people is concerned, "mores" is simply another word for "real" right and wrong. For, as Sumner [1906] has observed, the mores can make anything right and prevent condemnation of anything. Our mores define the killer as either a villain or a hero, according to the circumstances. Medieval mores made it right for the church to tolerate prostitution and even share in its income. Most of the Reformation churchmen, both Catholic and Protestant, who ordered the torture and burning of heretics were not cruel or evil but decent and often kindly men who did what the mores of the time and place required them to do. Mores of our recent past have approved child labor, slavery, and persecution of minorities and have condemned pacifism, woman suffrage, and sex education. And at all times and places, good people feel pure and righteous when following the mores, whatever they may be.

Institutions. Some folkways and mores are more important than others; for example, those concerned with forming families and raising children are more important than those concerned with playing football. *An organized cluster of folkways and mores centered around a major human need is called a social institution.* Five basic institutions found in most complex societies are the family, church, state, school, and economic system. Beyond these the concept tapers off into less important clusters of behavior patterns such as those surrounding football, hunting, or homecoming, which are sometimes loosely called institutions but probably should not be included because they are so much less important.

Institutions are among the most formal and compelling of the norms of a society. As already outlined, folkways emerge from the trial-and-error experience of the group; some of the folkways come to be viewed as essential to group welfare and are therefore supported by the mores; when the folkways and mores surrounding an important activity become organized into a quite formal, binding system of belief and behavior, an institution has developed. An institution thus includes a set of behavior patterns that have become highly standardized, a set of supporting mores, attitudes, and values, and generally a body of traditions, rituals and ceremonies, symbols and vestments, and other paraphernalia. Social institutions will be treated in detail in later chapters, but are introduced here because the concept must be used throughout our dscussion.

Laws. While some of the mores function simply as mores, there is a strong tendency for them to become incorporated into the religious teachings and laws of a society. Many people will obey the mores automatically or because they want to do the "right" thing. A few, however, are tempted to violate them. These people may be forced to conform by threat of legal punishment. Thus the law serves to reinforce the mores. Those who still will not conform are imprisoned or executed.

Some observers believe that law can be effective only when it seeks to support mores that are already firmly accepted by most members of the society. National prohibition is an example. The Eighteenth Amendment was ratified in 1918 to end all sale of intoxicating beverages in the United States. It clearly expressed the mores of many persons and groups. But for many others, the prohibition amendment was not a legal sanction of *their* moral beliefs but an effort by the state to impose an unreasonable restriction. To these people the use of alcoholic beverages was a part of family social life and sometimes of religious celebration. The members of these groups reinforced one another's belief that prohibition was absurd and obedience unnecessary. The bootlegger who sold liquor illegally became, not a criminal to be reported to the police, but a folk hero somewhat in the Robin Hood tradition. Under these circumstances law enforcement was ineffective. The Eighteenth Amendment was repealed in 1933, only fifteen years after it had been introduced. Other examples of laws unsupported by the mores include the Fugitive Slave Act, widely violated by persons who believed that escaped slaves should be helped to escape their owners, and World War II price and rationing controls, widely violated by Americans trained to believe they had a right to buy anything they could pay for. Such examples show how difficult it is to enforce a law that is not backed by a nation's mores.

In complex societies, law also becomes a means of regulating many kinds of behavior not clearly covered by the mores. Our culture changes rapidly, while mores develop slowly, and new situations must be handled in an orderly way. Hence a vast array of laws and regulations—building codes, zoning ordinances, business law, traffic codes, and many others—has developed to regulate matters that are too detailed, specialized, technical, or changeable to be controlled successfully by mores. Some sociologists [Odum, 1947, pp. 227–229] have used the term "stateways" to include all this regulatory machinery of the state, but the concept does not appear very often in sociological literature.

The Structure of Culture

A culture is not simply an accumulation of folkways and mores; it is an *organized system* of behavior. Let us see some of the ways in which it is organized.

Culture Traits and Complexes. The smallest unit of culture is called a *trait*. The definition is somewhat arbitrary, since what is a single unit to one individual may appear as a combination of units to another.

Hoebel's definition [1949, p. 499] is apt at this point: "A reputedly irreducible unit of learned behavior pattern or material product thereof." Traits of the material culture would include such things as the nail, the screwdriver, the pencil, and the handkerchief. Nonmaterial culture traits would include such actions as shaking hands, tipping hats, the practice of driving on the right-hand side of the road, the kiss as a gesture of affection between the sexes, or the salute to the flag. Each culture includes thousands of traits.

Is the dance a trait? No; it is a collection of traits, including the dance steps, some formula for selecting the performers, and a musical or rhythmic accompaniment. Most important of all, the dance has a meaning—as a religious ceremonial, a magical rite, a courtship activity, a festive orgy, or something else. All these elements combine to form a *culture complex*, a cluster of related traits. Another cluster of objects, skills, and attitudes forms the football complex. The saying of grace, the reading of the Bible, and evening prayers may form a family religious complex. Similarly, there is a dating complex that includes many activities and attitudes with which students may have some familiarity.

The complex is intermediate between the trait and the institution. An institution is a series of complexes centering around an important need. Thus the family includes the dating complex, the engagement and wedding complex, the honeymoon complex, the child-care complex, and several others. Some complexes are parts of institutions; other, revolving around less important activities—stamp collecting, for instance—are simply independent complexes.

Subcultures. Sometimes a particular group has a number of culture traits and complexes not shared by the rest of the society. Immigrant groups, for example, develop a blend of the culture of their host nation and of the mother country. Economic groups, whether of high, low, or middle status, usually develop ways of behavior that mark the group off from the rest of society. The adolescent has special styles of behavior, thought, and dress and a private vocabulary that adults can scarcely

The individual lives and functions mainly within certain of these subcultures.

translate, so that one may speak of "teen-age culture." Institutions tend to produce behavior patterns not required outside of the institutional setting, and the expressions "culture of the school" or "culture of the factory" suggest special sets of behavior patterns. Such terms as "army life," "preacher's kid," and "ivory tower" evoke pictures of a cultural setting different from the conventional one.

Clusters of patterns such as these, which are both *related to the general culture of the society and yet distinguishable from it*, are called *subcultures.* The subcultures in our society include occupational, religious, nationality, regional, social-class, age, and sex subcultures, and many others. Literature abounds in descriptions of subcultures, ranging from serious studies like Coleman's *The Adolescent Society* [1961] to Clausen's lighthearted description of carnival life in *I Love You, Honey, but the Season's Over* [1961].

Subcultures are important because all complex societies have, not a single, uniform culture, but a core of traits that all members share plus an assortment of subcultures. The individual lives and functions mainly within certain of these subcultures. The immigrant may live within the immigrant subculture, and the army wife on a military post may have very little contact with civilian people or civilian values. The child passes through several age subcultures and behaves according to their values, often distressing his mother, who applies the values of a different age subculture. The delinquent gang is not a group with no standards or moral values; it has very definite standards and a very compelling set of moral values, but these are part of a different subculture than the conventional middle-class one. Much of our social conflict and individual "misconduct" stems from the clash of opposing subcultures.

Age, sex, class, and occupational subcultures are probably inevitable in a complex culture, and economic specialization tends to increase them. Whether nationality, religious, and regional subcultures are desirable has been a subject of debate. Some countries, like Nazi Germany, sought ruthlessly to exterminate such subcultures; our country has sometimes protected and sometimes persecuted them.

Ethos. All the subcultures within a society will share some important norms and values in common. This core of norms and values which gives a characteristic feeling tone to the culture is called its *ethos.* A culture's ethos is almost impossible to define precisely, yet there is a difference in the cultures of various societies that goes beyond a more listing of the individual traits and complexes. This ethos is a sort of unifying bond or spirit running through all the aspects of culture, which sets the tone of the society.

Even the casual traveler senses a difference in the cultural atmosphere when he moves from Paris to Berlin or from Tokyo to New York. Our competition-success ethos contrasts sharply with the detached and contemplative ethos of the Indian Brahmin or the family-ancestor ethos of classical China. The many jokes about the Frenchman, the Englishman, the Irishman, the Scotsman, and others are popular oversimplifications of the ethos concept. It is easy to fall into misleading generalizations about ethos, yet a combination of distinct cultural patterns seems to lead to a different overall approach to life in different cultures.

Cultural Integration. The culture of the Plains Indians centered on the buffalo. From its carcass they drew most of their material culture, as they used its flesh, hide, tendons, bones, sacs, membranes, and every other part for one purpose or another. Their religion was mainly directed at ensuring the success of the buffalo hunt. Their status system measured success largely according to a man's hunting skill. Their nomadic way of life was attuned to the buffalo migrations. In other words the different parts of the culture all fitted together in an interrelated system of practices and values. When the white man killed off the buffalo, he did so in a deliberate and successful effort to demoralize the Indian by destroying the focal point of his culture.

Just as a pile of bricks is not a home, a list of traits is not a culture. A culture is an *integrated system* in which each trait fits into the rest of the culture. It is no accident that hunting peoples worship hunting gods, fishing peoples worship sea gods, and agricultural peoples worship sun and rain gods. The different parts of a culture must fit together if the culture is to function efficiently. Over a period of time a people tend to reject or discard inharmonious elements, thus gaining a reasonably integrated culture.

Linton [1936, pp. 189–195, 348–354] illustrates the concept of integration with a description of the Tanala of Madagascar. Their main crop was rice, grown on dry land by slash-and-burn agriculture. An extended family group of several adult males with their wives and children formed the basic social unit. This extended family formed a cooperative work force of the right size for clearing the land and growing rice. As land became exhausted, the village would move on to fresh lands. The family heads formed a tribal council whose main task was to reassign land annually to different families according to their size and needs. This system of land tenure prevented any great differences in wealth or income, and the society was quite democratic and equalitarian. The authority of the family head was limited and rested upon his personal leadership abilities more than upon inheritance. Religion was centered upon ancestor worship, with the founders of a family receiving special veneration. Whenever a family became much larger than necessary for working efficiency, it was likely to divide, some members leaving under the leadership of a new founder who was thus assured of great honor. When attacked by unfriendly neighboring tribes, they simply fled into the jungle, for their flimsy, temporary villages were easily rebuilt. Thus their family life, religion, tribal structure, defense measures, and economic procedures all fitted together into an efficient, mutually harmonious system. Stated differently, the culture of the Tanala was highly integrated around the dry-rice complex.

All this changed when wet-rice growing spread to the Tanala from neighboring peoples. It was adopted as an individual hobby rather than as a family activity. It took a great deal of work to prepare the necessary dikes and ditches along the river. Furthermore, the season was continuous and unending, so that such land never reverted to tribal ownership for the annual reassignment. Thus private ownership of land appeared, and differences in wealth developed. Disputes within each family arose over the division of work time between family work and private hobby, and over the sharing of the wet-rice crop. When the dry-rice land was exhausted and it was time to move the village, the wet-rice growers declined to abandon their laboriously prepared wet-rice plots. When white men arrived, they found a landed nobility of wet-rice aristocrats, living in permanent homes in well-fortified villages, and a landless proletariat of dry-rice growers, living in simple shelters and moving farther and farther away from the river, while the tie between the two branches of each family gradually weakened. In a few more generations they would have become two entirely separate societies. The addition of an important new culture trait had disrupted the existing integration and had brought about a new integration of the culture.

Failure to appreciate the integration of culture leads to many failures in dealing with other cultures. When the American Indians were herded onto reservations and supplied with cattle by the government, the Indians hunted the cattle instead of tending and milking them as expected. The idea of tending and milking cows did not tie in with anything in their culture; to introduce a completely foreign complex was a far more complicated task than had been imagined. Today the industrialization of the undeveloped areas of the world is delayed because "backward" patterns are tightly interwoven into the native culture. For example, the Bantu of South Africa are overgrazing their lands with oversized herds of scrawny, infected cattle. Reduction of herds and selective breeding are clearly indicated; but in the Bantu culture a man's wealth and status and his ability to purchase wives are measured by the number, not the quality, of his cattle. To introduce scientific livestock practices will require changes in customs and values that weave through the entire culture. Since a culture is integrated, we cannot change one part of it without producing some change in the entire culture.

Summary

Culture is the socially learned behavior norms and patterns accumulated and shared by a group and transmitted from generation to generation. A *society* is a group of people who share a common culture. Man's greatest difference from other animals is his ability to absorb and transmit culture, mainly through the use of language.

Folkways are types of habitual behavior that have the force of custom but do not have a moral connotation, while *mores* carry the ideas of right and wrong. Both folkways and mores develop gradually through social living, without conscious plan or design. Important clusters of folkways and mores centering around major activities are called *institutions*. Mores may become sanctified by religion and strengthened by incorporation into the law as part of the stateways.

A *trait* is the smallest unit of culture, and related traits are grouped into *complexes*. A *subculture* is the behavior system of a group that is really part of a larger society but that has certain unique cultural patterns marking it off as being a distinctive unit. The *ethos* of a culture refers to the distinctive emphasis of a large society or nationality group.

A culture is an *integrated* system of behavior, with its supporting ideas and values. In a highly integrated culture, all elements fit harmoniously together.

Questions and Projects

1. Which would give the greater understanding of the culture of the Romans—studying the ruins, sculptures, and public works that have been excavated or studying the records of the nonmaterial culture preserved in literature, letters, and legal documents?
2. How do you differentiate between society and culture?
3. Distinguish between the symbolic communication among human beings and the instinctive communication among animals.
4. What is meant by the statement that, when firmly established, the mores operate automatically?
5. Of the following acts, which would violate American folkways and which would violate American mores?
   a. Attending church in a bathing suit
   b. Nude bathing at a public beach
   c. Nonsupport of one's children
   d. "Standing up" a date
6. Classify the following in terms of trait, complex, and ethos:
   a. German orderliness
   b. American hot dogs
   c. Keeping on the right-hand side of a thoroughfare
   d. Fraternity rush week
   e. The American urge for success
   f. Home gardening
   g. Salesmanship

h. The funeral
7. Is the hospital an institution?
8. Why, when the government first gave cattle to the American Indians, did they hunt and kill the cattle instead of herding and milking them?
9. Apply your knowledge of the integration of culture in evaluating the proposal that our society should return to the "simple life."
10. Make a list of ten folkways on the college campus that are different from those in the rest of the community. Make a list of the folkways and mores of fraternity life.
11. Select an occupational group and describe the *special* behavior typical of that occupation.
12. Describe the traits, complexes, attitudes, and values making up the hospital subculture.
13. Make a list of the folkways and the mores of the nursing profession.

Suggested Readings

BERNSTEIN, WALTER: "The Cherubs Are Rumbling," *New Yorker,* Sept. 21, 1957, pp. 129–159. An account of the current juvenile gang mores.

LEZNOFF, MAURICE, AND WILLIAM WESTLEY: "The Homosexual Community," *Social Problems,* 3:257–264, April, 1956. A treatment of the folkways and mores found within this particular subculture.

LINTON, RALPH: *The Study of Man,* Appleton-Century-Crofts, Inc., New York, 1936. A classic analysis of the role of culture in human affairs. Chapters 5, 6, 20, and 25 are especially recommended.

SANDERS, IRWIN T.: *Societies around the World,* Holt, Rinehart and Winston, Inc., New York, 1956. Detailed description of six contrasting societies—Eskimo, Navajo, Banganda, Chinese peasant, Cotton South, and English Midlands.

SAUNDERS, LYLE: *Cultural Difference and Medical Care,* Russell Sage Foundation, New York, 1954, chaps. 3 and 4. A study of how the cultural background of Mexican-Americans affects the problem of bringing scientific medicine to them. Chapter 4 is reprinted in E. Gartly Jaco (ed.), *Patients, Physicians and Illness,* The Free Press of Glencoe, New York, 1954, pp. 189–206.

STEINBECK, JOHN: *The Grapes of Wrath,* The Viking Press, Inc., New York, 1939, pp. 264–269; reprinted under the title, "The Social 'World' of the Transients' Camp," in Edgar A. Schuler et al. (eds.), *Readings in Sociology,* Thomas Y. Crowell Company, New York, 1952, 1960, pp. 170–174, 221–225. A brief passage from a famous novel showing how human relationships become organized among a group of people who share the same kind of experiences.

SUMNER, WILLIAM GRAHAM: *Folkways,* Ginn and Company, Boston, 1906. A source book on folkways and mores.

WHYTE, WILLIAM F.: *Street Corner Society,* The University of Chicago Press, Chicago, 1955. Describes the subculture of street-corner gangs in a large Eastern city.

The Meaning of
Culture

"You said the fellow you killed provoked you?"

"So it was."

"He insulted Asiak?"

"Terribly."

"Presumably he was killed as you tried to defend her from his advances?"

Ernenek [her husband] and Asiak looked at each other and burst out laughing.

"It wasn't so at all," Asiak said at last.

"Here's how it was," said Ernenek. "He kept snubbing all our offers although he was our guest. He scorned even the oldest meat we had."

"You see, Ernenek, many of us white men are not fond of old meat."

"But the worms were fresh!" said Asiak.

"It happens, Asiak, that we are used to foods of a quite different kind."

"So we noticed," Ernenek went on, "and that's why, hoping to offer him at last a thing he might relish, somebody proposed him Asiak to laugh [have sexual intercourse] with."

"Let a woman explain," Asiak broke in. "A woman washed her hair to make it smooth, rubbed tallow into it, greased her face with blubber, and scraped herself clean with a knife, to be polite."

"Yes," said Ernenek, rising. "She had purposely groomed herself! And what did the white man do? He turned his back to her! That was too much! Should a man let his wife be so insulted? So somebody grabbed the scoundrel by his miserable little shoulders and beat him a few times against the wall—not in order to kill him, just wanting to crack his head a little. It was unfortunate it cracked a lot!"

"Ernenek has done the same to other men," Asiak put in helpfully, "but it was always the wall that went to pieces first."

The white man winced. *"Our judges would show no understanding for such an explanation. Offering your wife to other men!"*

"Why not? The men like it and Asiak says it's good for her. It makes her eyes sparkle and her cheeks glow."

"Don't you people borrow other men's wives?" Asiak inquired.

"Never mind that! It isn't fitting, that's all."

"Refusing isn't fitting for a man!" Ernenek said indignantly. "Anybody would much rather lend out his wife than something else. Lend

55

out your sled and you'll get it back cracked, lend out your saw and some teeth will be missing, lend out your dogs and they'll come home crawling, tired—but no matter how often you lend out your wife she'll always stay like new."

Hans Ruesch, *Top of the World*, Harper & Row, Publishers, Incorporated, New York, 1950; Pocket Books, 1951, pp. 87–88.

As this anecdote shows, a particular social situation gets its meaning from the culture in which it appears. A situation has very different meanings in two different societies. The members of each society are so completely immersed in their own body of belief and custom that they generally fail to sense that they are obeying *belief* and *custom*, and fail to wonder *why* they believe and act as they do. Only by imaginatively stepping outside his own body of belief and custom can a man become aware of his actual nature. The purpose of this chapter is to help us to *see* our own behavior as a system of beliefs and values, of customs and traditions, of gadgets and properties, and of social contacts and relationships that we call our culture.

A Purari youth in the Amazon basin awakens at sunrise from his sleep on a woven reed mat on the floor of the men's house. With other unmarried young men, he sleeps here because it would be shockingly indecent for him to sleep in the same house with his female relatives. He yawns, stretches, and rises to perform his first assigned task of the day—he checks the row of human skulls on the display racks to see that they are in neat and orderly array. He gazes at them and remembers the mighty enemies they represent. He wishes he were old enough to share in the next cannibal feast. Then the enemy's powers would surge through his own muscles and his enemy's craft would lodge in his own brain! Truly, it will be wonderful to be a Purari warrior!

But meanwhile there is work to do. He takes a quick plunge into a muddy stream, then goes to his father's house for a breakfast of sago sticks. He finds his mother and sisters in the house so he returns to the men's house to eat his breakfast, as any well-mannered young man should do. Today's work is to be a pig hunt, so he collects bow and arrows and joins several other young men, mostly relatives on his father's side of the family. While they are waiting, a Purari maiden strolls casually by with her grass skirt swinging gaily and he chats with her for a moment. He suspects that she may like him but their fingers do not even touch, for both are above any vulgar public display. As the party leaves for the jungle, her younger brother appears and unobtrusively falls into step with him. Quietly and wordlessly this boy slips a small gift—which happens to be a roll of tobacco leaves—into his hand and then drifts away. Now his step becomes more elastic and the set of his shoulders more assured. Now he knows that she likes him and that the costly love-magic he placed under his sleeping mat last night has worked well. Truly it would be good to be a Purari warrior, but meanwhile, it is good to be a Purari young man!

For descriptions of the Purari, see F. E. Williams, *The Natives of the Purari Delta, Anthropological Report no. 5,* Territory of Papua, Port Moresby, 1924; J. H. Holmes, *In Primitive New Guinea,* G. P. Putnam's Sons, New York, 1924; Robert F. Maher, *The New Men of Papua,* University of Wisconsin Press, Madison, Wis., 1961.

This sketch shows that a culture is a system of behavior norms that people follow habitually and unthinkingly. They seldom realize how closely their behavior is guided by system. In the culture of his own society a man lives and dreams, shapes his ideals, formulates his questions, stages his rebellions, trains his body, and disciplines his mind. He dreams those dreams his culture suggests, wishes those wishes his culture develops, and fears those fears his culture inspires. He takes pride in the achievements his culture applauds and feels shame at the impulses his culture condemns. Each person is, far more than he will ever know, *the product of his culture*. If we would understand people, we must study culture.

Some Functions of Culture

As we have seen, a culture is no more an assortment of curious ways of doing things than a heap of spare parts is an automobile. A culture is an *organized system of behavior*, together with its supporting ideas and values. How does the culture of a society—of any society—function to control and direct the life of the individual?

Culture Defines Situations. An early sociologist, W. I. Thomas, coined the phrase "the definition of the situation." Suppose someone approaches you with right hand outstretched at waist level. What does this mean? That he wishes to shake hands in friendly greeting is perfectly obvious—obvious, that is, to anyone familiar with our culture. But in another place or time the outstretched hand might mean hostility or warning. One does not know what to do in a situation until he has defined the situation. Each culture has many subtle cues that define each situation, revealing whether one should prepare to fight, run, laugh, or make love. The stranger who misinterprets the cues and wants to run when he should make love, or vice versa, is a stock comic figure in the literature of many cultures. Each society has its insults and fighting words. In many primitive societies a man would be undisturbed at the suggestion that his mother's husband was not his father, but it is unwise to call an American a "bastard" unless one is ready for a brawl.

The cues that define situations appear in infinite variety and subtlety. When a Dobuan man cuts or delouses a woman's hair in public, it means they have committed adultery and that he is challenging her husband to make something of it. Owen Wister's "Virginian" says, "When you call me that, smile!" A word spoken in one manner is an insult demanding manly vengeance; but delivered with a different inflection it becomes a bit of harmless banter. A person who moves from one society into another will spend many years misreading the cues, laughing at the wrong places, and committing *faux pas*. In fact, it is debatable whether a person who enters another society as an adult ever fully absorbs the endless nuances of meaning within that culture.

Culture Prescribes Attitudes, Values, and Goals. Each person learns from his culture what is good, true, and beautiful. It matters not whether female charm is represented by a flat-chested, straight-hipped flapper of the American 1920's, a chubby butterball of the French

Regency, or a mountainous heap of Dahomean blubber—to each, man has reacted with predictable longing, for each had been defined by his culture as desirable. When a Rhodesian chieftain told Lillian Russell, a famous beauty of the last century, "Miss Russell, had Heaven only made you black and fat, you would be irresistible," he revealed how his feelings were channeled by his society's concept of beauty.

Attitudes, values, and goals are defined by the culture, and the individual normally learns them as unconsciously as he learns the language. Sociology has no special definitions for these terms; they are used in their popular meaning by sociologists. Attitudes are tendencies to feel and act in certain ways. Values are measures of goodness or desirability; for example, we value private property, representative government, romantic love, and many other things and experiences. Goals are those attainments which our values define as worthy; for example, winning the race, gaining the affections of a particular girl, or becoming president of the firm. An interrelated and interdependent set of attitudes, values, and goals is an important part—probably the *most* important part—of any culture. Why will twenty-two healthy young Americans, after hours of grueling practice, pound one another into sweaty exhaustion in a mighty effort to boost the air-filled skin of a dead pig over a pair of posts? Why is it a moral obligation of every Marindese husband to hunt heads? Each culture defines the desirable goals and the praiseworthy values.

By approving certain goals and denigrating or ridiculing others, the culture channels individual ambitions. The American high school male graduate may wonder whether to become a carpenter, a salesman, or a physician, but he "decides" against being a dressmaker or a eunuch without even considering the matter. Young American women today wonder what career to enter—a question that did not arise a century earlier, when our culture approved no role for women except that of housewife. Since domesticity was the only goal for women the culture respected, it was the only role most women wanted.

In these ways culture determines the goals of life. The young person looking for a career may feel he has a free choice, but he will choose one of the lines of work his culture has taught him to value. Whether it is praiseworthy to become a mighty warrior, a powerful capitalist, a great landowner, or a wandering, penniless holy man—the choice is defined by the culture and sanctified by its religion. An extreme example of this channeling can be seen in Tibet where, prior to Chinese annexation, it is estimated that about one-third of the males became Buddhist monks. This occupational distribution would seem absurd to most other societies but is understandable in view of Tibetan cultural values.

Even one's play is culturally defined. Hunting, which was work for primitives, is play for moderns. To play golf is acceptable in the United States, but cricket or lacrosse, although far more vigorous, are not "masculine." Few American men will brag about their skill in the kitchen; but at a charcoal grill—that's different!

The cultural definition of goals helps to explain the achievements and failures of different societies. Why did Germany lead the world in music, Italy in art, and England in commerce during the eighteenth century? Laymen often attribute such achievements to some racial or national aptitude, but a more careful look shows that each society excels in those activities the culture rewards and encourages.

The individual may develop, modify, or oppose the trends of his culture, but he always lives within its framework. What would Bach have done in a culture with no musical instruments or Einstein in a culture without a number system? The "great man" is one whose talents can find an outlet in the culture; without appropriate cultural channels his genius will either take a different form or remain dormant. In more ways than there is space to tell, we are the reflections of our culture. It provides channels for our individual talents and shapes our general attitudes and view of life.

Culture Provides Myths, Legends, and Supernatural Beliefs. Myths and legends are an important part of every culture. They may serve as an inspiration, reinforce effort and sacrifice, and bring comfort in bereavement. Whether they are true is sociologically unimportant. Ghosts are

Culture provides myths.

real to people who believe in them and who act upon this belief. We cannot understand the behavior of any group without knowing something of the myths, legends, and supernatural beliefs they hold. Could the Jews have survived centuries of persecution without the chosen-people belief to sustain them? Try to explain the rise of Hitler without exploring the heritage of Teutonic mythological heroes with which he identified the Nazi movement! In an effort to promote loyalty and sacrifice, Communist

China is today reviving the ancient myth of Han superiority, the image of a favored people surrounded by barbarian hordes. The legend that one sturdy freeborn American can lick any number of decadent foreigners has helped keep us unprepared for every war we have entered. Myths and legends are powerful forces in a group's behavior.

Culture also provides the individual with a ready-made view of the universe. Questions such as the origin of the world, the nature of divine power, and the important moral issues are defined by the culture. The individual does not have to grope or select but is trained as a Christian, Buddhist, Hindu, Moslem, or in some other religious tradition. This tradition gives answers for the major imponderables of life and fortifies the individual to meet life's crises.

Culture Provides Behavior Patterns. The individual need not improvise; he need not go through painful trial-and-error learning to know what foods can be eaten without poisoning himself or how to live among people without fear of mayhem. He finds a ready-made set of patterns awaiting him which he needs only to learn and follow. This is a tremendously important fact. Without it we would still be living in caves and hollow trees—those of us who survived long enough.

For example, if a society is to survive without unbearable chaos, it must provide some standardized way of forming new families. In the United States our culture has encouraged a set of romantic attitudes and developed a dating system that lead to marriage. Other societies are shocked that marriage partners should be selected through youthful impulse and romantic illusion, and they have made different provisions. In some Arab groups the young man knows he is predestined to mate either with the oldest available female cousin of his father's brother or with the nearest kinswoman equivalent in relationship. In the Tinguian tribe of the Philippines, parents until recent years selected mates for their offspring and often arranged the betrothal in early infancy so that the matter would be settled at an early age. Different as these methods are, they have one feature in common: The culture maps out the path to matrimony. The individual does not have to wonder how one secures a mate; he *knows* the procedure because his culture has defined it. He accepts without question this path to matrimony because he has been trained to view it as the only proper way to get a mate, and considers himself fortunate to have been provided for in this manner.

From before he is born until after he is dead, man is a prisoner of his culture. His culture directs and confines his behavior, places his goals, and measures his rewards. His culture gets into his mind and shutters his vision so that he sees what he is supposed to see, dreams what he is expected to dream, and hungers for what he is trained to hunger. He may imagine that *he* is making choices or that *he* rules his destiny, but the choices of the normal person always fall within a series of possibilities that the culture tolerates. The individual is thus prepared to fill his role among his fellows, while the smooth, orderly operation of the society is assured. The occasional individual who deviates from these expected patterns is scorned and punished by his fellows, for he upsets the smooth operation of society, and if people are to be comfortable, society must carry on in an orderly and predictable manner.

Ethnocentrism

Oliver Wendell Holmes once observed that "the axis of the earth sticks out visibly through the center of each and every town and city." Sumner [1906, p. 13] called this outlook *ethnocentrism*, formally defined as "that view of things in which one's own group is the center of everything and all others are scaled and rated with reference to it." Stated less formally, ethnocentrism is the tendency for each group to take for granted the superiority of its culture. We assume, without thought or argument, that monogamy is better than polygamy, that young people should choose their own mates, and that it is best for the young married couple to live by themselves. Our society is "progressive," while the non-Western world is "backward"; our art is noble and beautiful, while that of backward societies is grotesque and degraded; our religion is true; others are pagan superstitions. Ethnocentrism makes our culture into a yardstick with which to measure all other cultures, which are "good" or "bad," "high" or "low," "right" or "queer" in proportion as they resemble ours. It is expressed positively in such phrases as "chosen people," "progressive," "superior race," "true believers," and negatively by epithets like "foreign devils," "infidels," "heathen," "backward peoples," "barbarians," and "savages." Like the Bostonian who "didn't need to travel because he was already here," we are usually quick to recognize ethnocentrism in others and slow to see it in ourselves. Thus it was often remarked that Americans could not possibly believe Hitler's claim that the Germans were a nation of supermen, because they knew this could only be true of Americans!

All known societies are ethnocentric. The "backward" native peoples to whom we feel so superior have a similar feeling of superiority to us. Even while they are adopting our technology, they generally view most of the rest of our culture as quaint and absurd. Worsley describes the New Guinean's evaluation of white men.

> The Europeans were not regarded as all-powerful, but as rather pathetic, ignorant people who could be easily cheated or stolen from. Their ignorance of sorcery was lamentable. "These are not men; they are merely gods," said the natives, judging the whites to be beings whose lives were inferior to those of

living men. Again, they spoke the indigenous tongues very badly; why should one bother trying to make out their uncouth speech?

Peter Worsley, *The Trumpet Shall Sound*, MacGibbon & Kee, London, 1957, pp. 208–209.

Most, if not all, groups within a society are also ethnocentric. Caplow [1958, p. 105] studied fifty-five sets of six organizations each, including fraternities, churches, insurance companies, colleges, and many others. He found that members overestimated the prestige of their own organizations eight times as often as they underestimated it. Ethnocentrism is a real human reaction, found in all known societies, in all groups, and in practically all individuals.

A few persons reject their group or some part of its culture. There are anti-Semitic Jews, anti-Negro Negroes, aristocrats who lead revolutions, intensively trained believers who abandon their faith, and so on. This rejection of one's group or culture has sometimes been called xenocentrism, although the term is rarely used in sociological literature. Such a reaction is a form of deviant behavior and will be discussed in a later chapter.

Some Reasons for Ethnocentrism. *Habit*. Groups are ethnocentric because man is a creature of habit. Man learns to enjoy the culture of his society. We come to *like* the food our society eats, prepared and served the way we serve it. In our churches, listening to familiar church music and familiar rituals, we feel worshipful, but a Buddhist prayer wheel or ragged holy man in India arouses in us no feelings of devotion. We enjoy our music, but the music of the Orient sounds to us like a lot of tuneless banging. Our form of family life seems normal and comfortable; we cannot imagine ourselves practicing wife-purchase, accepting a mate we have never even met, or submitting to ceremonial defloration. In short, since other culture traits do not arouse the appropriate feelings in us, we automatically rate them as inferior and undesirable.

Lack of Understanding. Groups are ethnocentric because they do not understand what a trait means to its user. Since we do not realize how other people feel in a situation, *we impute to them the feelings we would have* in such a situation. An American father who would sell his daughter in marriage to a man she did not already love would have to be crude, greedy, and unfeeling. Therefore the non-Westerner who permits wife-purchase must be crude, greedy, and unfeeling. The essence of ethnocentrism consists in *judging other groups in terms of our group's values*. This procedure practically guarantees that we will be comfortably reassured of our own superiority.

Since wife purchase is a custom foreign to Western culture, let us analyze it and see what meanings it carries for the people who practice it. Wife-purchase has been practiced by a good many primitive societies, but in none of them is the wife bought as merchandise; nor is she owned as a man owns his property. Rather, the purchase price is viewed as a property exchange between families that serves several functions. It recompenses the bride's family for raising her; it dramatizes a girl's desirability; it guarantees that only a "suitable" husband from a responsible family will become the son-in-law; it serves as a sort of deposit for good behavior. In some societies, if the husband abuses his wife, she may return to her family, while the husband and his family forfeit their purchase price. Since the purchase price is usually quite substantial, he is likely to be lonely for a long time. Conversely, if the wife proves to be a poor bargain, he may return her and demand either a refund or an exchange. The rejected wife will find that such a homecoming is decidedly chilly, since her family must now provide either another daughter or a large refund in exchange for this daughter whom no one is likely to want. Thus the purchase price operates to encourage both partners to do their part in making the marriage a success. (Possibly wife-purchase is what we need in our society!) The bride and her family are proud of the price she can command, and would be insulted at the suggestion that she give herself for nothing. People in these societies were puzzled by the Christian missionaries' disapproval of wife-purchase, and felt great pity for the Western women whose men had so little respect for them that they did not want to pay a flattering price for them. In other words, the "heathen" are just as ethnocentric as Christian Americans.

If we understand a pattern, we are less likely to make ethnocentric judgments about it and the people who practice it. If we know how they feel about this pattern, and realize the needs and purposes it fills in their culture, we may judge it according to *their* tastes and values and not according to ours.

Cultivation. We are ethnocentric because we are encouraged to be ethnocentric. Our culture complex of nationalistic patriotism is perhaps the greatest source of deliberately cultivated ethnocentrism. From early childhood we learn about national heroes and the national mythology. Self-appointed patriotic organizations comb our textbooks and pounce upon any statements lacking in ethnocentric coloration. Organized religion is busily engaged in the promotion of ethnocentrism. Many religions, including many branches of Christianity, proclaim themselves the one true faith. All other faiths are true only in so far as they agree with the one true faith; wherever others diverge, they are the false and evil corruptions of the Devil. Far from seeking a sympathetic understanding of other faiths, most religious bodies urge their members to reject absolutely any ideas that might weaken their own belief in the true faith.

Many other sources of ethnocentrism exist. Almost every race, social class, regional or sectional group, occupational group, recreational group, or group of any kind encourages the ethnocentrism of its members.

Personal Inadequacies. Some of us are ethnocentric as a defense against our own inadequacies. But not all persons in a group are equally ethnocentric. How can we explain this difference? Each person belongs to many groups and has many associations, and his personality is an integration of all these influences. Some evidence exists that, at least in our society, some persons develop a personality that is basically more ethnocentric than that of other people. Many research studies have explored this hypothesis. One group of studies [O'Connor, 1952; Brown, 1953] finds that the ethnocentric person is apt to have difficulty in following abstract reasoning and tends to be intolerant of ambiguity in a threatening situation. By "difficulty in abstract reasoning" we mean he has difficulty in placing specific events in the framework of a complicated chain of reasoning and therefore easily accepts simplified explanations that fit ethnocentric prejudices. "Intolerance of ambiguity" means that the ethnocentric person sees the experiences of life as polar opposites with no indeterminate shadings; that is, everything must be either "good" or "bad," with no confusing mixtures. This polarity is especially necessary when he feels that his status or his group's welfare is involved; his need for security demands that his enemies and friends must be clearly identified. He cannot attribute adversity either to his own limitations or to a complex chain of events, but must fix the blame on some specific personal or ideological devil. In this way he can simplify a baffling world and escape the need to deal realistically with his own shortcomings.

A number of research projects have given us information on the kinds of people most apt to hold strong ethnocentric views. One of these, *The Authoritarian Personality* [Adorno et al., 1950], sought to discover the personality types most apt to accept a fascist philosophy. Most of the data were gathered through interviews with people on the West Coast of the United States during and after World War II. The authors developed a scale designed to measure ethnocentrism. They found that the ethnocentric personality is not just prejudiced against one group but against many. The people they questioned who denigrated Negroes also expressed suspicion of other minorities in the society, and were distrustful of many "foreign" groups and influences. From this and other studies of ethnocentrism [Stouffer, 1955; Altus and Tabejian, 1953] we arrive at some general characteristics of the kinds of Americans who are most likely to be highly ethnocentric. Five social categories among whom ethnocentrism has been found to be higher are women, older people, the less educated, those less active in community affairs, and the religiously orthodox. The people in these categories may be more ethnocentric because they are somewhat restricted in their interaction with other groups in our society. Seclusion of one kind or another is obviously more characteristic of the aged, the less educated, and those who are inactive in community affairs. It is also true that many women are still confined to contacts with their families and those in the immediate neighborhood, although this situation is rapidly changing. The religiously orthodox are those who develop an intense and unquestioning loyalty to a religious creed while living in a society that permits religious variation. Religious orthodoxy, with its sharp distinction between truth and error, would seem to appeal to the desire of the ethnocentric person for definite, unambiguous answers and a positive identification of good and bad people.

These studies have also found ethnocentrism to be higher among people with certain personality characteristics: the sexually inhibited, those with obsessive compulsions, those with paranoid feelings (of persecution), those with stunted egos (lack of self-confidence), and the poorly socialized (ruthlessly self-centered). While this is not the place for a detailed psychoanalytic interpretation of ethnocentrism, it is clear that individual differences in ethnocentrism are related both to the group affiliations and to the personality structure of the individual.

We should remember that not everyone in each of these categories is highly ethnocentric; these are group averages. Also, we often find that a particular form of ethnocentrism is a local tradition that one absorbs along with the rest of the culture, without necessarily becoming ethnocentric about other topics. Thus Southern whites learn a set of ethnocentric reactions to Negroes; but Prothro [1952] finds no evidence that Southerners are more ethnocentric about other groups than comparable persons from other parts of the country. The intense ethnocentrism that some localities, such as Boston, cultivate in matters of local pride and history may not extend to other topics. In other words it takes more than one ethnocentric reaction to identify a person as highly ethnocentric.

Effects of Ethnocentrism. Is ethnocentrism good or bad for people? First we should have to decide how to define "good" and "bad," and even then we might find the question very unsettled. Ethnocentrism gets us into many of our muddles; yet it is doubtful whether groups can survive without it.

Promotion of Group Unity, Loyalty, and Morale. Ethnocentric groups seem to survive better than tolerant groups. Although most of the tolerant religions have disappeared, the ruthlessly ethnocentric ones have, in the main, survived and maintained missionary zeal. Ethnocentrism justifies sacrifice and sanctifies martyrdom. The attitude, "I prefer my customs, although I recognize that basically they may be no better than yours," is not the sort of faith for which dedicated believers will march singing to their death.

Ethnocentrism reinforces nationalism and patriotism. Without ethnocentrism, a vigorous national consciousness is probably impossible. Nationalism is but another level of group loyalty. Periods of national tension and conflict are always accompanied by intensified ethnocentric propaganda. Perhaps such a campaign is a necessary emotional preparation for the expected sacrifices.

Protection against Change. If our culture is already the world's most perfect, then why tinker with alien innovations? From the Biblical Hebrews to nineteenth-century Japan, ethnocentrism has been used to discourage the acceptance of alien elements into the culture. Such efforts to prevent culture change are never entirely successful; change came to both the Hebrews and the Japanese. Yet if people share a serene, unquestioning faith in the goodness of their culture—the sort of conviction that is so completely accepted that no proof is necessary—then change is delayed.

Ethnocentrism also acts to discourage change.

Ethnocentrism also acts to discourage change in the internal arrangements of a culture. Privileged and wealthy groups are apt to feel that their society is "the best of all possible worlds," since a society that treats them so well must be good. Ethnocentrism also brings comfort to those of low status. An example is seen in the attitude of Southern "poor whites" toward Negroes. Myrdal [1944, pp. 597–599] found that the poor whites, low in income and social status, were the strongest exponents of the doctrine of white supremacy. As Sinclair Lewis writes, "Every man is king so long as he has someone to look down upon." Belief in the moral and mental inferiority of Negroes and perhaps "damyankees" compensates for their own wretched position. These attitudes are powerful barriers to change in the American South.

In discouraging culture change, ethnocentrism is undiscriminating. It discourages both the changes that would disrupt the culture and the changes that would help it attain its goals. Ethnocentrism led the Biblical Hebrews to reject both the pagan gods that would have disrupted their culture and the superior farming techniques of their neighbors that would have advanced their culture. Since no culture is completely static, every culture must make some changes if it is to survive. Ethnocentrism in India today helps keep her from turning communist, but India may not remain noncommunist unless she rapidly adopts Western technology, and this change is delayed by ethnocentrism. In an age of atom bombs and push-button warfare, when probably the nations must either get together or die together, ethnocentrism helps keep the nations tied to concepts of national sovereignty. Under some circumstances, then, ethnocentrism promotes cultural stability and group survival; under other circumstances ethnocentrism dooms the culture to collapse and the group to extinction.

Bigotry. Ethnocentrism blinds a group to the facts about themselves and other groups. Our own interests at many times require an accurate appraisal of the motives, abilities, and accomplishments of another group. If a government misjudges the intentions and capabilities of other nations, it leads its people to destruction, as the Germans and Japanese have recently learned.

The history of colonialism offers many illustrations of the blunders into which ethnocentrism can lead. The nineteenth century saw the development of colonialism, a philosophy that calmly assumed that Western nations as the carriers of a superior culture had an obligation to take over the government of Asian and African regions. The ethnocentrism that made the colonial officials so obnoxious to the natives also made these officials unable to recognize how deeply they were resented. (*They* knew their presence benefited the natives; why couldn't the stupid natives see their conqueror's superiority?) Colonialism has therefore ended with a startling abruptness; and Western ethnocentrism is now being replaced by a still more rigid and intolerant native ethnocentrism of the African and Asian peoples.

An Evaluation of Ethnocentrism. We can see there is no simple answer to the question whether ethnocentrism is good or bad. It is inevitable. It has a number of effects, some of which most of us would consider good and some bad. Our interest is neither to justify nor to condemn it but to understand it. We must understand that no one can help being ethnocentric. As Ruth Benedict has observed:

> The life history of the individual is first and foremost an accommodation to the patterns and standards traditionally handed down in his community. From the moment of his birth the customs into which he is born shape his experience and behavior. By the time he can talk, he is the little creature of his culture, and by the time he is grown and able to take part in its activities, its habits are his habits, its beliefs his beliefs, its impossibilities his impossibilities.

Ruth Benedict, *Patterns of Culture,* Houghton Mifflin Company, Boston, 1934, pp. 2–3.

Rarely are we able to question the basic values of our culture until we come into direct contact with people from another background. Even at this point of contact our tendency is not to question the values of our culture but rather to defend them vigorously against the assaults of members of the other group whom we tend to classify as "backward" or "immoral" and therefore unworthy of serious consideration. To understand our own ethnocentrism will help us avoid being so gravely misled by it. We cannot avoid *feeling* ethnocentric, but with understanding, we

No one can help being ethnocentric.

need not *act* upon these irrational feelings. We may become able to base our actions on rationally perceived facts, rather than on thoughtless ethnocentric evaluations. For unless we can understand and control our ethnocentric impulses, we shall simply go on repeating the blunders of our predecessors.

Cultural Relativism

We cannot possibly understand the actions of other groups if we analyze them in terms of *our* motives and values; we must interpret their behavior in the light of *their* motives, habits, and values if we are to understand them. Consider, for example, the administration of justice in the far North. The Canadian Mounties are occasionally summoned to the arctic region to apprehend Eskimos who have committed a murder. This action in terms of our culture is a crime, a violation of the mores. In the culture of many Eskimo tribes, however, the killing may have been justified, since their mores demand that a man avenge an injury committed upon a kinsman. This type of revenge is not considered unruly or deviant but the only honorable kind of action a respectable member of the society could take. We would condemn the man who takes the law into his own hands and seeks revenge, while they would condemn the man who has so little courage and group loyalty as to allow his kinsman to go unavenged.

Few culture traits are so disturbing to most Americans as the primitive practice of headhunting, an apparently useless and bloodthirsty pastime. However, this trait nearly everywhere has a fairly complex meaning. Among the Marindese of New Guinea, a quite gentle and affectionate people, heads were hunted in order to provide names for their children [VanderKroef, 1956]. Since they firmly believed that the only way a child could get a name and a separate identity was to take it from a living person, they hunted heads from neighboring tribes. A Marindese husband had a moral obligation to have one or two head names on hand, in case he was presented with a child. Thus headhunting, like any other important trait, was deeply integrated into a total cultural system within which it was moral and necessary.

These illustrations show what we mean by cultural relativism—that *the function and meaning of a trait are relative to its cultural setting.* A trait is neither good nor bad in itself. It is good or bad only with reference to the culture in which it is to function. Fur clothing is good in the arctic but not in the tropics. Premarital pregnancy is bad in our society, where the mores condemn it and where there are no comfortable arrangements for the care of illegitimate children; premarital pregnancy is good in a society such as that of the Bontocs of the Philippines, who consider a woman more marriageable when her fertility has been established and who have a set of customs and values that make a secure place for the children. Adolescent girls in the United States are advised that they will improve their marital bargaining power by remaining chaste until marriage; adolescent girls in New Guinea are given the opposite advice, and in each setting the advice is probably correct. The rugged individualism and peasant thrift of early America would produce great unemployment if they were widely practiced in our present mass-production economy. From such examples we see that *any cultural trait is socially "good" if it operates harmoniously within its cultural setting to attain the goals the people are seeking.* This is a workable, nonethnocentric test of the goodness or badness of a culture trait.

The concept of cultural relativism does not mean that all customs are equally valuable nor does it imply that no customs are harmful. Some patterns of behavior may be injurious in any milieu, but even such patterns serve some purpose in the culture, and the society will suffer unless a substitute is provided.

Sociologists are sometimes accused of undermining morality with their concept of cultural relativism and their claim that almost "everything's right somewhere." If right and wrong are merely social conventions, say our critics, one might as well do whatever he wishes. This is a total misunderstanding. It is approximately true that "everything's right somewhere"—but not everywhere. The central point in cultural relativism is that in a particular cultural setting, certain traits are right because they work well in that setting, while other traits are wrong because they would clash painfully with parts of that culture. This is but another way of saying that a culture is integrated, and that its various elements must harmonize passably if the culture is to function efficiently in serving human purposes.

Real and Ideal Culture

In most societies some behavior patterns are generally condemned yet widely practiced. The people who follow these patterns cannot be considered "deviant," since their behavior is common in the society even though not sanctioned by the approved mores. In some cases these illicit behavior patterns have existed for centuries side by side with the norms that are supposed to outlaw them. As an example of this type of behavior, Malinowski cites the Trobriand Islanders, a group whose incest tabus extend to third and fourth cousins.

> If you were to inquire into the matter among the Trobrianders you would find that . . . the natives show horror at the idea of violating the rules of exogamy and that they believe that sores, disease and even death might follow clan incest. . . .
>
> [But] from the point of view of the native libertine, suvasova (the breach of exogamy) is indeed a specially interesting and spicy form of erotic experience. Most of my informants would not only admit but actually did boast of having committed this offense or that of adultery (kaylasi); and I have many concrete, well-attested cases on record.

Bronislaw Malinowski, *Crime and Custom in Savage Society*, Routledge & Kegan Paul, Ltd., London, 1926, pp. 79, 84.

Like all societies, the Trobrianders have some standardized ways of evading punishment, for Malinowski observes, "Magic to undo the consequences of clan incest is perhaps the most definite instance of methodical evasion of law."

This case illustrates the difference between the real and ideal culture. The ideal culture includes the formally approved folkways and mores that people are supposed to follow (the cultural norms); the real culture consists of those they actually practice (the statistical norms). For example, Warriner [1958] found that many residents of a town in Kansas, a legally "dry" state, drank in private while supporting the "temperance" morality in public. He concluded that the official morality served to prevent a disruptive public controversy, without interfering with their drinking behavior. There are many such divergences between the real and ideal culture in our society.

A clash between the real and ideal culture patterns is generally avoided by some kind of rationalization that allows people to "eat their cake and have it." For example Lowie [1940, p. 379] describes some Burmese villages that are Buddhist and hence forbidden to kill any living thing, yet are dependent upon the murderous occupation of fishing. The people evade this contradiction by not overtly killing the fish, which ". . . are merely put out on the bank to dry after their long soaking in the river, and if they are foolish and ill-judged enough to die while undergoing the process it is their own fault."

No society is free of such inconsistencies, and complex societies like ours have many patterns that are formally condemned, enthusiastically practiced, and skillfully rationalized. We cherish monogamous marriage but tolerate quasilegalized prostitution. The practices seem to be incompatible, but there is little conflict between them since our culture trains us both to applaud the virtuous woman and to tolerate the prostitute. Tax evasion is legally and morally wrong, but apparently it is practiced by most people who have the opportunity. Business life demands rigid honesty, but alongside this uprightness may be found a pattern of bribery and special favors that is said to facilitate the making of business agreements. All are equal before the law in America—except Negroes, immigrants, poor people, radicals, women, children, and the unemployed. Such contradictions could be extended into an impressive list for any modern society.

In some circumstances it may be possible that the illicit patterns of behavior allow society to engage in conduct that seems essential to the welfare of the group but for which it has not been able to find a moral sanction. Thurman Arnold expressed this viewpoint [1937]. He argued that the large-scale consolidation of industry was an essential part of modern technological development. This trend, however, is inconsistent with the American mores which sanction the value of small-scale competitive business. To meet the situation, he claims that the United States evolved unenforceable antitrust laws that expressed our moral condemnation of bigness in business and at the same time permitted business to gain the advantages of continued consolidation. This procedure reminds us of the practice in some primitive societies in which courtship and marriage procedures are so complicated that most marriages occur through a type of elopement that is vigorously condemned by the mores. If the couple are unusually awkward, they may be caught and severely beaten, but ordinarily they are able to make good their escape. After a period of penance, they are welcomed back into the social group. Thus society is able to maintain the expression of sentiments sacred to the mores along with the existence of a useful practice in violation of the mores, thereby promoting a type of adjustment that seems necessary to the smooth functioning of the culture.

Culture and Medical Care

Health beliefs and practices are a part of every culture. Most ancient and primitive societies had supernatural explanations for illness. The Dobuans believed that all illnesses and injuries were caused by witchcraft and could be prevented or cured only by witchcraft. In classic Greece, accidents and injuries were man-made, and were therefore treated rationally; illness was believed to be supernaturally caused, and was treated by magical rites and potions.

Christian societies until very recently viewed illness as a divine punishment for sin. Even today this view still clings to the venereal diseases. And there are many groups in our society—American Indians, Mexican-Americans, Puerto Ricans, and a great many of our uneducated people —among whom supernatural and superstitious health ideas abound.

Scientific medicine conflicts with the folk medicine of these subcultures. Scientific health workers often fail because they do not realize that they are dealing with a subculture that must be sympathetically understood. Suppose the doctor wants the Mexican-American woman to enter the hospital but her husband, whom she has been taught to obey, tells her to stay out of this strange, fearsome place and stay home and take care of the children. What does she do? As a good wife, she does what her husband tells her to do. To scold the husband is useless; he must be persuaded that his wife *needs* to enter the hospital.

Physicians and nurses must understand the subcultures with which they deal if they are to be effective. The wise physician does not discourage or ridicule the Navajo family that stages a *yebachai*, a healing dance for an ailing member, for he knows that though the rite is medically useless, it is emotionally most beneficial. It is good psychosomatic medicine, and a part of "total patient care" for the Navajo. He opposes folk medicine only where it is positively harmful, and encourages the patient to use both folk and scientific medicine. Saunders [1954b] and Gould [1957] have discussed this problem.

Summary

From before one is born until after he is dead, his life is circumscribed by his culture. His culture (1) defines the meaning of situations and thereby indicates the behavior expected; (2) defines the attitudes he should hold, the values he should cherish, and the goals that are worthwhile; (3) provides the myths, legends, and supernatural beliefs he will live by; and (4) gives him ready-made behavior patterns to carry out all of these.

All societies and all groups assume the superiority of their own culture, a reaction called *ethnocentrism*. We are ethnocentric because (1) we are so habituated to our culture's patterns that other patterns fail to please us; (2) we do not understand what an unfamiliar trait means to its user and therefore impute our reactions to him; (3) we are trained to be ethnocentric; (4) we find ethnocentrism a comforting defense against our own inadequacies. Ethnocentrism (1) promotes group unity, loyalty, and morale, and thereby reinforces nationalism and patriotism; (2) protects a culture from changes, including those needed to preserve the culture; (3) reinforces bigotry and blinds a group to the facts about themselves and other groups, sometimes preventing their successful adjustment to other groups and cultures. Sociology neither applauds nor condemns ethnocentrism, but seeks to understand it and its effects on society.

Cultural relativism describes the fact that the function and meaning of a culture trait depend on the culture in which it operates. Traits are judged "good" or "bad" according to whether they work efficiently within their own culture.

Every society has an ideal culture, including the patterns that are supposed to be practiced, and a real culture, including illicit behavior that is formally condemned but widely practiced. Clashes between the two are evaded by rationalization. In some cases illicit patterns are ways of getting necessary tasks done and thus, even though the mores do not approve the illicit actions, may actually contribute to cultural stability.

Every culture and subculture has its health beliefs and practices. Health personnel must understand them if they are to be effective.

Questions and Projects

1. Why must we "define a situation" before we can do anything?
2. What goals do you think are most widely approved in our society? How is your present behavior related to these goals?
3. Is ethnocentrism the opposite of cultural relativism? Explain.
4. How would you make a group or a nation less ethnocentric? More ethnocentric?
5. Is there any difference between ethnocentrism and patriotism? Are the most ethnocentric groups also the most patriotic?
6. In what ways does ethnocentrism aid in national survival in the modern world? In what ways does it jeopardize national survival?
7. What effects do you think an extended trip around the world is

likely to have on one's ethnocentrism?
8. Cheating in college is sometimes defended on the ground that it is necessary if the student is to reach the goal of graduation. Is this position defensible in terms of cultural relativism? Why or why not?
9. In terms of cultural relativism, how would you appraise the old Chinese custom of binding upper-class women's feet?
10. Are there any respects in which the real hospital subculture differs from the ideal hospital subculture?
11. In a perfectly integrated culture, would there be any divergence between the real and ideal culture patterns?

12. Occasionally a child dies because his parents refuse to authorize the indicated medical procedures. Why do they take this attitude?

Suggested Readings

"The American Way of Life," *Fortune,* February, 1950, p. 63. A comment on the goals, values, and regional subcultures of American life.

BAIN, READ: "Our Schizoid Culture," *Sociology and Social Research,* 19:266–276, January, 1935. A classic discussion of our cultural contradictions.

CHASE, STUART: "On Being Culture Bound," *Antioch Review,* September, 1949, pp. 293–306. Shows how the habit of thinking in terms of our own culture makes it difficult for persons from different cultures to understand one another.

GILLIN, JOHN: "The Old Order Amish of Pennsylvania," in *The Ways of Men,* Appleton-Century-Crofts, Inc., New York, 1948, pp. 209–220. A summary of John W. Kollmorgen's research on the Old Order Amish who are seeking to preserve a distinct subculture.

GOULD, HAROLD A.: "Some Implications of Technological Change for Folk and Scientific Medicine," *American Anthropologist,* 59:507–516, 1957; reprinted in Dorrian Apple (ed.), *Sociological Studies of Health and Sickness,* McGraw-Hill Book Company, New York, 1960, pp. 88–99. A brief discussion of the use of folk and scientific medicine in a village in India.

LA BARRE, WESTON: "Professor Widjojo Goes to a Koktel Parti," *New York Times Magazine,* Dec. 9, 1956, pp. 17ff. A brief, highly entertaining picture of our folkways as seen through the eyes of an imaginary

African anthropologist doing field work in "darkest America."

MC CABE, GRACIA S.: "Cultural Influences on Patient Behavior," *American Journal of Nursing,* 60:1101–1104, 1960. A description of how lack of medical understanding affected the reactions of uneducated Negro patients in a rural Southern hospital.

MERYMAN, RICHARD S., JR.: "South Dakota's Christian Martyrs," *Harper's Magazine,* December, 1958, pp. 72–79. A description of a group of Americans who are being persecuted because of their subculture, which includes a form of New Testament communism.

MICHENER, JAMES A.: *Return to Paradise,* Random House, Inc., New York, 1950; Bantam Books, 1952, section entitled, "Povenaaa's Daughter." A popular writer's hilarious tale of ethnocentric Americans' inability to comprehend the customs of Polynesian society, a fairly comfortable mixture of native and Western elements.

MINER, HORACE: "Nacirema Culture," *American Anthropologist,* 58:503–507, June, 1956. An anthropologist describes the quaint customs and odd values of a well-known modern culture that the student may recognize.

SAUNDERS, LYLE: *Cultural Differences and Medical Care,* Russell Sage Foundation, New York, 1954, chaps. 3 and 4. A study of how the cultural background of Mexican-Americans affects the problem of bringing scientific medicine to them. Chapter 4 is reprinted in E. Gartly Jaco (ed.), *Patients, Physicians and Illness,* The Free Press of Glencoe, New York, 1954, pp. 189–206.

WILLIAMS, ROBIN M., JR.: *American* *Society,* Alfred A. Knopf, Inc., New York, 1951, chap. 10, "Institutional Variation and the Evasion of Normative Patterns." A perceptive discussion of the differences between our real and ideal cultures.

CHAPTER
4

Socialization, Culture, and Personality

Every man is in certain respects
  a. Like all other men
  b. Like some other men
  c. Like no other man

Clyde Kluckhohn and Henry A. Murray (eds.), *Personality in Nature, Society, and Culture,* Alfred A. Knopf, Inc., New York, 1949, p. 35.

There are some elements of man's heredity, environment, and social experience that he shares with all other men, some that he shares with some other men, and some that he shares with no other man. What these are and how they operate is the subject of this chapter.

Factors in the Development of Personality

The factors in personality development include (1) heredity, (2) physical environment, (3) culture, (4) group, and (5) unique experience.

Biological Inheritance. A brick house cannot be built of stone or bamboo; but from a pile of bricks a great variety of houses can be built. Heredity provides the raw materials of personality, and these raw materials can be shaped a great many different ways.

Unlike many species, the human animal is sexually active throughout the entire year, and this characteristic guarantees the more or less constant association of the sexes. The human infant is born helpless and will survive only if given tender care for many years. Such biological facts provide a basis for man's group life. Some species are monogamous by instinct; that man is not is a biological fact that every society must deal with in some manner. Some of the similarities in man's personality and culture are due to his common heredity. As far as we know, every human group in the world inherits the same general set of biological needs and capacities. According to Montague [1958, p. 85], these needs include oxygen, food, liquid, rest, activity, sleep, bowel and bladder elimination, escape from frightening situations, and the avoidance of pain. Our common heredity thus explains some of our similarities in personality, while individual differences in heredity explain some of the individual differences in personality. But *group* differences in personality cannot be attributed to heredity unless there is convincing evidence that the groups differ in average inheritance.

The American Negroes were taken from a number of tribes, mostly in West Africa. Promptly upon arrival they began absorbing a culture and developing a personality quite different from that of their African kinsmen. Americans of many racial and national origins now share a common culture, and their differences in personality are not closely related to their different ethnic origins. We could cite dozens of examples of a rapid change in culture and personality without any apparent change in heredity. All that we know of heredity suggests that the heredity of a group does not change rapidly enough to account for such changes in group behavior. What heredity does is to provide the set of needs and capabilities that the other factors can use in shaping human personality.[1]

[1] See Ralph Linton, *The Study of Man*, Appleton-Century-Crofts, Inc., 1936, chap. 9, "The Raw Materials for Society," for a more extended discussion of the biological basis for man's culture and personality.

Physical Environment. Some of our earliest manuscripts are attempts to explain man's behavior in terms of climate and geography. Sorokin [1928, chap. 3] summarizes the theories of the hundreds of writers, from Confucius, Aristotle, and Hippocrates down to the modern geographer Ellsworth Huntington, who have claimed that group differences in behavior are due mainly to differences in climate, topography, and resources. Such theories fit beautifully into an ethnocentric framework, for geography provides a respectable, apparently objective explanation for our national virtues and other peoples' vices.

The difficulty with geographic explanations is that there are too many exceptions. If a hot climate favors dictatorship and a temperate climate encourages democracy, then how do we explain the Nazi and Communist dictatorships or the early Roman Republic? If the excitability of the Italians and the stolidity of the Scandinavians are climatically caused, then what explains the dour Dobuans and the good-natured Eskimos?

Tradition is more important than physical environments.

The fact is that most kinds of personality and culture are found in every kind of climate. We find sharply differing cultures in similar physical environments, as witness the American Indians and the American colonists, or Tibet and the Peruvian highlands. We also find similar cultures in differing physical environments, as in the British settlements in England, India, Australia, and South Africa. Tradition is more important than physical environment in shaping most of our behavior. Social life in an area sometimes changes rapidly, without any change in physical environment. Obviously the physical environment is only one of the factors in social life.

Physical environment sets the limits within which the culture can develop. A desert people will not use boats or live in log houses. They usually live as small nomadic bands or in remote oases, and their shifting habitation profoundly affects much of their social life. Physical environment is, unquestionably, a highly important factor in social life, especially among the more primitive societies. It accounts for some similarities in the social life of all desert peoples, highland peoples, seafaring peoples, or hunting peoples. Men can use only the materials present in their environment (at least until they develop trade and transportation). Diet is limited to those foods that are available; but it is further limited by cultural preference, for almost all societies reject some of the edible foods available to them. Environment is a persuasive but seldom a controlling factor in social life.

Socialization

The infant enters the world as an organism concerned only with his own physical comforts. He soon becomes a human being, with a set of attitudes and values, likes and dislikes, goals and purposes, patterns of response, and a deep, abiding concept of the sort of person he is. He gets these through a process we call *socialization*—the learning process that turns him from an animal into a person with a human personality. Put more formally, *socialization is the process whereby one internalizes the norms of his groups so that a distinct "self" emerges, unique to this individual.* This chapter seeks to show how group experience, unique personal experience, and culture interact with biological inheritance to shape the personality of the individual.

Group Experience and Socialization. As one's life begins there is no self, for the individual is simply an embryo whose life and growth come from the mother's body. Nor do birth and the severing of the umbilical cord produce any awareness of self. Even the distinction between the limits of the physical self and the rest of the world is a matter of gradual exploration as the infant discovers that toes are a part of his body, not like the rattle or the bars on his crib which belong to the external world.

The realization of a distinctive personality is an even more complicated process which continues throughout life. The child learns to differentiate between various other people by names—Daddy, Mummy, and Baby. At first, any man is a "daddy" and any woman a "mummy," but eventually he moves from names that distinguish a status to specific names that identify individuals, including himself. At about the age of two he begins to use "I," which is a sign of definite self-consciousness—that he is becoming aware of himself as a distinct human being [Cooley, 1908; Bain,

1936]. As time passes and social experiences accumulate, he forms an image of the kind of person he is—an image of self. One ingenious way of trying to get some impression of a person's self-image is the "Twenty Questions Test" [Kuhn and McPartland, 1954] in which the informant is asked to write twenty answers, exactly as they occur to him, to the question "Who am I?" One's formation of his image of self is perhaps the most important single process in personality development.

Social Isolates. To some degree personality is dependent on physical-growth processes. But personality development is not simply an automatic unfolding of inborn potentials, as is shown by the social isolates whose physical growth has not been accompanied by corresponding personality development. Several times each year the newspapers report instances of neglected children who have been chained or locked away from the normal family group. They are always found to be retarded and generally antisocial or unsocial. Without group experience, human personality does not develop. The most dramatic reports are those of so-called feral children, separated from their families and supposedly raised by animals [Singh and Zingg, 1942; Krout, 1942, pp. 106–114]. Social scientists doubt that a child could live for long in the care of animals, and suspect that these children had been lost or abandoned by their parents and then discovered by others shortly thereafter [Ogburn, 1959].

An explanation of the reported "animal" behavior of feral children is offered by Professor Bettelheim, who states that severe cases of infantile autism being treated at the Orthogenic School of the University of Chicago show symptoms like those of the feral children, although there was no claim that the Chicago children had ever been in a nonhuman environment.

> During one year a single staff member had to have medical help more than a dozen times for bites she suffered from Anna, and the children regularly bare their teeth when annoyed or angry. Different, and again reminiscent of animals, is their prowling around at night, in marked contrast to their quiet withdrawal to a corner during the day. . . . Then there is their great preference for raw food, particularly for raw vegetables. . . . Some of these children on seeing animals, respond as though they had found a dear long lost friend. One girl for example, became extremely excited on seeing a dog; she showed a strong desire to run toward it and cried or howled like an animal. . . . She fell on all fours, jumped like a dog with her head down and made biting gestures. Now had we believed in the feral origin of this girl—whose total life-history, incidentally, is well known to us—we would probably have been convinced that, on seeing that wolflike creature, she was filled with memories of her happy times among wolves and was reverting to what she had learned from them.

Bruno Bettelheim, "Feral Children and Autistic Children," *American Journal of Sociology,* 54:458, March, 1959. See also Bernard Rimland, *Infantile Dutism,* Appleton-Century-Crofts, Inc., New York, 1964.

It is highly doubtful, then, that allegedly feral children are examples of animal nurture. It does seem evident, however, that children who are emotionally rejected and deprived of normal loving care fail to develop the type of personality we usually consider human. This conclusion is consistent with the findings of a number of experiments in which animals were raised in isolation from their normal groups. Harlow [1961] raised monkeys in isolation, with only a heated terry-cloth-covered wire framework as a substitute "mother," from which they received their bottle and to which they clung when frightened. As infants, they seemed satisfied with this substitute mother, but as adults, they were almost entirely asocial. Many were apathetic and withdrawn; others were hostile and aggressive. None showed the social group behavior of normal adult monkeys. Apparently the substitute mother met the infant's need for affection and security but was unable to carry the monkey through any further stages of psychosocial development. Other animal experiments show similar failures of isolated animals to develop the behavior normal for their species [Krout, 1942, pp. 102–105]. Both animals and human beings need group experience if they are to develop normally.

Cooley and the Looking-glass Self. Just how does a person arrive at a notion of the kind of person he is? He develops this concept of self through a gradual and complicated process which continues throughout life. It is an image that one builds only with the help of others. Even the elementary knowledge that one is fat or thin, tall or short is a comparative judgment that we cannot make until we have had the opportunity to compare ourselves with others. Whether one is intelligent, average, or stupid; attractive, homely, or downright ugly; righteous or sinful; these and many other ideas of the self are learned from the reactions of our associates. This picture of oneself as it is reflected in the reactions of others has been labeled the "looking-glass self" by Cooley [1902, pp. 102–103], who carefully analyzed this aspect of self-discovery.

There are three steps in the process of building the looking-glass self: (1) our imagination of how we look to others, (2) our imagination of their judgment of how we look, and (3) our feelings about these judgments. Suppose that whenever you enter a room and approach a small group of people conversing together the members promptly melt away with lame excuses. Would this experience, repeated many times, affect your feelings about yourself? Or if, whenever you appear, a conversational group quickly forms around you, how does this attention affect your self-feelings? A wallflower is a person who learned early in life that she could not make bright conversation. How did she discover this?

Just as the picture in the mirror gives an image of the physical self, so the perception of the reactions of others gives an image of the social self. We "know," for instance, that we are talented in some respects and less talented in others. This knowledge came to us from the reactions of other persons. The child whose first crude artistic efforts are sharply criticized learns that he lacks artistic talent, while the child whose first efforts win praise from a considerate parent may build up a belief in his own ability in this field. As he matures, others will also give a reaction, although it may differ from that of his parents, for the social looking glass is one that is constantly before us.

Still more important are the impressions the individual receives as to whether he is an attractive person who inspires love or an inadequate person who is incapable of stimulating affection and respect. As with specific talents, this type of self-knowledge is first gained from parents and is modified by the reactions received from others in later life. It is difficult to change completely an impression formed in early childhood. A child who learns from his family that he is inferior and unwanted may cling to a belief in his personal inadequacy in spite of spectacular success in adult life. Conversely, one who seems to be a failure in life may carry a feeling of security, developed through favorable early childhood experience, that survives adult disappointments. This does not mean that personality is frozen in a rigid mold in early childhood, but it does suggest that the adult does not easily change his childhood conception of self. Sometimes he must reinterpret his childhood experience in great detail, with the aid of psychotherapy, before he can reconstruct a concept of self with which he can live more comfortably.

Another difference between the functioning of the "looking glass" in early childhood and in later life is that the child may be deeply affected by the response of anyone with whom he comes in intimate contact, whereas the older individual is more discriminating in appraising the importance of the response he receives from various individuals. The baby-sitter's responses affect the child more than they affect the parent. Thus we say that as one matures he develops *reference* groups to whom he gives special attention [Rosen, 1955, 1955a]. A child may base his estimate of his musical talents on the opinion of his parents regardless of their musical sophistication; an adult is more likely to give special attention to the opinions of musical experts and ignore the reactions of others. Not only do we become more selective in choosing the reference groups that comprise our social looking glass but we also are selective in the perception of the images that do influence us. We pay more attention to some reactions than to others; or we may misjudge the reactions of others. It may be that the ego-boosting remark that we take at face value is mere flattery; a scolding may have been caused by the boss's headache rather than by our own error. Thus the looking-glass self the individual perceives may easily differ from the image others have actually formed of his personality. Several research efforts have sought empirical evidence of the correlation between one's *perception* of responses of others and the *actual* judgments they have made of him. These studies find that most people perceive fairly accurately the judgments of others about them. Calvin and Holtzman [1953] found that individuals vary considerably in their ability to perceive accurately the judgments of others about them, and that the less-well-adjusted person was less accurate in these perceptions. Clearly, it is our perception of the responses of others and not their actual responses that shapes our self-image.

Mead and the Generalized Other. The process of internalizing the attitudes of others has been aptly described by George Herbert Mead [1934, part 3, pp. 140–141] who refers to it as "the generalized other." This means that the self becomes reflective, that the individual looks at himself as though he were another person and judges his actions accordingly. This theory may be illustrated in terms of the development of play activities. At first the young child simply imitates the actions of his elders without much realization of why they act the way they do. Later in games such as "hide and seek" he begins to make a partial response to what he assumes will be the actions of others; he tries to predict the places they would look, and seeks to find less accessible hiding places. Later in the organized game he finds that others have definite roles assigned to them and must act in a given manner. In order to play the game successfully he must internalize the expected actions of others as well as their expectations of his actions, and conduct himself accordingly. When a girl plays with a doll, she acts out the part of the mother and gives the doll the part of the child; she can doll-play *only* as she puts herself into the role of another. Thus the individual is never truly alone, for always in his own mind he is responding to a pattern of behavior he attributes to others. The self is thus inevitably social, since the individual incorporates the attitudes of others in his own mind. His developing awareness of the social expectations of others is a vital part of self-development.

Freud and the Antisocial Self. Our treatment thus far implies a basic harmony between the self and society. In the words of Cooley:

> A separate individual is an abstraction unknown to experience. . . . In other words "society" and "individuals" do not denote separate phenomena but are simply collective and distributive aspects of the same thing. . . . And just as there is no society or group that is not a collective view of persons, so there is no individual who may not be regarded as a particular view of social groups. He has no separate existence; through both the hereditary and the social factors in his life a man is bound into the whole of which he is a member, and to consider him apart from it is quite as artificial as to consider society apart from individuals.

Charles Horton Cooley, *The Nature of Human Nature*, Charles Scribner's Sons, New York, 1902, pp. 1–3.

This concept of the socialized self is challenged by Freud, who sees no identity of self and society. Freud believed that the rational portion of human conduct was like the visible portion of an iceberg, with the larger part of human motivation resting in the unseen, unconscious forces that powerfully affect human conduct. He divided the self into three parts: the *superego*, the *ego*, and the *id*. The superego, or the conscience, represents the social ideals that one has internalized; the ego is the acting individual; the id represents instinctive desires that may be viewed as an unsocialized aspect of human nature. Since society restricts the expression of aggression, sexual desire, and other impulses, the id is continually at war with the superego. The id is usually repressed, but at times it breaks through in open defiance of the superego, creating a burden of guilt that is difficult for the self to carry. At other times the forces of the id find expression in disguised forms that enable the ego to be unaware of the basis of its actions, as when a parent relieves his aggressions by beating his child, believing it is "for his own good." Thus Freud finds that the self and society are often opponents, and not merely different expressions of the same phenomena. He asserts:

> If civilization imposes such sacrifices not only on man's sexuality but on his aggressivity, we can understand better why it is hard for him to be happy in that civilization. . . . We may expect gradually to carry through such alterations in our civilization as will better satisfy our needs and will escape our criticisms. But perhaps we may also familiarize ourselves with the idea that there are difficulties attaching to the nature of civilization which will not yield to any attempt at reform. . . . In all that follows I adopt the standpoint, therefore, that the inclination to aggression is an original, self-subsisting instinctual disposition in man, and I return to my view that it constitutes the greatest impediment to civilization.

Sigmund Freud, *Civilization and Its Discontents*, newly translated from the German and edited by James Strachey. Copyright © 1961 by James Strachey. First American edition 1962. W. W. Norton & Co., Inc., New York, N.Y., pp. 62, 69.

Freud's theories have inspired bitter controversies, rival "schools," and numerous interpretations and revisions. There is no simple experimental way to determine whether the concepts of superego, ego, and id are validly descriptive. Social scientists today agree, however, that Freud was probably right in his claim that human motives are largely unconscious and beyond rational control, and do not always harmonize with the needs of an orderly society.

Social and Individual Aspects of the Self. On the other hand Cooley, Mead, and many others have demonstrated that the very emergence of the self is a social process. From this social process, however, a self emerges that is not altogether harmonious with the society that created it. Man's readiness to respond to sexual stimuli is far greater than any society has felt could be safely permitted, and his tendency to meet any kind of frustration with aggressive violence must likewise be restrained in the interest of social order. Further, he may lack the type of physical stature, muscular coordination, or ability to engage in complex thinking that his society values. The ability of the individual to develop a self in harmony with the image his society prefers may depend, at least in part, on his possession of biological traits needed to match the social image.

Multiple Groups and Socialization. Another reason for lack of harmony between the self and society is that society itself is torn by conflict, and the individual is presented with models of behavior that are rewarded at one time and condemned at another, or approved by some groups and criticized by others. Thus the boy learns that he should be tough and able to "stand up for his rights" and at the same time that he should be orderly, considerate, and respectful. Some people caution the girl that society demands modesty and maidenly reserve, while others show how a bold, provocative approach is rewarded. In a society where the individual participates in a number of groups, often with conflicting standards and values, he must work out some way of dealing with these conflicting pressures. Failure to do so is likely to bring personal maladjustment and mental illness. He may deal with this problem by compartmentalizing his life, developing a different "self" for each group in which he moves. Or he may select a favorite reference group to conform to and have his real life within, rejecting other groups, as in the case below.

> "Thirteen arrests." The judge shook his head over my file.
> "Gang fightings, shootings, burglary, stealing a car. . . . I don't know what to make of you. Your parents are hard-working, religious people in pretty good circumstances. Your I.Q. is extraordinarily high. Why do you do these things?"
> I shrugged. What a dumb question. Every boy I knew did these things. Maybe I just did more of them and better.

"A Gang Leader's Redemption," *Life*, Apr. 28, 1958, pp. 69ff.

This boy had adopted the standards of the peer group rather than those of his family. Research studies [Warner and Lunt, 1941, p. 351; Rosen, 1955*b*] have usually emphasized the power of the peer group to cultivate behavior patterns contrary to those of the family. Not all youth, however, are as firmly wedded to peer-group standards, and not all peer groups are as much in conflict with family or society. Most youths find their principal extrafamily group allegiance in athletic teams, church youth groups, neighborhood clubs, or middle-class youth cliques that are in harmony with the standards of adult society. Such groups frequently operate to support the parental standards, as seen in this case.

> Bill was a late adolescent who began to run around with a girl who not only lived on the other side of the railroad tracks, but who had most of the traits as-

sociated with that oft-used phrase. Bill's family was upper class. Bill was personally most attractive, and his mother knew the power of a peer group. Calling Bill to her, she explained with disarming friendliness that she had heard of his new girl and wanted to meet her. Wouldn't he bring her to the house, and to make it less formal, she would invite a few of his favorite friends. Upon securing Bill's wondering and semireluctant consent, the mother proceeded to promote, secretly, a gala event, to which she invited all of Bill's extended clique. Bill's relations with the new girl just barely survived until the end of the party.

James H. S. Bossard, *The Sociology of Child Development*, Harper & Row, Publishers, Incorporated, New York, 1948, p. 507.

Why do some youths select peer groups that generally support the socially approved adult values while others choose peer groups that are at war with adult society? The choice seems to be related to self-image. The habitual delinquent is usually one who sees himself as unloved, unworthy, unable, unaccepted, unappreciated; he joins with other such deprived youth in a delinquent peer group that reinforces and sanctions his resentful, aggressive behavior. The law-abiding youth sees himself as loved, worthy, able, accepted, appreciated; he joins with other such youths in a conforming peer group that reinforces socially approved behavior. Truly, seeing is behaving. How we see ourselves is how we behave.

Unique Experience and Socialization. Why is it that children raised in the same family are so different from one another, even though they have had the same experiences? The point is that they have *not* had the same experiences; they have had social experiences that are similar in some respects and different in others. Each child enters a different family unit. One is the firstborn; he is the only child until the arrival of the second, who has an older brother or sister to fight with, and so on. Parents change, and do not treat all their children exactly alike. The children enter different peer groups, may have different teachers, and survive different incidents. Identical twins, in addition to identical heredity, come very close to having the same experience. They enter a family together, often have the same peer groups, and are treated more nearly alike by other people; yet even twins do not share *all* incidents and experiences. *Each person's experience is unique in that nobody else perfectly duplicates it.* A detailed inventory of the daily experiences of the several children in the same family will reveal an impressive number of differences. Thus each child (excepting identical twins) has a unique biological inheritance, exactly duplicated by no one, and a unique set of life experiences, exactly duplicated by no one.

Furthermore, *experiences do not simply add up; they integrate.* Personality is not built by piling one incident upon another like a brick wall. The meaning and impact of an experience depend upon the other experiences preceding it. When a popular girl is "stood up" by her date, this is not the same experience for her as it is for the wallflower. Psychoanalysis claims that certain incidents in one's experience are crucial because they color one's reaction to all later experience. "Psychological" movies often imply that psychoanalysis consists of probing into one's unconscious and dredging up *the* traumatic experience that caused all the trouble. This is a gross oversimplification. No woman has had her personality blighted *because* papa stomped on her dollie at the age of five. But it is possible that such a traumatic episode might be the beginning of a series of mutual rejection experiences, and thus color the meaning of a great many later experiences. This means that each person's experience is an infinitely complicated network of millions of incidents, each gaining its meaning and impact from all those which have preceded it. Small wonder that personality is complex!

Still another factor appears in the selection of roles to play within the family. Children imitate each other a great deal, but they also strive for a separate identity. Younger children often reject those activities which their older siblings already do well and seek recognition through other activities. Parents may unwittingly aid this selective process. Mother may say, "Susie is mama's little helper, but I guess Annie is going to be a tomboy," whereupon Susie starts clearing the table while Annie turns a few handsprings. Sometimes a child in a well-behaved family selects the "bad boy" role, and scowls impressively while his parents describe their problem to the visitors. In large families a child may be hard pressed to find a role that has not already been annexed by an older sibling. Thus in these and many other respects each person's life experience is unique—unique in that nobody else has had exactly this set of experiences and unique in that nobody else has the same background of experience upon which each new incident will impinge and draw its meaning.

Culture and Personality

We have seen how group experience develops personality similarities within groups and personality differences between groups, while unique experience develops the individuality and the personal idiosyncrasies of the individual. We shall now see how cultural experience develops similarities in personality within a society.

Cultural Variation in Personality. Some cultural experience is common to all mankind. Everywhere infants are nursed or fed by older persons, live in family groups, learn to communicate through language, experience punishments and rewards of some kind, and have some other experiences common to the entire human species. It is also true that each society gives to virtually all its members certain experiences that many

Some cultural experience is common to all mankind.

other societies do not offer. From the social experience that is common to virtually all members of a given society emerges a characteristic personality configuration that is typical of many members of that society. DuBois [1944, pp. 3–5] has called this the "modal personality" (taken from the statistical term "mode," which refers to that value appearing most frequently in a series). How the modal personality may vary between two different societies is seen in the following contrast.

The Anxious Dobuan [Fortune, 1932; Benedict, 1934, chap. 5]. The Dobuan child in Melanesia might think twice about coming into this world if he had any choice in the matter. He enters a family where the only member who is likely to care much about him is his uncle, his mother's brother, to whom he is heir. His father, who is interested in his own sisters' children, usually resents him, for the father must wait until the child is weaned before resuming marital relations with the mother. Often he is also unwanted by his mother; abortion is common. Little warmth or affection awaits the child in Dobu.

The Dobuan child soon learns that he lives in a world ruled by magic. Nothing happens from natural causes; all phenomena are controlled by witchcraft and sorcery. Illness, accident, and death are evidence that witchcraft has been used against one and call for vengeance from one's kinsmen. Nightmares are interpreted as witchcraft episodes in which the spirit of the sleeper has narrow escapes from hostile spirits. All legendary heroes and villains are still alive as active supernaturals capable of aid or injury. Crops grow only if one's long hours of magical chants are successful in enticing the yams away from another's garden. Even sexual desire does not arise except in response to another's love magic, which guides one's steps to his partner, while one's own love magic accounts for his successes.

Ill will and treachery are virtues in Dobu, and fear dominates Dobuan life. Every Dobuan lives in constant fear of being poisoned. Food is watchfully guarded while in preparation, and there are few persons indeed with whom a Dobuan will eat. The Dobuan couple spend alternate years in the villages of wife and husband, so that one of them is always a distrusted and humiliated outsider living in daily expectation of poisoning or other misadventure. Because of numerous divorces and remarriages, each village shelters men from many different villages, so that none of them can trust either their village hosts or one another. In fact, no one can be fully trusted; men are nervous over their wives' possible witchcraft and fear their mothers-in-law.

To the Dobuans, all success must be secured at the expense of someone else, just as all misfortune is caused by others' malevolent magic. Effective magic is the key to success, and a man's success is measured by his accomplishments in theft and seduction. Adultery is virtually universal, and the successful adulterer, like the successful thief, is much admired.

On the surface, social relations in Dobu are cordial and polite although dour and humorless. There is very little quarreling, for to give offense or to make an enemy is dangerous. But friends are also dangerous, for a friendship may be a prelude to a poisoning or to the collection of materials (hair, fingernails) useful for sorcery.

What kind of personality develops in such a cultural setting? The Dobuan is hostile, suspicious, distrustful, jealous, secretive, and deceitful. These are rational reactions, for he lives in a world filled with evil, surrounded by enemies, witches, and sorcerers. Eventually they are certain to destroy him. Meanwhile he seeks to protect himself by his own magic, but he can never feel a sense of comfortable security. A bad nightmare may keep him in bed for days. As measured by Western concepts of mental hygiene, all Dobuans are paranoid to a degree calling for psychotherapy. But simply to call them paranoid would be incorrect, for their fears are justified and realistic; the dangers they face are genuine, not imaginary. A true paranoid personality *imagines* that other people are threatening him, but in Dobu, other people really *are* out to get him. Thus the culture shapes a personality pattern that is normal *and useful* for that culture.

The Cooperative Zuñi [Benedict, 1934, chap. 4]. The Zuñi of New Mexico are a placid people in an emotionally undisturbed world. The child is warmly welcomed, treated with tender fondness, and receives a great deal of loving attention. He is never disciplined or punished, yet becomes a well-behaved member of a society in which crime is rare and quarreling almost unknown.

Cooperation, moderation, and lack of individualism are carried into all Zuñi behavior. Personal possessions are unimportant and readily lent to others. The members of the matrilineal household work together as a group, and the crops are stored in a common storehouse. One works for the good of the group, not for personal glory. (Zuñi children do poorly on competitive examinations in the government schools, for it is impolite to answer any question whose answer may be unknown to one's classmates.)

The magical forces in the Zuñi world are never malevolent and often helpful. The supernaturals have the same tastes as living men, so need not be feared. Supernatural and magical aid is sought through many long ceremonials, yet the ceremonial dances are never frenzied or orgiastic. Violence or immoderation is distasteful, and even disagreements are settled without open bickering. For example, one wife who became weary of her husband's many amours decided to settle the matter. "So," she said, "I didn't wash his clothes. Then he knew that I knew that everybody knew, and he stopped going with that girl." Without a word the issue was settled. Unlike most Indians the Zuñi rejected alcohol because it tempts men to immoderate, undignified behavior. They do not use peyote or other drugs, or resort to self-torture or prolonged fasting in an effort to induce ecstasies, visions, or other unusual sensory phenomena. They desire only the normal sensory experiences of moderate behavior.

The Zuñi have no sense of sin. They have no picture of the universe as a conflict between good and evil, nor any concept of themselves as disgusting or unworthy. Sex is not a series of temptations but part of a happy life. Adultery is mildly disapproved, but is largely a private matter and a probable prelude to a change of husbands. Divorce is simple; the wife simply piles her husband's things outside the pueblo, where he finds them, cries a little, and goes home to his mother. Since the family is matrilineal and matrilocal, a divorce does not seriously disrupt the life of the family or of the child. Yet divorce is not very common, and serious misconduct is very rare.

The normal personality among the Zuñi stands in stark contrast to that of the Dobuans. Where the Dobuan is suspicious and distrustful, the Zuñi is confident and trusting; where the Dobuan is apprehensive and insecure, the Zuñi is secure and serene. The typical Zuñi has a yielding disposition and is generous, polite, and cooperative. He is unthinkingly and habitually conformist, for to be noticeably different from his fellows is something neither he nor they can tolerate. Apparently this serves to control his behavior without the sense of sin and the guilt complexes found in many societies, including our own.

The Cultural Patterning of Personality. As the two foregoing sketches illustrate, personality differs strikingly from society to society. *Each society develops a basic personality type that fits the culture.* The Dobuans do not consciously or intentionally train their children to be hostile and suspicious, yet the atmosphere of constant treachery and fear has this result. Each culture, simply by being what it is and by working the way it works, shapes personality to fit the culture. Let us consider some aspects of the culture that affect the process of personality development. *Norms of the Culture.* From the moment of birth, the child is treated in ways that shape the personality. Each culture provides a set of general influences that vary endlessly from society to society. As Linton writes:

> In some [societies] infants are given the breast whenever they cry for it. In others, they are fed on a regular schedule. In some they will be nursed by any woman who happens to be at hand, in others only by their mothers. In some the process of nursing is a leisurely one, accompanied by many caresses and a maximum of sensuous enjoyment for both mother and child. In others it is hurried and perfunctory, the mother regarding it as an interruption of her regular activities and urging the child to finish as rapidly as possible. Some groups wean infants at an early age; others continue nursing for years.
>
> In the techniques of caring for infants there is an even greater cultural range. One society may make the baby the center of attention for the entire family, various adults constantly carrying it about, playing with it, and giving it anything it wants. Another society may regard infants as a nuisance and pay little attention to them outside the satisfaction of their physical needs. In some societies the child is in almost constant bodily contact with its mother during the first two years. Madagascar mothers keep their infants in the backs of their dresses, leaving them there even when working in the fields. In other societies this constant bodily contact is lacking, but the child is handled frequently. In still others it is rarely touched except at feeding time. In some societies the child is allowed to tumble about without interference. In others it spends its first eighteen months bound to a board, even its arms sometimes being wrapped. . . .
>
> Turning to the more direct effects of culture patterns upon the developing individual, we have an almost infinite range of variations in the degree to which he is consciously trained, discipline or the lack of it, and responsibilities imposed upon him. Society may take the child in hand almost from infancy and deliberately train him for his adult status, or it may permit him to run wild until the age of puberty. He may receive corporal punishment for even the smallest offense or never be punished at all. As a child he may have a claim upon the time and attention of all adults with whom he comes in contact or, conversely, all adults may have a claim upon his services. He may be put to work and treated as a responsible contributing member of the family group almost from the moment that he is able to walk and have it constantly impressed upon him that life is real and earnest. Thus in some Madagascar tribes children not only begin to work at an incredibly early age but also enjoy full property rights. I frequently bargained with a child of six for some object which I needed for my collections; although its parents might advise, they would not interfere. On the other hand, the children in a Marquesan village do no work and accept no responsibility. They form a distinct and closely integrated social unit which has few dealings with adults. The boys and girls below the age of puberty are constantly together and often do not go home even to eat or sleep. They go off on all-day expeditions, for which no parental permission is required, catch fish and raid plantations for food, and spend the night in any house they happen to be near at sunset.
>
> Examples of such cultural differences in the treatment of children could be multiplied indefinitely. The important point is that every culture exerts a series of general influences upon the individuals who grow up under it. These influences

differ from one culture to another, but they provide a common denominator of experience for all persons belonging to a given society.

Some of the American literature on psychoanalysis and child development, drawing heavily on the theories of Freud, has attached great importance to specific child-training practices. Breast feeding, gradual weaning, demand-feeding schedules, and easy and late induction to bowel and bladder training have often been recommended, with the opposite practice being blamed for all sorts of personality difficulties. These recommendations are generally unsupported by any carefully controlled comparative studies, although dramatic case histories may be cited in illustration. One serious effort [Sewell, 1952] to test these recommendations made a comparison of American children who had been brought up according to different child-training practices. This study found that no measurable adult personality differences were associated with any particular child-training practices. Studies of personality development in other cultures have likewise failed to substantiate Freudian theories of the results of specific child-training practices [Dai, 1957; Eggan, 1943]. Apparently it is the total atmosphere and not the specific

Children are urged to copy.

practice that is important in personality development. Whether a child is breast-fed or bottle-fed is unimportant; what *is* important is whether the feeding is a tender, affectionate moment in a warmly secure world, or a hurried, casual incident in an impersonal, unfeeling, unresponsive environment.

Ideal Personality Types. A culture poses one or more ideal personality types that children are urged to copy. Among most of the Plains Indians, the approved personality for the adult male was that of a vigorous, self-reliant, aggressive warrior. Under many circumstances, to take what he wanted from the weak was a virtue. Any tendency to overlook insults or to compromise disagreements was a weakness. Since these personality characteristics were the only ones that were admired and rewarded, they were the ones most youths developed.

The most widely approved personality in our culture is probably the one who is friendly and sociable, somewhat cooperative yet quite competitive and aggressively individualistic, progressive, yet practical and efficient. Many features of our social life conspire to develop these characteristics within us. We live in a society where sociability has a cash value. Cordiality is taught and cultivated as a necessity in almost any career. The child is trained to make all requests with a "Please" and to receive all favors with a smiling "Thank you." Television commercials and clerks and salesmen maintain an unending barrage of smiling, friendly sounding appeals. While most of this outward show of friendliness is phony, it nonetheless surrounds one with an atmosphere of sociability that probably leaves some residue. Our society forces people to develop an acute consciousness of time, since nearly everything is done on a time schedule. The Indian's serene unconcern with time is exasperating to whites who have dealings with him, just as the white man's endless fretting and clock-watching perplexes and bores the Indian.

Until recently, most societies saw little if any change within a man's lifetime. People lived in an unchanging world, a world of customs seemingly unchanged over countless generations, of legends passed down from remote ancestors, and a world expected to extend endlessly into the future. We live in a culture permeated by change and expectations of change. Each child is surrounded by adults busily contrasting the present with their childhood reminiscences. Change is accepted, expected, and even discounted, since we base our future plans on the changes we expect to have taken place by the time our plans mature. Cultural influences such as these help to develop the bustling, restless, energetic personality that is admired in our culture.

A close relationship between personality and culture should be expected, because in a sense personality and culture are two aspects of the same thing. As Spiro [1951] has observed, "The development of personality and the acquisition of culture are not different processes, but are one and the same learning process. . . ." In a well-integrated society, personality is an individual aspect of culture, while culture is a collective aspect of personality. This discussion could be prolonged indefinitely, but enough has been said to illustrate the point that every culture, including our own, surrounds the individual with experiences that develop a normal personality, more or less perfectly reflected by most members of that society.

Subcultures and personality. This picture of a single approved personality type (for each sex and age level) in a society holds fairly true for the simple society with a well-integrated culture. But in a complex society with a number of subcultures, the picture changes. Are there personality differences between the Yankee and the Deep Southerner? Does the sharecropper think and feel as the urban professional? In a complex society there may be as many "normal personality types" as there are subcultures.

The United States has many subcultures—racial, religious, ethnic, regional, social-class, perhaps even occupational. The boundary lines are indistinct, and some subcultures are more important than others. For example, the Catholic and Protestant subcultures probably affect less of a member's life than the Jewish subculture and still less than the Amish subculture. Yet subcultures are real, and we have some justification for speaking of the "urban middle-class personality" or of the "typical salesman." Of course we must not exaggerate; it is likely that personality similarities within our culture greatly outnumber personality differences between subcultures, and there are individual personality differences within each subculture. But the physician, the minister, the carnival worker, and the migrant fruit picker show some personality differences from one another. Therefore we cannot describe *the* normal American personality without first naming the subculture we have in mind.

Individual deviation from modal personality. In even the most conformist of societies there is some individuality in personality. The modal personality merely represents a series of personality traits that are most common among the members of a group, even though comparatively few of them may have developed every one of the traits in the series. Wallace [1952a] used Rorschach tests on a sample of Tuscarora Indians, and concluded that only 37 per cent of them showed all twenty-one of the modal personality traits. Other similar studies [Kaplan, 1954; Wallace, 1952b] show that while a modal personality type characteristic of a society exists, it is not a uniform mold into which all members are perfectly cast. Likewise, in discussing the "typical" personality of nations, tribes, social classes, of occupational, regional, or other social groups, we must remember that the typical personality merely describes a series of personality traits, a *great many* of which are shared by *most* of the members of that group. Each society and each social group allows a certain amount of individual deviation from the modal personality. When this deviation extends beyond what the group or society considers "normal," then that person is considered to be a "deviant." Such deviation will be considered in some detail in Chapter 6.

Summary

We become human through *socialization*. Our *heredity* gives us a set of needs and potentialities that other factors may channel and develop;

our *physical environment* sets certain limits to our behavior; our *group experience* develops personality similarities within groups and differences between groups; our *culture* provides certain fairly uniform experiences for all members of our society; the *unique experience* of each person shapes his individuality.

Socialization requires group experience, and *social isolates* fail to develop a normal human personality. Socialization is heavily centered on the development of the concept of *self*. One's image of self is largely perceived in the looking glass of other peoples' reactions to him and his feelings about these perceptions. Through play and other group activities, one is also helped to perceive the feelings of others and their feelings toward him. Cooley viewed self and society as two aspects of the same thing, whereas Freud viewed self as basically antisocial, with most personality difficulties arising from the clash between the impulses of the self and the restraints of society.

In a complex culture with many kinds of groups, one may have difficulty in developing a satisfactory self-image and an integrated system of behavior. One may resolve this by compartmentalizing his life and acting differently in each group, or by conforming to one group while, if possible, ignoring any others whose standards conflict. Failure to do either may bring confusion and maladjustment.

The normal personality differs dramatically from society to society, as shown by the suspicious, treacherous, insecure Dobuan and the amiable, secure, cooperative Zuñi. Each society develops a normal personality which is produced by the total experience of a person raised in the society. Such cultural influences include the standard ways of treating people in the culture, the ideal personality types presented as models, and many other kinds of experience. All these influences tend to develop a modal personality type for the society.

The more complex societies may have a number of subcultures, each developing its characteristic personality and reducing the overall personality uniformity within the culture. Even in the simpler societies, there is no complete uniformity in personality; only a minority of the members share all the traits of the modal personality. In complex societies, the variation in personality is still greater.

Questions and Projects

1. How do we know that personality is not simply the maturing and unfolding of inherited tendencies?
2. What might be some possible differences in social life and human personality if human infants were normally born (and nursed) in litters instead of one at a time?

3. How is the self a social product?
4. How do games contribute to the development of the self?
5. Do you feel that Freud and Cooley are in basic disagreement on the nature of the self? Explain.
6. How can children in the same family develop such strikingly different personality traits?
7. It has been said that a person raised in one culture may learn to act like people in an adopted culture, but will never be able to think and feel like a person of his adopted culture. Do you agree?
8. If culture develops similarities in personality within a society, how do we explain personality differences within a society? Are such personality differences greater within a simple or a complex society? Why?
9. How would you explain the fact that groups that have a major socializing influence upon one person may leave another person in the same vicinity unaffected?
10. Can you recall a specific looking-glass incident in your experience? Write it up, describing your actions, others' reactions, your perception of their reactions, and your feelings about that perception. How do you think this incident affected you?
11. Write an account of a typical day in your life, listing all the standardizing cultural influences you have experienced along with nearly every other American, and state how you suspect each has helped shape your personality.
12. Describe the modal personality of the nursing profession. Do you detect any personality changes in yourself as you proceed with nursing training?
13. Prepare an analysis of the behavior of "Yank," the fireman in Eugene O'Neill's *The Hairy Ape.* Is his behavior consistent with what this chapter outlines about others and the concept of self?

Suggested Readings

BENEDICT, RUTH: *Patterns of Culture,* Houghton Mifflin Company, Boston, 1934; Penguin Books, Inc., Baltimore, 1946. Shows how each culture develops a behavior and personality that is normal and useful for that society.

BURTON, GENEVIEVE: *Personal, Impersonal and Interpersonal Relations: A Guide for Nurses,* Springer Publishing Company, New York, 1958, chap. 2, "Emotional Development and Illness." A brief, highly recommended chapter on emotional development and how it is affected by illness.

GOFFMAN, ERVING: *Presentation of Self in Everyday Life,* Social Science Research Center, University of Edinburgh, 1956; Anchor paperback, Doubleday & Co., Inc., Garden City, N.Y., 1959. A detailed picture of how the self emerges through everyday experiences.

HAVIGHURST, ROBERT J., AND ALLISON DAVIS: "A Comparison of the Chicago and Harvard Studies of Social Class Differences in Child Rearing," *American Sociological Review,* 20:438–442, August, 1955. Two separate studies show that cultural influences on personality development differ form one social-class subculture to another, and also differ by region, religion, and ethnic group within the same social class.

KUHN, MANFORD: "Self-attitudes by Age, Sex, and Professional Training," *Sociological Quarterly*, 1:39–55, January, 1960. Exploration of self-attitudes by members of different social categories through use of the Twenty Questions Test.

LEZNOFF, MAURICE, AND WILLIAM A. WESTLEY: "The Homosexual Community," *Social Problems*, 3:257–264, April, 1956. Describes efforts of homosexuals in a Canadian city to organize a "third-sex" community.

MEAD, MARGARET, AND MARTHA WOLF-ENSTEIN (EDS.): *Childhood in Contemporary Cultures*, The University of Chicago Press, Chicago, 1955. A number of studies of patterns of child development in different cultures.

MERRILL, FRANCES E.: "The Self and the Other: An Emerging Field of Social Problems," *Social Problems*, 4:200–207, January, 1957. An analysis of anxiety over others' image of the self in a society stressing achieved status.

CHAPTER 5 Role and Status

All the world's a stage,
And all the men and women merely players:
They have their exits and their entrances;
And one man in his time plays many parts.

William Shakespeare, *As You Like It*, Act II, Scene **7.**

Status is usually defined as the *position of an individual in a group* or of a group in relation to other groups. *Role* refers to the *behavior expected of one who occupies a certain status.* Children occupy a status usually subordinate to adults and are expected to show some degree of deference to adult authority. Soldiers occupy a status different from that of civilians, and their role calls for risks and duties other people are not expected to bear. Women have a different status from men; their role calls for "feminine" behavior. Each person may occupy a number of statuses and be expected to fill the roles appropriate to these statuses. In a sense, status and role are two words for the same phenomenon. A status is a set of privileges and duties; a role is the acting out of this set of duties and privileges.

Socialization through Role and Status

We become socialized largely through learning the various roles expected of us. We must learn to fill roles as child, student, parent, employee, organization member or officer, member of a particular racial and social class, citizen, resident of a community, and many others. Role learning involves at least two aspects: (1) We must learn to perform the duties and claim the privileges of the role and (2) we must acquire the attitudes, feelings, and expectations appropriate to the role. Of the two aspects the second is often the more important. Almost any young woman who can read can learn the mechanical skills of housekeeping fairly quickly; what she cannot learn quickly are the attitudes and expectations that make housekeeping a satisfying and rewarding activity. One cannot fill a role with complete success unless he has been socialized to accept that role as good, worthwhile, and satisfying.

Imagine the mental state of a young German Jew, raised in a prosperous, cultivated home, who graduated from medical school just as the Nazi government closed the professions to Jews; at best he could work only as a menial and live only as an outcast. Or consider the difficulties of a woman socialized to view the role of housewife as the only really rewarding role for a woman and finding herself an unmarried career girl living alone and competing in a man's world.

Role training for most of the important roles begins early in childhood as one starts to form attitudes toward those roles and statuses. Most of this role training is painless and unconscious. Children "play house," play with the toys given them, watch and help mother and father, hear and read stories, listen to family talk, and share in the countless incidents of family life. From all this experience they gradually form a picture of how men and women act and of how husbands and wives treat each other.

Social Roles and Personality. The child who assumes the role of his father while playing house is aware that he must think and act in a different manner than when he is simply playing his own role, that of child. At first he may have little understanding of the reasons underlying his father's actions, but this understanding grows, and his "pretend" roles actually help prepare him for the time when he does become a father. At a more mature level, pretend role playing has been a helpful aid in assisting people to understand the reactions of others in a diagnostic and therapeutic technique known as the psychodrama, developed by Moreno [1940] and others. Husbands and wives, for instance, in pretending to take the role of the other person, sometimes acquire a greater understanding both of the partner and of themselves.

The concept of role implies a set of expectations both of one's own be- behavor and of the reciprocal behavior of the others in the situation. Whether a new role is taken on a pretend basis or as a genuine result of acquiring a new status, the person is forced to analyze the attitudes and behavior of himself and of those about him [Turner, 1956]. Obviously the self does not remain unchanged after this kind of experience. The married woman is in a different status from that of the single girl. Her role is different, and in many ways she will seem a different personality. Occupational roles also produce personality changes, so that without knowing a person's occupation we may say that he "acts like" a teacher, a farmer, a businessman, or a minister. Personality and role have a reciprocal relationship in that certain personal characteristics favor or hinder the playing of social roles, while social roles in turn tend to develop the personal characteristics required. The extrovert, for instance, is a personality type who may find it easy to adjust to the role of salesman; conversely, the daily routine of salesman helps to develop an extroverted type of personality. Thus there is a constant interaction between role and personality.

People are unconsciously drawn to or repelled by certain roles because of features in their own personalities. For example, several comparative studies of women nursing students show how they differ from liberal-arts and education students. Elwood [1927] found nursing students to be more stable with fewer neurotic tendencies, highly extroverted, more ready to share things, more cooperative, more conventional in attitudes, and less self-conscious and less given to daydreaming. Lough [1947] found them to be more stable and somewhat more masculine in interests and attitudes. Beaver [1953] also found them to be more stable, more conventional and fastidious, more highly duty-inspired, and more likely to admire masculine qualities (briskness, emotional self-control, etc.) in their associates. Presumably these personality differences have a bearing on the choice of nursing as a career.

Ascribed and Achieved Status

Linton [1936, chap. 8] has noted that statuses are of two sorts: those ascribed to us by our society and those we gain through our own efforts.

Ascribed Status and Role. If a society is to function efficiently, people must perform a vast number of daily chores willingly and competently. The simplest way to ensure the performance is to parcel most of the routine work of the society into a series of *ascribed* roles and socialize people to accept and fill their ascribed roles. Since role training has to begin early in childhood, ascribed roles must be assigned according to some criterion that can be known in advance. Sex and age are universally used as a basis of role ascription; race, nationality, social class, and religion are also used in many societies.

Although role training may be largely unconscious, it is no less real. As a noted American educator has remarked, "Adults ask little boys what they want to be when they grow up. They ask little girls where they got that pretty dress." No wonder that by adolescence boys are becoming concerned about careers while girls are preoccupied with baiting the man trap! This is no accident, since a major part of the socialization process consists of learning the separate activities of men and women. The little girl plays with dolls, helps mother with the housework, and is rewarded for being a "little lady," meanwhile learning that "tomboy" activities, though possibly tolerated, are not really consistent with the feminine role. The boy finds out that dolls are for girls and babies and that no worse fate can befall him than to be a "sissy." Many years of differential training, if successful, will bring boys and girls to maturity with great differences in their responses, feelings, and preferences.

In mature life, sex differentiation continues, and the process of role definition becomes ever more complicated. The woman finds that she may have to become an economic provider as well as a mother and housekeeper and that she must do so without robbing her husband of his masculine ego feelings. She must be an informed citizen, an intelligent conversationalist, and an active community worker, yet not neglect her primary duties in the kitchen and nursery. She must be a seductive siren, skillful, patient, and responsive, but she must also be a chaste creature, modest and demure, learning with wonderment the facts of life from the lips of her husband. She must be a skillful—but not too skillful—sportswoman, yet remain a feminine clinging vine. She must be a household purchasing agent, business manager, and financial consultant when necessary; at all other times she must be completely ignorant of money matters. It is little wonder women often find it difficult to play this complex and paradoxical role.

We tend to attribute the complexity of sex roles in our society to the industrial revolution with its increase in women's occupational opportunities, but historical evidence suggests that any type of social change complicates the roles women perform. Before the United States became an industrial nation with women helping to man the offices and assembly lines, the pioneer women had already enlarged the feminine role.

> Though careful to preserve the illusion of soft helplessness these Western dames were mostly as hard as nails. Wives of the Donner party survived that awful winter of snowbound death far better than the males. While passing through Montana in September, 1849, the men of the Riker family parked the wagon with Janette Riker in it and went hunting. They never returned. Janette kept herself alive alone in the wagon until Indians found her the following April. . . . A woman in Washington territory was planting precious seed corn, which was eaten by a rooster. When she caught on, the woman pounced on the bird, cut it open on the spot, removed the kernels and planted them again. An officer's wife carried her baby across the Arizona desert in a champagne basket. Sarah Royce rode horseback with her baby in her lap, canteen and diapers in one saddlebag, a pan in the other and necessities hanging from the pommel.

Marshall Sprague, "On the Western Trail There Was Nothing Like a Dame," *New York Times Book Review*, Apr. 20, 1958, p. 6, reviewing Dee Brown, *The Gentle Tamers: Women of the Wild West*, G. P. Putnam's Sons, New York, 1958.

Obviously, what it means to be "feminine" varies with the needs of time and place.

Every society handles many of its tasks by making them part of the sex role. Yet most of the sex-linked functions can be performed equally well by either sex, provided they are socialized to accept the task as a proper one. Thus in Pakistan, men are the household servants; in the Philippines, pharmacists are usually women, but men are preferred as secretaries; in the Marquesas, baby-tending, cooking, and housekeeping are proper masculine tasks, while women spend much of their time primping; in many parts of the world the heavy agricultural labor is performed by women. Occasionally there is a direct challenge to the mores that support the traditional sex roles, as in the case of the feminist movement in England and the United States during the past century; but normally the sexes accept their ascribed roles with little protest.

The definition of masculine and feminine roles is subject to infinite variation, yet every society has an approved pattern that the people are expected to follow. Individuals may be permitted to bypass some parts of the pattern at times, but they risk estrangement from the society unless they can identify themselves with the role expected of their sex. A few individuals do fail to make this adjustment and become homosexuals or Lesbians, which means they try to ignore the roles expected of their sex. While such individuals may attempt to develop a unique status for a "third sex," the task is difficult, and they usually become marginal to the culture. Only a few societies have developed an accepted status for homosexuals, as in the case of the Plains Indians who consider the homosexual to be one who has been stricken by the gods and thereby merits special consideration. In the majority of cases the homosexual is normal physically, and his condition is now viewed as a failure of socialization in relation to sex roles rather than as some type of biological deviation. Even in the case of hermaphrodites, who are biologically intermediate between the sexes, their biological "closeness" to one sex or the other is less important than the social definition of them as "boy" or "girl" by their family and others. In other words "sex orientation is much more dependent upon hair style and clothes than upon the morphologic criteria of sex" [Jones and Scott, 1958, p. 49].

Each society also ascribes different roles according to age. The adjustment of age status is a perennial task; almost as soon as a person adjusts to one age level, he enters another with different status and role. Furthermore, in our society the socialization process is conspicuously inefficient in preparing for adolescence and old age. In most primitive societies the adolescent period is not marked by any unusual stress. At any given age in most primitive societies the individual has a clearly defined status and role; he, and everyone else, knows exactly what his duties and privileges are. His transition into adult life is marked at about the age of puberty by definite ceremonies called "rites of passage." He then assumes a new status and role and a new set of privileges and duties. At no time is there much uncertainty over what he should be and do. The system may provide little freedom, but it also creates little anxiety.

Our society has no clearly defined age statuses, except for the relatively minor legal maturity at twenty-one. The American youth and his parents have no standardized set of duties and privileges to guide them. Parents are uncertain as to just how much "maturity" to concede to him, and they bicker endlessly about his choice of companions, the hours he keeps, his use of money, the use of the car, and whether he is old enough to marry. In most primitive societies the adolescent enters a period of training that ends in an elaborate ceremony, in which he may endure ordeals or submit to circumcision, tattooing, or scarification. This ceremony establishes his status and announces that he is now ready to assume adult responsibilities, and his successful role performance is almost guaranteed. Our closest equivalents are found in such events as confirmation or first Communion, getting a driver's license, holding a full-time job, graduating from high school or college, and getting married. Yet we lack any systematic preparation or any general agreement upon the age, achievement, or type of ceremony that clearly establishes the transition into adult status.

The youth in primitive societies has few painful choices to make. There are no competing religious groups, political parties, or social clubs. Since occupations are limited, the youth escapes conflicting advice on the type of career he should choose. Religion, government, social activities, educational training, and occupation—all are traditional and clearly defined. By contrast the American youth must decide which, if any, of over 250 different churches he will join, decide whether to continue education or go to work, choose one of thousands of occupations, decide whether and whom to marry, and make many other choices. With so many alternatives, it is small wonder that many youths vacillate wildly before settling down or that others make decisions contrary to their parents' hopes and dreams.

The transition to middle age is not a happy one in our society, especially for women. Our accent on youth and glamour dooms every woman to feel her desirability slipping away from her. The menopause is a relentless announcement that youth, glamour, and romance are over; instead she can become "matronly." Plastic surgeons, cosmeticians, and beauticians make fortunes by catering to women's futile efforts to stave off the ravages of time. We suspect that many of the physical and emotional difficulties that sometimes accompany the menopause are due to this painful role transition.

Old age in many primitive or traditional societies is highly honored, perhaps because in a static society the ancient are the ones closest to the source of hallowed tradition. Thus in pre-Communist China the grandmother was the reigning female in a multiple-family home, and the grandfather was a patriarch whose whim was close to law. In contemporary industrialized society old age is a nuisance. A rapidly changing society looks for wisdom, not to the past but to the future, for people who were socialized two generations ago are likely to be behind the times. The compulsory retirement-at-sixty-five system is an expedient way of discarding the fossils. Multiple-family homes are scarce, and where they exist the aged are likely to be tolerated as a duty rather than revered as head of the household. The aged face a retirement in which their income is reduced, their responsibilities withdrawn, and their influence undermined, their main function in life being to divert themselves while waiting to die. The unhappy position of our aged demonstrates that a role transition is difficult when the characteristics that a person develops in one role can become useless or even troublesome as he moves into the next role.

Among the Plains Indians the warriors were trained from childhood to become aggressive, hostile, and uncompromising; then upon retirement to "old man" status, they were expected to be placid peacemakers. This called for an abrupt reversal in personality, and few of them could make the transition gracefully. An equally painful transition is demanded in our society. To be successful in the active adult role, a man must develop independence and self-reliance, learn to find satisfaction in useful work and in being adviser and protector of the young. As an aged person he must become dependent and submissive, able to respect himself with no useful work to do, and learn to keep his advice to himself while being ignored or patronized by the young. It is little wonder that many of our old people sicken and die soon after retirement, while many others become bored and fretful. The rapidly developing field of *geriatrics* indicates a serious concern with this topic, and the picture may change in the future. One such change is emphasis on the development of hobbies and activities that can be expanded on retirement, since they are not associated either with family or job. Another trend is the growth of specialized facilities that can provide pleasant living in a society segregated on an age basis. These include housing, either in rest homes or specially designed apartments; recreation centers, often with a name such as the Golden Years Club; or even the development of an entire village as a living place for retired people such as Longview, Washington. These trends are already changing the status of elderly people, but at present their role involves difficult adjustments at a time of life when such adjustments are not easy to make.

Sex and age are only two of many examples of ascribed status. All such statuses involve roles that can be filled successfully only when one has been socialized to expect and appreciate the role.

Achieved Status and Role. A social position secured through individual choice and competition is known as *achieved status*. Just as each person occupies a number of ascribed statuses, assigned without regard to individual ability or preference, so he occupies a number of achieved statuses that are secured through his ability, performance, and possibly good or ill fortune. The difference is aptly stated by Young and Mack.

> "Princess" is an ascribed status; where there is a hereditary royalty a girl does not work her way up to being princess. She is *born* a princess, and whether she is pretty or ugly, tall or short, intelligent or stupid, a princess she remains. *Achieved statuses,* on the other hand, are not assigned at birth, but are left open to be filled by the persons who compete most successfully for them. Being male is an ascribed status. It is determined at birth; either you are male or you are not. Being a husband is an achieved status; it does not result automatically from one's being born a male but depends upon a male's own behavior in the future. Negro is an ascribed status. One cannot change his color to white. But policeman is an achieved status. One is not born a policeman; he becomes one through his own talent or choice or action.

Kimball Young and Raymond W. Mack, *Sociology and Social Life,* American Book Company, New York, 1959, pp. 160–161.

In traditional societies most statuses are ascribed, with one's occupation and general social standing determined at birth. Industrialized so-

Being a husband is an achieved status.

cieties have a greater range of occupations, require a greater mobility of labor, and allow greater scope for the individual to change his status through his own efforts. The society stressing achieved status will gain in flexibility and in its ability to place people in occupations best suited to their talents. The price it pays for these advantages is seen in the insecurity of those unable to "find themselves" and in the strain of constant adjustment to new roles. Achieved status requires the individual to make choices not only of occupation but also of friends, organizations, schools, and place of residence. Further, it leads the individual into roles not foreseen or desired by his parents. In the traditional society where statuses and roles are ascribed, the individual is trained from childhood and guided through life by rules of conduct that he has carefully learned in preparation for the roles he is destined to play. In a society where the individual is free to experiment, he meets many situations far removed from the parental way of life and may have to feel his way awkwardly into unfamiliar roles.

Ascribed and achieved statuses are basically different, yet they interact with each other and may overlap. Thus it is easier for one with the ascribed status of male to reach the achieved status of President of the United States than it is for the one with the ascribed status of female. The achieved status of physician is open to both Negro and white, but in the United States whites reach it more easily than Negroes. General social standing in the community (social-class status) is partly ascribed, reflecting the status of one's parents, and partly achieved through one's own accomplishments. At many points the boundaries between achieved and ascribed status are indistinct, yet the concepts are useful.

Role Conflict and Personality

Many of man's personality difficulties and maladjustments can be analyzed and better understood in terms of role incompatibilities and conflicts. In saying this we do not deny the existence of the genetic or biological factor in personality disorder discussed in Chapter 6. It is agreed that whether people develop personality disorders depends partly on their biological inheritance and partly on the emotional stress they experience. Role conflicts are a major source of emotional stress and thus contribute to personality disorders. Role conflicts and role inadequacies are of several kinds.

Inadequate Role Preparation. The little girl singing lullabies to her doll, the small boy building a model airplane, the maiden filling her hope chest, the apprentice copying the work techniques of the mastercraftsmen—all are experiencing a continuity of socialization by learning skills and attitudes at one period of life that they can use at another. In this type of setting, each stage of life flows smoothly from the preceding stage and we use the earlier periods of life to anticipate the roles we shall carry out later on. A classic summation of this process is attributed to the Duke of Wellington: "The battle of Waterloo was won on the playing fields of Eton."

By "continuity in socialization" we simply mean that the experiences at each life stage are an effective preparation for the next stage. An example of how continuity in the socialization process provides a smooth transition into the adult role is seen in the child-training practices of the Cheyenne Indians described by Benedict.

> The essential point of such child training is that the child is from infancy continuously conditioned to responsible social participation while at the same time the tasks that are expected of it are adapted to its capacity. . . . At birth the little boy was presented with a toy bow and from the time he could run about serviceable bows suited to his stature were specially made for him by the man of the family. Animals and birds were taught him in a graded series beginning with those most easily taken, and as he brought in his first of each species his family duly made a feast of it, accepting his contribution as gravely as the buffalo his father brought. When he finally killed a buffalo, it was only the final step of his childhood conditioning, not a new adult role with which his childhood experience has been at variance.

Ruth Benedict, "Continuities and Discontinuities in Cultural Conditioning," *Psychiatry*, 1:161–167, May, 1938.

Such an easy transition from one status to the next is by no means universal. Our culture is characterized by built-in *discontinuities* which make the socialization experience in one age period of little use in the next. In frontier America, boys and girls learned their adult roles by simply observing and taking part in whatever was going on around them —clearing land, planting crops, caring for babies, and so on. Today there is less opportunity for such continuity. Most adult male work is performed away from home, where boys and youths cannot watch and share it. Many households offer only a poor opportunity for a girl to learn the skills, attitudes, and emotional rewards of the housewife. Children and youths have few important tasks in most households, and much of the child's play activity is not directly related to adult tasks and responsibilities. Our maidens find that when they have internalized the roles of glamour girl and career woman as presented in magazines and movies, they are suddenly enveloped in maternity and housekeeping duties for which their previous experience has done little to prepare them. Then when they have adapted to the housewife role, their children leave home, their housekeeping responsibilities diminish, and they must either face a late middle age of limited activity or transfer to roles much different from those they have known. Boys associate athletics with team sports such as basketball and football which are difficult for them to follow in later life; thus even the athletic youth may learn a form of recreation that will not provide the physical activity he needs as an adult. When men reach the age of sixty-five they are apt to find that a life dominated by work has not prepared them for the leisure that comes with retirement.

Another imperfection in our socialization process is that the moral training of boys and girls introduces them mainly to the *formal* rules of social behavior rather than to the informal modifications of these rules that operate in the adult world. In other words they are taught the ideal, not the real culture. The result is that young people become cynical as they find that the copybook maxims do not work out. The politician does not appear to be a public servant negotiating a livable situation between bitter opponents but a man who compromises on sacred principles; the businessman seems a greedy manipulator rather

Our culture is characterized by built-in discontinuities.

than an individual struggling to find his place in the market; the clergy-man is apparently not one who mediates between God and man but a huckster who fails to live up to the ideals of Holy Writ. Thus we run the gamut from youthful idealism to mature cynicism without ever reaching an understanding of the nature of culture that can enable us to appreciate the services of those who work out livable compromises with the unsolved problems of society.

Such discontinuities are also favored by rapid social change, since parents cannot possibly anticipate the type of world their children will face. While the emergence of new inventions is often recognized as a disrupting factor, the changing social climate is equally unpredictable. Thus the parent in Ceylon, who in the 1920s looked on Christianity as the religion of the enlightened and powerful, raised children who sometimes find this religious affiliation a social handicap, now that Buddhism has become identified with resurgent nationalism in a newly independent country. Conversely the African, trained as a child to respect the traditions of the tribe and the authority of the chief, may grow up to live as an urban laborer in a culture where chiefs are powerless and tribal traditions irrelevant. The American farmer may carefully train his children in the attitudes and techniques appropriate to farming, although it is a predictable certainty that many of these children are headed for an urban life and work.

Such examples could be multiplied indefinitely. They add up to the premise that it is impossible to prepare youth for precisely the roles they will play as adults in a changing society. Margaret Mead [1941] observes that the family and the school are adjusting to this situation by emphasizing the development of a broad range of qualities rather than attempting to prepare students for specific roles. Instead of training Susie to be a wife and mother *or* training her to be a career girl, Susie's home and school try to prepare her to fill either or both of these roles, as the occasion may demand. Thus "adjustment" is preferred to rote learning, and students are introduced to "methods of thinking" rather than being trained in specific vocational techniques that may soon be outmoded. The rapidity of change in our day may make even such generalized training of doubtful help in meeting major shifts in roles, and the presence of cultural discontinuities is a part of the price we pay for rapid social change.

The role of any occupation or profession can be filled only if the individual is properly trained. This training involves the learning both of the needed skills and of the attitudes and feelings appropriate to the role. Thus student nurses are assigned to hospital duties both so that they may learn the necessary skills and habits and so that they may acquire the proper attitudes and feelings. As Buerkle [1959] says, ". . . nursing students gradually internalize the universalistic norms of the hospital." The student nurse must learn to treat all patients, regardless of her personal feelings, with a balance of sympathetic tenderness and emotional detachment. In her professional capacity she must discipline her feelings about the privacy of the human body and at the same time maintain a normal, healthy attitude in her personal relationships. Those who fail to achieve these attitudes will fail as nurses. Mauksch [1963] has described how some of these changes are brought about in the course of nursing training, and Bloom [1963] has described how the medical student develops the emotional detachment needed for the physician role.

Conflicting Roles. A man fills not only a succession of roles throughout life but also several at the same time. In our society he may be filling roles as male, husband, father, son (to his aged parents), churchman, manager of a business enterprise, officer in the chamber of commerce, member of the local school board, and several others. And in a complex and changing society like ours, he will almost inevitably find some of these roles in conflict with one another.

Cultural conflicts become upsetting to the individual when they produce conflicting role pressures upon him. Cultural conflicts and inconsistencies are probably found in every culture. In well-integrated cultures, these inconsistencies are so well rationalized, compartmentalized, and fenced off from one another that the individual senses no inconsistency. Thus many primitives who treated one another with great tenderness were ruthlessly cruel to outsiders; their humanitarian mores applied only to tribal fellows, while outsiders were considered to be and treated like animals of the forest. By contrast, our belief in a universal God of all mankind makes it harder for us to shoot our enemies with a clear conscience. Our belief in democracy and our denial of equality to women and Negroes caused us few qualms as long as we believed that women and Negroes were on an intellectual level with children. Cultural contradictions are upsetting only when they subject the individual to conflicting pressures in a situation that demands a single action. For example, should a government or corporation official use his authority to find positions for his relatives? In our society such an official is not expected to find jobs for unqualified relatives, and is criticized if he does so. In many non-Western societies, his family role demands that he find jobs for as many of his relatives as possible, without too much regard to their qualifications. But in some countries now in transition to Western technology, it is becoming unclear which role takes precedence, so that family role and professional role come into conflict.

Role conflicts in our society are unavoidable. Our moral and ethical training teaches us values that are inconsistent with some of the roles we must fill. The church teaches us to be gentle, forgiving, and sympathetic, while compulsory military training prepares our youth to be tough, aggressive, and hostile. Our democratic ethos, as reflected in orations, legends, slogans, and schoolbooks, teaches us to be individualistic and independent, to stand up for our rights and not allow ourselves to be "pushed around." But when members of racial minorities follow this course of action, they court severe reprisals. Family and church encourage us to be generous, self-sacrificing, and helpful to the weak;

an indiscriminate application of these virtues in the business world would guarantee bankruptcy.

If one is successfully socialized, he develops a wardrobe of role personalities and slips into one or another as the situation demands. At home he is tender and indulgent; while working at the office he is brisk

He develops a wardrobe of role personalities.

and formal. This process of switching role personalities creates emotional strain whenever the attitudes called for in one role clash sharply with those needed in the other. Many a businessman, faced with the necessity of laying off employees, finds it painful to ignore their human needs and treat them impersonally as "cost factors in production." The dishonesties, deceptions, and exploitations that are a part of many occupational roles are inconsistent with the usual moral and religious training. If the individual is not fully successful in fencing his behavior off into compartments, these cultural contradictions become mental conflicts within him. Some psychiatrists [Horney, 1937] hold that such culture conflicts, and the mental conflicts they produce, are major causes of personality disorder.

Not only must the individual reconcile the conflicting pressures of his different roles; sometimes there are conflicting pressures and demands within a single role itself. For example, the clergy or priests in a well-integrated society have a definitely established role that places them in a well-understood position in relation to the rest of society. Today, however, clergymen of all faiths in our society complain of being asked to be many things to many men. They find it difficult to be at once a prophet, an executive, a hail-fellow-well-met, an ascetic saint, a social group worker, and a spiritual philosopher [Wilson, 1959]. In the nursing field, conflicts occur between the nurse's professional and bureaucratic roles. She is both a professional person, using her professional training and independent judgment in ministering to the needs of the patient, and a petty bureaucrat, carrying out the routines of the hospital [Corwin and Taves, 1962]. Occasionally she must break the rules in order to provide the good nursing service her professional role requires [Corwin, 1961].

Other conflicts are built into the nursing role. As Benne and Bennis [1959a] have noted, the nurse's concept of her role is drawn from several sources: (1) the expectations of the hospital or other employer; (2) the expectations of her working associates; (3) the expectations of the nursing school staff, professional associations, medical profession, and other related groups; (4) her own image of what a nurse should be and do. Sometimes these different sources are in conflict. The hospital may require procedures which, in the nurse's professional judgment, are unnecessary, or it may forbid procedures she thinks helpful. Nurse-doctor conflicts are fairly common, especially as nurses are today assuming a less subservient and more truly professional role which some doctors resist [Benne and Bennis, 1959b]. The doctor's image of the ideal nurse differs somewhat from the nurse's image of the ideal nurse. The nursing role today, like all changing roles, is beset by a number of conflicts and confusions, which impose some strain and tension on the practicing nurse.

Other roles in our society are beset with similar internal uncertainties. Should a wife and mother stay home and take good care of her husband and children, or should she take a job so that the family can live better? Our culture presses her to do both, and this is impossible. According to Komarovsky [1946a], neither role is, therefore, completely satisfying or free of guilt. From role uncertainties and conflicts such as these come much of the mental conflict and tension of our age.

Role Failure. In a well-integrated society with a high proportion of ascribed roles, most people fill these roles successfully. Most of the roles in any society can be filled by almost any member if he has been adequately prepared for them. But in a rapidly changing and less well-integrated society like ours, where we cannot predict all adult roles in advance and where discontinuities limit role preparation, a good deal of role failure is inevitable. Some persons even fail in their ascribed roles of male and female, as in the case of the homosexual, or of the woman with the complex of hostile, resentful, and aggressive attitudes toward men which is called the "masculine protest" pattern, or of the man who never outgrows his dependence upon mother. Even more persons fail in some of their achieved roles. Some of them fail to achieve the role they court—the boy fails to become a physician or executive, or the girl fails to get a husband and become a wife and mother. Others achieve a role but fail to fill it successfully. Many husbands and wives fail as marital partners, and face either the often shattering experience of divorce or a lifetime of mutual frustration. Many parents fail to socialize their children successfully. Only a few in any occupation or profession can be spectacularly successful, because for each manager there must be many subordinates. Those who crave the highest levels of a particular role are usually frustrated. Role failures of many kinds and degrees keep providing recruits for the relief rolls and the mental hospitals.

Role Personality versus True Personality. Each role requires a certain series of personality traits if it is to be filled successfully. These traits may or may not be those most truly characteristic of the individual. For the ascribed roles and statuses, enough role preparation usually ensures little clash between role personality and true personality. Thus most adult males can fill the male role simply by "being themselves."

For the achieved roles and statuses, which often are not selected until after one's adult personality has already been formed, a divergence between role and true personality is fairly common. For instance, in the role of salesman a man needs to be friendly, extroverted, and perceptive of the reactions of others. Suppose in his true personality he is shy, withdrawn, contemplative, and insensitive to the reactions of others. Such a person is unlikely to become a salesman or to succeed as one. If he does succeed, he does it by masking his true personality with an outward show of friendliness and a deliberately cultivated attentiveness to the clues to other's reactions. This role playing is not easy to accomplish successfully and may entail a good deal of emotional strain. If done successfully over a long period of time, however, the true personality may gradually be modified to come closer to the status personality. Mrs. Eleanor Roosevelt was a rather shy young woman and a hesitant and reluctant public speaker. In her role as wife to a politically ambitious but physically handicapped husband, she forced herself into vigorous political activity and became an eloquent public speaker. Apparently she found the role a rewarding one, for long after her husband's death she accepted a diplomatic appointment and remained a tireless world traveler and public speaker, and became perhaps the most remarkable woman of her age. On the other hand the wives of several men prominent in public life have rejected the role of politician's wife and divorced their husbands.

It is likely that a good deal of success and failure in achieved roles is explained by the degree to which the true personality coincides with the required role personality. Personnel management today is much concerned with this problem and makes use of job analyses, psychological tests, depth interviews, and other devices in an effort to fit people into jobs where there will be little clash between true and role personalities.

Psychic Costs of Achieved Status. The ideal of the society that permits most statuses to be achieved is to place people according to their abilities. To some extent this effort enables the highly talented to free themselves from the handicaps of lowly birth, but it also removes from the less talented their alibi for lowly social status. In a society where most status is ascribed, the individual is not expected to improve his lot. He receives low rewards and little prestige, but he does not feel any guilt in occupying the lowly position in which society has placed him. He is taught that his role and status are right and proper. He can take pride in his accomplishments without any need to compare them with those of persons in other statuses. He is freed from the sense of insecurity, the nagging of ambition, or the sting of failure. Socialization is eased because he is not expected to change his status; he has only to learn and accept his social roles.

It is difficult to rationalize low status when hereditary barriers are removed and positions are open to all on the basis of ability. If positions are filled on competitive examinations and if schooling is free to everybody, then the reason for low status must be incompetence, and this is not a comfortable explanation. The low-caste person in India could blame his status on the inexorable laws of the universe; the American university student who fails to graduate is hard put to it to find a similar justification. In self-defense the mediocre generally support the attempt to limit achievement by the imposition of seniority rules, group quotas, veterans' preference, and similar techniques to assure that the "right" people get the proper rewards.

Achieved status makes maximum provision for the attainment of roles on the basis of individual ability. It provides a high degree of choice and flexibility at the cost of psychic insecurity for the individual who has limited talents or has unequal opportunity to develop and employ them. The roles accompanying achieved statuses may be difficult to learn and mutually conflicting. In essence, the achieved status probably represents both the most efficient use of the human potential and the greatest threat to the individual's peace of mind.

Culture and Human Adjustment

Having discussed the concepts and interrelationships of culture, personality, socialization, role, and status, let us now turn to the problem of culture and human adjustment. Is culture a help or a burden to mankind? Some of each. It helps him solve some problems, gets in his way as he grapples with others, and itself creates still others.

Culture and Biological Adjustment. Man's culture contains many gadgets that help him in his unremitting battle with nature. Since man freezes and sunburns easily, he wears clothes and builds houses. Nature offers wild fruits, seeds, and berries; man domesticates them and increases their yield. His hands are poor shovels, but his bulldozers remake the surface of the earth. He cannot run fast, swim well, or fly at all; yet no living thing travels so fast as he. Man was created a fragile, delicate being, quickly prey to death through heat or cold, thirst or hunger. Through his culture, man can moisten the desert and dry the swampland, survive arctic cold and tropic heat, and even survive a trip through outer space.

While culture helps man to adjust to his environment, it also interferes with his biological adjustment in many ways. Every culture offers many examples of patterns that are harmful to man's physical well-being. The Hindu belief that man should not kill anything has filled India with stray dogs, scrawny cattle, and all manner of parasites, wasting food and spreading diseases. Man has improved his weapons until he can destroy the entire human race. He follows methods of agriculture and land use that destroy the soil and flood the land. He pollutes the air, fouls the streams, and poisons his foods. If he is rich enough he generally eats, smokes, and drinks more than is good for him. He eats polished rice or white bread which are stripped of vital food elements, while he may pass up beef, pork, horse meat, snake meat, snails, milk, or whatever valuable source of nourishment is under taboo in the culture of his particular group. If he were descended from cats instead of anthropoids, he would be better equipped for the night hours he likes to keep.

In nearly every culture men (and women) have twisted, stretched, squeezed, gouged, painted, trimmed, and scarred the human body in an effort to be beautiful. The clumsy platters inserted in the slit lips of the Ubangi, the foot binding as practiced on upper-class female children in classical China, and the precarious high heels of American women are all efforts to improve on nature by deforming and distorting the natural body contours—along with those interesting Western devices intended to squeeze, shift, and uplift various parts of the female anatomy. Our culture induces men to wrap themselves in useless garments in the summer and the fair sex to expose their legs to the icy blasts in winter. Our culture encourages men to dangerous overexertion in sports and discourages healthful exercise by asking them to take a car for a trip to the corner and by hauling their children to school when they would be better off walking. Automobile buyers are far more interested in a stylish appearance than in passenger safety—so much so that manufacturers have found it wise not to stress safety in their adver-

Efforts to improve upon nature.

tising. Our culture includes traits that lead communities to build new hospitals and other traits that cause them to oppose fluoridation programs to reduce tooth decay. American culture includes both the scientific milieu that developed an effective polio vaccine and the folkways and vested interests that make it difficult to develop an effective mass immunization program for the efficient use of this vaccine. When the values of the culture are not in harmony with the needs of biological adjustment, the culture may cause man to work against his own physical welfare.

Is culture, then, good or bad for man? It may be either. Culturally sanctioned behavior may prolong life or it may prevent man from using nature for his own physical welfare.

Culture and Social Adjustment. Just as culture may either promote or impair man's physical health, so it may either encourage or impede the harmonious operation of the society and the development of well-adjusted personalities. American culture, for instance, has so highly valued the "practical" pursuits that it has been hard to interest enough young people in theoretical science or higher learning. The term "egghead" is a cultural stereotype reflecting a disdain of intellectuality that slows our scientific development and threatens national survival. In the Ottoman Empire the military and agricultural activities were highly valued, while commerce was so disdained that the Turks could not maintain their leadership in a world increasingly dominated by industrialism.

In the Philippines the culture encourages an extremely high status for the legal profession, with the result that other occupations are neglected and thousands of lawyers are without a practice.

The culture provides patterns of behavior organized into a series of ascribed and achieved roles, thus providing for getting the routine work of society accomplished. It may even overelaborate these to a point of impracticality. It is said that Marie Antoinette was unable to get a glass of cold water; court etiquette required that it pass through so many hands that it was always tepid by the time it reached her. Rivers [1912] tells how on Torres Island in Melanesia, canoe building was surrounded with such an elaborate set of magical rites and taboos that only a small group of hereditary canoe builders dared to try to build one. Others were familiar with the manual skills for canoe building, but since they lacked the secret magic, it was unthinkable that they should build the craft. Hence when the hereditary canoe-building families died out, the islanders went without canoes despite their desperate need for them. If this deliberate frustration seems stupid to the reader, let him try to explain why in our society any people should be hungry, ill-housed, or ragged while food rots in warehouses and men rot in unemployment. In our society our building codes, union rules, and other monopolistic practices in the construction industry make building unnecessarily complicated and costly. In every society the culture organizes the work of the society in ways that are sometimes cumbersome and impractical; yet without a culturally organized system for getting things done, most of them would not get done at all.

If a culture is to survive, it must cultivate the values and practices necessary for its survival. A culture is weakened if it encourages the individual in lines of endeavor that will lead to personal frustration and rob his society of needed types of activity. The culture may lead the individual into successful activity or it may cause him to follow a blind alley. The culture may produce either a society with qualities that make for world leadership or a society that lacks the elements needed for survival in competition with other world societies.

Summary

Socialization takes place largely through the learning of social roles. A *role* is a cluster of duties and privileges; a *status* is the social position these duties and privileges create. Roles and statuses are of two sorts: those which are *ascribed* to individuals according to sex, age, race, or other characteristic and those which are *achieved* through personal choice or effort. In well-integrated, traditional societies most statuses are ascribed, while in rapidly changing societies many statuses are open to achievement.

Role conflicts may arise in several ways. Inadequate role preparation, especially in terms of attitudes and values, makes for difficult role adjustment. One's several roles may conflict with one another; or a single role may carry conflicting duties and pressures. One may fail in role performance, with consequent injury to the self. The role personality may call for traits that are not a part of one's true personality. In such cases one may reject the role; or he may counterfeit the required role personality; eventually he may somewhat modify his true personality in the direction of the role personality. Organizing society's work by ascribing statuses ensures that most roles will be filled fairly adequately, with a maximum of emotional security but some waste of unusual abilities. Opening many statuses to achievement probably makes more efficient use of talent, at the price of many failures and greater emotional insecurity.

Human adjustment is both aided and hindered by culture and socialization, which enable man to survive in an inhospitable physical environment even though in many minor respects they are physically injurious to him. Culture and socialization enable man to live with his fellows, but culture conflicts and discontinuities in socialization also impose upon him role uncertainties and contradictions, role failures, and emotional stresses. We could not live without our culture; sometimes it is not easy to live with it!

Questions and Projects

1. Are *role* and *status* two separate concepts or two aspects of the same phenomenon? Explain.
2. What is the function of children's play in socialization? How does play aid in role preparation?
3. Why is it a comparatively easy task to assume one's age roles in most primitive societies? Why do we not have a clearly defined set of age roles?
4. How does our culture make old age a difficult period? Is it a difficult period in any culture? Analyze our old-age problem in terms of discontinuities. In terms of conflicting roles.

5. Describe the shift from the status and role of a high school student to that of a nursing student in terms of cultural continuities and discontinuities in socialization.
6. In role preparation for most adult roles, which is more important: the attitudes and values that make that role acceptable, or the knowledge and skills necessary to fill the role? Illustrate for the roles of homemaker, schoolteacher, army officer, research scientist, nurse, and old age.
7. Is there any conflict between your roles as nursing student and as son or daughter? If you are a mar-

ried student, a third (and possibly a fourth) role is added. What possible role conflicts are added?

8. What social costs accompany an emphasis on achieved status? Ascribed status?

9. In what respects is your present role as nursing student preparing you for later roles? In what respects is your present role experience irrelevant or even dysfunctional?

10. Are there any respects in which you are already assuming role personalities that differ from your true personality? Are you aware of any stresses this acting a part produces?

11. Describe in some detail a role and status with which you are familiar and which involves a good deal of conflicting pressure within the role. How do persons in that role usually resolve these conflicts?

12. Describe some situation you know about where a person has been under pressure to fill two or more conflicting roles. How did he resolve the matter? Would you say his resolution was successful or unsuccessful?

Suggested Readings

BEAVER, ALMA PERRY: "Personality Factors in Choice of Nursing," *Journal of Applied Psychology,* 37:374–379, 1953. A comparison of student nurses with other college students.

BURCHARD, WALDO W.: "Role Conflicts of Military Chaplains," *American Sociological Review,* 19:529–535, October, 1954. Conflict between chaplain's role as clergyman and as army officer, based on interviews with chaplains and ex-chaplains in San Francisco Bay area.

CORWIN, RONALD G.: "The Professional Employee: A Study of Conflict in Nursing Roles," *American Journal of Sociology,* 66:604–615, 1961. A study of conflict between the professional and bureaucratic roles of the nurse.

GOWMAN, ALAN G.: "Blindness and the Role of the Companion," *Social Problems,* 4:68–75, July, 1956. The process through which the companion develops a role relationship satisfactory to the blind person and the changes that occur in the definition of the situation.

GULLAHORN, JOHN T.: "Measuring Role Conflict," *American Journal of Sociology,* 61:299–303, January, 1956. An attempt to measure role conflicts of labor union leaders.

JOHNSON, MIRIAM M., AND HARRY W. MARTIN: "A Sociological Analysis of the Nurse Role," *American Journal of Nursing,* 58:373–377, 1958. A discussion of the nurse's function in the doctor-nurse-patient relationship.

KOMAROVSKY, MIRRA: "Cultural Contradictions and Sex Roles," *American Journal of Sociology,* 52:184–189, November, 1946. A brilliant discussion of the role conflicts of the college-educated woman.

MAUKSCH, HANS O.: "Becoming a Nurse: A Selective View," *Annals of the American Academy of Political and Social Science,* 346:88–98, 1963. Describes how nursing training shapes the attitudes and feelings needed for the nursing role.

MC CORD, JOAN, AND WILLIAM MC-CORD: "Effects of Parental Role Models on Criminality," *Journal of Social Issues*, 14(3):66–75, 1958. A study of social-worker reports on the parents of delinquents; shows that some popular ideas are unsound.

WARDWELL, WALTER L.: "A Marginal Professional Role: The Chiropractor," *Social Forces*, 30:339–348, 1952; reprinted in E. Gartly Jaco, *Patients, Physicians and Illness*, The Free Press of Glencoe, New York, 1958, pp. 421–433. Description of a group that seeks but lacks full professional status.

Social Control and
Social Deviation

The Hawaiians had long obeyed some of the Kanawai [*laws*]. *They had always honored fathers and mothers, and their days had been long upon the land. They had utterly abolished idols before the* Longnecks [*whites*] *came.*

Theft they had dealt with in a way that had served well enough, though it could scarcely have been pleasing to Jehovah. In the old days if a man took something from one below him in the social scale, it was not stealing; for that which was taken had in reality belonged by virtue of rank of the taker. And if a commoner made off with the calabash or the weapon of a superior, the injured man could go to the thief's house and take back his possession, along with anything else he saw that he wanted.

But when the haoles [*white traders*] *came with their bean pots and silver spoons, their monkey wrenches and linen towels, their sawed lumber and their keen-edged axes, this method no longer served. Complaints from foreigners rang unceasingly in the governor's ears. White men did not want to go poking into native huts to find their lost articles. They wanted Boki to haul up the thief and arrange for restitution and punishment.*

Gradually the enlightened chiefs saw what they must do. Some of them put their men in irons for proven theft or set them free only to work and pay for what they had stolen. The boy prince Kauikeaouli, when his beloved kahu *was found accessory to a theft, consented quickly to the man's dismissal. "My* kahu *must go," he declared, "or by and by the foreigners will think that I myself am guilty."*

The haoles *applauded such measures. Here was a Commandment they liked to see enforced.*

Then there was the Commandment forbidding murder in a few short words. Once, if a native killed in sudden anger, it was proper for the victim's relatives to avenge the deed, unless the murderer took shelter in a place of refuge. If the guilty man were of equal rank with the victim's avenger, there might be an appeal to the king or the governor or to the chief of the district. The aggrieved one and the accused would then sit cross-legged in the judge's yard and each would eloquently argue his case till the magistrate made his decision.

But these customs failed when Honolulu swarmed with hot-headed sailors, and brown and white alike drank rum and got huhu [*very angry*]. *Again, as with theft, the traders wanted stern laws, strictly enforced, so that the riffraff of all nations would think twice before bashing their fellows on the head. They told the chiefs to build a lofty engine of death which would string up a murderer by the neck and leave him hanging limp from a rope's end—a potent reminder to the living to restrain themselves.*

Social control—the processes through which people are led to behave as expected—has long interested sociologists. They begin with the study of the social order within which people interact. Consider, for example, the orderly arrangements underlying the bustling confusion of a great city. Tens of thousands of people take their places and perform their tasks with no apparent direction. Thousands of vehicles butt their way through clogged canyons, missing by inches, but with only a handful of collisions each day. Thousands of kinds of merchandise arrive at the proper places in the proper amounts at the proper times. Ten thousand people whom one never sees will labor on this day so that meals will be ready for him when needed, drinking fountains will flow, drains will carry off the wastes, bulbs will blink and glow, traffic will part to let him pass, and his other needs will be met. A hundred people may serve him within an hour, perhaps without a word from him to any of them.

This is what is meant by *social order*—a system of people, relationships, and customs operating smoothly to accomplish a society's tasks. Unless people know what they may expect from one another, not much will get done. No society, even the simplest, can function successfully unless the behavior of most people can be reliably predicted most of the time. Unless we can depend upon police officers to protect us, workers to go to work on schedule, and motorists to stay on the right side of the road most of the time, there can be no social order. The orderliness of a society rests upon a network of roles according to which each person accepts certain duties toward others and claims certain rights from others. Orderly society can operate only as long as most people reliably fulfill most of their duties toward others, and are able successfully to claim most of their rights from others.

How is this network of reciprocal rights and duties kept in force? Sociologists use the term *social control* to describe *all the means and processes whereby a group or a society secures its members' conformity to its expectations.*

Social Control and Social Order

Social Control through Socialization. Fromm has remarked that if a culture is to function efficiently, "its members must acquire the kind of character which makes them *want* to act in the way they *have* to act as members of society. . . . They have to *desire* to do what objectively is necessary for them to do" [Fromm, 1944].

People are controlled mainly by being socialized so that they fill their roles in the expected way through habit and preference. How do we compel women to accept the endless drudgery of household and child care? Mainly by socializing them so that they *want* husbands and children, and feel cheated without them. How is man, unlike the male of most other species, persuaded to exchange his freedom for a sense of social responsibility toward the offspring he sires? Mainly by cultivating within him a set of cherished sentiments and yearnings this troublesome little creature promises to fulfill. As we saw in an earlier chapter, the crucial part of one's role preparation is his development of the attitudes and wishes that make the role attractive. Most role failures come not because one is unable to perform the role's tasks but because he is trapped in a role he does not really want or enjoy.

Socialization shapes our wishes, our habits, and our customs. Habit and custom are great timesavers. They relieve us of the need for countless decisions. If we had to *decide* whether and how to perform each act—when to arise, whether and how to wash, shave, dress, and so on— few students would get to class at all. The members of a society are schooled in the same customs and tend to develop much the same set of habits. Thus habit and custom are great standardizers of behavior within a group. If all members of a society share a similar socialization experience, they will voluntarily and unthinkingly act in very much the same ways. They will conform to social expectations without any conscious awareness that they are "conforming," or any serious thought of doing otherwise. The American college male's attempt to date a cute coed arises from motives less academic than a wish to "conform to the courtship pattern"; yet such conformity is the result.

Social Control through Group Pressure. In a novel by Sinclair Lewis, George F. Babbitt, a small-town realtor, somehow strays into "radical" notions about government and politics. Soon his business declines, his friends begin to avoid him, and he grows uncomfortably aware that he is becoming an outsider. Lewis describes with rare perception how Babbitt's associates apply a variety of subtle pressures until, with a sigh of relief, Babbitt scurries back to a comfortable conformity [Lewis, 1922, chaps. 32, 33].

LaPiere [1954] sees social control as primarily a process growing out of the individual's need for status within his primary groups. He claims that these groups are most influential when they are small and intimate, when the individual expects to remain in the group for a long time, and when he has frequent contacts with them. All authorities agree that our need for status within intimate groups is a most powerful lever for the use of group pressure toward group norms.

The individual experiences this group pressure as a continuous and largely unconscious process. Its operation is illustrated by the life of one of the author's acquaintances. He spent most of his working life as a small farmer in central Michigan; like most of his neighbors he thought conservatively, voted Republican, and scolded labor unions. During

World War II he moved to Detroit and worked in a war plant, joined a union, became a union officer, and voted Democratic. After the war he retired to a small central Michigan village where he again thinks conservatively, votes Republican, and scolds labor unions. He explains these about-faces by claiming that the parties and the unions have changed. He does not realize that it is *he* who has changed. Like most of us, he soon came to share the views of his group associates. This tendency to conform to group attitudes is so compelling that the Catholic church in France found it necessary to abandon its worker-priest program, an effort to stem the drift of French workers toward communism by sending out priests who would take ordinary jobs and work beside the workers, meanwhile leading them back to the church. After a ten-year trial when it became evident that the workers were converting the priests to the Marxian view of the class struggle, the program was curtailed [Brady, 1954].

Social psychologists [Sherif, 1935; Bovard, 1951] have made a number of experiments showing how a person tends to bring his expressions in line with those of the group. The method is such experiments usually consists of asking the members for individual estimates, attitudes, or observations on a topic, then informing them of the group norm, and finally asking for a new expression from each member. Many of the informants modify their second expression in the direction of the group norm. In a series of ingenious experiments, Asch [1951], Tuddenham [1961], and others have shown that many people will even alter an observation they *know* to be correct rather than oppose the group. Each subject in these experiments was surrounded by a group which, by secret prearrangement, made factual observations the subject *knew* to be wrong; yet one-third of these subjects accepted the wrong observation when opposed by a unanimous group opinion to the contrary. Schachter [1951] has also shown experimentally how the member who sharply deviates from group norms in opinion is rejected by the group.

Our need for status within intimate groups.

We often notice that a new member of a group is more carefully conformist and more fiercely loyal than the old members. Religious converts and naturalized citizens often show a zeal that puts lifelong members to shame. An experiment by Dittes and Kelley [1956] helps explain this loyalty. They found that among members who equally value their membership in a group, those who feel *least accepted* are the most rigidly conformist to the group's norms. Meticulous conformity is a tool for gaining acceptance and status within a group, while rejection is the price of nonconformity.

It is probable that no other structure even approaches the tremendous controlling power of the group over the individual. Any parent who has tried to counter a teen-ager's argument, "*All* the kids are wearing them!" is fully aware of the controlling power of the group.

Informal Primary-group Controls. Groups are of two kinds, primary and secondary; these concepts will be analyzed in detail in a later chapter. For our present discussion it is sufficient to note that primary groups are small, intimate, informal, face-to-face groups, like the family, clique, or play group, while secondary groups are larger, more impersonal, more formal, and more utilitarian, like a labor union, trade association, church congregation, or student body.

Within primary groups, control is informal, spontaneous, and unplanned. The members of the group react to the actions of each member. When a member irritates or annoys the others, they may show their disapproval through ridicule, laughter, criticism, or even ostracism. When a member's behavior is acceptable, a secure and comfortable "belonging" is his usual reward. Countless novelists have used the subplot in which a character violates the norms of his group in some way, is disciplined by group disapproval which he cannot endure, and must earn his way back into group acceptance through penitence and renewed conformity.

In most primitive societies where virtually all groups were primary groups there was very little serious misconduct. Each person was born into certain kinship groups—a family, a clan, or a tribe. He could not move on to another tribe or clan, for a man divorced from his kinship ties had no social existence—that is, no one who was obligated to regard and treat him as a fellow human being. If a man was to survive, he *had* to get along with the groups in which he found himself. Since there was little privacy and no escape, the penalty of serious noncomformity was an intolerable existence. Lowie describes the use of scorn and ridicule by a number of American Indian peoples:

> When a Fox Indian boy in Illinois was taught not to steal and never to abuse his wife, his elder did not hold up to him any tangible punishment here or hereafter nor any abstract rules of morality. The clinching argument was, "The people will say many things about you, although you may not know it."
>
> Gossiping sometimes took special forms of ridicule. An Alaskan youth thus reports his experience: "If you do not marry within your village, they joke about

you—they joke so much that it makes it disagreeable." The Crow sang songs in mockery of a miser, a bully, or a man who should take back a divorced wife—the acme of disgrace. Certain kinsmen had the privilege of publicly criticizing a man for breaches of etiquette and ethics, and there was nothing he would fear more than to be thus pilloried. This system was developed by the Blackfoot along slightly different lines. "For mild persistent misconduct, a method of formal discipline is sometimes practiced. When the offender has failed to take hints and suggestions, the head men may take formal notice and decide to resort to discipline. Some evening when all are in their tipis, a head man will call out to a neighbor asking if he has observed the conduct of Mr. A. This starts a general conversation between the many tipis, in which all the grotesque and hideous features of Mr. A.'s acts are held up to general ridicule, amid shrieks of laughter, the grilling continuing until far into the night. The mortification of the victim is extreme and usually drives him into a temporary exile or, as formerly, upon the warpath to do desperate deeds."

A primitive man sacrifices half his property lest he be dubbed a miser; he yields his favorite wife if jealousy is against the code; he risks life itself, if that is the way to gain the honor of a public eulogy. That is why savages of the same tribe are not forever cutting one another's throats or ravishing available women, even if they lack written constitutions, jails, a police force, and revealed religion.

In many societies the group is held responsible for the acts of each of its members. For example if a Tlingit murders a member of another clan, his own clan must provide for execution a person equal in social status to the murdered victim, while the actual murderer is punished by living with the knowledge that he has been responsible for the execution of a kinsman. In our military units, one dirty rifle or messy locker may deprive an entire platoon of their weekend passes. Such forms of collective punishment may seem unjust, *but they work*. A soldier whose carelessness has once caused his platoon to lose their weekend passes is unlikely to repeat his error—or to be permitted to forget it.

A great deal of "leadership" and "authority" rest upon the skillful manipulation of the group as a control device. The successful schoolteacher, for example, often uses the class to maintain discipline; she manipulates the situation so that the child who misbehaves will look ridiculous before the class. But if she allows a situation to develop wherein the misbehaving child appears as a hero or a martyr to the class, her control is lost.

Normal people everywhere need and seek the approval of others, especially of the primary-group associates upon whom they depend for intimate human response. Thousands of novels, dramas, and operas have elaborated this theme. Most people will give almost anything, even their lives if necessary, to retain this approval and the comforting feeling of belonging to the group. It is the overwhelming need for group approval and response that makes the primary group the most powerful controlling agency known to man.

Secondary-group Controls. As we shift from primary- to secondary-group situations, we also shift from informal to more formal social controls. Secondary groups are generally larger, more impersonal, and specialized in purpose. We do not use them to meet our need for intimate human response but to help us to get certain jobs done. If a secondary group does not meet our needs, we can generally withdraw with no great anguish, for our emotional lives are not deeply involved. To maintain our status in the secondary group is desirable, but it is not a desperate emotional necessity as it is in the primary group. True, it is possible in our society for people to change their primary groups—leave their families, divorce their mates, find new friends—but the process is generally painful. The secondary group is a less compelling control agency than the primary group.

The secondary group is still an effective control. Some of the informal controls still operate in the secondary group. No normal person wants to appear ridiculous at the union meeting, the church worship service, or the chamber of commerce banquet. Such informal controls as ridicule, laughter, gossip, and ostracism operate in secondary-group settings, but generally with a reduced impact. Meanwhile other more formal controls are characteristic of secondary groups—parliamentary rules of order, official regulations and standardized procedures, propaganda, public relations and "human engineering," promotions and titles, rewards and prizes, formal penalties and punishments, and still others.

The more formal controls of the secondary group are most effective when reinforced by a primary group. A prize or decoration is more sweet when an admiring family and an applauding clique of close friends can watch the presentation ceremony. Within the large impersonal secondary group may be many very closely integrated primary groups, such as many squads within an army or many work crews within a corporation. These primary groups can either reinforce or undermine the formal secondary-group controls and greatly affect the performance of the secondary group. Much of the human-engineering approach in industry is an effort to use these primary groups to reinforce the controls and objectives of the corporation [Gross, 1953].

Control through Force. Many primitive societies succeeded in controlling the behavior of individuals through the mores, reinforced by the informal controls of the primary group, so that no formal laws or punishments were necessary. But with larger populations and more complex cultures, formal governments, laws, and punishments are developed. Wherever it becomes possible for the individual to become lost in the crowd, informal controls are inadequate and formal controls are necessary. For example in a clan of one or two dozen adult kinsfolk, informal food sharing is practical; each person can take what he needs and contribute whatever he can catch, while informal group pressures can be trusted to prevent laziness and control greed. But in a village of hundreds of persons, it would be impossible to keep tab on each person informally; individual laziness and greed would make a system of informal food sharing unworkable. Some *system* of assigning work and distributing rewards becomes necessary. Thus with larger populations and cultural complexity comes a shift to impersonal secondary-group controls—laws, regulations, councils, and formalized procedures.

When the individual does not wish to follow these regulations, the group seeks to compel him to do so. Informal group pressures have not made him conform, for in such large groups he is too anonymous for informal group pressures to be brought to an effective focus upon him. Furthermore, in larger groups with complex cultures, some subcultures conflicting with the culture of the majority are likely to develop. The individual who rejects the conventional regulations of the society may find emotional support from other persons who think and act as he does. Although he is still subject to group pressure, it now comes from a nonconforming group that insulates him from the pressures of conventional society. So conventional society uses force on him—force in the form of laws and formal punishments—to compel his conformity. This force is not always successful, yet no complex culture has survived without it.

Situational Determinants of Behavior. When a layman sees some behavior he does not like, he often attributes it to evil human nature, wicked impulse, weak character, or some other *individual* cause. What separates the sociologist from the layman here is the sociologist's habit of looking for *social* factors in the causation of behavior. True, when one individual or a few people change in character or behavior, the explanations may be purely individual. But when any *large number* of people change their character or behavior in the same way, we look for the probable cause in some change in the social and cultural influences on behavior.

To a far greater degree than most people recognize, one's behavior in a particular situation is a result of the needs, pressures, and temptations of that situation. There is ample evidence that many people who would not cheat a blind newspaper man will cheat the national supermarket if they get a chance to do so; war veterans who did not rob their neighbors back home "liberated" many articles from the enemy population; people do things as part of a mob they would never do as individuals. War atrocities are committed by all armies. Whether a surrendering enemy is shot or taken prisoner depends more on the circumstances at the moment of surrender than on the character of the capturing troops

[Draper, 1945]. Kinsey's data show that most civilian husbands are faithful to their wives, at least most of the time; but it appears that most

Behavior in a particular situation is the result of the needs of that situation.

overseas military personnel, when long separated from their wives, seized almost any attractive opportunity for infidelity. Labor union officials believe in labor unions—except for their own employees. Thus when the employees of the large unions seek to organize and bargain collectively with their bosses, these union official–bosses seem to react just like any other employers.[1] Boys from satisfactory homes in stable neighborhoods rarely become seriously delinquent, but most boys from an unsatisfactory home in a slum neighborhood will become seriously delinquent [Glueck and Glueck, 1959]. Illustrations of how the total behavior situation affects the behavior outcome could be multiplied almost without end. Many more are found in the chapter on collective behavior.

True, the character one brings to a situation is a factor in his behavior, and occasionally the determining factor. A few people are honest in *all* situations; a few husbands will be faithful despite *any* temptation. But more often than our folklore admits, a behavior situation develops a characteristic kind of behavior among most of the participants. This is why the upper floors of girls' dormitories are forbidden to male callers. A major part of social control consists of trying to manipulate the kinds of situations people enter, for we know that most of them will respond with the kind of behavior a particular situation encourages.

This is not a complete catalogue of the means of social control. There are many others which are described by Lumley [1925] and by Landis [1939, 1956]—symbols, traditions, myths, legends, threats, intimidations, tortures, and still others—but they would be only an elaboration of the above outline.

Social Deviation

No society succeeds in getting all its people to behave as expected all the time. The term *social deviation* is given to *any failure to conform to the customary norms of the society*. Deviation takes many forms. The juvenile delinquent, the hermit, the ascetic, the beatnik, the sinner and

[1] See "The Class War," *Reporter*, Jan. 9, 1958. p. 8.

the saint, the artist starving in his garret and the miser gloating over his wealth—all have deviated from the conventional social norms.

In a simple society where all members accept a single set of norms, deviation is easy to define. In a complex society with many different competing norms, the problem grows more complicated. In a neighborhood where most of the boys are delinquent and many of the adults are repeatedly violating the law, who is the deviant—the delinquent or the nondelinquent? Obviously, deviation needs more detailed definition.

Basic Types of Deviation. *Individual and Group Deviation.* A boy in a "good" neighborhood of stable families and conventional people may reject the norms surrounding him and become a delinquent. In this case the individual deviates from the norms of his subculture. He is thus an *individual deviant.* In a complex society, however, there may be a number of *deviant subcultures* whose norms are condemned by the conventional morality of the society. Thus in the deteriorated areas of the city, Cohen [1955] finds a delinquent subculture in which many of the youths participate. For many of them the life of the street gang is the only life that seems real and important. In such neighborhoods, delinquent behavior is as "normal" as law-abiding behavior. When boys from these neighborhoods become delinquent, they are not individually deviant from their subculture; it is their subculture that is deviant from the conventional norms of the society. It is the group, not the individual, that is deviant.

We therefore have two ideal types of deviants: (1) individual deviants, who reject the norms surrounding them and deviate from their subculture, and (2) group deviants, wherein the individual is a conforming member of a deviant group. In practice, deviant persons are not sharply divided into two such distinct groups. The "ideal type" always is a clearcut expression of an idea, while most real persons fall somewhere between the sharply contrasting images presented by the ideal types. This is the reason for constructing the ideal types; they clearly express an idea. Meanwhile, we remember that very few people perfectly fit into an ideal type but are intermediate; for example, few people are either "dominant" or "submissive"; most people show some of each characteristic.

In the case of deviant persons, many deviants are not perfect examples of either individual or group deviation but show elements of both. Rarely is an individual deviant *completely* surrounded by conventional groups and influences. If he were, it is unlikely that he would ever deviate at all! But even the most carefully sheltered child hears about crimes and immorality, comes across literature his parents would censor, and observes other children violating the norms his parents revere. In other words even a highly conventional subculture does not completely isolate the person from deviant patterns that he can observe and follow.

Furthermore, deviant persons tend to join with other similar persons into deviant groups. The "bad boys" in the schoolroom tend to form a clique, reinforcing one another's boisterous behavior. Individual hot-

They tend to become subcultures.

rodders, beatniks, drug addicts, or homosexuals tend to drift together into groups of deviants. These groups reinforce and sanction the deviation, give the member emotional protection against conformist critics, and possibly help to cultivate new deviants. These groups of deviants tend to develop a private language and a set of rigidly stereotyped behavior norms of their own. In short, they tend to become subcultures. Thus it becomes hard to say whether the beatnik is a deviant nonconformist or a rigidly conforming member of a deviant subculture. In practice, then, the distinction between the individual and the group deviant becomes blurred; yet the theoretical distinction is an important one, as our later discussion will elaborate.

The Private Vocabulary of a Deviant Subculture
A Glossary of Street Gang Argot

a fair one A fair fight between gangs or gang members, fought in some accordance with rules.

bop To fight.

bopping club A fighting club.

bread Money (term used mostly by drug addicts).

busted Arrested.

cheesy Traitorous.

cool An uneasy armistice.

cool it! Take it easy!

coolie A nongang boy.

debs Girl affiliates of gang boys.

diddley bop A first-class gang fighter.

dig To understand.

dig it! Get this!

duke To fight (with fists).

fish An erotic dance similar to the burlesque-house grind.

gig A party.

go down To attack another gang, declare war.

grind An erotic dance, similar to the fish.

heart Courage.

hurt To kill or wound seriously.

jap To ambush or attack an individual.

jazz Worthless talk, poor excuse.

junkie A drug addict.

meet A meeting, usually of gang chiefs.

piece A gun, weapon.

pot Narcotics.

punk out To display cowardice.

pusher A drug salesman.

rumble   A gang fight.

shakedown   A police inspection to see if a boy is carrying weapons.

shin battle   An intragang practice fight, sham battle.

shuffle   To engage in a fist fight.

snag   To attack an individual, usually by surprise.

snake   A spy.

sneaky Pete   Cheap wine.

sound   (Noun), Talk, argot; (Verb) to joke or taunt.

swing with a gang   To be a gang member.

tight   Friendly, as between gangs.

Abridgement of "A Glossary of Street Gang Argot," from *The Shook-up Generation* by Harrison E. Salisbury. Copyright © 1958 by Harrison E. Salisbury. Reprinted by permission of Harper & Row, Publishers, Incorporated, New York.

Cultural and Psychological Deviation. One may deviate from the norm in his social behavior, in his personality organization, or sometimes in both. Sociology is primarily interested in the cultural deviant, who deviates in his behavior from the norms of his culture. Psychologists are primarily interested in the psychological deviant, who deviates from the norm in his personality organization—the psychotic, the neurotic, the paranoid personality, and others. These two categories often converge. Deviant behavior may spring from personality abnormality, and many studies of deviant behavior report evidence of such an association. Radical political behavior is often interpreted as an outlet for emotional hostilities [Ernst and Loth, 1952; Almond, 1954]. The prostitute is often explained as a product of an emotionally deprived childhood, with little opportunity to integrate a secure personality [Greenwald, 1959], and other sex deviations along with alcoholism, drug addiction, and compulsive gambling are often attributed to personality disorder of some sort.

Personality disorder, however, is far from the sole cause of deviant behavior. While some psychologically abnormal people have a compelling urge to be bad, other psychologically abnormal people have an equally compelling urge to be good. These disturbed people become overconformists. The insecure, complex-ridden neurotic who *must* do his work perfectly, cannot stand disagreements, obeys all the mores, and finds comfort in meticulously following all the rules and regulations is fulfilling a neurotic need to conform. This shows that cultural and psychological deviations are related, but not in any simple cause-and-effect relationship. The puzzling question of why personality abnormality sometimes leads to deviant behavior and sometimes to conforming behavior is one that continues to interest both psychologists and sociologists.

Culturally Approved Deviation. Deviant behavior is culturally evaluated. Some deviation is condemned; some is applauded. The wandering holy man of one society is the worthless bum of another; the rugged hero of the raw frontier is the uncouth boor of the urban community. In our society, the genius, the hero, the leader, and the celebrity are among our culturally approved deviants. Social scientists have shown some interest in studying the reasons for such individual distinction, but because the culturally disapproved deviation is the more troublesome, it has attracted the greater study.

Culturally Disapproved Deviation. One may become deviant either because of an actual *inability* to conform or because of some *unwillingness* to conform, or perhaps some combination of both.

Deviation through Inability to Conform. Those with physical or mental defect may be incapable of normal achievements or normal social behavior. The term *mental defect* refers to limited learning capacity, either through inheritance or brain damage. The diagnosis and treatment of physical or mental defect lie largely outside the field of sociology. Popular beliefs about mental defect, however, and social policies concerning defectives do interest sociologists. The popular belief that all mental defectives multiply like hamsters is incorrect. Birth rates are high only among the "high-grade morons" or borderline defectives; among the more seriously defective, the greater the defect, the lower the birth and survival rates tend to be. Most inherited severe mental defect appears among children of normal parents who carry recessive gene defects, so that only a small fraction of severe mental defect could be prevented by sterilizing all mental defectives. Since all true mental defect and most physical defect are incurable at present, social policy is concerned mainly with preparing defectives to be as socially useful as their abilities permit.

Mental illness is a disorganization of behavior rather than a lack of learning capacity. In mental illness a person within the normal range of learning capacity is unable to perceive and respond to realities in an orderly and rational manner. His reality perceptions may be so distorted that he imagines people are persecuting him or that he hears strange voices and commands, or he becomes disoriented and forgets where he is and what he is doing. His self-perceptions may become so distorted that he becomes obsessed with his own worthlessness, sinfulness, or incompetence, or perhaps develops delusions of grandeur and power. His reactions to reality may become confused and erratic, or he may withdraw from reality into an inner world of fantasy.

The classification, diagnosis, and treatment of mental illness lie in the fields of psychology, psychiatry, and medicine. Sociologists are mainly interested in the social and cultural factors involved in producing mental illness, and in our social attitudes and policies toward it.

The causes of mental illness appear to be both physical and social, but in unknown proportions. All students of mental illness agree that heredity is a factor, but the exact degree and operation of the hereditary factor have not been established [Jost and Sontag, 1944; Kallman, 1946]. The fact that mental illness often runs in a family is not very helpful, since the members of a family generally share both a similar heredity and a similar social experience. Yet each individual is biologically and biochemically unique. Williams [1956] has shown that individuals vary considerably, even to the size and location of internal organs, the chemical composition of body fluids, the number of branch arteries, the branching of trunk nerves, and in many other respects. It is known that severe malnutrition can induce personality disorders [Keys, 1952; Wilder, 1952]. Kretschmer [1925] and Sheldon and Stevens [1942] have demonstrated how at least some types of mental illness seem to show some association with constitutional body type, but constitutional factors and their exact roles remain to be established. The entire question of the hereditary, constitutional, or organic causation of mental illness is not yet settled.

There is widespread agreement among scientists that most mental illness is precipitated, or "triggered," by mental conflicts, especially the conflicts provoked by guilt, frustrations, and anxieties. Yet some people survive terrific stress without becoming disorganized, while others succumb quickly. Obviously, people differ in their ability to endure mental conflicts. It is not known whether this difference is partly physical; some people may be constitutionally able to endure greater mental conflict without becoming disorganized. Certain physical changes or disorders may make a healthy person become susceptible to mental illness. There is widespread agreement among scientists, however, that the socialization process is extremely important. It may develop a secure and confident personality, well able to meet the stresses and conflicts of social life, or it may develop an insecure and complex-ridden personality, unable to survive even ordinary stress without disorganization.

Many people develop a mental illness when they assume a highly stress-filled role. Many servicemen became mentally ill after entering the service. Executives sometimes develop a mental illness (or more often a psychosomatic physical illness) after a promotion to greater responsibilities and hence greater anxieties. Many occupational roles produce great anxieties, and one must find ways of controlling or reducing those anxieties if he is to remain healthy. For example Menzies [1960] has studied the anxieties the nurse experiences in an atmosphere of constant pain, death, and the possibility of tragic error. He describes several defenses through which this anxiety is reduced: Several nurses share the responsibility for each patient so that the outcome bears less heavily on any one nurse. Depersonalization—viewing the patient as a "case"—helps to avoid personal involvement. Sometimes ritual task performance becomes a way of avoiding difficult decisions. These and other devices help to control anxiety and maintain emotional stability. Similar sets of defenses could probably be found for any anxiety-creating role.

Sociologists are especially interested in the ways a culture may create mental conflicts in individuals. The culture may impose difficult role transitions, such as our transition from youth into adulthood or from active adulthood into retirement. It may require difficult choices, so arranged that neither alternative is fully comfortable; an example is the American wife who is under pressure to get a job so that the family can live better, and also under pressure to stay home and take care of the family. Our massive advertising campaigns guarantee that people's wants will constantly outrun their means, a course that may be economically useful but that is emotionally costly. Our culture teaches many contradictory values: Be generous, but hang on to your money; be modest and unassuming, but be sure to get ahead; don't take advantage of another's hardship, but remember that business is business; be thrifty and saving, but keep spending lest you touch off a recession; be virtuous, but don't be inhibited; love your enemies, but extend no sympathies lest you be disloyal. Any complex, changing culture includes many such culture conflicts that can become mental conflicts for individuals. To some students of mental illness, such conflicts within the culture are largely responsible for the mental conflicts that precipitate much of our mental illness [Horney, 1937].

Simple, well-integrated societies, then, should provoke fewer mental conflicts and have less mental illness than we have. There is some evidence that this is true [Carothers, 1947], but it is difficult to be certain. Many difficulties arise when an observer from our society tries to diagnose and measure mental illness in a different cultural setting. Sometimes later studies of a group have concluded that the earlier studies underestimated the amount of mental illness in that group [Kaplan and Plant, 1956]. Furthermore, if increasing cultural complexity produces mental illness, then our rates should have increased during the past century. Whether they have is uncertain; one study [Goldhamer and Marshall, 1953] concludes that there has been no noticeable increase between 1840 and 1940. Yet it is significant that "no field worker has reported a high rate of schizophrenia [our most common form of mental illness] in a stable primitive society which is isolated from white influences. Wherever schizophrenia is recorded, the society is in the process of change" [Miller and Swanson, 1960, p. 45]. Until more is definitely known, we may only conclude that it *seems likely* that the mental conflicts produced by the culture are a major factor in mental illness.

Social attitudes toward mental illness show a fascinating variety. Some primitive societies assumed that the mentally ill were supernaturally favored and gave them special privileges and recognition. Medieval Europeans blamed mental illness on demon possession and therefore tortured and abused the victim to chase the demons from his miserable body. (There are no reliable data measuring the success of this heroic treatment!) Even today, many people cannot accept mental illness as an illness without connotations of humiliation or disgrace. This attitude is revealed by their preference for the euphemism "nervous breakdown," their unwillingness to admit that an illness is mental, their refusal to visit patients at a mental hospital or to accept them back into the family when they are ready for release [Weinberg, 1952, pp. 466–473; Freeman, 1961]. Such attitudes have the effect of prolonging mental illness, since they lead people to delay treatment, and make recovery more difficult even after treatment is instituted. As long as such prescientific attitudes persist, they will remain part of the "causes" of mental illness.

Deviation through Failure to Conform. Some persons fail to behave in the usual ways even though they are physically and mentally capable of learning conventional behavior. Criminals, bums, sex deviants, alcoholics, drug addicts, political extremists, hermits, and "cranks" of many varieties are examples. What causes such deviation?

Causes of Failure to Conform. *Some Debatable Theories.* Several theories have become quite popular, although evidence for them is either contradictory or incomplete.

1. *Physical-type theories* attempt to associate deviant behavior with body type. A number of students, including Lombroso [1912], Kretsch-mer [1925], Hooton [1939], Von Hentig [1947], and Sheldon [1949], have made studies claiming to find that certain body types are more prone to deviant behavior than others. The most recent and elaborate theory is that of Sheldon, who identifies three basic body types: endomorph (round, soft, fat); mesomorph (muscular, athletic); and ectomorph (thin, bony). For each type, Sheldon describes an elaborate series of personality traits and behavior tendencies. For example, he finds that delinquents and alcoholics are generally mesomorphs. He attributes neurosis largely to one's effort to be different from what his body type predisposes him to be.

Body-type theories appear occasionally as "scientific" articles in popular magazines and Sunday papers. They have become quite popular, possibly because they seem to offer a simple, scientific way of classifying people and predicting or explaining their behavior. Social scientists, however, are quite skeptical of the body-type theories [Clinard, 1957, pp. 119–125]. Although these theories are supported by impressive empirical evidence, critics have noted serious errors in method that cast doubts on their findings. For example, the process of classifying subjects into the several body types included no adequate methodological safeguards against unconscious bias; consequently a borderline subject may have been placed in whatever body-type class he "belonged" in order to support the theory. The subject groups used in most of these studies were composed of institutionalized delinquents, who are not properly representative of all types of delinquents. Furthermore, none of the studies used adequate control groups of "normal" people. For example, over half of Hooton's control group were firemen and militiamen, persons who are especially selected for physical fitness. Because of such errors in method, most social scientists doubt that a reliable association between physical type and deviant behavior has yet been established.

2. *Psychoanalytic theories* of deviant behavior are also popular, and have provided many plot themes for TV and "adult westerns." Psychoanalysis is firmly rooted in Freud's concepts of the id, ego, and superego, as described in Chapter 5. Deviant behavior is attributed to conflicts between the id and the ego or between the id and the superego. Crime, for example, takes place when the superego, the civilized self-control of the individual, is unable to restrain the savage, primitive, destructive impulses of the id [Zilboorg, 1943; Abrahamsen, 1944].

Are the id, ego, and superego valid concepts that help us in understanding and changing behavior? Do death wishes, castration-complexes, and oedipal stages actually exist in the normal personality, or does the psychoanalyst unconsciously plant the expected symptoms in the patient's mind and dig them up in subsequent interviews? We do not definitely know. Psychoanalytic theory is almost totally unsubstantiated by empirical research, while a number of such efforts have been inconclusive or nonconfirmatory. In Chapter 4, Sewell's findings [1952] cast doubt on psychoanalytic theory about specific child-training practices. Barnes [1952] sought to test the Freudian theory of the successive oral, anal, and phallic levels of psychosexual development and concluded that "the Freudian theory of levels of psychosexual development has not been supported as a whole." In all, comparatively few empirical attempts to test psychoanalytic theory have been made. It would, in fact, be quite difficult to design research that would either establish or disprove the existence of the id or the ego. But until such research is attempted, psychoanalytic theory remains debatable, even though it is widely used in the treatment of behavior disorders. Its clinical success is sometimes cited as proof of psychoanalytic theory; that is, since some of the patients improve under psychoanalytic treatment, the theory must be sound. But such claims for successful treatment are not accompanied by a comparison of these patients with a control group of untreated patients, who often improve without treatment. Consequently we cannot know whether the patients improved because of the treatment or because of other factors.

If, without using psychoanalytic terminology, it is merely stated that culture often frustrates biological drives, little argument is possible. While the id may be debatable, there is no doubt about the existence of biological drives such as hunger and sex, or about the organic reactions associated with fear and anger. Clearly, too, culture often frustrates these drives and impulses. Our culture, for example, makes no socially approved provision for the sexual drives of the unmarried, widowed, or separated. If one gratifies such impulses in defiance of cultural taboos, he is engaging in deviant behavior. If, however, he disposes of the impulse by *repressing* it into his unconscious (to return to psychoanalytic theory), it does not go away but remains as part of his unconscious motivation and may still give rise to deviant behavior of some kind. Thus the sex-starved spinster may repress her sex drives into her unconscious, where they remain active, perhaps impelling her to extreme prissiness, religious fanaticism, health anxieties, or some other emotional "cover-ups." Stated in this less tortuous manner, psychoanalytic theory, while still unproved, becomes a highly plausible explanation for much deviant behavior.

Failures in Socialization. Every member of a society is frustrated by the clash of his biological drives with the taboos of his culture. But not everyone becomes a deviant. Why, when most persons conform to the norms of the culture, do some become deviant? There is no convincing evidence that most of these deviants differ significantly from the conformists in their inherited or constitutional behavior impulses. Therefore, *social scientists assume that they are deviant because of some failure in the socialization process whereby cultural norms are integrated into the individual's personality.* Where the socialization process is successful, the individual adopts the norms that surround him so that the approved goals and values of the culture become his own emotional needs, while the taboos of his culture become a part of his conscience. He *internalizes* the norms of his culture so that he automatically and mechanically acts in the expected manner most of the time. His lapses are rare, and both he and others recognize that they are lapses from his normal behavior.

Behavior scientists are agreed that moral values and behavior norms are learned mainly in the family. When the child is socialized in a happy, affectionate, conventional family, he usually develops a secure, well-adjusted personality, behaves conventionally in most respects, marries successfully, and provides a happy, affectionate, conventional home for his children, who then repeat the cycle. Where family life is unsatisfactory, the children often develop personality difficulties and behavior deviations. The Gluecks [1959], after many years of carefully controlled comparisons of delinquent and nondelinquent youth, predict that juvenile delinquency is at least a 90 per cent probability when the "five highly decisive" factors in family life are unfavorable: father's discipline (harsh, erratic, unsympathetic); mother's supervision (indifferent, unconcerned); father's affection (lacking); mother's affection (cold, indifferent, hostile); cohesiveness of the family (unintegrated, empty of companionship). Where all five of these factors are favorable, they find virtually no serious delinquency.

The exact manner in which one's family life molds personality into conforming or deviant channels shows an endless variety. Some families make no real effort to transmit the cultural norms to their children, while others try but fail, as shown in this personal history taken from the author's files.

> As far back as I can remember anything, I can recall those scenes which always ended with my mother's tearful lament, "Why can't you be more like your brother?" while I kept to myself the thought, "Be like that big sissy? Not on your life." He was older and was expected to look after me, which I resented. So anything he counseled against, I promptly did. I think it was emotionally necessary for me not to be or do anything he was or did. He was studious; I avoided school books like they were disease germs. He was neat, orderly, punctual, and methodical; I shunned these weaknesses. He did exactly what our parents and teachers asked; I did nothing they asked. He was a "good boy" and they showed their pride in him on every occasion; they were never proud of me. He and my father were close confidants and companions; my only companions were other "bad boys" from whom my parents made strenuous—and unsuccessful—efforts to separate me. When I finally stood, dry-eyed, beside my father's casket while my brother sniffled, my only thought was, "Why don't you die too, you stupid square!"

We cannot be certain just why this boy rejected parental values and standards while his brother was accepting them. One might guess that his parents showed some favoritism and perhaps a lack of sympathetic interest, and made a clumsy use of the older brother as model. Yet a similar family atmosphere had an opposite effect on another child, as shown in this case.

> All my life I have been competing with my older brother. From the first I felt that he was better, smarter, and more handsome than I. He was the one whom my parents loved the more, criticized more gently, praised more highly, and proudly showed off before the relatives and guests. I recall that at such moments, I harbored no feelings of resentment, but only feelings of wistful longing that I might also deserve such appreciation. I became very dutiful and obedient, and my intense efforts to do what they wished were sometimes rewarded.
>
> Today, as a middle-aged adult, I feel a good deal of resentment toward them. I suppose that my dedicated efforts to earn their affection are responsible both for my success, which greatly surpasses my brother's, and for my anxieties and tensions, which are considerable. Although both parents have been dead for years, my persistent emotional need to seek approval through perfect performance is both my virtue and my curse. I often wonder what I would be today, had I received the warm acceptance my brother always enjoyed.

These two cases illustrate the fact that *there is no social situation that has uniformly predictable effects on all persons in that situation.* All attempts to link predictably a particular behavior outcome with a particular type of family experience are doomed to failure. The most we can say is that certain kinds of family experience usually produce well-adjusted, conforming people, while family life that is deficient is more likely to produce poorly adjusted personalities and behavior deviation. The specific deficiencies may be of many sorts—parental neglect or abuse, lack of sympathy and affection, harsh or erratic discipline, lack of family cohesiveness, excessive parental demands and unrealistic standards, or any of a number of other defects that keep the home from being a pleasant, comfortable place.

Inadequate parents may fail in at least two general ways: (1) They may fail to provide a satisfactory model of normal behavior for their children to copy. If the parents are themselves deviant persons, their children have little opportunity to learn the conventional behavior norms. There is a good deal of speculation on the possibility that much alcoholism, drug addiction, sex deviation, marital inadequacy, and other behavior difficulty may stem from a boy's inability to identify with his weak, ineffectual father, so that the son was never able to form a satisfactory masculine self-image. Feminine difficulties are often attributed in like manner to a girl's unsatisfactory mother-model. This theory is plausible, although as yet largely unsubstantiated. (2) They may strive to instill the cultural norms in their children, but may succeed only in arousing their resistance. Perhaps they are too demanding, too critical, too strict, too erratic, or too unloving. At any rate a child sometimes develops a strong emotional need to resist parental goals and standards and to shock parents and others by unconventional behavior. A study of American ex-Communists by Ernst and Loth [1952] found that most of them were resentful, somewhat unhappy children of conventional, domineering parents, and had joined the Communist party briefly during young adulthood as a means of emancipation from and revenge on their parents. Psychiatrists are convinced that some alcoholics are resentful persons who, probably unconsciously, are revenging themselves on their families by destroying themselves [Podalsky, 1960; Fox, 1956]. L. Young [1954] studied 1,350 unmarried mothers and concluded that most of them *wanted* an illegitimate child as a form of revenge, usually on their mothers. An endless variety of behavior difficulties are often traced to some such disturbance in the parent-child relationship. Such conclusions are difficult to prove or disprove, but are widely held by behavior scientists.

Cultural Conflicts. In a well-integrated culture with a single set of behavior codes and moral values, socialization is smooth and untroubled. Parents express the cultural norms, in their words and actions, and these are reinforced by the rest of the society. But in a heterogeneous, changing society there is no single set of norms; instead there are many competing sets of norms and values. Many parents find that their efforts to train their children are undermined by other groups and influences. Parents who wish their teen-age children to remain chaste and sober must struggle not only against the rash, exploratory self-confidence of youth but also against a variety of commercial panderings and group encouragements that tempt youth to seek "sophistication" and indulgence. Our formal mores demand chastity until marriage, but young people are subjected to a ceaseless barrage of commercial sex stimulation, are exposed to a pseudoscientific literature that encourages and justifies indulgence, and largely removed from any effective adult chaperonage. It is not surprising that most unmarried young people dally on the borders of unchastity while at least half of them step across it [Reiss, 1960].

Anomie and Deviation. From such a variety of conflicting norms arises a condition Durkheim [1897] called *anomie,* a condition of "normlessness." He did not mean that modern societies have no norms; instead they have many sets of norms, with none of them clearly binding upon everybody. Later, sociologists extended the term to include the state of mind in which the person has no firm sense of belonging to anything dependable or stabilizing. As Parsons writes, anomie is

> . . . the state where large numbers of individuals are in a serious degree lacking in the kind of integration with stable institutions which is essential to their own personal stability and the smooth functioning of the social system. . . . The typical reaction of the individual is . . . insecurity.

Talcott Parsons, *Essays in Sociological Theory,* The Free Press of Glencoe, New York, 1954, pp. 125, 126.

Merton [1938] believes that anomie in our society is largely a result of disharmony between our cultural goals and our institutionalized means for reaching them. He notes that while our society encourages *all* its members to aspire to wealth and social position, our approved modes of attaining these goals are so restrictive that only a few have any realistic prospect of reaching them. True, an exceptional Negro or poor boy reaches wealth and fame, and these rare exceptions help to preserve the myth of equal opportunity. But a Negro youth or poor boy with a family background of ignorance and apathy and without valuable "connections" has only a slender chance of success even if he is highly talented. If he has only average abilities, he has virtually no chance of ever reaching the goals our culture holds before him unless he violates the rules for seeking them. So Merton concludes:

> It is only when a system of cultural values extols, virtually above all else, certain *common* success-goals *for the population at large,* while the social structure rigorously restricts or completely closes access to approved modes of reaching these goals *for a considerable part of the same population,* that deviant behavior ensues on a large scale. . . .

The moral mandate to achieve success thus exerts pressure to succeed, by fair means if possible and by foul means if necessary.

Robert K. Merton, "Social Structure and Anomie," *American Sociological Review*, 3:672–682, 1938.

Whereas Merton sees deviation growing from one's inability to achieve culturally inspired goals, Riesman [1950] sees it growing from the shift to *other-direction* in modern society. In traditional societies, people are *tradition-directed;* that is, they are guided by a coherent set of traditions that they follow with little deviation. Later the society becomes *inner-directed*, with people guided by a conscience that has internalized the rather authoritarian indoctrination of family and other groups in a stable community. Today man is increasingly *other-directed*, for lack of a coherent tradition or a stable community is leaving him with no clear guide to conduct except the judgments of other people. But since modern societies have many groupings, with differing norms, other-direction provides no dependable guide to conduct. Consequently the behavior of the individual often lacks consistency and is conformable to no dependable norm. Since it is impossible, in our complex and changing society, to re-establish stable communities, Riesman looks to the development of "autonomous" persons who can order their lives responsibly without being rooted in stable communities or being puppets of their peer groups. Whether this is possible remains an unanswered question.

Significance of Deviant Behavior. Is deviant behavior good or bad for a society? The question is not easy to answer. Much of what we term progress was first conceived in the mind of some brilliant person whose imagination climbed out of the conventional ruts and channels—and who often suffered because of his unconventionality. Deviation is responsible both for much of the progress and much of the trouble of a society. And the same conditions that encourage disapproved deviation—rapid change, conflicting norms and values, weakness of traditional patterns—may also encourage approved forms of deviation. Finally, approved deviation in the form of brilliant discoveries and inventions may produce social changes that further undermine traditional behavior, and thus contribute to further deviation of both kinds. Deviation is both a threat and a protection to social stability.

Summary

A society must have *social order* if it is to function smoothly. A society maintains *social control* over its members in three principal ways. First, it socializes them so that they will want to behave as they should. Second, society imposes *group pressure* on the individual so that he must conform or be punished by his group. This group pressure may be expressed through the informal controls of the primary group—approval and disapproval, praise, scorn, ostracism, etc.; or it may operate through the more formal controls of secondary groups—rules and regulations, standardized procedures, propaganda, rewards, titles, penalties, etc. Finally, control through *force* is used where other controls fail. But in many social situations, behavior is more greatly controlled by the needs and pressures of the situation—the *situational determinants of behavior*—than by the character one brings to the situation.

Social deviation arises whenever a person fails to conform to the usual norms of the society. Deviation may be individual, in that a person deviates from the normal behavior of his group; or it may be group deviation, in which the entire group deviates from social norms, so that the individual is a conforming member of a deviant group or subculture. In practice, these two types tend to merge, since deviants tend to seek out other deviants and form deviant groups. Deviants are also divided into *cultural deviants* and *psychological deviants*. Cultural deviants simply deviate from the expected behavior norms. Psychological deviants are deviant from the norm in their personality integration; in their social behavior they may be either deviant or conformist.

Some forms of deviation are approved by the culture—the leader, hero, genius, and saint are often (though not always) honored and revered. Many forms of deviation are disapproved. Deviation through *inability* to conform—often caused by physical or mental defect or illness—is usually viewed with sympathy. The role of social and cultural influences in producing mental illness cannot be exactly measured, but there is widespread agreement that our culture provokes mental conflicts that contribute to mental illness.

Other deviation arises through *failure* to conform, and the causes are debatable. Physical-type theories are popular but unproved. Psychoanalytic theories are popular and plausible but also unproved. Most of the disapproved individual deviation probably stems, at least partly if not entirely, from failures in socialization, so that the norms and values of the culture are imperfectly integrated into the personality of the individual. The family plays the key role in socialization and is the main channel through which the child absorbs the culture's norms and values. Unsatisfactory family life is therefore the principal factor in disapproved individual deviation. The family, however, is a part of the culture, and unsatisfactory family life is often a reflection of conflicts within the culture. Such conflicts surround cultural norms with uncertainty, and by thus imposing conflicting pressures on individuals, help to produce a state of normlessness called *anomie*. The disharmony between our cultural goals and our means for attaining them encourages anomie and deviation. Thus deviation, while an enemy of social stability, is also a means of introducing the changed norms that become necessary if a changing society is to remain reasonably integrated and efficient.

Questions and Projects

1. How does social order depend on predictability of behavior?
2. Many ancient societies required many human sacrifices. Why did these people consent to die quietly instead of revolting?
3. Evaluate this statement: "Only weaklings follow the herd. A person with true strength of character will do what he knows is right without being swayed by the group."
4. In the factory a "rate-buster" is a worker on piecework who produces and earns so much that management may revise the piecerate downward. How do the other workers treat him? Is he anything like a "course-spoiler" in college, who works so hard in a course that the professor begins to expect more from the other students?
5. What do you think of the Tlingit practice of holding the entire group morally responsible for the acts of each member? Does it make for effective social control? How widely could we follow it? Is it consistent with our ethos? Does our society have the kind of group structure in which such a practice is workable?
6. In the hospital, does a sense of group responsibility for the actions of each member develop? What effect does this feeling have on individual performance of duty?
7. Under what circumstances will practically all students cheat? When will very few students cheat? How does this contrast in attitude illustrate "situational determinants of behavior"?
8. Distinguish between individual and group deviants. How do these two ideal types tend to merge in practice?
9. In what ways was Florence Nightingale a deviant? What were the consequences of her deviation?
10. Is overconformity a mark of successful or unsuccessful socialization?
11. Why do "backward" or primitive societies have less crime and fewer violations of the mores than "progressive" societies like ours?
12. How would you interpret our high Negro crime rate in terms of Merton's theory of cultural goals and institutionalized means?
13. Read one of the disaster studies such as William Form et al., *Community in Disaster*, Harper & Row, Publishers, Incorporated, New York, 1958, or Harry E. Moore, *Tornados over Texas*, University of Texas Press, Austin, Tex., 1958. Show how social order breaks down, and then is restored, following a physical disaster.
14. Compare and explain the differing success of two families in their effort to insulate their children from the influences of a slum neighborhood as described in Betty Smith, *A Tree Grows in Brooklyn*, Harper & Row, Publishers, Incorporated, New York, 1963, and in James T. Farrell, *A World I Never Made*, Vanguard Press, Inc., New York, 1936.

Suggested Readings

BINGER, CARL: "The Pressures on College Girls Today," *Atlantic Monthly*, February, 1961, pp. 40–44. A popular account of contemporary emotional stress.

BROWN, PAULA: "Changes in Ojibwa Social Control," *American Anthropologist*, 54:57–70, January, 1954. Tells how loss of traditional controls and lack of effective replacements leave the Ojibwa with an unsolved problem of social control.

GREEN, ARNOLD: "Why Americans Feel Insecure," *Commentary*, 6:18–28, July, 1948; reprinted in Edgar A. Schuler et al. (eds.), *Readings in Sociology*, 2d ed., Thomas Y. Crowell Company, New York, 1960, pp. 812–821.

HORNEY, KAREN: *The Neurotic Personality of Our Time*, W. W. Norton and Company, Inc., New York, 1937. A classic description of how a competitive, stressful society encourages mental disorders.

MERTON, ROBERT K.: *Social Theory and Social Structure*, rev. ed., The Free Press of Glencoe, New York, 1957, chaps. 3 and 4, "Social Structure and Anomie," and "Continuities in the Theory of Social Structure and Anomie." A classic statement concerning anomie and deviation in modern society; chap. 11, "The Self-Fulfilling Prophesy," is a description of the self-fulfilling prophesy as a basic process in society.

Groups and
Associations

Take each of us alone, a man apart from the Cheyenne people who remember the same things and wish for the same things. Take each one of us that way, and you have nothing but a man who cannot respect himself because he is a failure in the white man's way. A man who does not respect himself cannot make a good future. There is no strength in his spirit. Now take all of us together as Cheyenne people. Then our names are not the names of failures. They are the names of great and generous hunters who fed the people, fighters who died for freedom just as white men's heroes died, holy men who filled us with the power of God. Take us together that way and there is a drink for every man in the cup of self-respect, and we will have the strength of spirit to decide what to do and to do it. We will do good things as a tribe that is growing and changing that we cannot do as individual men cut off from their forefathers.

From a statement by the Northern Cheyenne, quoted by Oliver la Farge in *Indian Affairs*, News Letter of the Association for American Indian Affairs, Inc., no. 37, New York, June, 1960.

The Cheyenne are not the only people who find that individual strength and character come from association with the group. All men, regardless of race or culture, find personality fulfillment through group life. The infant becomes "human" as he takes his place in the family; the autistic children mentioned in Chapter 4 are extreme examples of the results of a lack of normal family interaction. As the child moves beyond the family circle he enters into still other group relationships which will continuously remold his personality until death ends the process.

To define a "group" presents some problems because all groups are aggregations or collections of persons but not all aggregations are groups. Bogardus [1949, p. 4] suggests this definition: "A number of persons who have common interests, who are stimulating to each other, who have common loyalty and participate in common activities." The definition covers the groups in which the members come to know each other personally but does not fit groups such as the national fraternal order, the political party, or the national state. Yet all these and many similar aggregations are important in groups in society. For a more inclusive definition let us say that *groups are aggregates in which people have a consciousness of membership and interaction.* This definition includes both the large groups in which one never sees most of the members and the smaller groups such as the family.

The definition excludes certain types of aggregations. A busload of passengers would not ordinarily be a group because they have no consciousness of interaction with each other but simply happen to be in the same place. It is possible that interaction may develop in the course of the trip and groups may form. When children begin to play together, when boy meets girl, when businessmen discover a common interest in the stock market or the baseball game, groups begin to develop—transient and amorphous though they be. On occasion the entire aggregate may become a group as in this instance related by Bierstedt.

> Subway passengers in New York, for example, are notoriously indifferent to one another. But only the slightest stimulus is needed to transform [them] . . . into a social group. The writer was in a fairly crowded car one evening in the spring when a very young, very tipsy Scandinavian sailor happened to stroll in from the adjoining car. He began to sing aloud in his native language, a gay, pleasant song, and the passengers, aroused from their reveries and their newspapers, responded warmly to his effort and began to exchange smiles with one another. With unexpected and, indeed, unusual solicitude for subway passengers, several of the men in the car asked the sailor where he wanted to go and made sure that he did not ride past his destination. After he left, the remaining passengers, augmented now by others who were strangers to the episode, returned to their reveries and their newspapers. The spell was broken. What for a few transitory moments had been a social group became once again . . . people with no more in common than their accidental togetherness at the same time and

place, enough to give them a consciousness of kind but not enough, without this extra stimulus, to induce them to enter into social relations with one another.

Robert Bierstedt, *The Social Order*, McGraw-Hill Book Company, New York, 1957, p. 257.

The essence of the social group is not physical closeness but a consciousness of joint interaction. The passengers in the subway car were close together, but until the entry of the sailor gave them a common interest they were not engaged in joint interaction. This consciousness of interaction depends on many factors and may be present even when there is no personal interaction between individuals. Thus we are members of a national group and think of ourselves as nationals even though we are acquainted with only a tiny fraction of those who make up our nation. Nevertheless we interact through political campaigns, the payment of taxes, the use of government services, the response to symbols such as the flag and the national anthem, and perhaps most of all in a consciousness that as citizens of one nation we are bound together in a way that distinguishes us from the citizens of other nations. Groups vary tremendously in size, purpose, and degree of intimacy among their members, and the individual is involved with them in many different ways.

The Group and the Individual

Our individualistic ethos tempts us to assume that the individual is in full command of his behavior and blinds us to the degree to which individual behavior is controlled by group experience. This assumption is revealed by the popular reaction to the announcement that American soldiers, held prisoner by the Chinese in the Korean War, had collaborated with the enemy far more than in any other war in our history. There was a popular disposition to blame individual weaknesses and character defects, but a more scientific inquiry found that the captured soldiers had been demoralized by a systematic attack on their group loyalties.

To explain this process we have to know the types of conduct in question. First, all evidence shows that the American soldiers were patriotic men who fought bravely and surrendered only in hopeless situations. There were no wholesale conversions to communism, for when prisoners were given their choice at the end of hostilities, only twenty-one Americans chose to remain with the Chinese forces as against over twenty thousand Chinese prisoners who chose to go to Taiwan rather than return to mainland China.

While scarcely any American defected to the enemy, virtually all American prisoners developed a passivity that contrasted strangely with their reputation in other wars as being extremely troublesome prisoners. For the first time in history, American prisoners sat through a war without making any organized escape attempts [Kinkead, 1959, p. 7]. One out of three prisoners collaborated to some extent in giving propaganda material to the Chinese, and a 38 per cent death rate in the prison camps indicated the American prisoners' lack of concern for the welfare of their companions. The net results were that the Chinese did not have to divert large forces to guard prisoners and were able to use some of the prisoners in a manner embarrassing to the United States.

Physical hardship, poor food, limited medical attention, and inadequate shelter played a part in weakening the resistance of the American prisoners, but these conditions were not considered sufficiently severe to account for their behavior. Torture and, more frequently, the threat of torture did take place on occasion but affected only a minority of the prisoners. The major means of demoralization used by the Chinese was something more powerful than physical force—*the systematic attack on group ties*, described by Biderman [1960] and Schein [1960]. Just as "dying is easy for anyone left alone in a concentration camp,"[1] death came easily to prisoners of war who were isolated from their fellows.

The Chinese used such techniques as solitary confinement, isolation of small groups of prisoners, and frequent shifting of personnel to hamper the formation or survival of cohesive groups. More important, they also sought to divide the prisoners in their attitude to each other and to cut them off from any feeling of effective links with the homeland. Casual information gathered in interviews was used to convince them that all other Americans were informers and that they might as well give in too. If a prisoner resisted what he thought were improper demands from the Chinese, the whole unit was denied food or a chance to sleep until the objector had been forced to come around by his own buddies. The following description of mail censorship gives an idea of some of the procedures used:

> Another method of isolating these people from each other was through their selection of mail. . . . This effectively separates people one from another by shearing away what ordinarily serves as a common basis for unified effort and unified activity. When two soldiers get together and compare their letters from home about their kids and about their family and about their house, this has a unifying effect. This binds men closer together. But when your letters are restricted to letters which very often announce some major or minor domestic crisis, when your letter turns out to be a notice from a collection company, or what a soldier calls a "Dear John" letter, this isn't the kind of thing you get together with your buddy and talk about. Consequently, men were deprived of this common emotional basis for sticking together.

[1] An anonymous concentration-camp survivor quoted in *Life*, Aug. 18, 1958, p. 90.

They also used this control of the mail to make men feel that what the Communist says about capitalism and what it does to its members was demonstrably true, in this respect: It said that our system of free enterprise leads to selfishness, grasping, caring only for what is in it for you, little regard for another individual, especially if he is not there. They said, "Your people at home have forgotten about you. They don't really care about you." What little mail you got was likely to bear this out. Of course this helped make men feel that they were alone and abandoned and isolated. . . .

They cut these people apart, making them isolated and thus obviously much more helpless. . . .

Testimony before the permanent Subcommittee on Investigations; testimony of Major William E. Mayer, Medical Corps, United States Army, before the Committee on Government Operations, U.S. Senate, 84th Cong., 2d Sess. Cited in Eugene L. Hartley and Gerhart D. Wiebe, *Casebook in Social Processes,* Thomas Y. Crowell Company, New York, 1960, pp. 76–77. Our general treatment of this topic is based on testimony by Major Mayer and Major Marion R. Panell.

Normally the GI is a gregarious soul, looking for amusement in the company of his buddies and anxious to maintain his home ties. Observers reported that over half of the first group of liberated American prisoners passed up an offer for a free long-distance phone call to the States and that when given leave in Tokyo they went to town alone. These are clues to the success with which they had been isolated—from their buddies, from their families, from everyone. How this separateness contrasts with the kind of group experience that makes a soldier effective may be seen in a dispatch by the late Ernie Pyle, a World War II correspondent.

The ties that grow up between men who live savagely and die relentlessly together are of great strength. There is a sense of fidelity to each other among little corps of men who have endured so long and whose hope in the end can be but so small.

One afternoon while I was with the company, S. Sgt. Buck Eversole's turn came to go back to rest camp for five days. The company was due to attack that night.

Buck went to his company commander and said, "Lieutenant, I don't think I better go. I'll stay if you need me."

The lieutenant said, "Of course I need you, Buck, I always need you. But it's your turn and I want you to go. In fact, you're ordered to go." . . .

I walked with him toward the truck in the dusk. He kept his eyes on the ground and I think he would have cried if he knew how, and he said to me very quietly:

"This is the first battle I've missed that this battalion has been in, and I sure hope that they have good luck."

And then he said:

"I feel like a deserter."

He climbed in and the truck dissolved into the blackness. I went back and lay down on the ground among my other friends, waiting for the night orders to march. I lay there in the darkness thinking—terribly touched by the great simple devotion of this soldier who was a cowboy—and thinking of the millions far away at home who must remain forever unaware of the powerful fraternalism in the ghastly brotherhood of war.

The remarkable tenacity with which the German army survived two years of unbroken defeats in World War II is testimony to the importance of group unity to fighting effectiveness. During the war, the Allies nursed the hope that "psychological warfare" could undermine the German soldier's faith in his cause and his loyalty to his government and thus impair his fighting morale. Postwar studies [Shils and Janowitz, 1948] have shown that this approach was not very effective. It was rooted in the unsound theory that the soldier is sustained mainly by loyalty to his country and faith in the rightness of its cause, whereas postwar investigations found that he is sustained mainly by his unity with and loyalty to the small military units to which he is attached. As long as the soldier's immediate group—the primary group which we shall analyze within a few pages—remained integrated, he continued to resist. Even those who were critical of their "cause" remained effective soldiers because of their group loyalties. Among the comparatively few German deserters, their failure to have become fully absorbed into the primary group life of the army was far more important than any political or ideological doubts. Long after their cause was clearly lost, most German units of all sizes continued to resist until their supplies were exhausted or they were physically overwhelmed.

Such is the sustaining power of a unified group. When bound to his fellow soldiers by shared experience and group loyalties the soldier was able to face death itself in heroic fashion, but when he was cut off from the support of his group his fighting effectiveness quickly ebbed. Individual qualities certainly played a part, but beyond them was the vital question of whether the soldier was an isolated individual or a member of a group drawing strength from the consciousness of his relationship to others. Pasley [1955] has shown how, of the twenty-one Korean prisoners who defected, eighteen had never taken part in school activities or sports during their school life. This shows that these were men who had *never* really "belonged" and were therefore easily open to treason.

In *every* kind of behavior, a person's relation to his group has a profound effect on how he will perform. Even in a hospital setting, a patient's recovery is affected by his group associations. Gilbert and Wells [1957] has shown how the improvement of patients in mental hospitals is associated with their social relationships within the ward.

The concept of group, then, is not just a sociological plaything. It is a vital social reality, with great bearing on the behavior of individuals in all social situations. Cut a man off from all group ties, and in many cases he soon sickens and dies; unite him in group loyalty, and his endurance and sacrifice are almost beyond belief.

Some Major Group Classifications

In-groups and Out-groups. There are some groups to which I belong— my family, church, clique, profession, race, sex, nation—any group I precede with the pronoun "my." These are *in-groups*, because I feel I belong to them. There are other groups to which I do not belong— other families, cliques, occupations, races, nationalities, religions, the other sex—these are *out-groups*, for I am outside of them.

The least advanced primitive societies live in small, isolated bands that are usually clans of kinsmen. It was kinship that determined the nature of the in-group and the out-group, and when two strangers met, the first thing they had to do was establish relationship. If kinship could be established, then they were friends—both members of the in-group. If no relationship could be established, then in many societies they were enemies and acted accordingly.

In-groups and out-groups.

Modern society is based on many ties besides those of kinship, but the establishment and definition of in-groups are equally important to us. People placed in a new social situation will usually make cautious conversational feints to find out whether or not they "belong." When we establish that people have a common economic level with ourselves, a common religious background, a common political viewpoint, are interested in the same types of sports or music, then we may have some assurance that we are in an in-group. Members of the in-group are likely to share common sentiments, laugh at the same jokes, and have a common definition of the activities and goals of life. Members of the out-group may share many of the same cultural traits, but they lack certain essentials considered necessary to break into this particular social group.

In modern society, we find that individuals belong to so many groups that a number of their in-group and out-group relationships overlap. A member of the senior class will consider that a freshman belongs to an out-group; yet the same senior and freshman may both be members of an athletic team in which they have an in-group relationship to each other. Similarly men who have an in-group relationship based on membership in the same church may discover that this association does not extend to economic relationships; and women who work together in the PTA may find they are no longer in the same in-group when making plans for a party at the country club.

Exclusion from the in-group can be a brutal process. Most primitive societies treated outsiders as part of the animal kingdom; many had no separate words for "enemy" and "stranger," showing they made no distinction. Not too different was the attitude of the Nazis, who excluded the Jews from the human race. Rudolf Hoess [1960], who commanded the Auschwitz concentration camp in which two million Jews were put to death, characterized this slaughter as "the removal of racial-biological foreign bodies." It is impossible to understand the repeated brutalities of history without understanding in-groups and out-groups. This distinction makes it psychologically possible for even decent and humane men to commit cruel acts. Trevor-Roper writes:

> Seventeenth-century Englishmen were generally tolerant and humane. Even in their civil war and revolution, they constantly remembered that their enemies were like themselves; they fought them with mildness and courtesy. Oliver Cromwell himself was ahead of his age in tolerance. But when Cromwell invaded Ireland, he assumed a new character. To him and his followers, the Irish were quite different. A generation of ideological propaganda against creatures safely invisible in another island made it possible for Englishmen to regard the Irish as "sub-human," and for Cromwell (who was surprisingly tolerant of Roman Catholics in England) to write from Drogheda that his "knocking on the head" of obstinate Irishmen was "a righteous judgment of God [on] these barbarous wretches."

H. R. Trevor-Roper, *New York Times Magazine,* Sept. 17, 1961, p. 108.

In-groups and out-groups are important, then, because they affect behavior. From fellow members of an in-group, we expect recognition, loyalty, and helpfulness. From out-groups, our expectation varies with the kind of out-group. From some out-groups we expect hostility; from others, a more or less friendly competition; from still others, indifference. From the sex out-group we may expect neither hostility nor indifference, yet in our behavior a difference undeniably remains. The twelve-year-old boy who shuns girls grows up to become a romantic lover and spends most of his life in matrimony. Yet when men and women meet on social occasions they tend to split into one-sex groups, for each is bored by many of the conversational interests of the other.

Social Distance. We are not equally involved in all our in-groups. One might, for example, be a passionate Democrat and a rather indifferent Rotarian. Nor do we feel equally distant from all our out-groups. Our loyal Democrat will feel far closer to the Republicans than to the Communists. Bogardus [1958, 1959] and others [Westie, 1959] have developed the concept *social distance* to measure the *degree of closeness or acceptance we feel* toward other groups. While most often used with reference to racial groups, social distance refers to closeness between groups of all kinds. Pearlin and Rosenberg [1962] have studied nurse-patient social distance in a mental hospital. They find, for example, that social distance is greater when nurse and patient differ greatly in age and among nurses who are especially obedient and worshipful toward authority.

Social distance refers to group, not individual, relationships. One may feel quite distant toward a group, yet have warm personal feelings toward certain of its members. The racial bigot may have a real affection for a faithful Negro servant, and many anti-Semites have a favorite Jew. Yet social distance discourages close personal feelings and associations. Social distance is measured either by direct observation of the relationships people have with other groups or, more often, by questionnaires in which people are asked the relationships in which they would accept or reject members of certain other groups. In these questionnaires a number of groups may be listed (Jews, Catholics, English, Japanese) and the informants asked to check whether they would accept a member of each group as a neighbor, as a fellow worker, as a marriage partner, and so on through a series of relationships. Table 2 shows a study of social-distance reactions of a sample of Americans to thirty different racial or national groups.

The social-distance questionnaires may not accurately measure what people actually would do if a member of another group sought to become a friend or neighbor. The social-distance scale is only an attempt to measure one's feeling of unwillingness to associate equally with a group. What a person will actually do in a situation depends both upon his feelings of distance and the circumstances of the situation, a point that will be discussed at some length in the chapter on race and ethnic relations.

Table 2 RACIAL REACTIONS BY REGIONS IN THE UNITED STATES, SPRING, 1956

	North-east (N = 424)	South (N = 524)	North middle (N = 487)	Pacific west (N = 613)	Difference between high and low
1. Americans (U.S. white)	1.09	1.23	1.07	1.03	.20
2. Canadians	1.17	1.28	1.16	1.12	.16
3. English	1.22	1.43	1.19	1.17	.26
4. French	1.47	1.73	1.41	1.32	.41
5. Germans	1.62	2.09	1.45	1.33	.76
6. Scots	1.63	1.97	1.41	1.39	.58
7. Swedish	1.64	2.02	1.36	1.34	.68
8. Hollanders	1.65	2.13	1.43	1.44	.30
9. Norwegians	1.67	2.26	1.39	1.37	.89
10. Jews	1.75	2.18	2.02	2.12	.43
11. Irish	1.77	1.87	1.42	1.29	.58
12. Finns	1.78	2.15	1.75	1.66	.49
13. Italians	1.81	2.29	1.81	1.68	.61
14. Poles	2.04	2.79	1.77	1.74	1.05
15. Spanish	2.08	2.33	2.00	1.97	.46
16. Czechs	2.09	2.78	1.89	1.90	.49
17. Greeks	2.12	2.46	2.05	1.80	.66
18. Russians	2.32	3.68	2.32	2.19	1.49
19. Armenians	2.34	2.47	2.36	2.15	.32
20. Japanese Americans	2.40	2.57	2.16	2.23	.41
21. Indians, American	2.44	2.31	2.32	2.32	.13
22. Filipinos	2.45	2.58	2.42	2.52	.16
23. Mexican Americans	2.50	2.70	2.49	2.49	.21
24. Negroes	2.53	2.74	2.80	2.89	.36
25. Chinese	2.54	2.84	2.51	2.59	.33
26. Turks	2.62	3.14	2.46	2.48	.68
27. Japanese	2.71	2.88	2.59	2.77	.29
28. Indians from India	2.72	2.96	2.76	2.76	.24
29. Mexicans	2.77	2.99	2.75	2.72	.27
30. Koreans	2.87	3.09	2.63	2.75	.46
Arithmetic means of 61,590 reactions	2.06	2.40	1.96	1.97	.44

SOURCE: Emory S. Bogardus, "Racial Reactions by Regions," *Sociology and Social Research,* 43:286–290, March, 1959. Based on a survey of 2,048 persons. A score of 1.00 would indicate complete acceptance, while higher scores reveal increasing degrees of rejection. A low figure in the last column shows that a particular group is about equally accepted or rejected in all four regions. What do you think the bottom row shows?

Primary and Secondary Groups. *Primary groups* are those in which we come to know other people intimately as individual personalities.

We do this through social contacts that are *intimate, personal,* and *total* in that they involve many parts of the person's life experience. In the primary group, such as family, clique, or set of close friends, the social relationships tend to be informal and relaxed. The members are interested in one another as persons. They confide hopes and fears, share experiences, gossip agreeably, and fill the need for intimate human companionship. In the *secondary group* the social contacts are *impersonal, segmental,* and *utilitarian.* One is not concerned with the other person as a person but as a functionary who is filling a role. His personal qualities are not important, only how he performs his role. Only that part or segment of the total personality involved in playing this role is important. The secondary group might be a labor union or a trade association, a country club, a PTA, or it might be two persons bargaining briefly over a store counter. In any case the group exists to serve a specific, limited purpose involving only a segment of the personalities of the members.

The terms "primary" and "secondary" thus describe a type of relationship rather than the relative importance of the group. The primary group may serve objective functions such as the provision of food and clothing, but it is judged by the quality of its human relationships rather than by its efficiency in meeting material needs. The secondary group may function in pleasant surroundings and develop some pleasant associations, but its principal purpose is to fulfill a specific function. One does not consider a family as successful because the house is clean, nor does one judge the New York Stock Exchange mainly by the pleasant way the broker's clerk answers the phone; indeed telegraphic communication is apt to eliminate even this vestige of a human touch. In brief, *primary groups are relationship-directed and secondary groups are goal-oriented.*

A labor union or a trade association is a secondary group in which personal relationships play only a minor role; the family is an example of a primary group in which personal relationships are of major importance. Many social groups cannot be quite as sharply defined, having both primary and secondary elements in their operation. The college fraternity that makes a primary-group emphasis on fellowship may find that it has to turn to goal orientations, such as an adequate scholarship record, in order to survive. On the other hand the army, which is so impersonal that human lives are the price of its activity, finds that its morale depends upon the formation of small groups of soldiers with an intense "buddy" type of relationship. The nurse-patient relationship is primary-group-like in its intimacy and expressed personal concern;

yet it is impersonal in that professional duty, not personal involvement, inspires the nurse's tender concern—she gives all patients the same concern regardless of her feelings toward them. Sometimes a genuine primary-group association eventually develops between nurse and patient, especially in a smaller hospital where a patient remains for a prolonged stay. Like other social classifications, primary and secondary are not polar opposites but are terms for general tendencies, both of which are present to some degree in all human groups.

Primary and secondary groups are important because feelings and behavior are different. It is in the primary group that personality is formed. In the primary group one finds intimacy, sympathy, and a comfortable sharing of many interests and activities. In the secondary group one finds an effective mechanism for achieving certain purposes, but often at the price of suppressing one's true feelings. For example, the saleslady must be cheerful and polite, even when she has a splitting headache and the customer is a boor. Sociology uses few of its concepts more often than the concepts of primary and secondary groups.

Modern Trend toward Secondary-group Association

Our sentiments and emotional ties are centered in primary groups, but an accelerating trend toward a secondary-group society has become irresistible. An industrialized urban society attacks the primary group in at least two ways. First, it increases the relative proportion of secondary-group contacts, as one activity after another is withdrawn from the primary group and assumed as a secondary-group function. Second, the remaining primary-group associations are at the mercy of secondary-group developments. Changes in industry may move the wage earner about, disrupting his local associations. Industrial changes also influence the roles played in the family. A prolonged depression, the result of a maladjustment of secondary relationships, may deprive the father of his earning power and substitute the wife and the relief administrator as symbols of authority. Changes in office and factory work lead to the employment of women, so that the mother has the same kind of career as the father, and both share in the domestic tasks of the home. Changes in the international political scene may take the husband or son out of the family locale and move him to the other side of the world. The worker's family must adjust itself to whatever working hours the corporations finds most profitable. Negotiations between the international union and the corporation may result in work changes that break up informal primary groups formed on the job. The "little red schoolhouse" where a small group of children and a teacher formed an intimate primary group lasting for years is succeeded by the consolidated school drawing hundreds of children from a large area and shifting them about from class to class and teacher to teacher. Scores of similar examples show how primary groupings have become transient and changing units, swept along by the heedlessly changing trends of a secondary-group-dominated society.

Such a trend is not universally welcomed. Critics maintain it produces shallow and rootless personalities that lack the calm certainty and deep friendship that supposedly characterized personal relationships in the traditional society. A visiting Filipino educator expressed this view in his reaction to America's largest city.

> In New York, people seem so busy and so deeply concerned with their own affairs that they no longer know how to smile. Some of them wear masks like "guys and dolls" who conceal their inner world from the busy chatter outside. They walk hurriedly—tack! tack! tack!—on the sidewalks, like robots, unfeeling and unconcerned.

Vidal A. Tan, "Visit to America," *Sunday Times Magazine*, Manila, Philippines, Dec. 28, 1952.

Durkheim [1897] in his study of suicide came to the conclusion that not only high rates of suicide but many other behavior difficulties are explained by the lack of traditional and personal ties in a secondary society, where the individual is engulfed by anomie. Many students of society have followed his lead in regarding the secondary trends of the modern world as an evil force destructive of the relationships that assured man of membership in a warm and secure society where his tendencies toward crime or despair were curbed by his obligations to a stable and intimate social community.

Contributions of the Secondary Group. While the secondary group has brought problems to man, it has also brought contributions. The most obvious is the efficiency of large-scale impersonal organizations in which sentiment is subordinated to the need to get the job done in the most practical way. The tremendous advances in material comfort and in life expectancy in the modern world would be impossible without the rise of goal-directed secondary organizations in which the paternal squire has been replaced by the efficiency expert and the production manager.

These changes have opened channels of opportunity and specializations of function which, while they fragment society, also open a greater chance to develop individual talents. The contrast between the thousands of occupations in the metropolis and the handful of pursuits in the rural village shows how a society dominated by secondary groups opens the way for specialized careers. Today this process has gone so far that not only is the talented individual able to rise from an obscure background but society actively seeks out those whose abilities may be developed along professional, artistic, scientific, or managerial lines. Without secondary-group organization, the modern world would be impossible.

Persistence of Primary Groups. The secondary group has overshadowed but not destroyed the primary group. In fact the two major primary groups, the clique and the family, appear to be stronger than ever. The clique is a small group of intimates with intense in-group feelings based on common sentiments and interests. It may develop in almost any situation, and nearly every secondary group shelters a large number of cliques that add a highly personal note to an otherwise impersonal environment. As for the family, more people get married today, and get married earlier, than in any other period on which we have reliable data. Furthermore, today's family is steadily becoming less directed toward mundane goals and more concerned with human relationships. Yesterday's family was primarily a work crew, sometimes a brutally repressive one; today's family is primarily a companionship group, and a perfect example of primary-group persistence.

Primary groups persist in a secondary-group-dominated world because the human need for intimate, sympathetic association is a persisting need. Man cannot function well unless he belongs to a small group of people who really care what happens to him. Wherever people are ripped from family and friends and thrust into large, impersonal, anonymous groups, as in a college dormitory or an army camp, so great is their need for primary groups that they promptly re-form them.

Primary Groups in a Secondary Setting. If we classified groups according to the extent to which they show primary- or secondary-group traits the result would be a listing of secondary groups such as the army, the corporation, and the national state and a listing of primary groups such as the family, the clique, and the gang. Proceeding in this fashion we would then contrast the impersonal, goal-directed nature of the large organization with the personal, relationship-oriented focus of smaller intimate groups. Such a separation is often assumed when we attempt to analyze the efficiency of large organizations. If we are interested in the productivity of industrial labor, we might study the goals, techniques, and rewards of the factory and then look at the character and training of the individuals who make up the labor force.

Primary groups persist in a secondary-group-dominated world.

The fallacy of this approach is that it overlooks the extent to which every large organization is a network of small primary groups. A person is not simply a unit in an organization chart designed by top management; he is also a member of a smaller informal group with its own structure and its own system of statuses and roles defining the behavior of its members. In the factory the workman finds his place in a group of his fellows with its own leadership, from which the foreman is usually excluded since his very position bars him from this in-group relationship. Since the workman needs the approval and support of his clique more than he needs the approval of his supervisors, he responds to the demands of management only as these demands are consistent with his primary-group relationships.

The influence of the primary group is one reason why incentive-pay plans giving the worker a bonus for greater output have frequently been ineffective. The logic of such plans is that many workers who fail to exert their maximum efforts will work harder if paid in proportion to the work they do. The major defect in such plans is that their effective operation destroys the unity of primary groups. Rather than a number of equals cooperating together, the work gang would become a number of competing individuals each striving to outdo his fellows. Aside from the strain of continuous competition, this situation threatens the workers' social relationships. As a defense, factory cliques develop a norm of a "fair day's work." The man who attempts to ignore this norm is the butt of ridicule, ostracism, and possible violence. Management may employ time-and-motion-study experts to decide a "reasonable" output, but new norms cannot be effective unless they are also accepted by the group [Roethlisberger and Dickson, 1939, chaps. 22, 23; Moore, 1947, chap. 15].

While the primary group in the secondary setting can be an obstacle, it can also be a positive aid in the accomplishment of organizational objectives. Gross [1953] has examined the way in which informal cliques that cut across formal work assignments may lead to cooperation and smoother functioning of the organization. He finds that the clique may even reinforce the idea of organization loyalty, as one private secretary reveals.

A private secretary is the top of the heap. You need something else besides the ability to type and take shorthand. You've got to feel that you are working for the company and not just for yourself. Now Mildred and Emma (other private secretaries), we see eye to eye on that. Louise—she's a good little stenographer, but she'll never be a secretary. She doesn't fit into our crowd. When we go out for coffee she usually tags along. Then she'll complain about her boss. She can't accept the idea that you don't work for a boss, you work for the company.

Edward Gross, "Some Functional Consequences of Primary Controls in Formal Work Organizations," *American Sociological Review*, 18:372, August, 1953.

At times the primary groups may even violate the rules of the larger secondary organization in order to get things done. Since the formal rules are not always workable in all situations, primary worker groups simply trim some corners—that is, break a few rules—in order to get the work out [Roy, 1955].

Perhaps the most dramatic of all illustrations of the influence of the group is found in studies of the extent to which American combat soldiers actually fired their guns in combat. Since soldiers are trained to shoot and may die if they fail to shoot, one would take their reaction for granted. Actually many men found that at the crucial moment they were unable to fire. In fact, studies in World War II [Marshall, 1947; Davidson, 1952] indicated that only 12 to 25 per cent of combat soldiers in a position to fire were able to pull the trigger. It appears that the soldiers had been so strongly conditioned against taking human life that even when self-defense and the call of duty demanded that they kill the enemy, they were unable to overcome the effect of the mores of the civilian culture. Research on combat behavior found that patriotism, hatred of the enemy, military training, and fear of punishment are not very effective in making a man perform well in combat. The main variable determining how well a man will fight is his degree of integration with his unit. Men who will not shoot to save themselves will shoot to save their comrades, if they have any. Highly integrated units fought bravely. Poorly integrated units, although identical in individual abilities and training, fought poorly, with a high proportion of nonshooters, deserters, and mental breakdowns. The authors of the research study, *The American Soldier*, conclude [Shils, 1950] that the primary group "served two principal functions in combat motivation: it set and emphasied group standards of behavior and it supported and sustained the individual in stresses he would otherwise not have been able to withstand."

Training methods and combat techniques now are designed to create the closest possible unity of member and group. For example, two men are assigned to a foxhole instead of being scattered as much as possible. Instead of keeping silence in combat, men are now encouraged to yell and scream while attacking, as this binds them into a group. Officers are told to spend their time crawling from foxhole to foxhole to keep the mob psychology going. In such ways the primary group may be used to achieve secondary-group objectives.

Integration of Primary and Secondary Groups. Just as it is unrealistic to consider the individual apart from society, so secondary and primary groups can best be understood in relation to each other. In modern society the functions and influence of primary groups have been weakened by a growth of impersonal, goal-directed secondary groups that are assuming an increasingly dominant role. Most of these secondary groups, however, create a new network of primary groups which provide intimacy and personal response in an otherwise impersonal situation. While many primary groups are destroyed or modified by the impact of secondary groups, the primary groups in turn exert a major influence on the secondary groups. Primary groups may resist the goal-directed efforts of secondary organizations, or they may help to integrate disparate parts of the organization and provide an emotional security that reinforces the individual's ability to play the roles demanded by his status in the secondary group.

Voluntary Associations

When Alexis de Tocqueville, the perceptive French observer of American life, visited the United States in 1835 the pervasive influence of voluntary associations impressed him as a major part of the society. In his words:

> The political associations that exist in the United States are only a single feature in the midst of the immense assemblage of associations in that country. Americans of all ages, all conditions, and all dispositions, constantly form associations. They have not only commercial and manufacturing companies, in which all take part, but associations of a thousand other kinds—religious, moral, serious, futile, extensive or restricted, enormous or diminutive. The Americans make associations to give entertainments, to found establishments for education, to build inns, to construct churches, to diffuse books, to send missionaries to the antipodes; and in this manner they found hospitals, prisons, and schools. If it be proposed to advance some truth, or to foster some feeling by the encouragement of a great example, they form a society.

Alexis de Tocqueville, *Democracy in America,* tr. by Henry Reeve, ed. by Henry Steele Commager, Oxford University Press, Fair Lawn, N.J., 1947, p. 319.

The round of activities of many Americans today would tend to bear out de Tocqueville's observation. For illustration, consider how voluntary associations affect the life of many a businessman. After luncheon at the chamber of commerce he rushes back to the office to get in a little work before spending the rest of the afternoon soliciting for the community chest. When he returns home after a weary round of pledging he finds that his children have gone on an overnight hike with the scout troop and that dinner is delayed because his wife spent the afternoon at a board meeting of the Children's Aid Society. In the evening his wife will be attending a League of Women Voters' session while he joins an initiation ceremony at his lodge. During the week his leisure and working hours are sprinkled with club luncheons, committee sessions, and organization meetings. On weekends he and his family spend much of their time at the country club, and on Sundays the children are apt to find themselves involved in a church youth group. These are only the beginning. He or his family are sought by the symphony society, the art center, and the little-theater group; the taxpayers' association, the good-government league, and a dozen reform organizations beckon to him; the PTA, several church groups, and a dozen welfare organizations crave his support.

Voluntary associations attract many types of people. The young businessman finds he is expected to take a major part in civic organizations, and labor leaders view invitations to serve in such groups as a sign that they have begun to be recognized by the rest of the community. Smaller towns supposedly offer a sense of community that might make formal organizations less necessary, but a survey [Scott, 1957] of a New England town of about 7,500 found a higher level of participation in organized groups than in most large cities. Surveys of participation usually show less activity among Negroes than among whites, but the existence of 4,000 associations among Chicago's Negroes indicates that any Negro-white gap in this respect will probably be of short duration [Myrdal, 1944, pp. 952–955]. Roman Catholicism has usually not encouraged voluntary associations, and Catholic membership in such groups is usually low in Catholic countries and among Catholic minorities in other countries. In the United States, however, the Catholic Church met the attraction of secular associations by promoting a large number of Catholic organizations in an effort to keep the voluntary-association tendency within the Catholic framework. In short, voluntary associations in great variety and number are a conspicuous feature of American life. It is said that whenever three Americans are stranded, the first thing they do is form an organization, elect officers, and appoint a committee.

An *association* is defined by Sutherland [Fairchild, 1944] as "an organized group formed in pursuit of some common interest with its own self-contained administrative structure and functionaries." Its formal organizational structure distinguishes it from informal primary groups. It differs from an institution by having a rather narrowly limited purpose (e.g., to enjoy bowling, to protect neighborhood property values, or to secure a particular social reform), while the institution pursues a series of rather broad, general purposes. Also, an institution is basically a set of *norms* and *ideas*, together with the necessary people and procedures, while an association is basically a group of people who have organized to pursue a particular activity or objective. Some associations are attached to an institution, helping it pursue one, or a few, of its purposes. Thus the PTA and the alumni association serve the school, while the church has its youth groups, men's clubs, and ladies' guilds. Other associations, like the photography club or the neighborhood-improvement association, may be independent of any institutional connection. Rose [1954,

p. 52] makes a distinction between *expressive* associations such as sports groups and hobby clubs and *social-influence* groups such as taxpayers' associations, chambers of commerce, and the National Association for the Advancement of Colored People. The expressive groups provide activities for their members, while the social-influence groups are directed toward achieving some sort of social power.

Functions of Voluntary Associations. *An Outlet for Individual Interests.* The major appeal of the voluntary association lies in its ability to provide a means of satisfying the proclivities of a number of citizens even though their interest is not shared by the total society. A few men interested in playing golf can band together and provide a country club even though the city council may be cool to the use of tax money for adult playgrounds. A few people may band together to found a planned-parenthood association to take action in a controversial field where it is politically unwise for the government to act. Rose [1954, p. 58] maintains that a variety of voluntary associations provides a type of "cultural pluralism," in which varied interests may be supported within the same society. Whatever the purpose, the voluntary association enables a minority of the people to take some action toward realizing their aims without being held back by a hostile or indifferent majority.

A Testing Ground for Social Programs. The voluntary association can develop a program and so demonstrate its values that it is ultimately taken over by the church or the state. The Sunday school began as an individual project by Robert Raikes, then was promoted through the London Sunday School Society, and is now an organic part of most Protestant churches. Most of the welfare functions of the modern state were born in voluntary associations that saw a social need, pioneered a program, and educated the public to the point where government was expected to assume the responsibility.

A Channel for Purposive Social Action. The voluntary association enables the private citizen to share in the making of major social decisions. Many observers feel that this is a vital part of the democratic process. One sociologist observes:

> More specifically, the hypothesis is that the voluntary associations have three important functions in supporting political democracy in the United States: (1) They *distribute power over social life* among a very large proportion of the citizenry, instead of allowing it to be concentrated in the elected representatives alone, so that the United States has a little of the character of the ancient Greek democratic city-state, as well as of the modern European centralized republic. (2) The voluntary associations *provide a sense of satisfaction with modern democratic processes* because they help the ordinary citizen to see how the processes function in limited circumstances, of direct interest to himself, rather than as they grind away in a distant, impersonal, and incomprehensible fashion. (3) The voluntary associations *provide a social mechanism for continually in-*

stituting social changes, so that the United States is a society in flux, constantly seeking (not always successfully, but seeking nevertheless) to solve long-standing problems and to satisfy new needs of groups of citizens as these needs arise.

Arnold Rose, *Theory and Method in the Social Sciences*, The University of Minnesota Press, Minneapolis, 1954, p. 52.

Voluntary associations are almost the only means whereby the average citizen can share actively in democratic policy formation. It is indeed doubtful whether American democracy could survive without them.

Participation in Voluntary Associations. Activity in voluntary associations is so conspicuous in the American community that observers tend to view it as a universal interest. Thus the historians Charles and Mary Beard [1930, pp. 730–731] report: "It was a rare American who was not a member of four or five societies. . . . Any citizen who refused to affiliate with one or more associations became an object of curiosity if not suspicion." Statements of this kind reflect the impressions that men of social prominence have when they observe their peers. It is true that the better-educated and higher-income groups participate actively in association work. Careful surveys reaching a cross section of the population, including those whose economic and educational handicaps make them less conspicuous, present a different picture.

A look at the characteristics of people who participate actively will tell us a good deal not only about voluntary associations but also about the general topic of social participation in American society [Scott, 1957; Wright and Hyman, 1958; Komarovsky, 1946b; Bell and Force, 1956; Foskett, 1955; Axelrod, 1956]. High rates of participation characterize the upper-income groups, the more highly educated, and those living in high-status urban communities. Men have a higher rate of participation than women, and Jews and Protestants a higher rate than Catholics. Studies of high school youth [Stone, 1960] show higher organizational participation in youth whose families come from higher-income and educational levels. They also show a higher rate among girls than boys, and a higher rate among youth who classify their family relationship as satisfactory than among those who have family problems.

PARTICIPATION IN VOLUNTARY ASSOCIATIONS IN THE UNITED STATES

High participation	Low participation
Protestants	Roman Catholics
Jews	No religious affiliation
Men	Women
College-educated	Elementary school only
Children of native-born parents	Children of foreign-born parents
Business and professional occupation	Manual occupation

Colleges, like urban communities, have many organizations in which some students participate to a great extent, others moderately, and many not at all. Organization work might be thought to conflict with studies, but surveys show that the better students are the ones most apt to be members and officers of numerous organizations [Burma, 1947; Chapin, 1931]. Among nurses, organizational activity reaches a peak around middle age, and is higher among nurses who are no longer working, as is shown in Table 3.

Table 3   AGE AND MEMBERSHIP IN NONPROFESSIONAL CLUBS AND ORGANIZATIONS (NURSES IN KANSAS CITY, 1956)

Number of clubs or organizations	Age of working nurses					Age of nonworking nurses				
	20–29	30–39	40–49	50–59	60+	20–29	30–39	40–49	50–59	60+
None	65	48	44	46	56	43	30	23	31	44
One	20	23	21	21	18	23	17	12	15	18
Two	9	17	16	16	13	21	21	26	12	20
Three or more	6	12	19	17	13	13	32	39	42	18

SOURCE: Community Studies, Inc., A Survey of the Social and Occupational Characteristics of a Metropolitan Nurse Complement, Community Studies, Inc., Kansas City Mo., 1956, p. 20.

From our study of voluntary associations we find that they have provided a means of social interaction through which the citizen can understand and to some extent control his society. But voluntary associations are largely an activity of the middle and upper classes. Apparently the better-educated and more prosperous persons find organization activity a useful means of adjusting to a complex modern society, and their children acquire the same pattern at an early age. The manual workers, the less educated, and the residents of substandard neighborhoods are indifferent to appeals to join in such activity. Neighborhood-improvement associations flourish in prosperous areas where they might seem superfluous and founder in deteriorating neighborhoods that seem to need some concerted attempt to improve community life. Bewildered and lonely individuals seldom find their way into associations, while the well informed and gregarious are overwhelmed with organization activity. Those who might gain the most from voluntary associations are least equipped to participate in them and least inclined to seek them.

Group Dynamics

For a long time sociologists were busy trying to convince a skeptical world that the group was real and not simply a collection of individuals.

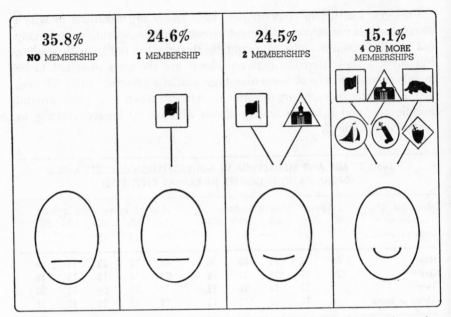

FIGURE 2 A Nation of Joiners? *Organizational Participation Reported by Residents of a Small New England City.*

SOURCE: Based on a survey in Bennington, Vermont, reported by John C. Scott, Jr., "Memberships and Participation in Voluntary Associations," *American Sociological Review*, 22:315–326, June, 1957. Surveys in other communities arrive at quite similar conclusions.

Only recently have sociologists turned their attention to the specific factors affecting the functioning of groups. Obviously many possible patterns may occur. A group may be dominated by one or two individuals or it may involve the participation of all its members; leadership may be democratic or authoritarian, transitory or enduring; the group may stimulate productivity or hold it down; its atmosphere may be relaxed and friendly or tense and charged with hostility; it may forge new approaches to problems or stick to old routines. These and many other patterns have often been observed. The question arises, "What factors produce one or another type of group life and how can these factors be controlled?"

The academic interests of sociologists in expanding the frontiers of knowledge in this area have been stimulated by demands from organizations that want help in solving their problems. Social agencies such as the Scouts and the YMCA and YWCA wish to use leaders more effectively and secure more intensive participation from their members. Governmental bodies hope to make their employees more efficient and more responsive to the needs of the people. The armed forces are constantly revising their policies in the search for the type of organization that will lead to the most effective use of military manpower. Industrial corporations seek knowledge that will help them plan their work groups in a way to minimize friction and to secure the maximum efficiency in their operations. Hospitals wish to make more effective use of their staffs.

These practical needs of organizations, joined by the intellectual curiosity of scholars, have led to a field of research usually labeled either "group dynamics" or "small-group research." Such research painstakingly records the interaction that actually occurs in group activities, oftentimes using such devices as a conference room in which one-way visibility enables observers to see the interaction and record conversations without being noticed by the participants. Study of the "nursing team" is another kind of group-dynamics research [Newcomb, 1953; E. Lambertsen, 1953; Kron, 1961]. The research on the nursing team seeks to find how total patient care can best be provided by organizing various personnel—professional nurse, practical nurse, nurse's aide, occupational therapist, and others—into an integrated group rather than having each service be an independent activity. This kind of research is gradually enlarging our understanding of the nature of group operations. Since it would be hopeless to try to summarize many volumes of research [Strodtbeck and Hare, 1954; Cartwright and Zander, 1953; Bales, 1959] in a few pages, we shall limit our discussion to a short exposition of two topics in the hope that students will gain some idea of the questions usually raised and the type of research that has developed.

Formal and Informal Structures. In the armed forces a table-of-organization chart shows the exact rank and duties of every category of personnel. The recruit soon learns that he must "go through channels," that is, take up his business with the appropriate officer, without going over his head to any of this officer's superiors. In a short time, however, the perceptive soldier will learn that the organizational chart does not really tell how the army operates. He will find that sometimes, but not always, a sergeant or secretary has more to do with decision making than the commanding officer. As he continues in an army career he will, if successful, learn that there is a "shadow" table of organization, different for

The individual who can discern the real pattern of power will find adjustment easy.

every unit and not printed in any headquarters, which he must learn in order to get things done. This shadow table is a list of the men who have "influence." Sometimes they are the men named in the official organization chart, other times not; but the individual who can discern the real pattern of power will find adjustment easy in the armed forces, whereas the man who relies on the official table of organization will experience bewildering delays and frustrations.

All groups have a *structure*, that is, *a network of relationships between the members*. Primary groups have no formal structure, no list of officers, ranks, or formal duties. But within the group certain members have influence over others, some assume leadership while others follow, and definite roles within the group are filled. The group has a real structure, based on a network of personal relationships instead of an organizational chart.

Secondary groups have both a formal and an informal structure. The formal structure is that which can be shown on an organizational chart —positions or ranks, duties and privileges of each, lines of authority, and the like. The informal structure is the network of personal relationships found in every formal organization. It arises from the fact the formal pattern is developed on a relatively impersonal basis, giving weight to such factors as hereditary social position, seniority, education, and proficiency in passing examinations. This formal pattern becomes limited in its effectiveness as people develop relationships based on the primary-group traits that cause them to be accepted or rejected as persons. Even under the best of personnel systems the two patterns will not completely coincide. There will be natural leaders who acquire power greater than their position in the organization chart would warrant. These persons get enthusiastic support from their subordinates and favorable attention from their superiors. They can often gain through persuasion the decisions they lack the authority to command. There are other officials who have formal authority but no personal influence. They get little real support from subordinates and no special consideration from superiors. They can accomplish nothing beyond the measures they have the authority to order, and these orders may be frustrated by delay and concealed resistance.

Organizations have devised ways to protect themselves from the strain of deviation between their formal and informal structures. Thus members of a religious group are advised to honor the clergyman regardless of his personal traits, and soldiers are told that they "salute the office not the man." It still remains true, however, that the group is more efficient if the formal and informal systems support each other. The priest is more effective in his work if he is pious and devout than if he is lecherous and dissolute. The army officer can better command his troops if he inspires personal confidence as well as respect for his office.

The relative emphasis on formal and informal organization will vary in different associations. Frequently, in the beginning stages of an association people will be drawn together by ties of congeniality and common interest. The association, be it a good-government league, stamp-collectors' club, or society to aid unmarried mothers, has few formal rules and operates with the volunteer labor of its members. Decisions are made through the personal influence of the individuals involved rather than according to rules as to the authority or responsibility of different functionaries. Eventually the members of the association feel a need for professional employees with definite responsibilities, to be supervised by a set of association officers with definite authority. Often this need for a more formal bureaucratic structure comes when enthusiasm has waned and it is more difficult to secure member participation on an informal basis. In a study of the formalization trend in a voluntary association, Chapin and Tsouderos [1955, 1956] found that informal contacts between members declined as expenditures for hired personnel increased and a more formal organization was adopted. In other words the formal organization devices used to strengthen the informal organization had the reverse effect. The paid executive may draw up a more coherent program, keep better accounts, and put out more attractive publicity material, but the members now feel that the formal organization can handle matters and that the association no longer requires their personal efforts. This result does not mean that the total effectiveness of the association has decreased but simply that the gain from the greater efficiency of the association must be balanced against the loss from a decline in the informal participation of its members.

Communication Patterns. One of the important problems in any group is communication between its members. Communication is not merely a matter of the language spoken and the types of printed or audio-visual material used to get across messages, even though these are important. Communication is also a matter of the structure of the group and the physical and social proximity of its members. Any group must devise some way for its members to share their information. There are many possible ways of arranging the flow of communication, and it may be that not all of these patterns have the same effect on the work of the group and the relationship among its members.

The influence of different patterns of communication in a problem-solving group has been listed by Bavelas [1953]. He arranged groups of five men in different communication patterns which may be described as the circle, the chain, the Y, and the wheel. In the circle everyone had an equal chance to communicate with everyone else; in the other patterns the man in the center had maximum communication and the others were restricted. Morale and leadership turned out to be closely related to centrality of position. Member satisfaction with the situation was greatest in the circle, where no one man emerged as a leader. In the wheel where the man in the center became the leader, production was greater but group satisfaction less. As an offset to the loss in production, the circle was found to adapt more quickly to new tasks than the other patterns.

Effective communication promotes satisfaction of the individual with the group and enables him to express himself freely and to receive the impressions of others. A centralizing of communication focuses the attention of group members on specific topics and promotes a concentration of effort. The implications for the organization of school classrooms and industrial work plans depend on whether the major emphasis is on routine productivity or on developing flexibility and achieving satisfaction in the group situation. Research on the lecture versus the discussion method of college instruction, for instance, reports that students memorize as much even in very large groups with the lecture method (analogous to the wheel pattern) but that they have greater stimulus to do their own thinking in the discussion method (analogous to the circle pattern) [Bloom, 1954, pp. 37–38]. These are a few examples of how small-group research can help in solving practical problems.

Summary

Both strength and weakness are largely the result of the manner in which a person is integrated into a network of groups. A fundamental distinction is that between *out-groups* and *in-groups,* a distinction that has been measured by the use of the concept of *social distance.* Emotional conditioning is largely the result of *primary-group* contacts, but our society is increasingly affected by the growth of *secondary-group* relationships. While many groups may be easily characterized as either primary or secondary, the two types of influence interact, each influencing the other.

Voluntary associations represent a type of organization in which small groups of citizens may work for goals not yet accepted by a more lethargic majority, or pursue special interests not shared by everyone. Voluntary associations are most prominent in the highly industrialized areas, chiefly the United States, and even here involve mainly the middle- and upper-class citizens.

Formal patterns of group interaction based on the standards of secondary relationships are accompanied by informal patterns arising out of primary-group relationships. Group members usually have unequal access to communication, and it has been found that this inequality affects both morale and participation. Small-group research is now providing much knowledge useful to administrators and others responsible for group management.

Questions

1. Which of the following social aggregates are groups: citizens of a country; commuters waiting for a train; husband and wife; members of an international labor union; residents of cities of between 50,000 and 100,000 population?

2. Comment on this statement: "A group is made up of individuals; and the characteristics of a group are the sum of the characteristics of its members."

3. Is courage an individual character trait or a response to group patterns?

4. What differences are found in the in-group–out-group distinction in primitive and modern societies?

5. Do nurses view the physician as part of their in-group, or as an out-group?

6. Why are primary and secondary groups important? In-groups and out-groups?

7. Is the nurse-patient contact primary-group or secondary-group in nature?

8. To what extent would you expect social distance to coincide with geographical distance?

9. College is often an introduction to the complexities of secondary-group relationships. Is this experience worthwhile for a young woman whose major interests are centered in the primary-group relationships of family life? Defend your answer.

10. Suppose that production engineers design a new layout in a factory that spaces the work force differently and thereby achieves a smoother flow of goods from the raw material to the finished product. Is this a case of secondary- or primary-group behavior? What types of resistance would the engineers be apt to encounter in putting their plan into effect?

11. A new employee has thoroughly studied the organization chart of a company where he is going to work. Will this enable him to understand the distribution of power and influence among the employees?

12. Does the conduct of American prisoners of war in Korea indicate that a greater knowledge of communism is essential for our soldiers? What other needs are indicated by this experience?

13. The early Christians were sometimes crowded into large prison cells and later marched into the Colosseum to be crucified or fed to the lions before thousands of spectators. They could save themselves by denying their faith, but few did so. Why?

Suggested Readings

BOGARDUS, EMORY S.: "Racial Distance Changes in the United States during the Past Thirty Years," *Sociology and Social Research*, 43:127–

135, November, 1958. Shows how the acceptance and rejection of different racial or national groups has changed during this period.

COMMUNITY STUDIES, INC.: *A Survey of the Social and Occupational Characteristics of a Metropolitan Nurse Complement,* Community Studies, Inc., Kansas City, Mo., 1956. Describes the background, activities, and memberships of nurses.

DAVIDSON, BILL: "Combat Soldiers Fail to Shoot," *Colliers,* Nov. 8, 1952, pp. 16–18. Popularly written account of the relationship between primary-group ties and military performance.

GROSS, EDWARD: "Some Functional Consequences of Primary Groups in Formal Work Organizations," *American Journal of Sociology,* 18:368–373, August, 1953. A description of some ways in which primary groups may support the aims of secondary groups.

KRON, THORA: *Nursing Team Leader-*ship, W. B. Saunders Co., Philadelphia, 1961. A description of the operation of the nursing team.

SCHEIN, EDGAR H.: "Interpersonal Communication, Group Solidarity and Social Influence," *Sociometry,* 23:148–161, June, 1960. Describes how group disintegration was used as a technique of psychological warfare against American prisoners in Chinese camps.

SHILS, EDWARD A., AND MORRIS JANOWITZ: "Cohesion and Disintegration in the Wehrmacht in World War II," *Public Opinion Quarterly,* 12:280–315, Summer, 1948. Tells how morale and resistance continued in the German army as long as primary-group structures remained intact.

WHYTE, WILLIAM FOOTE: *Street Corner Society: The Social Structure of an Italian Slum,* The University of Chicago Press, Chicago, 1943. A classic study of informal groups in lower-class urban American society.

CHAPTER 8 Social Institutions

*Work expands so as to fill the time available for its completion.
General recognition of this fact is shown in the proverbial phrase,
"It is the busiest man who has time to spare." Thus, an elderly
woman of leisure can spend the entire day in writing and dispatch-
ing a postcard to her niece in Bognor Regis. An hour will be spent
in finding the postcard, another in hunting for spectacles, half an
hour in a search for the address, an hour and a quarter in composition, and twenty minutes in deciding whether or not to take an
umbrella when going to the mailbox in the next street. The total
effort that would occupy a busy man for three minutes all told may
in this fashion leave another person prostrate after a day of doubt,
anxiety, and toil.*

*Granted that work (and especially paperwork) is thus elastic in
its demands on time, it is manifest that there need be little or no
relationship between the work to be done and the size of the staff
to which it may be assigned. . . . The thing to be done swells in
importance and complexity in a direct ratio with the time to be
spent. . . . The fact is that the number of the officials and the
quantity of the work are not related to each other at all. The rise
in the total of those employed is governed by Parkinson's Law and
would be much the same whether the volume of work were to increase, diminish, or even disappear. The importance of Parkinson's
Law lies in the fact that it is a law of growth based upon an analysis of the factors by which that growth is controlled.*

C. Northcote Parkinson, *Parkinson's Law and Other Studies in Administration*,
Houghton Mifflin Company, Boston, 1957, pp. 2–4.

In this famous essay, Parkinson has written with tongue in cheek of the tendency for all bureaucracies to expand. Bureaucratic behavior is only one of the many forms of institutional behavior that interest sociologists. What are social institutions, and what is their importance?

Sociologists have not been entirely consistent in their use of the term "institution." Some have applied the term to any large-scale organization, like the American Legion or the YMCA, using the term "association" for smaller organized groups like the local photography club. This makes the distinction between institution and association purely one of size, and obscures the basic difference in nature between institution and association. The more common practice is to call any organized group of any size an association, and to define an institution [Bierstedt, 1957, p. 299] as "an organized way of doing something." Kingsley Davis [1949, p. 71] defines the institution as "a set of interwoven folkways, mores, and laws built around one or more functions." Hertzler [1961, p. 77] calls them "great clusters of established, accepted, and implemented ways of behaving socially." Clearly, the association is an organized *group of people* while an institution is an organized *system of behavior.*

All these definitions of institutions imply both a set of behavior norms and a system of social relationships through which these norms are practiced. Let us suggest a formal definition which clearly includes both ideas: *An institution is an organized system of social relationships that embodies certain common values and procedures and meets certain basic needs of the society.* In this definition "common values" refers to shared ideas and goals; the "common procedures" are the standardized behavior

An institution embodies certain common values and procedures.

patterns the group follows; the "system of relationships" is the network of roles and statuses through which this behavior is carried out. Thus the family includes a set of common values (about love, children, family life), a set of common procedures (dating, child care, family routines), and a network of roles and statuses (husband, wife, baby, teen-aged child, fiancé) that form the system of social relationship through which family life is carried out. Five important basic institutions in complex societies are the familial, religious, governmental, economic, and educational institutions. Beyond these the concept tapers off into less important clusters of behavior patterns which, when highly standardized and formalized, widely expected, and generally approved, may be called an institution.

While they are separate concepts, institutions and associations are not entirely separate from each other. An institution is a set of relationships and a system of behavior, and these require *people*. Although the institution itself consists of relationships and norms, it is people who fill these relationships and practice these norms. And people organize themselves into groups, forming associations. Thus each institution has many satellite associations that carry out institutional behavior. *Institutional behavior* means the carrying of institutional norms and values into practice. Institutional behavior is carried out, in large part, through these satellite associations. The church has its organized local congregations, Sunday schools, clubs, and groups of many kinds carrying out the work of the church; the school has its PTA, alumni association, and athletic association; the state has its political organizations, voters' leagues, taxpayers' associations, and organized pressure groups. Institutions and associations are very much interrelated, yet the concepts are distinct and should not be confused.

The Development of Institutions

The Process of Institutionalization. Institutions emerge as the largely unplanned products of social living. People grope for practical ways of meeting their needs; they find some workable patterns that harden through repetition into standardized customs. As time passes, these patterns acquire a body of supporting folklore that justifies and sanctions them. The institution of "dating" developed as a means of mate selection. Banks gradually developed as the need for storing, transferring, borrowing, and lending money gave rise to a series of practices for accomplishing these purposes. From time to time men might gather to codify and give legal endorsement to these practices as they continued to develop and change. In such manner, institutions arise.

Institutionalization consists of the establishment of definite norms that assign status positions and role functions in connection with such behavior. A norm is a group expectation of behavior. Institutionalization involves the replacement of behavior that is spontaneous or experimental with behavior that is expected, patterned, regular, and predictable. Thus the preinstitutional period of a religious movement brings forth spontaneous, ecstatic, and often confused behavior as the followers of the new leader respond to his dynamic appeal. Every day is an adventure and every religious meeting an unpredictable sequence of emotional events in which no man is able to predict what he will do. As the institutionalized church emerges, the participants acquire definite roles, and their activities begin to follow a routine pattern. Some people are merely worshipers; others assume specialized roles such as choir member, clergyman, teacher, usher, secretary, janitor, and so on. Novelty and excitement fade as procedures come to be governed by definite norms and as the behavior of each participant becomes standardized and predictable.

A tavern brawl is noninstitutionalized behavior; a professional boxing match is institutionalized behavior. A set of social relationships has become institutionalized when (1) a regular system of statuses and roles has been developed and (2) this system of status and role expectations has been generally accepted in the society. Dating in American society meets both of these qualifications. A rather clearly defined set of courtship roles has emerged in which the duties and privileges of each party are defined (he asks, she accepts, he pays, etc.) and safeguarded with some limitations or restraints (e.g., no all-night dates) intended to prevent complications.

Dating has *institutional status*, meaning it is generally accepted by the society as a necessary and proper activity whereby young people mature emotionally and eventually find agreeable partners. Many societies have also institutionalized premarital sexual intercourse, making it a normal and expected part of the activities leading to marriage. Although premarital intercourse is fairly common in American society, it has not been institutionalized; that is, it is not a part of a standardized, approved, and culturally safeguarded pattern of behavior.

Even carefully organized patterns of behavior differ in the extent to which they receive social acceptance. In American society the corporation has full institutional status. The labor union, on the other hand, would be classified as an *emergent* institution, not yet completely accepted as a proper and necessary part of society.

The hospital in America has full institutional status. Voluntary health insurance, highly controversial and strongly opposed by medical associations three decades ago, today comes very close to full institutional status. Compulsory or national health insurance, which enjoys full institutional status in England and many other countries, has not gained acceptance in the United States. Although the need for some basic social institutions is recognized in all societies, their subsidiary units vary. Time will see the acceptance of some subsidiary institutional forms and the passing of others from the scene. As an example, Smith [1955] gives an interesting account of psychiatry as an emergent institution.

Individual Roles in Institutional Behavior. Not all roles are institutionalized. The "bad boy" and "mother's little helper" roles in the family are noninstitutionalized roles, while "son" and "daughter" are institutionalized roles. An institutionalized role is a set of behavior expectations that leaves little room for personal eccentricity. All judges act a good deal alike when on the bench, however much they differ at other times. Every Methodist minister and every Catholic priest finds that his duties and privileges are quite precisely defined by his institutional role; to deviate from his expected role in any way is hazardous. Even presidents and kings, apparently so powerful, are in fact most highly circumscribed in their freedom of action. If they fail to operate within the role expectations of the institution they generally lose their influence.

A recent example of the persistence of institutional roles is seen in the transition of the English coal mines from private to public ownership [Koenig, 1948]. Under private ownership the miners were supervised by the "boss," an agent of the private capitalists who owned the mines. Acting in this role, the boss sought to get the greatest production at the least possible cost. When the government took over the mines, some of the miners thought the new ownership meant the end of annoying rules and regulations. The boss, however, was still with them. Although now an agent of the state, he still had the job of making the nationalized mines produce the greatest possible amount of coal at the lowest possible cost. Ownership and, in some cases, personnel had changed, but the system of roles that had grown up in response to institutional needs remained pretty much the same.

This lack of change in the role of the supervisor in the coal mines under nationalization is not an isolated example, for similar experiences occur in other institutional settings. Occasionally a man contrasts the smooth and efficient way in which his secretary anticipates his needs in the office with the rather demanding attitude of his wife at home. Sometimes a discontented husband divorces the wife and marries the secretary, only to find that when the secretary assumes the role of wife, she begins to act like a wife! The boss gets better work if he is considerate and appreciative of his secretary; she marries him and sees him change into an inconsiderate and thoughtless husband who "takes her for granted." Many an employee who is promoted to a supervisory role tries to retain his old rapport with his former crew; this rarely succeeds, for the new role inevitably alters his relationship to the old buddies whom he now bosses.

It is true that individual personality differences do affect institutional behavior to some degree. One foreman is grouchy and another cheerful;

one professor is stimulating and another dull. But the range of individual variation is limited and is greatly overshadowed by role requirements. The conflicts that arise within an institution are sometimes due to clashes of personality, but more often they are due to the clash of institutional roles. The foreman and the inspector clash because the foreman must keep production going while the inspector keeps finding defects that must be corrected. The salesman is frustrated when the credit manager refuses to extend more credit to a slow-paying customer. The medical staff's wish for all the latest hospital equipment clashes with the administrative staff's wish to keep down expenses. Many such clashes are inherent in the inter-relation of roles within an institution. With some modification Gertrude Stein's famous statement "A rose is a rose is a rose" may be applied to in-stitutional roles. A wife is always a wife, a husband is always a husband, and a supervisor is always a supervisor. The difference made by individual personalities in institutional roles is comparable to the difference between a mediocre and a highly talented actor in a dramatic production. The highly talented actor realizes more fully the potentialities of the part he is playing, but at the same time his expression must be channeled within the limitations of the role. Institutions function most smoothly when they can attract competent personnel, and sometimes they are handicapped by personnel unequal to the roles they assume. Regardless of differences in personnel, however, the persistence of role requirements will require some degree of uniformity in the conduct of those who carry out institu-tional roles.

Institutional Traits

While each institution is unique each institution is also like all others in some respects. All institutions must maintain the loyalty of their par-ticipants, assign authority to different functionaries, formulate standards of behavior, and develop methods of dealing with other institutions. Since these are common problems, it is not surprising that institutions with very different goals may use quite similar techniques.

Cultural Symbols. All institutions develop symbols that serve as a shorthand reminder of the institution. The citizen is reminded of his alle-giance to the state by the flag, to the church by a crucifix, crescent, or star of David, to the family by a wedding ring, to the alma mater by the school colors or animal totem (mascot), and to the business concern by brand names and trademarks. Music also has symbolic meanings. Na-tional anthems, school songs, religious hymns, and the singing "com-mercials" all use the art of melody to strengthen institutional ties. Build-ings may become institutional symbols so that it is hard to think of home without a house, religion without a church edifice, education without a school building, or government without the White House or king's palace.

Codes of Behavior. Along with a general sense of loyalty, institutions must prepare their members to carry out the roles the institution has assigned them. These roles are often expressed in formal codes, such as the oath of allegiance to the country, the marriage vows, the medical profession's oath of Hippocrates, and the codes of ethics of several other groups.

A formal code of behavior, however impressive, is no guarantee of proper role performance. Husbands and wives may prove unfaithful to marital vows, citizens who fervently repeat the oath of allegiance may commit treason, and church members who have sworn fidelity to their religion may lapse into indifference. If the affirmation of a verbal or written code is the climax to a long process of attitude formation and role preparation, the code may be observed; if not, and if there are no swift and sure punishments for violation, it may be quietly ignored.

A formal code is only a part of the total behavior that makes up an institutional role. Much of the behavior in any role—parent, soldier, priest, professor, physician, politician—consists of an elaborate body of informal traditions, expectations, and routines that one absorbs only through long observation and experience with the role. Children who have never lived in a harmonious family setting are likely to have difficulty in filling the roles of parent and husband or wife [Terman, 1938]. They have had no good chance to observe these roles in successful operation or to absorb the attitudes needed for successful role performance. Like roles of all kinds, institutional roles can be filled most successfully by those who have fully learned the proper role attitudes and behavior.

Ideologies. An ideology may be loosely defined as a *system of ideas that sanction a set of norms.* The norms define how people are expected to act; the ideology explains *why* they should act that way, and why they sometimes fail to act as they should. The ideology of an institution includes both the central beliefs of the institution and an elaboration of these beliefs which will explain the rest of the world in terms acceptable to the participants in the institution. Whereas the repetition of an oath formally binds the individual to follow institutional norms, the ideology gives him a rational justification for the application of institutional norms to the problems of life.

For instance, juvenile delinquency is a problem in all complex societies. All institutions tend to develop an explanation for this problem consistent with their basic norms. Juvenile delinquency may be interpreted by the Communist as the result of capitalist exploitation, by the conservative businessman as the result of coddling by a paternalistic government, by the churchman as caused by the neglect of religious teaching

Table 4   TRAITS OF MAJOR AMERICAN SOCIAL INSTITUTIONS

	Family	Religion	Government	Business	Education
Attitudes and behavior patterns	Affection Loyalty Responsibility Respect	Reverence Loyalty Worship Generosity	Loyalty Obedience Subordination Cooperation	Efficiency Thrift Shrewdness Profit making	Love of knowledge Class attendance Studying "Cramming"
Symbolic culture traits	Marriage ring Wedding veil Coat of arms "Our song"	Cross Ikon Shrine Hymn	Flag Seal Mascot Anthem	Trademark Patent sign Slogan Singing commercial	School colors Mascot School song Seal
Utilitarian culture traits	House Apartment Furnishings Car	Church building Church equipment Literature Liturgical supplies	Public buildings Public works Office equipment Blanks and forms	Shop, factory Store, office Office equipment Blanks and forms	Classrooms Library Stadium Books
Code of oral or written specifications	Marriage license Will Genealogy Marriage law	Creed Church law Sacred books Taboos	Charter Constitution Treaties Laws	Contracts Licenses Franchises Articles of incorporation	Accreditation Rules Curricula Graduation requirements
Ideologies	Romantic love "Togetherness" Familism Individualism	Thomism Liberalism Fundamentalism Neo-orthodoxy	Nationalism States' rights Democracy Republicanism	Laissez faire Managerial responsibility Free enterprise Rights of labor	Academic freedom Progressive education Three "r"s Classicism

SOURCE: Adapted from F. Stuart Chapin, *Contemporary American Institutions*, Harper & Row, Publishers, Incorporated, New York, 1935, p. 16.

and practice, by the educator as the result of an inadequate school system, and by the family-oriented person as a symptom of the breakdown of the home.

Ideological explanations persist in spite of changing circumstances. In Russia, after more than forty years of Communist rule, juvenile delinquency is still viewed as either the result of organic ailments that might resist even a perfect social order, or is attributed to the fact that the

Soviet Union is still in the process of transition to the ideal communist state [Alt and Alt, 1959, pp. 201–202, 216, 217]. Similarly in African or Asian countries under Western rule, nationalist leaders have long attributed social problems to the evil effects of foreign rule. After independence is achieved, social problems are still attributed to a "colonialism" now said to be all the more potent because it is disguised [Lava, 1958]. The Communist party in the United States was viewed as a major menace by many Americans who called for stern measures of repression. But now that the party has practically disappeared, J. Edgar Hoover [1958, p. 78] warns us that it is more dangerous than ever. Such examples might be extended indefinitely. The point they illustrate is simply that an ideologically satisfying explanation of a social problem is not easily abandoned even when changing circumstances make it outmoded.

The usefulness of an ideology is measured not by its literal correctness but by its ability to inspire the loyalty and cooperation of an institution's participants. Any shortcoming in society is blamed on competing institutions or on the inadequate devotion of the institution's own followers. Institutional leaders claim credit for practically all favorable developments and define all problems as simply a challenge to greater efforts along present lines. Criticisms of institutional ideology are defined as heretical or subversive attacks that must be repelled. False doctrine (any belief that attacks the ideology) breaks down the attitudes supporting institutional role performance and so strikes at the heart of institutional functioning. The medical profession's bitter opposition to national health insurance is, among other things, an example of how institutions resist changes that threaten to disrupt traditional role arrangements.

Institutional Structures

Institutions have *structure*. The *normative* structure is the cluster of norms—of expectations, rules, and procedures—written or unwritten, formal or informal. The *personnel* structure is the network of persons, roles, and statuses through which the activities of the institution are carried on. Both the normative and the personnel structures can be closely or loosely structured.

Closely Structured and Loosely Structured Institutions. Some institutions are termed *closely structured* because authority is highly centralized and procedures highly standardized with little autonomy for either local groups or individuals. Other institutions having less centralization and allowing more freedom of action are classified as *loosely structured*. In the closely structured institution, roles are rigidly defined, with specific rules for most situations; in the loosely structured institution, roles are less rigidly defined and may be adjusted by the individual or local group as circumstances may warrant. The army is normally a closely structured institution with a precisely defined role and status for each rank, rigid obedience to orders, and detailed organization patterns. The family in our society is a loosely structured institution in which roles and statuses are so uncertain as to be sometimes confusing. The hospital has been a rather loosely structured institution but is now becoming more closely structured. Bureaucratic procedures, written policies, and formal lines of authority are replacing the more informal arrangements of the past [Wilson, 1963].

Institutions with a similar ideology may differ in structure. The Catholic Church is a closely structured institution with a strong central authority, elaborate organization, and detailed rules and procedures. The Baptist Church is very loosely structured. Baptist congregations are highly autonomous; they select and dismiss their own ministers, run their own affairs, and are very loosely tied together into a denominational organization. Likewise the Communists and Socialists both base their ideology on the writings of Karl Marx. Yet the Communist party is one of the most closely structured institutions ever developed, whereas the Socialist parties operate in a loosely structured system somewhat resembling the congregationally organized Protestant churches.

Which is more effective—the closely structured or the loosely structured institution? The answer depends on the particular situation. A large army must be fairly closely structured; a smaller military unit can be quite loosely structured. Under some circumstances loosely structured guerrilla units are the more effective, as in the defeat of the carefully organized troops of General Braddock by a less orderly collection of French and Indians. Churches and political parties apparently can be effective with varying degrees of close or loose structuring. Any intrinsic superiority of close or loose structuring is difficult to prove. The loosely structured institution is apt to pride itself on freedom, tolerance, and individual responsibility while being criticized for inconsistency, laxness, and ideological deviations. The closely structured institution prides itself on the purity and consistency of its ideology and the close integration of its component parts while it is criticized as dogmatic, intolerant, and heedless of local problems far removed from the central office.

Formal and Informal Structure of Institutions. Institutions have a formal and informal structure quite similar to the formal and informal structuring of groups as discussed in Chapter 7. An organizational diagram of an army would show the ranks from general to private, with the powers and duties of each. It would show the formal structure of the army, with every task and duty accounted for. The hospital also has a formal structure [Henry, 1954] in some ways similar to that of the army. But an institution is more than a system of formal roles. These are filled by a network of people who relate themselves to one another in ways not covered by the organizational diagrams. A constantly changing network of personal friendships, antagonisms, obligations, and admirations is operating behind the facade of institutional titles and formal roles. It is this network of personal relationships that either fulfills or frustrates the purposes of the institution.

A crucial distinction must obviously be made between *authority* and *influence*. Authority is an official right to make and enforce decisions; influence is the ability to affect the actions of others apart from any authority to do so. Authority stems from rank; influence rests largely upon personal attributes. Authority is based on the status one holds; influence is based on the esteem one receives. A professor has authority to make assignments and assign grades; he may have much or little influence on his students, depending on how they feel about him. An admired institutional officer will have both authority and influence; an unpopular officer has authority but little influence; a competent, popular subordinate may have much influence even though he has little authority.

This informal structure grows partly from the personality differences among individuals and partly from the fact that no system of rules is completely successful in meeting all needs of the institution. In order to get things done, it is often easiest to go outside regular channels and use

It is often easiest to go outside regular channels.

the informal structure of the institution. This procedure is sometimes risky, and must be done skillfully if it is not to backfire; yet it is very common. The navy even has an institutionalized name—"cumshaw"— for the use of this informal structure. Without informal structures and procedures, many things would not get done quickly or efficiently.

The real operation of an institution cannot be understood without understanding its informal structure. In an institutional unit we may find the "operator" who can pull strings and get things done outside the usual channels; there is the old-timer whose support is valuable because he knows all the routines and because he knows "where all the bodies are buried"—that is, he knows of past errors and incidents that can be used as gentle blackmail; there are the friends and relatives of the higher officials who presumedly have influence on them; there is the "fair-haired boy" who appears to have been selected for promotion; there is the subordinate who is so widely admired and respected that the officials find it wise to consult him; there is even the pariah who is so disliked that his support is to be avoided. The interplay of such personalities has great effect on the decisions made by those in authority and on the way these decisions are interpreted and carried out in practice. The interaction of authority and influence in the upper levels of government is described in the popular novel *Advise and Consent* [Drury, 1959].

Institutional Functions

Society is so complex and its forces so interrelated that it is impossible to foresee all the consequences of a particular action. Institutions have *manifest* functions, which are easy to recognize as part of the professed objectives of the institution, and *latent* functions, which are unintended and may be unrecognized, or, if recognized, are regarded as by-products [Merton, 1957b, pp. 19–84]. The manifest function of the corporation is to make profits through business operations; its latent functions may be to promote urbanization, alter family life, promote the growth of labor unions, redirect education, and produce many other changes. The latent functions of an institution may support the professed objectives, or be irrelevant, or even lead to consequences quite damaging to the norms of the institution. A brief look at some of the latent functions of educational and health institutions will illustrate some of the types of unintended consequences.

Latent Functions of Educational Institutions. The manifest function of mass public education is to enable all to share in the knowledge and skills once confined to a privileged few. Some of the latent functions of this activity would include keeping youth off the labor market, weakening the control of parents, promoting the Americanization of immigrants, and altering the class system.

To a great extent the mixed public response to the schools is a reaction to these latent functions. Keeping youth off the labor market may be attractive to labor unions, but it appears in a different light to farmers who need seasonal workers or to other employers who rely on cheap and unskilled labor. Parents want their children to achieve higher status through education but are distressed when their children learn about ideas that conflict with parental norms; immigrant parents who wish children to cling to the practices and customs of a foreign culture have mixed feelings about the Americanization of the school. Altering the class system by enabling youth from low-income families to get the education needed for higher-status positions likewise meets with a mixed response. Some laud this as a step toward a better society; others fear the increase of competition. The American school system is now engaged in probably the most bitter controversy in its history—over whether its latent functions should include the promotion of racial integration.

Latent Functions of Health Institutions. The manifest functions of the health institutions are to relieve human suffering and promote health. Success in achieving these manifest functions is bringing a number of latent consequences. Health advances have helped to increase the proportion of aged people who must be cared for. A falling death rate together with a stable birth rate have produced the "population explosion," so that population pressure has become a grave problem in many parts of the world. This in turn has encouraged the spread of abortion and contraception, which arouse bitter controversy in many areas. Medical science has largely eliminated the quick-killing illnesses, with the result that people now live to die of expensive, lingering illnesses. This inflates the costs of medical care and encourages the public demand for national health insurance which the medical profession strongly opposes. Thus a number of problems have been created or intensified as latent functions of our health institutions.

Manifest Functions of Institutions. Every institution has two types of manifest functions: (1) the pursuit of its objectives in a world often indifferent or hostile to these objectives and (2) the preservation of its own internal cohesion so that it may survive. The family, for instance, is concerned both with raising its children and with maintaining harmony and loyalty among its members so that it does not dissolve in the divorce courts. The national state must serve its citizens and protect its boundaries and at the same time escape the peril of revolution or conquest. The church which seeks to convert outsiders and increase its influence must also hold the loyalty of its members and enhance their feeling of satisfaction with the institution. When an institution fails in either of these manifest functions, it must either change itself or die. Such changes often take the form of a characteristic life cycle.

Cycles of Institutional Change

The birth or death of an institution is a comparatively rare event. New institutional norms may replace old norms, but the institutional generally goes on. For example, the modern family has replaced a set of strongly patriarchial norms with a set of more equalitarian norms, while *the family* continues. When feudalism "died," government did not end; one pattern of institutional structure with its attendant associations was replaced with a different one. Governmental and economic functions continued to be fulfilled, although according to changed norms. All the basic institutions are thousands of years old; the present institutional

norms and the forms of association that carry out institutional functions
are much newer. This establishment of new institutional norms and supporting associations often follows a familiar sequence of stages, as is
suggested by Dawson and Gettys [1948, pp. 705–709] and by Hertzler
[1961, pp. 155–157].

The Initial Phase. Winning recognition as a new institutional norm is
often the outgrowth of a struggle—the culmination of a successful social
movement. The successful establishment of a new satellite association
also involves a struggle for acceptance from an often skeptical or hostile
society. The battle for acceptance often develops a heroic loyalty the
founders never forget. Countless novels and epic poems have immor-
talized the burning faith of the founders of a new religion or a new
religious order, the patriotism of revolutionary armies, and the zealous
conviction of the founders of a new political party. Individual interests
have been largely submerged in dedication to the establishment of the
new norm or association, and its progress gives its members new roles
providing them with a sense of fulfillment. If personal rivalries develop,
they are handled in an improvised and perhaps violent manner. Stern
and even harsh actions are justified by the belief that they are necessary
to protect the institution. The leader during this period is often a person
of magnetic personality who receives a fanatical devotion from his followers. In his person people see a "charisma" that personalizes their image of the crusade and sustains their loyalty.

The Consolidation Phase. An institution cannot survive on spontaneous
enthusiasm; it must be organized. In this period the thrill of novelty is
largely gone, and the new roles and statuses become routinized. People
no longer are fighting for a cause; instead they accept the remodeled institution as a natural part of the social order and seek to find in it a desirable personal status. The virtues of dignity and responsibility replace
spontaneous enthusiasm among participants. Capable administrators replace magnetic personalities as leaders. In rare cases the early popular

The battle for acceptance often develops a
heroic loyalty.

leader is able to develop administrative talents and retain institutional
leadership; in others he is shoved aside by coldly efficient "organization men." The religious saint or martyr is succeeded by the ecclesiastical
diplomat, the daring business promoter gives way to the efficiency expert,

and the revolutionary hero yields to the shrewd political administrator.

During the initial phase, institutional change is supported by an ideology that is a flaming faith inspiring a challenge to the social order. Now it becomes a comfortable system of beliefs serving to reinforce the *status quo*. The consolidation process generally demands some compromises in the original beliefs. When the early Christian faith—communal, frugal, and pacifistic—gained recognition as the official faith of the wealthy and powerful Roman Empire, some compromises were necessary. Those who cannot make such compromises may become a nuisance and, like Trotsky in Russia, may have to be silenced. Thus "the revolution devours its children," as ardent devotees of the early ideals give way to practical men who can adjust their ideological beliefs to the needs of institutional power.

The major activity in this period is the development of institutional procedures. It is a time when the statuses become formalized so that titles and established privilege mark off one status from another. Decisions become the precedents for future action. Many personal rivalries appear, and in dealing with them the institution develops a rigid pattern of procedures. Changes do occur, but these must be pictured as though they were logical and proper developments from the past, latent always in the life of the institution.

The Disorganization Phase. The routinization of the institution during the period of consolidation does not mean it has lost its attractiveness Indeed, the very fact that it can be sustained without fanatical enthusiasm may indicate that people generally find it a satisfying way of meeting their needs, and it may continue to gain fairly complete and uncritical acceptance for a long period of time. Eventually, however, social changes are apt to bring about situations that the institution fails to meet successfully. Gunpowder and trade destroyed feudalism; nationalism destroyed the Holy Roman Empire; today the atom bomb is undermining nationalism in the advanced countries. Social change will shake the firmest institution. The first symptom is often a widespread cynicism about the motives of the leaders of the institution, followed by demands for reforms and then by the threat of replacement of present norms and associational structures by alternative ones.

In this period of change the associational structures attached to the institution may fail to attract either the idealist or the practical citizen. The practical man seeking a career may look elsewhere for personal opportunities; the idealist may be dismayed by the traditional inertia that seems to make the institution unresponsive to human needs. The institutional officers are apt to be either aristocrats who inherited their position, opportunists callously exploiting the institution for personal advantage, or passionate antiquarians living in a bygone world. As acceptance dwindles and criticism mounts, there may be frantic attempts to restore prestige through the sporadic persecution of critics and the expansion of symbols of wealth and power. Often the most impressive monuments are completed just as an institution or state enters a period of disorganization and perhaps decline—the Hanging Gardens of Babylon, the Acropolis at Athens, St. Peter's Cathedral at Rome, or the Palace at Versailles. Such displays of institutional splendor do not regain the loyalty of an apathetic public.

If an association fails to adjust to changing conditions, it dies. A corporation whose products no longer appeal to its customers will become bankrupt. If the corporation as an institutional system of business organization fails to adapt itself to meet changing social needs, it is either compelled by outside pressures to change or is discarded in favor of some other form of business organization. The church whose doctrines and activities are out of touch with current needs will lose its followers to other churches. An ineffectual political system will be replaced by a competing institutional form as monarchies yield to republics or democracies to dictatorships. History is strewn with the wreckage of once powerful institutions that relied on prestige, wealth, or force instead of making adaptations to a changing scene.

The Reorganization Phase. But institutions seldom die. If all churches were to become irrelevant to the spiritual or emotional needs of people, would religion die? More likely some different kind of religion would appear. Has Russia abolished religion, or merely replaced a supernatural religion with a secular Marxist faith with its own set of sacred writings, saints and martyrs, and eternal truths? Associations and institutional norms may die, only to be replaced by others as the institution is reorganized.

It is not easy for institutions to reformulate their norms and structures, for they are highly resistant to change. The institution tends to become tradition-encrusted and its procedures and symbols become sacred, so that a proposal for change appears to be subversive and wicked. It was traitorous and sinful to question the absolute authority of thirteenth-century kings or nineteenth-century husbands.

An institution tends to become so involved in its procedures that it loses sight of its objectives. A church may become preoccupied with its rituals, a government with its paper work, an army with its parades, equipment, and traditional training procedures, and a school with its established courses of study. The *means* of the institution may have become the *ends* of the institution. Proposed changes in procedures are bitterly denounced as attacks upon the institution itself.

To reorganize an institution demands leadership capable of adapting the institution to meet changing needs. Such leadership rarely arises within an institution, for it generally promotes men who venerate its traditions and respect its present operation. To get leaders who will make drastic changes new blood must be brought in. The reorganization may involve new procedures, new objectives, new associational structures, or perhaps a reinterpretation of neglected earlier ideals of the institution.

Religious institutions offer many examples of institutional reorganization. To Western eyes Buddhism and Islam appear as outmoded faiths, irrelevant to the needs of the modern world. But a skillful alliance with the newer nationalism has made Buddhism in Burma, Ceylon, and Thailand a symbol of national unity with which every ambitious man must be identified [Cady, 1953]. In Africa a similar identification with nationalism has brought a fresh dynamism to Islam [Northcott, 1959]. An enlargement of objectives has strengthened both faiths. Meanwhile the struggle of the Christian faith to gain institutional status in Asia and Africa has been severely, and perhaps fatally, handicapped by its identification with Western colonialism [Jacob, 1957].

Sometimes an institutional reorganization consist of a change of methods as in the counterreformation led by Ignatius Loyola, which helped the Catholic Church to regain some of the ground lost in the Protestant Reformation. Sometimes an emphasis on latent ideals that have been neglected in practice may gain new power for the church. A case in point here is the emphasis of American Negro pastors on the ideals of brotherhood and nonviolent resistance, a strategy enabling their churches to assume a prominent position in fields of politics, education, and business. Problems and methods of coping with them may vary, but all institutions face the necessity of periodic changes of norms, objectives, procedures, and leadership if they are to survive in a changing society. In modern societies, change is so rapid that most institutions are in a continuous state of disorganization and reorganization.

The Interrelations of Institutions

No institution operates in a vacuum. One cannot understand a social institution unless one studies its relationships with the rest of society. Religion, government, business, education, and the family all exist in a constant state of mutual interaction. Business conditions determine the number of people who feel able to marry; marriage and birth rates affect the demand for goods. Education creates attitudes that influence the acceptance or rejection of religious dogma; religion, in turn, may either exalt scholarship as revealing the truths of God or denounce scientific inquiry as a threat to the faith. Businessmen, educators, clergymen, and the functionaries of all other institutions seek to influence the acts of government, since governmental action may make the difference between success and failure in their institutional enterprises.

The interrelationship of institutions explains why institutions are seldom able to control their members' behavior in a manner fully consistent with institutional ideals. Schools may offer a standard curriculum to all children, but the reaction of students depends on many factors outside the control of the educational institution. Children from a home that offers stimulating conversation and challenging reading materials are more apt to acquire intellectual interests than are children in homes where comic books and confession magazines are the reading fare and where television replaces conversation. Churches profess high ethical ideals, but their members often feel obliged to compromise these ideals in their adjustment to business, politics, or the process of securing a mate. Patriotism glorifies self-sacrifice and a devotion to the welfare of the state, but a little tax evasion helps to raise the family standard of living.

The family affects participation in other institutions and in turn is the object of attention from other institutions. The state regulates the process of marriage and divorce along with setting minimum standards for the care of children. The schools provide "family-life" courses and seek family cooperation through the formation of parent-teacher associations. Churches set ideals for family life and strive to keep the observance of family ceremonies in the religious setting. Business advertises its products as essential to proper family life.

All institutions face a conflict between career loyalty and family loyalty on the part of their functionaries. Business concerns strive to secure "corporation wives" [Whyte, 1951] who will cheerfully adjust their family concerns to harmonize with the demands the corporation makes on its executives. The army discourages marriages for privates and encourages marriage for the upper-officer ranks by trying to provide living quarters that will enable them to adjust their family life to the needs of military service. The most thorough effort to control family influence is seen in the Roman Catholic Church which strives to free its priesthood entirely from family entanglements through the requirement of celibacy.

All institutions face the necessity of continuously adapting themselves to a changing society. Changes in one institution compel changes in other institutions. Since family patterns change, the state sets up a system of social security. Since workers drift from farm to factory, the church must revise its language, its procedures, and possibly its doctrines. No institution can avoid affecting other institutions, nor avoid being affected by other institutions.

Summary

As roles are defined by mores, folkways, and laws, role behavior becomes predictable or institutionalized. Such role behavior is carried on in a regular pattern that is relatively independent of the personalities involved. Institutions tend to interpret both their own behavior and that of the rest of society in ideological terms. This mode of interpretation strengthens the institution by enabling its adherents to explain events in terms consistent with the intellectual assumptions of the institution.

Institutions may be so loosely structured that no central authority has the power to make binding decisions, or their system of defining role behavior may be so closely structured that rigid specifications for all participants in the institution are centrally determined. Institutional functions are either manifest or latent depending on the degree to which they are deliberately planned. Latent functions may be completely at variance with the professed aims of the institution, and devoted members of the institution may be unaware of their existence. Manifest functions include activities sustaining the internal functioning of the institution and also measures designed to extend its influence in the total society. Functions, morale, ideology, and type of personnel vary at different periods in the life cycle of the institution, and behavior that is common in one period may be unusual in another.

Regardless of the unique qualities of the institution, its functioning is affected by its relationship to the rest of society. This relationship is seen both in behavior patterns that spread unconsciously from one institution to another and in the conscious efforts to establish the supremacy of church, state, business, or family. Institutions are interrelated, so that changes in one institution affect the others in a continuous, mutual, cause-and-effect relationship.

Questions and Projects

1. What changes occur as a procedure becomes institutionalized?
2. "Turn the rascals out" is a frequent battle cry in politics. Comment on the effectiveness of this procedure as a means of changing role behavior.
3. Is the role of the nurse an institutionalized role?
4. Is the hospital a closely structured or a loosely-structured institution?

Would a Veterans' Administration hospital and an independent local hospital differ in this respect?

5. Is it correct to say that modern labor unions are a latent effect of changes in business enterprise brought about by the industrial revolution?
6. Religious institutions are often charged with having abandoned the faith as originally conceived.

How does this charge relate to the theory of the life cycle of institutions?

7. What is meant by the interrelationship of institutions? How does the shift from rural to urban living affect the church? Can the development of the social security system be related to any other changes in economic institutions? In the family?

8. Make a comparison of the Communist party and the Christian church(es) as institutional structures. (William Ebenstein, *Today's Isms*, Prentice-Hall, Inc., Englewood Cliffs, N.J., 1954, 1958, chap. 1, is a good source on the Communist party.) For each, identify its sacred writings, saints and martyrs, absolute truths, symbols, codes of behavior, manifest and latent functions, and recent examples of disorganization and reorganization.

Suggested Readings

DE HARTOG, JAN: *The Hospital*, Atheneum Publishers, New York, 1964. Describes a successful effort of laymen to organize volunteer help in an understaffed charity hospital despite administrative indifference and apathy.

ETZIONI, AMITAI (ED.): *Complex Organizations*, Holt, Rinehart and Winston, Inc., New York, 1961. A collection of essays and research on the structure and functions of large organizations.

HENRY, JULES: "The Formal Structure of a State Mental Hospital," *Psychiatry*, 17:139–151, 1954. A rather difficult but penetrating analysis of the organizational structure of a hospital.

HERTZLER, J. O.: *American Social Institutions*, Allyn and Bacon, Inc., Boston, 1961. A textbook in social institutions.

HOULT, THOMAS FORD: *The Sociology of Religion*, Holt, Rinehart and Winston, Inc., New York, 1958, especially chap. 4, "The Institutionalization and Differentiation of Religion." Discusses principally the relationship of religion to other social institutions.

HUNT, CHESTER L.: "Moslem and Christian in the Philippines," *Pacific Affairs*, 18:331–350, 1955. Interaction between religious, economic, and political institutions in the southern Philippines.

MERTON, ROBERT K.: "Manifest and Latent Function: Toward the Codification of Functional Analysis in Sociology," *Social Theory and Social Structure*, The Free Press of Glencoe, New York, 1957, pp. 19–84. A discussion of latent and manifest functions.

SMITH, HARVEY L.: "Psychiatry: A Social Institution in Process," *Social Forces*, 33:310–317, 1955. A description of the factors affecting the success of psychiatry in gaining institutional status.

SMITH, HARVEY L.: "Two Lines of Authority: Are One Too Many," *The Modern Hospital*, 84, no. 3, 59–64; reprinted in E. Gartly Jaco, *Patients, Physicians and Illness*, The Free Press of Glencoe, New York, 1958, pp. 468–477, under tit'

"Two Lines of Authority: The Hospital's Dilemma." Shows how the informal structure of the hospital is affected by the clash between medical and lay authority.

WILSON, ROBERT N.: "The Social Structure of a General Hospital," *Annals of the American Academy of Political and Social Science*, 346:67–76, 1963. Describes the changing structure of the hospital.

The Family

It happened one morning when Johnny [an American ex-G.I.] came to work and found Maggi, Kim Sing, Povenaaa and three other men rolling dice. Teuru [Johnny's native girl] stood nearby, watching the game with interest, advising Maggi, "You better try harder! You need three more sixes!"

"What's the game?" Johnny asked.

"Dice," Teuru said.

"I can see that. What's it about?"

Teuru blushed and looked away, so Johnny asked Povenaaa. "Don't bother me now," the excited man cried. Suddenly there were shouts of triumph and Maggi swore the Chinaman had cheated, but Kim Sing grinned happily and picked up the dice.

"The damned Chinaman gets the baby," Povenaaa spat.

"Gets what?" Johnny asked.

"The baby."

"Whose baby?"

"Teuru's."

"I didn't know Teuru had a baby."

"She doesn't . . . yet."

"You mean . . . my baby?" Johnny fell back with his mouth gaping. Then he yelled, "Hey! What's this about my baby?"

"He won it," Maggi said disconsolately.

Grabbing Teuru the American cried, "What are they talking about?"

"When it's born," Teuru said. "All the people in Raiatea would like to have it. So we rolled dice."

"But it's your own baby!" he stormed.

"Sure," she said. "But I can't keep it. I'm not married."

"Your own flesh and blood!"

"What's he mean?" Teuru asked Maggi.

Johnny Roe looked beseechingly at the fat woman and asked, "Would you give away your own baby? Would you give away Major?"

The crowd in the vanilla shed burst into laughter and Johnny demanded to know the joke. "It's Major!" Povenaaa roared, punching Johnny in the ribs. "Major's not her baby. She's Hedy's."

"You mean that Hedy . . ."

"Of course," Maggi explained. "Hedy had to go to Tahiti for a good time before settling down. So she gave me Major."

Johnny Roe had heard enough. He stormed off and bought two

bottles of gin, and when Teuru found him he had returned to his Montparnasse days except that now he blubbered, "Our baby! You raffled off our baby with a pair of dice!"

He kept this up for a whole day and Teuru became afraid that it was the start of another epic binge, so she broke the gin bottles and said, "All girls give away their first babies. How else could they get married?"

Johnny sat upright, suddenly sobered. "What do you mean, married?"

"What man in Raiatea would want a girl who couldn't have babies?"

"You mean . . . the men don't care?"

"Very much! Since people find I'm to have a baby, several men who never noticed me before have asked when you were going away."

"What happens then?" Johnny asked suspiciously.

"Then I get married."

Johnny fell back on his pillow and moaned, "It's indecent. By God, it's indecent."

James A. Michener, *Return to Paradise,* Random House, Inc., New York, 1951, pp. 115–117.

As this passage reveals, family patterns show a fascinating variation from society to society, and persons from one society who become involved in the family patterns of a different society generally react in a predictably ethnocentric manner. Why, if the family is so important, has mankind been unable to find and agree upon some ideal pattern of family life that best serves human needs?

In the most primitive societies, the family is the only institution. Among the polar Eskimos, there are no other institutions—no chiefs or formal laws, no priests or medicine men, no specialized occupations. Within the family all the business of living is fulfilled. In other words, they have no physical or social needs calling for an institutional structure other than that provided by their family.

As a culture grows more complex, its institutional structures become more elaborate. The family is an adequate structure for handling the economic production and consumption of primitive hunters and farmers. But what happens when they develop trade with neighboring or distant tribes? Before long there are traders, shippers, and other specialists whose work is no longer a part of the family life of the society. Later, specialized craftsmen begin to produce trade goods, giving rise to further occupational differentiation. Economic institutions exist whenever economic functions are performed in routine ways by specialists operating outside their family roles and functions.

In the most primitive societies, order is maintained with no formal laws, police, or courts. The only authority known in many simple societies is family authority; that is, certain family members have certain authority over others. With increasing tribal size and growing cultural complexity, more formal political organization is needed. Family heads are joined into tribal councils, tribes combine into confederations, and bureaucracies begin to develop. Warfare, in both primitive and modern societies, is a powerful stimulus to political organization, for only through political organization can an aroused rabble be mobilized for an effective military effort.

The family, then, is the basic social institution, from which the others have grown as increasing cultural complexity made them necessary. A study of the family will tell us something about the family and about institutions in general.

Structure of the Family

Like all institutions the family is a system of accepted norms and procedures for getting some important jobs done. The family is defined as a *kinship grouping that provides for the rearing of children and for certain other human needs.* If a society is to survive, people must find some work-

Where family patterns are concerned, almost everything is right some place.

able and dependable ways of pairing off, conceiving and raising children, and fulfilling the other functions of the family. These family functions vary less than the family forms through which people seek to meet them. In fact if one were to list every possible way of organizing family life, a search of anthropological literature would probably reveal that each form of organization was the accepted pattern in at least one society. With only a few exceptions, where family patterns are concerned, everything's right some place.

Composition of the Family Group. When we speak of the family we think of a husband and wife, their children, and occasionally an extra relative. This is called the *conjugal family,* since its core is the married couple; or it is sometimes called the "nuclear family." The *consanguine* family is founded not on the conjugal relationship of two people but on the blood relationship of a large number of people. The consanguine family is an extended clan of blood relatives together with their mates and children. Sometimes it is called the "joint" or "extended" family. There are certain technical differences between the joint and the extended family [see Queen et al., 1961, p. 69], but they need not concern us here. While we use the consanguine-family pattern for family reunions and other ceremonial purposes, our important family functions proceed on a conjugal-family basis. Our folklore warns against in-laws and urges the couple to set up a household of their own. Our laws require a husband to maintain his wife in a home apart from other relatives if she desires, and she generally does. Our laws require parents to support their own children, but impose only slight obligation to care for their parents, and no obligation to care for brothers and sisters, cousins, uncles and aunts, nephews and nieces, or other relatives.

The consanguine family has a very different atmosphere. Whereas the conjugal family has a married couple at its core, surrounded by a fringe of blood relatives, the consanguine family has a group of brothers and sisters at its core, surrounded by a fringe of husbands and wives. In most instances of the consanguine family, a married man (or woman) remains primarily attached to his parental family, and remains a semioutsider in his wife's (or husband's) family. This attachment has important consequences. One's principal responsibilities are toward one's family of birth, not of marriage. Sometimes the family of marriage is called the "family of procreation," while the family of birth, the socially significant family group by which one is surrounded, is called the "family of orientation." In our society these two are much the same, but in many societies they are quite different. Thus a woman may depend not on her husband but on her brothers for protection and help in raising her children. Her husband does not escape, however, for he is saddled with his sister's children. [For descriptions of the consanguine family see Linton, 1936, chap. 9; Murdock, 1949, chap. 3.]

In such a family, affection and responsibility are widely diffused among a fairly large group of people. Children are the joint responsibility of the entire family, and a child develops a relationship with his aunts very like that with his mother. He is surrounded by many adults, any of whom may momentarily act as parent toward him. Such a family tends to turn out personalities with less individuality than ours, since each child has more nearly the same socialization experience. Such a family protects the individual against misfortune. If a child's mother dies or is neglectful, good substitutes are at hand. The consanguine family offers little opportunity for individuality and little danger of loneliness or neglect.

Obviously the consanguine family is not practical everywhere. Where both the family of birth and the family of marriage are in the same

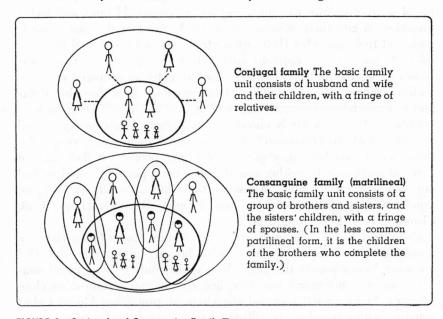

Conjugal family The basic family unit consists of husband and wife and their children, with a fringe of relatives.

Consanguine family (matrilineal) The basic family unit consists of a group of brothers and sisters, and the sisters' children, with a fringe of spouses. (In the less common patrilineal form, it is the children of the brothers who complete the family.)

FIGURE 3 Conjugal and Consanguine Family Types.

village, it is easy to be with one's mate while fulfilling one's family obligations. If they are in different villages, a strain is imposed. In a highly mobile, individualized, specialized society like ours, the consanguine family would be unworkable. But for the Tanala of Madagascar, whose farm work required a cooperative team of a half dozen or more adult males, the consanguine family was ideal [Linton, 1936, chap. 12].

Forms of Marriage. The path to marriage is lined with a variety of impediments, requirements, preliminaries, and ceremonials that would be downright discouraging—were not the objective so compelling. Rare is the society that simply allows a couple quietly to pair off and start playing house. Marriage is too important for such casual arrangements. Marriage is *the approved social pattern whereby a couple establish a family*. It involves not only the conceiving and rearing of children (who are sometimes conceived as an institutionalized preliminary to marriage) but also a host of other obligations and privileges affecting a good many people. Every society has, therefore, developed a pattern for guiding these marriages.

In this matter of guidance, our ethnocentrism is likely to be evident. To us it is monstrous that parents should arrange and compel the marriage of two persons who may never even have met. How do they know they will love each other? Why are not their wishes consulted? Our reaction illustrates the usual error of ethnocentrism—assuming that people of another culture will think and feel as we would think and feel if transplanted into their situation. It overlooks the fact that most people wish and feel only what their culture trains them to wish and feel. We think of marriage as a romantic adventure with a person we have come to love. The girl in classical China, about to enter an arranged marriage with a stranger, eagerly anticipated her marriage as a desirable status and a comfortable companionship with a man she would come to love, because he had been wisely chosen by her parents. Each society viewed the other with an ethnocentric pity; we pitied their young people for their lack of freedom; they pitied our young people for their lack of parental assistance. In neither case did the young people themselves feel any need for pity. Today, of course, the Chinese family is changing rapidly and painfully under the new Peoples' Republic [Levy, 1949; Chandrasekhar, 1959; Yang, 1959].

Endogamy and Exogamy. Every society limits choice in marriage by requiring that one select a mate outside his own group. This is called *exogamy*. In our society the prohibition applies only to close blood relatives; one may not marry his sister, first cousin, and certain other close relatives. Many societies extend the circle of prohibited kin to forbid marriage within the clan, the village, or sometimes even the tribe.

Most societies also require that mates be chosen within some specified group. This is called *endogamy*. Clan, village, and tribal endogamy are quite common among primitive societies. In our society, racial endogamy is required by law in many states, and custom and social pressure strongly discourage racial intermarriage in the rest of our country. With varying degrees of pressure, we also encourage religious endogamy and class endogamy in our country, although they are not enforced by law.

Every society practices both exogamy and endogamy, specifying the limits of group closeness (exogamy) and the limits of group distance (endogamy) within which mates must be found. Sometimes between these two limits there is little room for hunting! The Aranda of Central Australia have a complicated marital pattern known to anthropologists as an "eight-class system with exogamy and indirect patrilineal descent." To skip the detailed explanations, this means that a man can marry only a woman from a particular group within the proper subsection of the opposite half of his tribe [Murdock, 1936, pp. 27–30]. In a number of societies a formula such as this makes an actual choice unnecessary, for only one girl may be in the permissible category for a boy to marry. If there is none at all, then the couple who are supposed to become his parents-in-law normally adopt a marriageable girl from another family with a surplus. After all, an institution is a structure for meeting human needs, and it usually does so in one fashion or another.

Marital Choice. The process of arranging a marriage shows a fascinating range of possibilities. As shown above, some societies follow a formula whereby the children of certain socially designated kinsmen marry each other, so that individual choices may be unnecessary. Where actual choices are necessary, there are many ways of making them. The couples can do their own choosing, in some cases with parental guidance or parental veto. The parents can arrange the marriage with or without considering the couple's wishes. A wife may be purchased, or perhaps a complicated series of gifts exchanged between families. Wife capture is now unknown. All these patterns exist as the standard way of arranging marriages in some of the world's societies. All of them work—within the society in which they exist—and are supported by the values and practices of the culture. Wife capture worked very well for the Tasmanians, who practiced village exogamy and were not greatly concerned over the differences between one woman and all the others. For our society, it would be less practical.

Monogamy and Polygamy. To us, the only decent and civilized form of marriage is *monogamy*—one man to one woman (at a time). Yet a majority of the world's societies have practiced *polygamy*, allowing a plurality of mates. There are three theoretical forms of polygamy. One is *group marriage*, in which several men and several women are all in a marriage relationship with one another. While this is an intriguing theoretical possibility, there is no authentic instance of it among human beings, with the possible exception of the Marquesans at one time. A very rare form is *polyandry*, where several husbands share a single wife. The Todas of Southern India provide one of our few examples. Here as in most other cases polyandry was fraternal, meaning when a woman married a man she automatically became wife to all his brothers, and they all lived together with little jealousy or discord. Toda polyandry becomes understandable when one learns that it accompanied female infanticide and a shortage of women [Murdock, 1936, pp. 120, 121; Queen et al., 1961, chap. 2]. Only where some situation has created a shortage of women is polyandry likely to be found [Unni, 1958]. But the scattered handful of societies that practice polyandry serve to show how a practice that seems to us to be contrary to human nature can still be the accepted and preferred pattern for people who are socialized to expect it. The usual form of polygamy is *polygyny*—a plurality of wives, not necessarily sisters and generally acquired at different times during one's life.

Mention of polygyny will arouse a predictably ethnocentric response from almost any American. He conjures up images of female degradation and helpless enslavement, and rises to impressive heights of moral indignation at such heathen brutishness. The facts are otherwise. It would be difficult to show that women have generally had a more satisfactory status in monogamous than in polygamous societies. Even in most polygynous societies, most of the marriages are monogamous. It is generally only the more successful and powerful men who can afford or attract more than one wife. In many polygynous societies the second wife fills the status function of the second Cadillac in our society. Far from feeling resentful, the first wife often urges her husband to take more wives, over whom she generally reigns as queen bee. Polygyny in operation takes many forms in different societies, all of them far removed from the imagination of the normal ethnocentric American.

Divorce. What is to be done when a married couple can't stand each other? Although most societies make some provision for divorce, some make it very difficult or perhaps give the privilege of divorce only to the men. Some make divorce very simple. Among the Hopi, divorce is rather rare. It is also uncomplicated—the husband merely packs up and leaves, or in his absence his wife tells him to get lost by piling his things outside the door.

The social and family structure of many societies makes divorce a fairly painless and harmless operation. Where there is no great emphasis on romantic love and no intense individual love attachments, divorce entails no great heartbreak. Where the consanguine family surrounds the child with a protective clan of kin and designates the mother's brother as the responsible male in a child's life, the loss of a child's father is hardly noticed. The meaning of divorce depends on how it relates to other aspects of the institution of the family. In our society, with its strong accent on individual love attachments within an independent conjugal family unit, a divorce is likely to mean the collapse of the emotional world for both child and adult.

Other Variations in Family Structure. We could extend the list of "odd" family patterns indefinitely. Some societies, like ours, encourage an informal camaraderie between brother and sister; among others, such as the Nama Hottentots, brother and sister are expected to treat each other with great formality and respect; they may not address each other directly or even be alone together. Such *avoidances* are found in many societies. Mother-in-law avoidance is a very common one; the Crow husband may not look at or speak to his mother-in-law, or even use a word that appears in her name. In many societies avoidance taboos demand extreme decorum toward other relatives. Thus the Crow, who must act with great decorum toward his sister, mother-in-law, son-in-law, and his wife's brother's wife, is socially expected to show great familiarity toward his sister-in-law, to joke with her and engage in various immodesties. Among the Nama Hottentots, brother-sister incest is the worst of all offenses, but cross-cousins[1] enjoy a joking relationship that includes loose talk, horseplay, and sexual intimacy. All this is merely to say that the family includes a varying number of people whose relationship to one another is defined differently in different societies.

Is there any sense in all this, or is the family an irrational jumble of odd notions and historical accidents? Two things we should remember. First, many different patterns will work as long as all members of the society accept them. Wife purchase, wife capture, or wives-for-the-asking —any one of these patterns work out acceptably provided the people view it as the proper way to stake out a mate. Thousands of societies have been in existence at some time or other. It is not surprising that most of the possible ways of organizing human relationships have been tried out sometime, somewhere. Many of them have survived, showing that man is a highly adaptable animal capable of being trained to find his satisfactions in a remarkable variety of ways.

Second, we invoke the concept of cultural relativity and repeat that how a custom works depends on how it relates to the rest of its cultural setting. Where wife purchase exists, the transaction is not merely a way of arranging marriages but a central feature of the entire economic and social system. The consanguine family exists in certain societies because

[1] Cross-cousins are the children of a brother and a sister; where the related parents are of the same sex, the cousins are called *parallel cousins*.

it is an efficient *economic* unit, and not just because it is nice to have the family together [Sahlins, 1957; Nimkoff and Middleton, 1960]. As we saw in the preceding chapter, institutions are interrelated.

Functions of the Family

The family in any society is an institutional structure for getting certain tasks done. What are the tasks commonly performed through the family?

The Sexual-regulation Function. The family is the principal institution through which societies organize and regulate the satisfaction of sexual desires. Most societies provide some alternative sexual outlets. With varying degrees of indulgence, each society also tolerates some sex behavior in violation of its norms. But in all societies it is expected that most sexual intercourse will occur between persons whom their institutional norms define as legitimately accessible to each other. These norms sometimes allow for considerable sexual variety, yet no society is sexually promiscuous. In every society there are mores forbidding certain persons access to one another. What may look to us like promiscuity is more likely to be a complicated system of sexual permissions and taboos we do not fully understand.

A clear majority of the world's societies allows young persons to experiment with sexual intercourse before marrying [Murdock, 1949; 1950]. Many societies think the idea of virgin marriage is absurd. Yet in such societies, this premarital sex experience is viewed as a preparation for marriage, not as a recreational pastime. Its principal purpose is generally to determine fertility; a girl who conceives shows her readiness for marriage. Most of these societies have not merely *allowed* premarital sexual behavior; they have *institutionalized* it. They have defined it as a proper and useful activity and have developed a supporting set of institutional arrangements making it safe and harmless. Since there is full social approval, there is no fear, shame, or disgrace. The family structure and living arrangements in such societies are generally of a sort where one more baby is no special inconvenience or burden. Premarital sex experience can be a useful and harmless preparation for marriage in a society that has institutionalized it. Ours has not, as many young people learn to their dismay.

Some societies provide for the sexual needs of virtually all adults; others do not. Many primitive societies provide for the unmarried through some form of sexual hospitality or occasional license. An unmarried or widowed brother may be permitted occasional access to his brother's wife. A widow may automatically become wife to her deceased husband's brother (the *levirate*), and, less commonly, the widowed husband may become husband to his deceased wife's sister (the *sororate*). Celibacy is exceedingly rare in primitive societies. Contemporary Western societies are less solicitous. No approved sexual outlet is provided for the widowed or the unmarried adult. Just how easily Western societies *could* make such provision without severe disruption of other institutions and values is a matter of debate. Yet the war-decimated populations of countries like Germany and Russia have several millions of women condemned to a life without husband, legitimate children, or a legitimate sex and love experience. In this respect contemporary Western society is perhaps less well organized than many primitive societies.

The Reproductive Function. Every society depends primarily on the family for the producing of children. Other arrangements are theoretically possible, and many societies do arrange to accept children produced outside the family. But no society has established a set of norms for providing children except as part of a family.

The Socialization Function. All societies depend primarily on the family for the socialization of children into adults who can function successfully in that society. Thinkers from Plato to Huxley [1932; 1958] have speculated about other arrangements, but the family survives as the standard arrangement for looking after children. The family is the child's first primary group, and this is where his personality development begins. By the time he is old enough to enter primary groupings outside the family, the basic foundations of his personality are already firmly laid.

One of the many ways in which the family socializes the child is through providing models for him to copy. He learns to be a man, a husband, and a father mainly through having lived in a family headed by a man, a husband, and a father. Some socialization difficulties are encountered where such a model is missing and the child must rely on the secondhand models he sees in other families or on other relatives. There is no fully satisfactory substitute for a mother and a father.

Sometimes although both parents are present, they are not satisfactory models. If the father is an ineffectual, timid, hesitant incompetent in a society that expects men to be bold, confident, and successful, the son is torn between his need to identify with a father as a model and his growing awareness that he should not grow up to be like his father. A girl's mother may be aggressive and masculine, with a resentful hostility toward men; she may be exploitatively feminine, selfishly using femininity to manipulate men; she may be timid, overdependent, and insecure, lacking any confidence in her ability to function as a wife and mother. A girl with such a mother has no opportunity to imitate the attitudes and skills needed for a successful adult role in our society. Many psychiatrists trace many personality difficulties to one's childhood lack of suitable parental models [Parsons, 1947; LaPiere and Farnsworth, 1949, chap. 8].

The function of models in socialization can be seen in the role-taking play of children. Children often "play house," passing out roles among one another ("You be the mama and you be the papa and I'll be the little girl and you be the baby!"). They proceed to act out these roles as they perceive them, and they perceive them largely as they have seen them being played in their own families. Many a parent, overhearing such play, has been chagrined to learn how his child perceives his behavior! All this, however, is more than just "play." Through such role taking, the child's perception of adult roles is refined and corrected ("You stop doing that and act like a papa is supposed to act or we won't play!"). Such play probably contributes insights into the feelings of others. When in play a child "misbehaves" and is "punished" by the "papa," each of them probably gains some insight into the feelings of the real father who punishes a child. Both are also recognizing the boundaries of conduct when they define an act as misbehavior. Role-taking play is thus a way of socializing children to accept and fill both their present and their future family roles.

The Affectional Function. Whatever else he needs, man needs intimate human response. Psychiatric opinion holds that probably the greatest single cause of emotional difficulties, behavior problems, and even of physical illness, is *lack of love*, that is, lack of a warm, affectionate relationship with a small circle of intimate associates [Fromm, 1956; Schindler, 1954, chap. 10]. A mountain of data shows that the serious delinquent is typically a child whom nobody cares very much about. Infants who get good physical care but do not get cuddled, fondled, and loved are likely to develop a condition medically known as *marasmus* (from a Greek word meaning "wasting away"). They lose weight, fret and whimper listlessly, and sometimes even die [Ribble, 1943, chap. 1]. Several studies have shown how children in the sterilized but impersonal atmosphere of hospital or foundling home will suffer in emotional development and often show startlingly high rates of illness and death [Spitz, 1945]. Lack of affection actually damages an infant's ability to survive.

The evidence is overwhelming that our need for companionship and intimate, affectionate human response is vitally important to us. Indeed, this is probably our strongest social need—far more necessary than, for example, sex. Many celibates are leading happy, healthy, and useful lives, but it is hard to find a happy, healthy person who has never been loved.

Most societies rely almost entirely on the family for affectionate response. The companionship need is filled partly by the family and partly by other groupings. Many primitive societies had organizations and clubs somewhat like modern lodges and fraternities, filling much the same functions. Yet even these were often organized on a kinship basis and were therefore another aspect of the family.

The Status Function. In entering a family one inherits a string of statuses. One is ascribed several statuses within the family—age, sex, birth order, and others. The family also serves as a basis for ascribing several social statuses—as, for example, a white, urban, middle-class Catholic. Class ascription is especially important, for the class status of a child's family largely determines the opportunities and rewards open to him and the expectations through which others may inspire or discourage him. Class status can be changed through some combination of luck and personal efforts, as described in a later chapter. But each child *starts out* with the class status of his family, and this initial placement probably has greater effect on achievement and reward than any other single factor. The assignment to a class may seem unfair, yet it is inevitable. The family cannot avoid preparing the child for a class status similar to its own, for the process of living and growing up in such a family is preparation for its class status. The child normally absorbs from his family a set of interests, values, and life habits that make it easy for him to continue in the class status. Sometimes a family deliberately tries to ensure the upward mobility of its children and to teach them the values, habits, and skills that will help them climb upward. At best the effort is only partly successful. No family can fully succeed in socializing children in a way of life not practiced by the family.

The Protective Function. In all societies the family offers some degree of physical, economic, and psychological protection to its members. In many societies any attack on a person is an attack on his entire family, with all members bound to defend him or to revenge the injury. In many societies guilt and shame are equally shared by all family members. In most primitive societies the family is an extended food-sharing unit that starves or fattens together; as long as a man's relatives have food, he has no fear of hunger. And in many primitive societies, as in ours, very few persons outside one's family really care what happens to him.

The Economic Function. As stated earlier, the family is the basic economic unit in many societies. Its members work together as a team and share jointly in their produce. In some societies the clan is the basic unit for working and sharing, but more often it is the family. This situation, however, is now changing, as will be seen in the following section.

The Changing American Family

The family is a prime example of the interrelatedness of institutions, for the changes in the family mirror the changes in the other institutions

into which it dovetails. For example in most hunting societies the men
are clearly dominant over women, who make inferior hunters because
of their limited strength and incessant child bearing. But as the economic
base shifts from the hunt to the hoe, women's role in the family grows
somewhat more influential, for women can and do perform most of the
hoe agriculture. As the plow replaces the hoe, male dominance again
tends to grow, for plowing generally calls for the greater strength of
the male. Thus there is some relation between one's power within the
family and the importance of his (or her) economic contribution. Other
examples of interrelatedness will follow.

Changing Family Structure. *The Size of the American Family Has
Decreased.* It is no secret that the twelve-child families of the last century are rare today. The birth rate in the Western world began falling
about a century ago, reached its low point during the Great Depression
of the 1930s, and has since risen somewhat from that figure. Today there
is much popular talk about "the large family coming back." Yet the facts
are that, while three- and four-child families have grown in popularity
in the past two decades, the proportion of families with five or more
children has not shown a proportionate increase, as is seen in Figure 4.
The talk about the large family "coming back" merely means that among
the middle class (accustomed, as usual, to view *their* world as *the*
world), the over-two-child family has regained popularity.

Why has overall family size declined in the Western world? Contraceptive devices have provided the means but not the motive. Contraceptives are not the cause of smaller families any more than ropes are the
cause of suicides. The motives for desiring smaller families carry us into
many other aspects of the culture. The shift from an illiterate agricultural
society to a literate, specialized, industrialized society has changed children from an economic asset into an expensive burden. Shifts in patterns
of recreation, in aspirations for education and social mobility, and changing concepts of individual rights have all united to curb indiscriminate
child bearing. Thus changing technology, changing economics, and
changing values are all involved in the change in family size.

The Status of Divorce Has Changed. Divorce is the object of much
agonized dismay by Americans who cannot accept divorce as an integral
part of the modern American family system. A society can secure a very
low divorce rate in at least four ways. First, it can deemphasize love.
In many societies marriage is a working partnership, but not a romantic
adventure as well. If less is expected of marriage, more will be "successful." Second, it can separate love from marriage. Romantic love
appeared in Western societies several centuries ago, but only recently
has it become the standard basis for marriage. A number of societies
have a series of men's clubs for companionship, and allow a wide free-

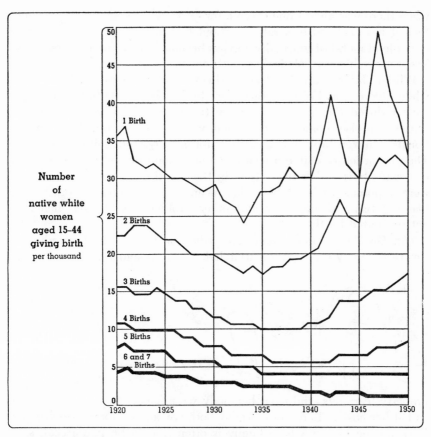

FIGURE 4 Family Size in the United States since 1920.

SOURCE: Reproduced from *Life,* copyright Time, Inc., 1952, by permission.

dom to prowl in search of sex adventure. Here again, less is demanded
of the marriage. Or the society can socialize its members to be so much
alike in personality and expectation that practically all marriages will
work out successfully. The stable, well-integrated society generally succeeds in accomplishing this leveling; our society does not. Finally, divorce
can be made so difficult that most unhappily married couples are unable
or unwilling to seek divorce as a solution. Our society has actually done
none of these. It socializes people so that they differ more and more
greatly in personality and expectation, gives them values that lead them
to expect a great deal of marriage and to demand a high level of love
satisfaction in marriage, and provides no approved outlet for their frustrated marital needs when they fail. All this makes a fairly high rate
of marital failure and divorce an inescapable part of our modern family
structure. The American divorce rate reached its peak in the mid-1940s,

when there was almost one divorce for every three new marriages. Since then it has declined to a ratio of about one to four. From being a rare example of moral disgrace, divorce has become a fairly common, more-or-less respectable way of dealing with an intolerable marriage.

Where children are involved, a divorce creates a broken home. But while divorce has been creating more broken homes, falling death rates have reduced the homes broken by the death of parents. When both causes of broken homes are combined, we find that we now have proportionately fewer broken homes than formerly [Landis, 1960, pp. 3–4]. The proportion of children who reach adulthood under the care of their own parents is higher today than in the "good old days" when families were supposed to be stable. This means that the popular practice of blaming rising delinquency and other problems on broken homes is not supported by the facts.

The Division of Labor and Authority Has Changed. The traditional American family was highly patriarchal. A century ago a married woman's

They differ more and more greatly in personality and expectation.

property, earnings, and even her body were legally beyond her control and at her husband's disposal. Today both law and custom have changed. Even among groups whose family is often said to be patriarchal, such as Catholics, immigrants, or farmers, recent investigation shows that ". . . the patriarchal family is dead" [Blood and Wolfe, 1960, p. 29]. In their investigation of 909 Detroit-area marriages they found that power or domination of decision making was about equally divided between white husbands and wives [p. 35]. Among Negro couples, the wife was normally the more dominant, perhaps because our economy offers more steady jobs to Negro women than to Negro men [Kephart, 1961, pp. 217–222].

Blood and Wolfe's research clearly shows the relationship between economic role and family role. Husbands exercised less dominance over working wives than over nonworking wives; unemployed husbands of working wives ranked far down the dominance scale. The more highly educated, prosperous, and successful the husband, the greater his degree of dominance over the wife [Blood and Wolfe, 1960, pp. 37, 40–41, 60–61; Wolfe, 1959]. Thus the upper-class family more nearly approaches the patriarchal tradition than the lower-class family.

The "Quiet Revolution" in Women's Employment. Perhaps the greatest change of all has been the increase in "working wives." Women today make up one-third (32 per cent) of our labor force. Slightly over one-half (52 per cent) of all women are in our labor force at any single moment, and three-fourths (76 per cent) of these are married. Of the married workers, almost half (7.5 million) have children under eighteen, and one-sixth (2.9 million) have children under six years old. Almost one-third of all mothers with children under eighteen are employed, and about 4 million preschool children have working mothers [Herzog, 1960, p. 3; Women's Bureau, 1961]. From these figures the "normal" pattern of the American woman emerges. Typically she begins working before marriage, works until her children arrive, takes off a few years, then returns sometime after her children get into school [Smutz, 1959, p. 60]. Obviously it has become normal for the American wife to work for a major part of her lifetime.

Historically a woman who worked was living evidence that she had no husband able and willing to support her. A survey of 140 married women workers in 1908 found only 6 whose husbands held jobs above the grade of unskilled laborer [Bureau of Labor Statistics, 1916, pp. 163–164]. By 1956, among husbands earning between $7,000 and $10,000, placing them in the top eighth in income, half the wives with no children at home were working. The working wife, once a lower-class phenomenon, is increasingly found among the prosperous middle classes. There is no reason to believe this trend will be reversed. The "American standard of living" now assumes two incomes. Of families in the $7,000 to $15,000 income range in 1956, 70 per cent had at least two workers. As the "normal" standard of living increasingly becomes insupportable on a single income, the pressure grows on the nonworking wives to get a job. A large majority of the readers of this textbook will be either working wives or the husbands of working wives for a major portion of their married lives.

This quiet revolution has transformed the household division of labor as well. A French study finds that married women workers actually work, at job plus housework, only six to eight hours more a week than nonworking wives with several children [Stoetzel, 1956]. Blood and Wolfe's study shows that husbands of working wives must expect to help out more at home. Many of the readers of this text will (if they have not already done so) eventually perform certain experiments that will tell whether their husbands' masculinity will dissolve in dishwater!

Changing Family Functions. Structure and function are two aspects of the same thing. Changes in one are both cause and effect of changes in the other. What changes in function accompany these changes in family structure?

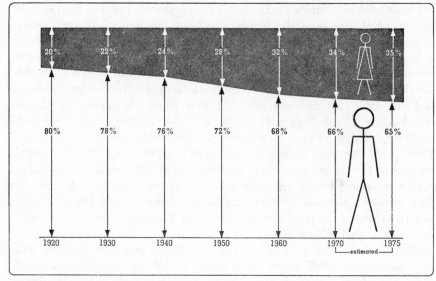

FIGURE 5 Women in the Labor Force (*United States, 1920–1975*).
SOURCE: Department of Commerce, Bureau of Labor Statistics.

The Sexual-regulation Function Probably Shows No Great Change.
Illicit sexual behavior is fairly common, but according to Kinsey at least
90 per cent of all American sexual intercourse is marital [1948, p. 588].
There is evidence of a good deal of premarital sexual intercourse, most
often with one's intended marital partner, while evidence is mixed as
to whether such behavior has been increasing. But is premarital sexual
intercourse evidence of the *failure* of family regulation of sex? Or are
we developing premarital relations with an intended mate as a form of
family regulation of sex? In other words are we actually beginning to
institutionalize premarital sex relations? Some scholars suspect so [Ehr-
mann, 1959; Reiss, 1960].

The Reproductive Function Is Little Changed. True, birth rates are
lower than a century ago, but if one considers only the average size of
the *surviving* family, even the birth rate is not so greatly changed. A
century ago nearly half the babies died in infancy or childhood; today
nearly all survive. Today's American family of three or four surviving
children is about what it has been through most of recent Western
history.

The Socialization Function Claims Increased Attention. The family
remains the principal socializing agency, although the school now plays
an important role. Other social agencies are occasionally called in for
guidance. The major change has been in our *attention* to the socialization function. An earlier generation knew little about "personality devel-

opment"; today nearly every literate parent knows about Dr. Spock [1945, 1957]. We know something today of the role of emotional development in school progress, career success, physical well-being, and practically all other aspects of the good life. Our great-grandparents worried about smallpox and cholera; we worry about sibling jealousies and peer-group adjustment.

How Has the Quiet Revolution Affected the Socialization Function? Does the child suffer when mother takes a job? There have been several dozen studies of this question [reviewed by Stolz, 1960; Herzog, 1960]. The earlier studies failed to control for such variables as social class or family composition. As a result the working-mother sample had a higher proportion of poor, uneducated slum dwellers, widows, and divorcees than the nonworking-mother sample. Such poorly controlled studies seemed to show that children suffered when mother worked. Later studies compared children of working mothers with children of *otherwise comparable* nonworking mothers. These studies show no significant differences between the children, and conclude that, when other things are equal, the child is as likely to benefit as to suffer when mother works.

Perhaps the most careful study was that of the Gluecks [1957] who compared five hundred delinquents with five hundred nondelinquents, carefully matched for social class, age, ethnic-racial derivation, and intelligence. They found no difference between the delinquency rates of the children of nonworking and regularly employed mothers, while children of irregularly employed mothers had a much higher delinquency rate. The fact of working or nonworking was unimportant, but the irregularly employed mother was more likely to be a disorganized, irresponsible person who was a poor mother whether working or not. Apparently it is the kind of person the mother is, and not whether she works, that determines how she fulfills the functions of a mother.

The Affectionate and Companionship Functions Have Gained. Among Blood and Wolfe's 909 families, "Companionship has emerged as the most valued aspect of marriage today" [1960, p. 172]. Here we have two apparently contradictory developments. We have become *more* dependent on the conjugal family for affection and companionship while we have become *less* dependent on the extended family, the clan of relatives. We are so mobile and so individualized in our interests that we sometimes find we have nothing in common with our cousins, uncles, and aunts except our ancestors. The extended family is less effective in offering companionship, and this lack increases our dependence upon the immediate family. Furthermore, the primary community, the small group of neighbors who knew one another well and had a lot in common, has disappeared from the lives of most Americans. Urbanization and specialization have destroyed it. In an increasingly heedless, impersonal, and ruthless world, the immediate family becomes the bulwark of emotional support. A man may be insulted by his boss, patronized by his colleagues, and ignored by his neighbors, but at home he can be King Solomon to his wife and Samson to his children! Herein lies one of the greatest functions and strengths of the family.

Herein also lies one of the greatest weaknesses of the modern American family. When the family fails to provide affection and companionship—the key functions of the modern American family—little is left to hold it together. Most of the other functions can be performed for the individual outside the family relationship. We can even question whether the married man is better off, economically or sexually, than the bachelor. Yet most people marry, perhaps because sex without enduring affection is not enough. Nonetheless, when we place so much responsibility on the conjugal family group for providing the basic emotional support for the individual, many will fail.

The Status-definition Function Continues. Many families continue to prepare children to retain the class status of the family; a growing fraction seek to prepare their children for social mobility. They do this mainly by giving children the kind of ambitions, attitudes, and habits that prompt them to struggle for a higher status.

The Protective Functions Have Declined. The traditional family in Western society did most of what organized social work does today—nursed the sick, gave haven to the handicapped, and provided shelter for the aged. Today we have a medical technology only specialists and hospitals can handle. Today's urban household is an impractical place to care for many kinds of handicapped people. Family care of the aged was a practical arrangement when the aging couple stayed on the farm, joined by a married child and mate. The parents could retire gradually, shifting to less strenuous tasks but remaining useful and appreciated. This pattern is available today to only a tiny minority, and many elderly couples feel—and are—useless and unappreciated in the homes of their children. Our rapid rate of social change also means that many tensions may develop when three generations live under one roof. So for a variety of reasons—most of which have nothing to do with selfishness or personal irresponsibility—many of the protective functions of the traditional family have been shifted to other institutions.

The Economic Functions Have Changed Most Greatly. A century ago the American family was a unit of economic production, united by shared work on the farm. Today only one-tenth of our families are farmers, and even the farm family is not the self-sufficient unit of the past. Except on the farm, the family is no longer the basic unit of economic production; this has shifted to the shop, the factory, the office. The family is no longer united by shared work, for its members work separately. Instead the family is a unit of economic *consumption,* united by companionship, affection, and recreation together.

Health and Family Life

The observation has often been made that good health runs in some families and frequent illness in others. Specific diseases may strongly run in certain families. For example Graham and Lilienfeld [1958] find that gastric cancer is twice as common in families of cancer patients as in other families. Why is this so? Shared living habits and hereditary susceptibility may be factors, although very little is definitely known about hereditary susceptibility to most diseases. But a good deal is known about frequent illnesses and unsatisfactory family relations. Two carefully controlled studies found that three-fourths of all general-hospital admissions were for psychosomatic illnesses. Most psychosomatic illness is rooted in unsatisfactory family relationships [Schindler, 1954, p. 4]. Schindler flatly states that "the family is our number-one cause of illness" [p. 126] and describes several kinds of family atmosphere that are highly productive of illness-prone people—atmospheres of constant criticism and constant complaint, dislike, selfish egoism, in-law domination, the kill-joy attitude, and others. He illustrates:

> Ellen was the youngest of seven children in a home where no one really cared about anyone else. Being the youngest, she was the target of everyone else's ill will. Every member of the family was criticizing Ellen as soon as she was old enough to understand. "Oh, she's dumb." "She isn't going to be able to get through school." No one ever helped Ellen.
>
> By the time she got into school she had a deeply grounded inferiority complex. She looked past her teachers because everyone told her she was stupid. When Ellen, after a hectic childhood, at last grew up, she married a boy who had the same kind of a past and the same kind of an inferiority complex. When she had children, she was sure she lacked the ability to rear them; she had no confidence in her ability as a housewife. Hers was a constant life of worry.
>
> Ellen has been sick most of the time since childhood and is still sick today.

John A. Schindler, *How to Live 365 Days a Year,* Prentice-Hall, Inc., Englewood Cliffs, N.J., 1954, pp. 130–131.

People whose emotional life is unsatisfactory generally haunt the doctor's office with an endless string of complaints. The illnesses are genuine, but a purely medical treatment is seldom effective, because the underlying causes are emotional. If one ailment does respond to treatment, another soon develops. Clearly, a comfortable, relaxed, affectionate family life is the greatest health asset anyone can inherit.

The Future of the Family

The family is unquestionably here to stay, but its forms and functions will constantly change along with the rest of the society. Our family has largely completed the transition "from institution to companionship" [Burgess and Locke, 1953, p. vii]—from a family wherein the role of each person was rigidly fixed by tradition and enforced by law, custom, and social pressure to a family wherein the roles and tasks are arranged according to the wishes of the members. It is united not by work and external pressures but by shared interests and affections. It shows a far greater variety, since no uniform set of marriage roles and duties are impressed upon all without regard for individual preferences and aptitudes. Such a family has a far greater potential for personality development and individual fulfillment than the traditional pattern allows. This potential is not always realized, but it is the form our family is taking.

A look at our other institutions tells us why this is so. Our economic system demands specialization and mobility. The American standard of living, supported by advertising and salesmanship, guarantees the continuing march of women from the kitchen to the time clock. No amount of lecturing and posturing about "women's place" will change the trend. In time we shall adjust our family life to this fact. Our value system prizes individuality and personal happiness at the expense, if necessary, of family stability. In a society of mass production, automation, and the forty-hour week, family play takes the place of family work as the great unifying agent. Under our political system the welfare state has assumed many of the protective functions that the mobile, urban, individualized family is poorly adapted to fulfill. Our religious institutions have tempered their former preoccupation with sin and eternity with a concern for individual fulfillment in the present world.

The modern American family is thus moving in harmony with the rest of our institutions. There is little reason to believe that present trends will be reversed. Our family will for some time continue to be medium in size, to accept and appreciate mothers who work, to have a fairly high divorce rate, and to be integrated around companionship and common interests. Only major changes in our other institutions would be likely to change these trends.

Summary

The family is the basic social institution. It varies greatly in form. The Western family is normally *conjugal,* composed of man, wife, and children. But in many societies the family unit is *consanguine,* a much larger group of blood relatives with a fringe of spouses. All societies follow *endogamy*, requiring selection of mates within some specified groups, as well as *exogamy*, requiring that one go outside certain of his groups for selection. Although most marriages are *monogamous*, many societies permit *polygamy*, generally polygyny, wherein it is the husband who has more than one mate at at time. Most societies provide for divorce, with wide variance in grounds and procedures. The fascinating variety of family forms shows how man's basic needs can be satisfactorily met under a great variety of institutional arrangements. In all societies the family performs certain functions—regulates sex relations, provides for reproduction, socializes children, offers affection and companionship, defines status, protects its members, and serves as a working and sharing team.

The present American family is in the midst of sweeping changes. It is somewhat larger than a generation ago, perhaps a little smaller than a century ago. Divorce has become common and almost respectable. Male authority has declined and the division of labor has changed, since it has now become normal for the wife to hold a job during a considerable part of her married life. This development has aroused many alarms over the welfare of children, but the evidence suggests that these alarms are largely unjustified.

The sex-regulatory, reproductive, and status-definition functions of the family have probably been the least affected by recent social changes. In economic function, the production activities of the family have been largely absorbed by separate economic institutions, leaving the family mainly a unit of economic consumption. The protective functions have been largely shifted to other institutions. The socialization and affectionate functions of the family have gained greatly in relative importance, both because of changes in other institutions and because of our increased knowledge about man's personal and social needs. It is likely that these trends will continue and that tomorrow's family in America will be equalitarian and oriented toward companionship and family recreation. Unsatisfactory family life is our greatest cause of illness; successful family life is one's greatest health asset.

Questions and Projects

1. Why is the family found in all societies? Would it be possible, with modern technology, to dispense with the family?

2. Why do American parents today play only a limited role in guiding the courtship choices of their children? Would it be desirable that they play a larger role in determining marriage choices?

3. In a society such as the Trobriand, where a man has no special duties

of particular affection for his own children, how can he possibly take a truly "fatherly" concern for his sister's children?

4. What could be said for allowing polygynous marriages in American society? What could be said against such permission?

5. We use the term "uncle" for the brothers of either father or mother. Among the Todas the term "father" includes not only one's father but all his uncles. What is the importance of such variations in terminology? Some societies have no word for "illegitimate" or "adultery." What does the omission signify?

6. How do recent and current family changes illustrate the interrelationship of institutions?

7. Discuss these two propositions: (1) "Divorce is a necessary and useful institution for a society like ours." (2) "Divorce is cause and evidence of family breakdown in our society and should be discouraged."

8. Discuss these two propositions: (1) "The proper socialization of the child requires the intimate, continuous, affectionate supervision only a full-time mother can give." (2) "An uninterrupted mother-child contact encourages an excessive dependence; the child develops most healthfully when cared for by several warmly responsive adults."

9. Discuss these two propositions: (1) "The American family is badly disorganized by the sweeping social changes of the past century." (2) "The American family is reorganizing itself to meet the changing needs of a changing society."

10. Read Hans Ruesch, *Top of the World,* Harper & Row, Publishers, Incorporated, New York, 1950; Pocket Books, 1951, a novel about Eskimo life. Evaluate the Eskimo family as an institutional structure for meeting the needs of people in a particular environment.

Suggested Readings

BLOOD, ROBERT C., JR., AND DONALD M. WOLFE: *Husbands and Wives* (The Free Press of Glencoe, New York, 1960). A research study that presents evidence contradicting many widely held notions about American family life.

BURTON, GENEVIEVE: *Personal, Impersonal, and Interpersonal Relations: A Guide for Nurses,* Springer Publishing Company, 1958, chap. 3, "Growing Up in the Family." A highly readable treatment of personality development in the family, as it affects and is affected by health and illness. Also, chap. 5, "Family Adversity and the Nurse." Discusses effects of illness on family life, and the role of the nurse.

DOTEN, DANA: *The Art of Bundling,* Holt, Rinehart and Winston, Inc., New York, 1938. An entertaining account of the rise and fall of a quaint American custom, showing how it related to the rest of the culture.

FOLSOM, JOSEPH K.: The Family, John Wiley & Sons, Inc., 1934, 1943, chap. 1, "The Family Pattern." An interesting parallel-column comparison of the American and Trobriand family patterns.

LINTON, RALPH: *The Study of Man,* Appleton-Century-Crofts, Inc., New York, 1936, chap. 10, "The Family," chap. 11, "Marriage," and chap. 12, "Social Units Determined by Blood." An anthropologist's account of various forms of marriage and family life.

QUEEN, STUART A., ROBERT W. HABENSTEIN, AND JOHN B. ADAMS: *The Family in Various Cultures,* J. B. Lippincott Company, Philadelphia, 1952, 1961. Readable descriptions of the family in a dozen cultures, primitive and civilized, ancient and modern.

REISS, IRA L.: *Pre-marital Sexual Standards in America,* The Free Press of Glencoe, New York, 1960. A research study of contemporary sex standards.

SCHINDLER, JOHN A.: *How to Live 365 Days a Year,* Prentice-Hall, Inc., Englewood Cliffs, N.J., 1954, chap. 10, "Achieving Emotional Stasis in the Family." A popularized description of how unsatisfactory family life produces physical illness.

YOUNG, KIMBALL: *Isn't One Wife Enough? The Story of Mormon Polygamy,* Rinehart and Winston, Inc., New York, 1954. A readable analysis, by a Mormon and distinguished sociologist, of the only serious attempt to establish polygamy in America.

CHAPTER 10 **Social Class**

CAPTAIN: (. . . walks upstage, then turns to ROBERTS) *I think you're a pretty smart boy. I may not talk very good, Mister, but I know how to take care of smart boys. Let me tell you something. Let me tell you a little secret. I hate your guts, you college son-of-a-bitch! You think you're better than I am! You think you're better because you've had everything handed to you. Let me tell you something, Mister—I've worked since I was ten years old, and all my life I've known you superior bastards. I knew you people when I was a kid in Boston and I worked in eating-places and you ordered me around . . . "Oh, bus-boy! My friend here seems to have thrown up on the table. Clean it up, please!" I started going to sea as a steward and I worked for you then . . . "Steward, take my magazine out to the deck chair!" . . . "Steward, I don't like your looks. Please keep out of my way as much as possible!" Well, I took that crap! I took that for years from pimple-faced bastards who weren't good enough to wipe my nose! And now I don't have to take it any more! There's a war on, by God, and I'm the Captain and you can wipe my nose! The worst thing I can do to you is to keep you on this ship! And that's where you're going to stay! Now get out of here.*

Thomas Heggen and Joshua Logan, *Mister Roberts*, Random House, Inc., New York, 1948, pp. 87–88.

In these lines from the play *Mr. Roberts,* the captain explodes with resentment against those whose class origin is higher than his. Popular literature abounds with dramatic illustrations of class attitudes, class prejudices, and class-typed behavior. What is social class, and how does it affect behavior?

What Is Social Class?

Is social class purely a matter of money? If so, the rich gambler would outrank the minister, nurse, or professor. While money is a factor, social class is not directly measured by one's bank account. A social class is defined as *a stratum of people of similar social position.* The social position of the janitor is not the same as that of the college president; a student will not greet them in exactly the same manner. We are deferential toward those whose social position we believe to be above ours; we are condescending to those whose social position we believe to be below ours. These processes of snubbing and kowtowing, of trying to claw one's way in or of shouldering out the person who doesn't "belong"—these provide the inexhaustible material for hundreds of novels, plays, and scripts every year.

The members of a social class view one another as social equals, while holding themselves to be socially superior to some other groups and socially inferior to still others. In placing a person in the proper social class, two main questions are asked: "To whose dinner party will he be asked as a social equal?" or "For whose daughter will his son be an 'acceptable' suitor?" The members of a particular social class often have about the same amount of money; but what is much more important is that they have much the same attitudes, values, and way of life.

How many classes are there? This question is hard to answer. Classes are not sharply defined status groupings like the different ranks in an army. Social status varies along a continuum, a gradual slope from top to bottom rather than a series of steps. As "youth," "middle-age," and "old age" are points along an age continuum, the several social classes may be viewed as points along a status continuum. Consequently, the number of social classes is not fixed, nor do any definite boundaries and sharp status intervals separate them. Instead, persons are found at all status levels from top to bottom, just as persons are found at all weights and heights, with no abrupt gaps in the series. Such a series can be broken up into any convenient number of "classes." Clothing makers have found it practical to divide people into a dozen or more size classifications. Earlier students of social class broke up the status continuum into three classes—upper, middle, and lower. Later students found this division unsatisfactory for many communities, because it placed persons in the same class even when they were much too far apart to treat one another as equals. Later students have often used a sixfold classification by breaking each of these three classes into an upper and lower section. The top, or *upper-upper* class, is composed of the wealthy old families who have long been socially prominent and who have had money long enough for people to have forgotten when and how they got it. The *lower-uppers* may have as much money but have not had it as long, nor has their family long been socially prominent. The *upper-middle* class includes most of the successful business and professional men, generally of "good" family background and comfortable income. The *lower-middle* class takes in the clerks, other white-collar workers and semiprofessionals, and possibly some of the foremen and top craftsmen. The *upper-lower* class consists mainly of the skilled and semiskilled workers, and is often described as the "working class" by those who feel uncomfortable about applying the term "lower" to honest workmen [Miller and Riessman, 1961]. The *lower-lower* class includes the unskilled workers, the irregularly employed, the unemployable, migrant laborers, and those living more or less permanently on public assistance.

This sixfold classification, used by Warner and Lunt [1942] in studying an old New England town, probably is fairly typical of the large and medium-size cities in the more settled parts of the country. In the rapidly growing Western regions, "old family" may be less important. In smaller towns, the class system is less complex. In studying a small city in the Midwest, Hollingshead [1949] used a fivefold classification in which the two upper classes were combined into one. In a small rural community, West [1945] found no agreement among the residents on the number of classes, although the status range probably would correspond to the bottom half of the six-class system of an urban society. Lynch [1959], studying the class system of an impoverished agricultural community in the Philippines, found only two classes—the self-sustaining and the destitute.

People *do* classify others into equals, superiors, and inferiors.

The number of social classes, therefore, varies from place to place; possibly it also varies with the observer's appraisal of the number of social strata whose members have the same general status. When we speak of, for example, the middle class, we do not refer to a group of people who are clearly set off from others by a definite status interval; we refer to a group of people who cluster around a mid-point in a status scale and who view and treat one another as social equals. The fact that the terms have no distinct boundaries does not keep the terms from being useful concepts and research tools. Social class is a significant social reality, not just a theoretical construct, for people *do* classify others into equals, superiors, and inferiors. Whenever people define certain other people as social equals, and treat them differently from those who are not so defined, their behavior creates social classes.

Social Classes as Subcultures

> It is, after all, this division into working class and business class that constitutes the outstanding cleavage in Middletown. The mere fact of being born upon one or the other side of the watershed roughly formed by these two groups is the most significant single cultural factor tending to influence what one does all day long throughout one's life; whom one marries; when one gets up in the morning; whether one belongs to the Holy Roller or Presbyterian church; or drives a Ford or a Buick; whether or not one's daughter makes the desirable high school Violet Club; or one's wife meets with the Sew We Do Club or with the Art Student's League; whether one belongs to the Odd Fellows or to the Masonic Shrine; whether one sits about evenings with one's necktie off; and so on indefinitely throughout the daily comings and goings of a Middletown man, woman, or child.

Robert S. Lynd and Helen H. Lynd, *Middletown,* Harcourt, Brace & World, Inc., 1929. Copyright, 1929, by Harcourt, Brace & World, Inc., renewed (c) 1957 by Robert S. Lynd and Helen H. Lynd and reprinted with the publisher's permission.

Each social class is a system of behavior, a set of values, and a way of life. While some overlapping and some exceptions occur, it remains true that the average middle-class child has a vastly different socialization from the average lower-class child. Let us take just one aspect of socialization—those experiences that shape ambition, education, and work habits—and see how they differ between two social class worlds.

The typical upper-middle-class child lives in a class subculture where he is surrounded by educated, cultivated persons who speak the English language correctly most of the time, enjoy classical music, buy and read books, travel, and entertain graciously. He is surrounded by people who are ambitious, who go to work even when they don't feel like it, and who struggle to make their mark in the world. He is acquainted with the successes of ancestors, relatives, and friends, and it is normal for him simply to assume that, like them, he is going to amount to something in the world.

When he goes to school, scrubbed and expectant, he finds a teacher whose dress, speech, manner, and conduct norms are much like those he already knows. He is met by a series of familiar objects—picture books, chalk board, and others—and introduced into a series of already familiar activities. The teacher finds him an appealing and responsive child; he finds school a comfortable and exciting place. When the teacher says, "Study hard so you can do well and become a success some day," her words make sense to him. His parents echo these words; meanwhile he sees people like him—older brothers, relatives, family acquaintances— who actually *are* completing educations and moving on into promising careers. For him, to grow up means to complete an advanced education and get himself launched into a career.

The lower-lower class child lives in a class subculture where scarcely anybody has a steady job for very long. To be laid off and go on relief is a normal experience, carrying no sense of shame or failure. He lives in a world where one can spend his weekends in drinking, gambling, and sexual exploration and miss work on Monday without sacrificing the respect of his friends or neighbors. In his world, meals are haphazard and irregular, many people sleep three or four to a bed, and a well-modulated voice would be lost amid the neighborhood clatter.

He goes to school, usually unwashed and often unfed, and meets a woman unlike anyone in his social world. Her speech and manner are unfamiliar, and when he acts in ways that are acceptable and useful in his social world, she punishes him. The classroom objects and activities are unfamiliar. The teacher, who usually comes from a sheltered middle-class world, is likely to decide he is a sullen, unresponsive child, while he soon concludes that school is an unhappy prison. He learns little. The school soon abandons any serious effort to teach him, defines him as a "discipline problem," and concentrates on keeping him quiet so that the other children can learn. When the teacher says, "Study hard so you can do well and become a success some day," her words make no sense to him. They receive no reinforcement from his parents, who are likely to be hostile and uncooperative toward the school. More important, he sees almost nobody *like him*, nobody in his world, who actually *is* using school as a steppingstone to a career. In his world the big cars and slender blondes are possessed by those who picked a lucky number or got into the rackets or found an "angle." Thus the school fails to motivate him. For him, "growing up" means to drop out of school, get a car, and escape from the supervision of teachers and parents [Davis, 1952]. His horizon of ambition seldom extends beyond the next weekend. His work habits are casual and irregular. Soon he marries and provides for his children a life that duplicates the experiences of his own socialization. Thus the class system operates to prepare most children for a class status similar to that of their parents.

Such differences in class behavior are found in virtually every facet of life—food habits, personal care, discipline and child care, reading tastes, conversational interests, vocabulary and diction, religious behavior, sleeping arrangements, sex life. According to Kinsey [1948, pp. 355–357], even the procedures followed in making love show important class differences. This is what is meant by class subcultures—that a great many of the normal life experiences of people in one class differ from those of people in another class. It is true that there are no sharply defined boundaries. From top to bottom one kind of behavior gradually shades off into another; for example vocabulary gradually becomes less genteel and diction less precise as we descend the class continuum. But if we pick several points along this continuum for comparison, then the class differences are easy to see.

Determinants of Social Class. What is it that places one in a particular social class? Is it birth, money, occupation, or what? The answer is "Yes," for all these attributes are involved.

Wealth and Income. Money is necessary for upper-class position, yet one's class position is not directly proportional to his income. An airline pilot has less status than a college professor at half the income; a clergyman may outrank a prizefighter at fifty times his income.

To understand the place of money in class determination we must remember that a *social class is basically a way of life.* It takes a good deal of money to live as upper-class people live. Yet no amount of money will gain *immediate* upper-class status. The "new rich" have the money but lack the way of life of the upper-class person. They can buy the house, cars, and clothes and hire a decorator to select the proper furnishings, books, and paintings. It takes a little longer to learn the formal manners of the upper class, but some careful observation, plus intensive study of Emily Post or Amy Vanderbilt, will probably suffice. But to acquire the attitudes and feelings and habitual responses of the upper-class person takes far longer. Unless one is born and socialized in an upper-class subculture, he is almost certain to make occasional slips that betray his plebeian origin. Novels and plays abound with social climbers who never quite "make it" because they occasionally use the wrong word or reflect the wrong attitude and thereby betray their humble origin. Most of the "new rich" are no more than marginal members of the upper classes during their lifetimes.

Their children, however, have a better chance, and for their grandchildren, a secure upper-class status is practically assured. Money, *over a period of time,* usually gains upper-class status. People who get money begin to live like upper-class people. By the time their grandchildren

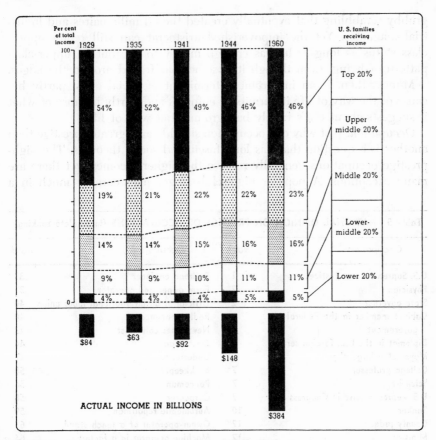

FIGURE 6   Share of Total U.S. Income Received by Family Groups.

SOURCE: Herman P. Miller, "Is the Income Gap Closed? No." *New York Times Magazine,* Nov. 11, 1962, p. 50.

mature, they are becoming "old family," while the grandchildren have fully absorbed upper-class behavior. Thus the two requisites of upper-class status are fulfilled.

Money has other subtle overtones. Inherited money is better than earned money, for inherited wealth shows family background. Income from investments also suggests family background. Income from genteel professions is better than wages; money from speculating on stocks is better than money from gambling on horses. The nature and source of one's income carry suggestions as to one's family background and probable way of life.

Money one used to have is almost as good as money one has now. The "real" aristocracy of the South, for example, no longer has great wealth, partly because its class values prevented it from engaging in the

grubby scrabbling that eventually created the oil millionaires and industrial magnates. Yet the impoverished aristocrat can still retain upper-
class status as long as he has enough money to eke out an upper-class
pattern of living, even though it is somewhat frayed around the edges.

Money, then, is an important determinant of social class, partly because of the way of life it permits or enforces and partly because of what
it suggests about one's family background and way of life.

Occupation. Just why one occupation should carry greater prestige than
another is a question that has long fascinated social theorists. The high-
prestige occupations generally receive the higher incomes, yet there are
many exceptions. A popular night-club singer may earn as much in a

Table 5   NATIONAL OPINION ON PRESTIGE OF OCCUPATIONS (incomplete ranking)

Occupation	Rank	Occupation	Rank
U.S. Supreme Court justice	1	Railroad engineer	37
Physician	2*	Farm owner and operator	39
State governor	2	Official of an international labor union	40*
Cabinet member in the Federal		Radio announcer	40
government	4*	Newspaper columnist	42
Diplomat in the U.S. foreign service	4	Electrician	44
Mayor of a large city	6	Undertaker	47
College professor	7*	Bookkeeper	50
Scientist	7	Policeman	54
U.S. Representative in Congress	7	Carpenter	58
Banker	10	Automobile repairman	59
County judge	12*	Owner-operator of a lunch stand	61
Minister	12	Machine operator in a factory	64
Architect	15*	Barber	66
Dentist	15	Clerk in a store	67
Lawyer	15	Truck driver	70
Member of board of directors, large		Singer in a night club	74
corporation	15	Farm hand	76
Nuclear physicist	15	Taxi driver	78
Civil enginer	23	Restaurant waiter	79
Airline pilot	24	Dock worker	81*
Owner of factory, 100 employees	26	Night watchman	81
Accountant for a large business	28*	Janitor	86
Musician in symphony orchestra	28	Sharecropper	87
Author of novels	29	Garbage collector	88
Building contractor	33	Street sweeper	89
Public schoolteacher	36	Shoe shiner	90

* Two or more occupations tied for same rank.
SOURCE: National Opinion Research Center, "Jobs and Occupations: A Popular Evaluation,"
Opinion News, 9:3–13, 1947. Reprinted in Reinhard Bendix and Seymour M. Lipset (eds.),
Class, Status and Power, The Free Press of Glencoe, New York, 1953, pp. 411–425. (Nursing
not included in survey.)

week as a Supreme Court justice earns in a year. The relatively low-paid clergymen, diplomats, and college professors rank far above the higher-paid airline pilots and building contractors, and have about equal ranking with the far wealthier physicians and lawyers, as shown in Table 5. The high-ranking occupations generally require advanced education, but again the correlation is far from perfect. The importance of the work is an unsatisfactory test, for how can we say that the work of the farm hand or policeman is less valuable to society than the work of the lawyer or corporation director? In fact it has been suggested that the low-ranking garbage collector may be the most essential of all workers in an urban civilization!

Obviously, the prestige ranking of occupations cannot be easily explained on a purely rational basis; yet it can hardly be an accident that all complex cultures have developed much the same occupational status hierarchy. A survey of data from many countries by Inkeles [1960] finds that a particular occupation has about the same status rating in all urbanized, industrialized societies. Apparently the industrial system fosters

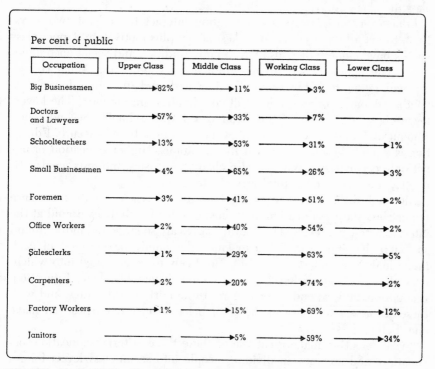

Per cent of public

Occupation	Upper Class	Middle Class	Working Class	Lower Class
Big Businessmen	82%	11%	3%	
Doctors and Lawyers	57%	33%	7%	
Schoolteachers	13%	53%	31%	1%
Small Businessmen	4%	65%	26%	3%
Foremen	3%	41%	51%	2%
Office Workers	2%	40%	54%	2%
Salesclerks	1%	29%	63%	5%
Carpenters	2%	20%	74%	2%
Factory Workers	1%	15%	69%	12%
Janitors		5%	59%	34%

FIGURE 7   The Public Classifies Occupations in the United States.

SOURCE: Joseph A. Kahl, *The American Class Structure*, Holt, Rinehart and Winston, Inc., New York, 1953, p. 81. Based on data in Richard Centers, "Social Class, Occupation, and Implied Belief," *American Journal of Sociology*, 58:543–555, May, 1953.

certain attitudes, perceptions, and status relationships wherever it develops. And in all societies, industrial or preindustrial, we see that persons tend to be assigned a class status according to their occupation, and that they will find those occupations most easily open to them which are appropriate to their inherited class status.

Occupation is an exceedingly important aspect of social class because so many other facets of life are tied in with occupation. If we know a man's occupation, we can make some fairly accurate guesses about the amount and kind of education he has had, the standard of living he can afford, the kind of people he associates with, the hours he keeps, and the daily routines of his family life. We can even make some guesses about his reading tastes and recreational interests, his standards of moral conduct, and his religious affiliations. In other words each occupation is part of a way of life that differs considerably from the concomitant circumstances of certain other occupations. It is one's total way of life that ultimately determines which class one belongs to, and occupation is probably the best *single* clue to one's way of life, and therefore to one's social class membership.

Education. Social class and education interact in at least two ways. First, to get a higher education takes money plus motivation. Upper-class youths have money; they also have family tradition and social encouragement. The upper-class or upper-middle-class youth asks, "What college are you going to?" Lower-middle-class and perhaps upper-lower-class youths ask one another, "What will you do after graduation?" The lower-lower-class youth asks, "How soon can I quit school?" Second, one's amount and kind of education affect the class rank he will secure. Education is one of the main levers of the ambitious. Higher education brings not only occupational skill but also changes in tastes, interests, goals, etiquette, speech—in one's total way of life.

Although a distinguished family background is a necessity for secure upper-class status, education may substitute for family background at the intermediate-class levels. The middle classes are so large and move around so much that it is impossible to know the family background of each individual. Newcomers to a locality are likely to be accepted into whichever of the middle or lower classes their behavior fits them. Education, occupation, and expended income are three fairly visible clues, and with these are associated most of the other behavior characteristics that make one "belong."

Social scientists make great use of these three criteria—education, occupation, and income—in dividing people into social-class levels for research purposes. As we have already learned, these are fairly reliable clues to the total way of life distinguishing social classes. Furthermore, these criteria are fairly easy to objectify. It would, for example, be dif-

TABULAR PRESENTATION: per cent of total employed in each group, 1959

	Elementary: Nongraduate	High School: Nongraduate	High School: Graduate	College: Nongraduate	College: Graduate
Professional	1	2	7	23	65
Managerial	6	9	12	19	15
Clerical and Sales	4	14	35	33	13
Skilled and Semiskilled	37	44	29	15	4
Laborers, Farm, Service	52	31	17	10	3
	100	100	100	100	100

GRAPHIC PRESENTATION: per cent of total employed in each group

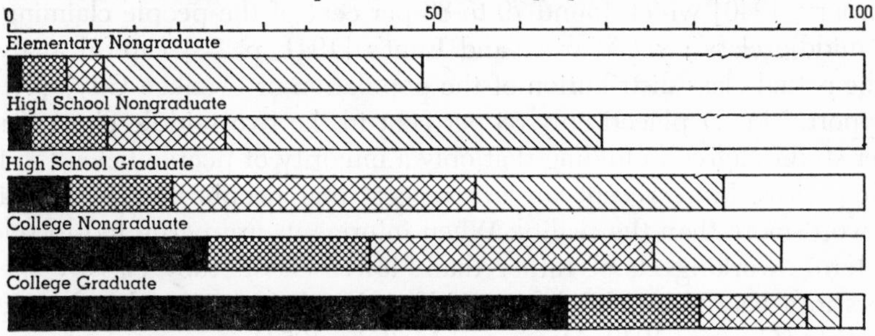

FIGURE 8 Education and Occupation in the United States, 1959.

SOURCE: The National Industrial Conference Board.

ficult to use "crude or cultivated speech" as a test of class rank in a research study, because speech, though easy to notice, is hard to measure. Finally, the data on education, occupation, and income are available from the census reports, broken down by "census tracts," or areas of a few blocks each. Suppose a sociologist wishes to compare death rates, polio rates, average family size, or practically anything that may vary between social classes. Using census data on occupation, education, and average income of the different census tracts within the community, he could easily locate an upper-class tract, a middle-class tract, and a lower-class tract for comparison. While social class involves more than these three criteria, they are adequate to identify social classes for most research purposes.

Self-identification and Class Consciousness. Sociologists view social class as a reality which exists even if people are not fully aware of it.

American democratic beliefs emphasize equality and tend to inhibit a frank recognition of class lines. People will deny that there are social classes in their community, yet state this denial in terms that reveal that classes really do exist. Lantz cites one of many such statements by the residents of a small town.

> You see, this no-class idea makes it a good place to live. The Company houses are called "Silk Stocking Row" but I would feel as good with the mining superintendent's wife as I would with anybody else. You see, this is a melting pot. Our people, you see, all came from foreign countries. Why, my grandparents came from England. You see, I belong to the D.A.R. I can trace my family tree all the way back through the Revolutionary War into England. I take a great deal of pride in this. Why, I can trace my ancestry back to a captain who was a friend of Washington's in the Revolutionary War.

Herman R. Lantz, *People of Coal Town*, Columbia University Press, New York, 1958, p. 216.

The belief that the American people lack "class consciousness" was supported by early surveys [Cantril, 1943; Gallup and Rae, 1940; *Fortune*, February, 1940] which found 79 to 88 per cent of the people claiming to be "middle class"; yet Warner and Lunt's [1941, p. 88] careful analysis of the actual class distribution of the population of "Yankee City" (Newburyport, Mass.) placed only 38 per cent in the two middle classes, and other studies agree in finding that only a minority of people belong in the middle class. More recent surveys suggest that people may be resisting the word more than the reality. When informants are permitted to select the term "working class" rather than "lower class," they classify themselves in a way more closely resembling the class division by the social scientists [Centers, 1949; Manis and Meltzer, 1954].

A comparison of the Warner findings with two self-identification studies, as shown in Table 6, shows how informants avoid the term "lower class." Apparently most of those in the lower-lower class placed themselves in the "working class"; otherwise the two studies agree fairly well with Warner's findings. Another self-identification study [Eulan, 1956] compared informants' self-rankings with their class position as measured according to occupation, education, and income. It was found that 75 per cent of those whom the social scientist placed in the "working class" and 65 per cent of those in the "middle class" had placed themselves in the class in which they objectively belonged. These studies show that, while people strenuously resist the term "lower class," the majority have a fairly realistic conception of their own class status.

Is one's class membership, then, determined by his feeling that he belongs in a particular class, or by the facts of his occupation, education, and income? Largely by the latter, for they determine his overall way of life. Yet his *feeling* of class identification is of some importance, for he tends to copy the behavior norms of the class with which he identifies

Table 6   CLASS DISTRIBUTION IN THE UNITED STATES

According to Warner's "Yankee City" study		Self-identification, two national cross sections of white males		
			July, 1945 N = 1,097	February, 1946 N = 1,337
Class	Per cent	Class	Per cent	Per cent
Upper-upper	1.44			
Lower-upper	1.56	Upper	4	4
Upper-middle	10.22			
Lower-middle	28.12	Middle	43	36
Upper-lower	32.60			
Lower-lower	25.22	Working	51	52
Unknown	.84	Lower	1	5
		Don't know	1	3

SOURCES: W. Lloyd Warner and Paul S. Lunt, *The Social Life of a Modern Community,* Yale University Press, New Haven, Conn., 1941, p. 88; Richard Centers, *The Psychology of Social Classes,* Princeton University Press, Princeton, N.J., 1949, p. 77.

himself. The above study, for example, showed that those informants who placed themselves in a class in which they did not objectively belong, shared the political attitudes of the class they claimed rather than those of the class in which they belonged. Self-identification with a social class apparently has some effect on behavior, whether one actually belongs to that class or not.

Size of Each Social Class. Since we do not completely agree on the number of classes, we can hardly agree on the size of each. Table 6 gives two estimates, one based on Warner's "Yankee City" study and the other on a national self-identification survey; both place about 57 per cent of the population in the two lower classes. Kahl [1953, p. 187] estimates that 10 per cent of the population are lower-lower class, on the grounds that although about 20 per cent of the population have incomes below $2,000 a year, half of these are pensioners whose present income does not reflect their total life situation. Davis [1952, pp. 22–23] feels that each of the two lower classes claims about one-third of the elementary school children. These and other studies generally agree in placing something over half the population in the two lower classes, using Warner's six-class typology, with each higher class becoming progressively smaller.

Measurement of classes is complicated by the fact that there are several criteria of membership in a given class and many families do not show *all* the characteristics of any one class level. For example the "ideal type" lower-lower-class family would live in an urban slum or rural shack; one or more adult members would drink quite heavily, and the male family head would not be consistently in the household; it would have little education or interest in education; and its low income would derive partly from intermittent unskilled labor and partly from welfare sources. Probably comparatively few lower-lower-class families meet all of these conditions. While class differences are real, the boundaries and membership of each class cannot be clearly fixed.

Class distribution appears to be changing in the United States. The middle class and possibly the upper classes are growing while the lower classes are shrinking. Changing technology is destroying lower-class jobs and creating middle-class jobs. In 1900 "unskilled laborers" comprised 13 per cent of the labor force; by 1950 they had fallen to 8 per cent and are expected to fall to 4 per cent by 1975; meanwhile the "professionals" in the labor force have risen from 4 per cent in 1900 to 8 per cent in 1950 and are expected to reach 14 per cent by 1975 [National Education Association, 1959]. Almost every kind of middle-class job is expanding as the changes in economic life continually demand more technical and professional personnel. Furthermore, as technology changes the content of jobs, their status also changes. Historically, most factory jobs were dirty and

Table 7   HOW LARGE IS OUR LOWER CLASS? Proportion of United States Population in Selected Educational, Occupational, and Income Categories

(Arranged in Order of Descending Magnitude)

Type of Individual or Group	Approximate percentage of population	Year or period
Adults (over 25) who did not complete high school	60	1953
Adults in civilian labor force in "semiskilled" and "unskilled" positions	40–50	1910–50
Household heads in large Northern cities who did not enter high school	42	1950
Consumer units with annual incomes under $3,000	42	1952
Adults in civilian labor force in "unskilled" positions	25–30	1930–40
Consumer units with annual incomes under $2,000	30	1954
Household units in large cities reporting female household head	20	1950

SOURCE: Walter B. Miller, "Implications of Lower-class Culture for Social Work," *Social Service Review*, 33:219–236, 1959. Copyright, 1959, by The University of Chicago.

filled by men who were comparatively unskilled and low paid. Today a growing fraction of factory jobs are clean and call for men who are highly trained and well paid. Some of these workers seem likely to move into the middle class. We have not yet become a "middle-class" society in the sense that the middle class is becoming the largest class, but we seem to be moving in that direction.

The Significance of Social Classes

Determine Life Opportunities. From before one is born until after he is dead, his opportunities and rewards are affected by his class position. A study of Chicago death rates in 1940 found a life expectancy at birth of 61 years for the lower-class female and 70.3 years for the upper-class female, while for males the expectancies were 58.7 and 67.8 years, a difference of over 9 years for each sex. A comparison of the death rates for the highest economic group and the rest of the city indicated that 21 per cent of all Chicago deaths in 1940 would have been avoided if the style of life, attitudes, and use of medical care for the rest of the city had been equal to that of its most prosperous segment [Mayer and Hauser, 1950].

In mental health the disparity is even greater [Hollingshead and Redlich, 1958]. The lower the class, the higher is the rate of mental illness; the increases, however, are small at all levels except the lowest class, whose rate is much higher than the others [Miller and Mishler, 1959]. The "treatment" received by the lower-class mentally ill is sometimes only custodial, which simply removes the patient from society, rather than the complete medical and psychotherapeutic treatment that might effect a cure. In no other major form of health care is the disparity between the classes as great as in the treatment of mental illness [Hollingshead and Redlich, 1953; Robinson et al., 1954].

If he survives his infancy, the lower-class child usually attends one of the old and dingy schools in the community, often staffed largely by beginning teachers and weary drudges who have been unable to get themselves transferred to a nicer neighborhood. He lives in a neighborhood of drab, crowded housing, of irregular family life, and of persons whose goals are short-term just as their grasp on jobs, health, and housing is short-term.

When the lower-class youth comes to seek a job, he has neither the education, the work habits, nor the poise and bearing to command a job with a promising future. The lower-class occupations such as farm laborer, unskilled laborer, or dock worker carry low wages, irregular employment, and few welfare or "fringe" benefits. Often they involve high-accident danger or health hazards, yet this class can afford only the poorest living conditions and the least medical care. In wartime the lower-class youth is less likely to be deferred as a college student or essential worker; when drafted he is less likely to become a commissioned officer or earn a specialist's rating. There is one place where his chances are better; he has a better chance of being killed, as is seen in Table 8.

Table 8 KOREAN WAR CASUALTY RATE PER 10,000 OCCUPIED DWELLING UNITS
by Median Income of Census Tract, Detroit, Michigan

Median income, dollars	Casualty rate per 10,000 occupied DUs
Under 2,500	14.6
2,500–2,999	10.8
3,000–3,499	9.1
3,500–3,999	8.6
4,000–4,499	7.5
4,500–4,999	6.6
5,000–5,499	5.8
5,500 and over	4.6

SOURCE: Albert J. Mayer and Thomas Ford Hoult, "Social Stratification and Combat Survival," *Social Forces,* 34:155–159, 1955. Copyright (c) 1955, The University of North Carolina Press, Chapel Hill, N.C.

Colors Personality Development

The debuante ritual is a *rite de passage* which functions to introduce the post-adolescent into an upper-class adult world, and to insure upper-class endogamy as a normative pattern of behavior, in order to keep important functional class positions within the upper class.

E. Digby Baltzell, *Philadelphia Gentlemen: The Making of a National Upper Class,* The Free Press of Glencoe, New York, 1958, p. 60.

The debutante ritual is part of the upper-class subculture just as going on relief is part of the lower-class subculture. Since social classes are subcultures, the personality development of the child is affected in many ways [Davis and Havighurst, 1946; Sears et al., 1957; Havighurst and Davis, 1955]. As we have already seen, his goals, interests, and habits are affected by the kind of social world he lives in. His moral standards are equally class-typed. The lower-class family is less stable, more often broken by death or separation. It is larger in size, yet occupies smaller living quarters. At almost every point of contact between child and parent, there are class differences in socialization experience. Middle-class child training encourages individual achievement and the urge to "succeed," encourages competition and rivalry while discouraging direct aggression, uses parental love systematically as a control device, avoids severe physical punishment, imposes numerous restrictions, and produces a good many anxieties and guilt feelings. Lower-class child training pushes the child more rapidly into adult roles, places less stress on individual achievement, accepts the idea that the child will probably retain the social status of his father, seldom uses parental love as a systematic reward, uses physical punishments readily, imposes fewer restrictions on organic functions and pleasures, accepts direct aggression and encourages aggressive self-defense, places little stress on language facility, literacy, or school advancement, and probably produces fewer guilts and anxieties. Middle-class socialization is strongly oriented toward upward social mobility through risk taking; lower-class socialization in a risk-filled world is strongly oriented toward reducing risks by attaining economic security and stability [Miller and Riessman, 1961]. The clashing views of labor and management on union "featherbedding" are one consequence of this difference in class socialization.

The differences in socialization produce many kinds of adult personality difference. As compared with lower-class personality, adult middle-class personality tends to be more ambitious, more competitive but less aggressive physically, more rigidly conformist to conventional mores, outwardly more poised and self-assured but possibly beset by greater inner guilts and self-doubts. Such differences are not predictably true for all members of either class, for there are many exceptions and much overlapping. But such differences are frequent enough to be socially significant [Barber, 1957, chap. 12].

Shapes Life-adjustment Patterns. The way people handle life situations varies with social class, as is illustrated by the following incident reported to the author by a perceptive student.

> I was in a small two-man garage on a Saturday morning, making small talk with the proprietor as he worked on my car. He pointed to another car parked nearby. "How much do you think that car is worth?" he asked.
> I studied it a moment and ventured, "Oh, perhaps $300."
> "I bought it a few minutes ago for $150," he remarked.
> "Now, I wonder why a fellow would sell his car so cheaply," I mused.
> He paused a moment and said, "Oh, you wouldn't understand."
> Suddenly I did understand. The proprietor was saying, "You, in your sheltered middle-class world of careful plans, long-term goals, and wisely rationed puritan pleasures, are unable to understand how a fellow would turn his car into quick cash to gratify a pressing impulse. Perhaps his eye is on something he can't wait to buy, or he needs money to finance a big weekend or to gain a new girl friend's gratitude. In his world, these may be more important than protecting his capital investment."

Social class affects the way people deal with virtually every aspect of reality. Suppose, for example, a street-corner loafer makes an insulting remark as a couple pass. The upper-class couple will walk on in cold disdain; a brawl would be ungentlemanly. The lower-class escort would be more likely to react aggressively, for to "knock the guy's block off" would make him look manly in his girl's eyes. Our "definition of the situation" reflects our class background; our behavior response is equally class-typed. When the middle-class youth gets a part-time job, he is expected to save part of his earnings, probably for his college education. He is rewarded with the approval of his class associates. But if the lower-class youth saves his money instead of sharing it with his pals, he is being stingy and snobbish and is rewarded by exclusion from his group. Thus is the class system perpetuated.

Influences Social Participation. Social class largely determines which parts of the culture one will experience—opera, country club and cotillion, or jukebox, tavern, and brawl. This is illustrated by class differences in degree of social participation. In general, the lower the social class, the fewer are the associations and social relations of the individual. In Chapter 7 we saw that lower-class people belong to fewer organizations of any kind—clubs, civic groups, or even churches—than do middle- and upper-class people. It might be assumed that this lack of organized sociability is compensated by greater informal contacts, but we find that these also diminish as we go down the class continuum. Lower-class people have fewer acquaintances, fewer friends, gossip with and about fewer other people, and do less informal visiting [Shuval, 1956].

The age of mass communications cuts across class lines, and while the lower classes read and travel less than other classes, they spend more time with radio, television, and movies [Bogart, 1958, p. 91]. This greater audio-visual exposure is still a selective process, since lower-class listeners shun "serious" programs and stick as far as possible to entertainment, which in turn is shaped along stereotypes already accepted in lower-class culture. Mass communication undoubtedly speeds the acceptance of new gadgets, but other than this, its influence on lower-class listeners would appear to be mainly to intensify their social conservatism. In substance, then, the lower-class person has only limited participation in any kind of social interaction that might lead to the rapid acceptance of new ideas.

Assigns Social Responsibilities and Privileges. A lot of unpleasant work must be done in any society, and someone must be persuaded to do it. Occasionally special rewards may be used—honor for the warrior or wealth and fame for the prizefighter, for example. But each complex society relies mainly on the class system to compel someone to do the drudgery. A combination of cultural background, educational limitation, and job discrimination all work together to make the lower-class person

There is a lot of unpleasant work.

unable to compete for the better jobs; as a result only the poorer jobs are left. Though the result may be unintentional, it is no less real. Social class gets the grubby work of the world done by excluding part of the people from the nicer jobs.

The lower class also functions as a storehouse for surplus unskilled labor. Our economy requires a good deal of seasonal or irregular labor, especially in farm labor and construction projects. Those who are not continuously needed are "stored" in the lower class, where the class sub-culture makes it possible to survive periods of unemployment and go on relief without guilt or sense of failure. The lethargy, lack of ambition, and willingness to accept squalor that middle-class people criticize so self-righteously are, in fact, the *necessary and useful* life adjustments of the lower class. Such attributes are necessary to the mental health and sanity of our "stand-by" unskilled labor supply.

The lower-class culture makes a positive contribution to the society. The men who seem to lack ambition and responsibility have shouldered jobs that were rough, monotonous, temporary in duration, and often far from settled communities, yet essential to the economic life of the nation. The lower-class women, often frowned upon by higher-status women because of their irregular family life, have learned to adjust to the unreliable habits of fathers and husbands whose lives had been shaped by irregular and uncertain employment. These women have reared children in manless households and at the same time cleaned the homes and offices used by other classes. Lower-class life produces people able and willing to work and live under conditions those raised in other class levels would find intolerable.

Other social classes also provide their members with distinctive sub-cultures that prepare them for specialized functions in society. Looking at the upper class, one sees a group removed from the fear of being unable to make a fairly adequate income. Their position in society does not have to be earned by unusual achievement, although they may have to validate their status through some form of public service. At its best this class produces men like Franklin D. Roosevelt, Nelson Rockefeller, and the Kennedys, who have been able to devote a major portion of their lives to public service without having to worry about personal fortune. The fact that all these men accept government programs commonly identified with lower-class interests indicates both an emancipation from economic concern and an acceptance by the masses of the leadership of an elite whose wealth and background are strikingly different from those of the common man.

Cultivates Class Ethnocentrism. There is an anecdote of a private tutor in a wealthy family who sought to teach her pupil about the life of the poor. Then the little rich girl wrote a story about the poor, beginning,

"Once upon a time there was a very poor family. The Papa was poor, the Mama was poor, the children were poor, the cook was poor, the maid was poor, the butler was poor, the gardener was poor. *Everybody* was poor."

Members of one class cannot help judging members of other classes in terms of their own class expectations and values. The middle class scorns upper-class snobbishness but strives desperately to raise its own children in a "good" neighborhood. People at every class level tend to see those above themselves as effete, snobbish, and pretentious, and those beneath as either disgusting or pathetic, good-for-nothing or "awfully pushy." At all intermediate status levels one tends to attribute one's own status to personal achievement, the status of those above to luck, and that of those beneath to inability and laziness. Miller suggests that, of all forms of ethnocentrism, class ethnocentrism is one of the most difficult to restrain.

It is considerably easier to manifest "tolerance" for the ways of the Zulu, Navaho, or Burmese than to achieve emotional acceptance of features of lower-class culture in our own society; in the former case it is relatively easy to recognize that disapproved or exotic behavior is a direct product of the group's culture and to accept such behavior on the grounds that it is "their way" of doing things, a way which is different from ours. In the case of lower-class culture, however, there is an almost automatic tendency to view certain customary behaviors in terms of right and wrong and to explain them on blameworthy deviations from accepted moral standards rather than as products of a deep-rooted cultural tradition. It is not too difficult to view the device of polygamous marriage and the mother-centered household among the Zulus as one alternative arrangement for meeting the problem of marriage and child-rearing; it is much harder to see the practice of serial mating and the female-based household in our own society as social forms which may constitute a practical or effective adaptation to the milieu in which they are found.

Walter B. Miller, "Implications of Urban Lower Class Culture for Social Work," *Social Service Review*, 33:232–234, 1959. Copyright, 1959, by The University of Chicago.

Middle-class Mores Define the Conventional Morality. The classes do not merely differ in etiquette; they also differ in moral judgments. The term "loyal worker" has one meaning in the union hall, another at the chamber of commerce. Kinsey [1948, pp. 375–379] has shown how sex mores differ between the classes. The lower-class emphasis is on naturalness, not on chastity; thus premarital sex experience is viewed rather tolerantly, since it is "natural"; but the lower classes strongly condemn as degenerate and "unnatural" the adolescent masturbation that the middle classes view more tolerantly, or the elaborate love play the middle-class marriage manuals recommend. On almost every point of moral conduct, class-typed mores differ.

Middle-class mores, however, tend to become the conventional mores.

The chuch, the school, and the welfare and "uplift" agencies are middle-class institutions staffed and run by middle-class persons, and dedicated to the cultivation of middle-class values. Political candidates must be models of middle-class virtue; stupidity is forgivable but not immorality. The laws are written by middle-class legislators and enforce middle-class values. The mass magazines righteously reflect middle-class mores, while the "confessions," aimed at the lower-class market, are even more undeviating in their unctuous approval of middle-class conventionality [Gerbner, 1958]. The upper classes may own or control these agencies, but it is not to their advantage to veto a middle-class morality that helps to protect upper-class interests. Thus the middle-class mores tend to become the official or conventional morality of the society.

This tendency creates certain strains for the lower-class person. He often finds that behavior that is normal and acceptable in his class subculture is condemned and punished when he steps outside this subculture, as he must do at school and in nearly all his dealings with persons in positions of authority. A good deal of resentment and class antagonism accumulates among the lower classes, who feel they are constantly being prodded, scolded, and "pushed around" by middle- and upper-class persons.

The lower classes feel that they are constantly being prodded, scolded, and "pushed around."

Affects Health Attitudes and Practices. Physicians and nurses share a middle-class ethnocentrism that makes them highly impatient with the haphazard health practices of the lower class. In the middle class, medical care is defined as important, so that prenatal care and regular infant care are routine, and any disturbing symptom calls for prompt medical consultation. All this concern is absent in the lower-class world. It simply does not occur to them to seek a physician just because Junior is feverish. Most of them see a physician only in a major medical emergency, or when someone else—school officer, factory official, or welfare worker—marches them to the clinic. Most of the less dramatic forms of illness, along with a good deal of actual physical impairment, are simply accepted as "natural," and not defined as situations calling for medical consultation. As one of Koos's lower-class informants stated:

> I'd look silly, wouldn't I, going to see a doctor for a backache. My *mother* always had a backache as long as I can remember, and didn't do anything about it. It didn't kill her either. . . . . If I went to the doctor for that, my friends would hoot me out of town. That's just something you have, I guess. Why let it get you down?

Earl Lomon Koos, *The Health of Regionville,* Columbia University Press, New York, 1954, p. 36.

Table 9 shows how differently a series of symptoms were defined by Koos's upper-, middle-, and lower-class informants.

Table 9 PERCENTAGE OF RESPONDENTS IN EACH SOCIAL CLASS RECOGNIZING SPECIFIED SYMPTOMS AS NEEDING MEDICAL ATTTENTION *

Symptom	Upper class (N–51)	Middle class (N–335)	Lower class (N–128)
Loss of appetite	57	50	20
Persistent backache	33	44	19
Continued coughing	77	78	23
Persistent joint and muscle pains	80	47	19
Blood in stool	98	89	60
Blood in urine	100	93	69
Excessive vaginal bleeding	92	83	54
Swelling of ankles	77	76	23
Loss of weight	80	51	21
Bleeding gums	79	51	20
Chronic fatigue	80	53	19
Shortness of breath	77	55	21
Persistent headaches	80	56	22
Fainting spells	80	51	33
Pain in chest	80	51	31
Lump in breast	94	71	44
Lump in abdomen	92	65	34

* Percentage rounded to nearest number.
SOURCE: Earl Lomon Koos, *The Health of Regionville,* Columbia University Press, New York, 1954, p. 32.

When the lower-class person does recognize a health problem, his usual response is self-medication. He either uses a home remedy or he gets a tonic from the drugstore. One important reason is cost. Scientific medical care is beyond the means of most lower-class people. While free clinics and services are more or less available, these often involve embarrassing red tape, inconvenient locations, and long waits. To secure free services requires a determination beyond that of most lower-class persons. Class ethnocentrism is another barrier. Middle-class physicians and nurses sometimes treat lower-class patients disrespectfully, treating them with a hurried impersonality, or curtly scolding them for not following middle-class health practices. Finally, the lower-class person seldom knows much about scientific medicine or has any great faith in it. If he seeks medical consultation, he is uneasy among all the unfamiliar people and equipment, and subjected to diagnostic procedures, often uncomfortable, that he cannot understand. What he *can* understand is that after an uncomfortable and expensive trip to the physician, he often leaves feeling worse than when he arrived, while a two-dollar bottle of tonic from the drugstore makes him feel better immediately.

Research has clearly established the class differential in health- and medical-care practices. Yeracaris [1962] has shown that the higher classes are far more acceptive of medical innovation. Deasy [1956] studied a community where free polio shots were offered to all schoolchildren whose parents would sign a slip giving consent; only one-half as many of the lower-class parents gave consent. These and other studies show that the health-care problem of the lower classes is not simply one of costs; it is also one of class-typed attitudes toward health needs and scientific medicine.

Many Other Group Differences Are Class Differences. Many other kinds of group differences—racial, religious, regional—are really class differences. For example, almost any Negro-white comparison will prove to be very flattering to whites. Negroes have proportionately more crimes, more venereal disease, more illegitimate births, more drunkenness, more desertions, more broken families, and proportionately more people on relief. This poor record is due largely to the fact that discrimination and lack of opportunity have kept most Negroes in the lower class. When Negroes and whites are compared as racial groups, therefore, we are comparing an overwhelmingly lower-class group with another group having vastly larger middle- and upper-class segments.

Variations in the class composition of religious groups affect comparisons between them. Thus one would expect Baptists and Catholics to have a higher rate of juvenile delinquency than Episcopalians and Congregationalists simply because juvenile delinquency usually has a greater incidence in lower-social-class groups. For the same reasons exclusive residential suburbs of Long Island will have lower death rates than slum districts in New York City. Therefore, whenever data for two groups are compared, the critical observer will always wonder, "Are these groups comparable in class composition?" If not, some very misleading conclusions may be drawn.

Summary

A social class is made up of people of similar social status who regard one another as social equals. Each class is a subculture, with a set of attitudes, beliefs, values, and behavior norms differing from those of other classes. Social class is based on total social and economic position in the community, including wealth and income, occupation, education, self-identification, hereditary prestige, group participation, and recognition by others. Class lines are not clearly drawn but represent points along a continuum of social status. The exact size and membership of a given class are difficult to establish.

Social class is an important social reality. Social class largely determines one's life opportunities and colors one's personality development. Social class molds the life-adjustment patterns of the individuals; the lower the class level, the more limited tends to be the participation of the individual in social and community life. Social class assigns privileges and responsibilities to individuals, and thereby helps to get necessary work accomplished. Social-class subcultures breed a highly subtle and tenacious class ethnocentrism that prevents classes from fully understanding one another. It is mainly the standards of the middle class that are written into law and sanctioned by the conventional morality. Social class greatly affects the health practices and peoples' attitudes toward and use of scientific medical care. Many differences ordinarily assigned to race, religion, ethnic group, or to some other kind of group difference are actually class differences; confusion arises from the fact that racial, religious, and other groups may be unevenly distributed along the class continuum.

Questions and Projects

*1. Distinguish among *evaluated participation, status characteristics,* and *self-identification* as methods of determining social-class status. Which method do you think is best? Why?

2. Are Americans class conscious? Can class lines exist when people deny their existence?

3. How can social classes really be subcultures when children of all class levels attend school together?

4. Given unlimited money, how hard would it be to provide children with complete "equality of opportunity"?

5. Is there a relation between the problems of health and education and the attitudes engendered by lower-class life? Explain.

6. When a college student from a wealthy family takes a summer job working in a factory, how much does he learn about the "working class"?

7. Which of the problems of the public-health nurse grow out of social-class factors?

8. Nurses' associations have been considerably more favorable toward Medicare (health care for the aged through social security payments) than the medical associations. Have you any idea why?

9. Make a chart of officers in your

senior high school class (or some other organization you know well). From which social-class level does each come? Are the officers proportionately representative of the social class present in the organization? Do members from different social classes view the group in the same way? Wherein, and why, do they differ?

10. Read and analyze the treatment of social class in one of the following novels: *Kitty Foyle* by Christopher Morley, *Marjorie Morningstar* by Herman Wouk, *Studs Lonigan* by James T. Farrell, *The Forge* by Thomas S. Stribling, *Mansfield Park* by Jane Austin, *The Age of Innocence* by Edith S. Wharton, *Fraternity* by John Galsworthy, *Tobacco Road* by Erskine Caldwell, *Hunky* by Thomas R. Williamson, *Babbitt* by Sinclair Lewis, *So Little Time* or *B. F.'s Daughter* by John P. Marquand.

Suggested Readings

American Journal of Sociology, vol. 58, 1953. Entire issue devoted to social stratification in the United States, Latin America, China, and France.

BALTZELL, E. DIGBY: *Philadelphia Gentlemen: The Making of a National Upper Class,* The Free Press of Glencoe, New York, 1958, chaps. 2 and 4. Brief descriptions of the American upper class.

BENDIX, REINHARD, AND SEYMOUR LIPSET (EDS.): *Class, Status, and Power,* The Free Press of Glencoe, New York, 1953. A collection of essays and research studies on social class.

HOLLINGSHEAD, AUGUST B.: *Elmtown's Youth,* John Wiley & Sons, Inc., New York, 1949. A study of the effects of social class on youth in a small Midwestern community.

MANIS, JEROME, AND BERNARD MELTZER: "Attitudes of Textile Workers to Class Structure," *American Journal of Sociology,* 60:30–35, 1954. A study of class consciousness among textile workers in an Eastern American city.

MILLER, WALTER B.: "Implications of Urban Lower-class Cultures for Social Work," *Social Service Review,* 33:219–237, 1959. A description of the problems faced by social workers in serving lower-class clients.

WARNER, W. LLOYD, AND PAUL S. LUNT: *The Social Life of a Modern Community,* Yale University Press, New Haven, Conn., 1941, chap. 7, "Profiles of Yankee City." A long chapter, reading like a novel, in which the attitudes and behavior of the different classes are dramatized.

ZORBAUGH, HARVEY W.: *The Gold Coast and the Slum,* The Univerity of Chicago Press, Chicago, 1929. A highly readable study of our two extremes of social class; now dated in detail but still sound in principle.

CHAPTER   **Social**

11   **Processes**

The background of partition [of India and Pakistan] is long and involved. It was the culmination of more than a century of dual struggle—the struggle for national independence against England, and the struggle for power inside India between Hindu and Moslem. . . .

And in those days of uncertainty and confusion people became panicky. Whatever the animosity had been between Hindu and Moslem before Independence, the people had managed to live side by side. With partition, however, millions of people suddenly became jittery and insecure. A Hindu who lived in a city near the border like Lahore wondered what was to happen to him now that Lahore was to become a part of Pakistan. A Moslem who lived on the outskirts of Calcutta wondered what was to happen now that there would be a separate Moslem Government in Pakistan that did not include him. The insecurity and confusion became multiplied as millions of people decided to move in order to be governed by their own group.

Then came violence. At first there were only sporadic incidents. A Moslem in Dacca, for example, would smash the shopwindows of a clothing store owned by a Hindu, claiming he had heard that Hindus were looting Moslem shops in Calcutta or Delhi. A Hindu in Calcutta would set fire to a Moslem home, in open view of a crowd, yelling that he had heard that Moslems were burning homes of Hindus who remained behind in Dacca or Karachi. Some Hindus or Moslems would try to take advantage of the National turmoil by seizing business properties or homes.

Each incident, of course, fed on rumors and begat even greater rumors. Outrages were carried out in the name of retaliation. Soon a civil war without battle-lines or armies raged throughout the subcontinent. People rushed through the streets with sticks or torches or whatever could be used to kill a man.

Norman Cousins, "Where Violence Begins," *Saturday Review*, Jan. 18, 1954, pp. 22ff.

Here we have an example of social processes—accommodation, competition, and conflict. What are social processes, and what is their importance?

The term "social processes" refers to *repetitive forms of behavior that are commonly found in social life*. One of the most extensive treatments of social process is found in Park and Burgess's *Introduction to the Science of Sociology* [1921]. This highly influential textbook of an earlier period is primarily devoted to the classification and analysis of social processes. In recent decades sociologists have become less interested in social processes themselves and more interested in the intensive analysis of behavior in specific institutional and cultural settings. Yet it still remains important for the student to be aware of the major social processes to be found in all groups and all societies. The most frequent classification of the major social processes is in terms of *cooperation, competition, conflict, accommodation,* and *assimilation*.

Cooperation

Cooperation is derived from two Latin words *co* meaning *together* and *operari* meaning *to work*. It may be formally defined as *joint activity in pursuit of common goals or shared rewards*. Cooperation may be found in groups as small as the dyad (group of two persons) and as large as the United Nations. Forms of cooperative endeavor in primitive societies are usually traditional and are acted out without any conscious design. Trobriand Islanders do not "decide" to fish cooperatively; they just go fishing in the same manner as their fathers. The more technologically advanced cultures often carry out elaborate plans for deliberate cooperative activities. Cooperation implies a regard for the wishes of other people and is often regarded as unselfish, but men may also find their selfish goals are best served by working together with their fellows [Bogardus, 1946].

Deliberate Primary-group Cooperation. Cooperation by members of small groups is so common in our society that the life history of most individuals may be written largely in terms of their attempts to become a part of such groups and to adjust to the demands of cooperative group life. Even the most ardent individualist will find that much of his life satisfaction arises from the give and take in the family, recreation groups, and work associates. The need for cooperation in these activities is so much taken for granted that we sometimes forget that whether one has a stable and enjoyable group experience depends largely on his ability to enter comfortably into cooperative relationships. The person who cannot cooperate easily and successfully is likely to be isolated and perhaps maladjusted.

Not only is primary-group cooperation important in itself; it is also

Deliberate primary-group cooperation.

closely related to secondary-group cooperation. Most large organizations are networks of smaller primary groups in which cooperation functions on a face-to-face basis involving many highly personal relationships.

Deliberate Secondary-group Cooperation. Usually, when we think of cooperation, we have in mind the kind engaged in deliberately by secondary groups. Consumer and producer cooperatives are an example. Consumer cooperatives are organizations of consumers that operate wholesale and retail stores and divide the profits (usually called "patronage dividends") among their members in proportion to their purchases. One form of consumer cooperative, the credit union, pools the savings of members to form a loan fund handled on a similar basis. Members are paid the going rate of interest for their savings and are able to borrow funds at a set rate of interest, with rebates being divided among borrowers when there is a margin available. Producer cooperatives are most frequently used in the marketing of agricultural produce. Groups of farmers hope to reserve for themselves the profits made by commercial middlemen through establishing their own warehouses and selling channels. Neither consumer nor producer cooperatives try to "undersell" other business concerns; they do business at competitive prices, then distribute profits among members in proportion to their purchases from or sales to the cooperative.

In the Scandinavian countries and in England, such cooperatives do a major proportion of the total business in the country. In the United States they handle only a small fraction of the total business but are highly important in dairy and fruit farming, and consumer co-ops are strong in some areas. Scandinavian immigrants have carried this pattern with them to the United States, and cooperatives seem to be strongest where a cohesive ethnic group regards them as a traditional part of the culture [Kercher et al., 1941].

These "cooperatives" are but one of many forms of large-scale cooperative activity. The desire of people to work together for common goals is expressed through governments, fraternal bodies, religious organizations, and a host of special-interest groups. Such cooperation not only involves many people in the local community but also extends to a network of organized cooperative activity involving state, regional, national, and international relationships. Problems in such cooperation include decisions as to the geographical extent of cooperation, obtaining a consensus on the ends to be pursued and the means of reaching them, conflicts with other cooperative groups, and the inevitable difficulty of reconciling the conflicting claims of individuals and the subgroups with which they are associated.

Impersonal and Symbiotic Cooperation. The world of nature is sometimes pictured as a world of conflict. Yet the concept of universal strife is contradicted by animals who hunt in packs, by insects who work together to maintain colonies, and even by the cooperation of dissimilar organisms. This cooperative interdependence of different species or orders on one another is known in biology as *symbiosis*.

A great deal of human cooperation may be said to be on the symbiotic level, since it unites people in a mutual interdependence although they may have made no deliberate choice to cooperate. The marketplace draws men into a network of cooperation even though each wishes only to buy or sell for his own needs. The farmer, for instance, produces for the market that will give him the greatest net profit, but in this process he cooperates with many people about whom he neither knows nor cares. Most of our economic life is organized on the principle of pursuing self-interest by selling one's labor or goods at the highest price he can get. The goal is self-interest, but the effect is to maintain a network of cooperative relationships in which men work to furnish goods and services needed by other men.

Competition

Competition is the struggle for possession of rewards that are in limited supply—money, goods, status, power, love—anything. It may be formally defined as *the process of seeking to monopolize a reward by surpassing all rivals*. It is based on the inexorable fact that it is never possible for all people to satisfy all their desires. It flourishes even in circumstances of abundance; in a time of full employment rivalry is still keen for the top jobs. Regardless of the sex ratio, we find in many societies a bitter contest within each sex for the attentions of certain partners. Competition may be personal, as when two rivals contest for election to office, or it may be impersonal, as in a civil service examination in which the contestants are not even aware of one another's identity. Whether personal or impersonal, competition is conducted according to standards that focus attention on the surpassing rather than on the elimination of rivals.

Competition a Culturally Patterned Process. While competition is present to some degree in all societies, it differs greatly in degree from society to society. The fiercely competitive Kwakiutl and the relatively noncompetitive Zuñi offer a striking contrast. The Kwakiutl work very hard to accumulate wealth which is used primarily to establish status rather than for material comfort. The competition for status reaches its height at the famous potlatch in which the chiefs and leading families vie with each other to see how much they can give away or destroy [Murdock, 1936, pp. 242–248]. A family may spend a lifetime accumulating wealth, then bankrupt themselves in a single potlatch, thereby establishing the social status of their children. A family that persisted in keeping their wealth would be criticized for their unwillingness to "do anything" for their children. The Zuñi, on the other hand, disdain any emphasis on the accumulation of wealth or the demonstration of individual skill. Most wealth is owned by the entire community, and it is bad form to demonstrate individual superiority of any kind. Thus the Zuñi child does not grow up believing he should make the most money, get the highest grades, or run the fastest race.

Even such strong encouragement of competition as is found among the Kwakiutl does not mean that cooperation is completely absent. As the anthropologist Margaret Mead points out:

> Nevertheless, no society is exclusively competitive or exclusively cooperative. The very existence of highly competitive groups implies cooperation within the groups. Both competitive and cooperative habits must exist within the society. There is furious competition among the Kwakiutl at the one stratum of society— among the ranking chiefs—but within the household of each chief cooperation is mandatory for the amassing of the wealth that is distributed or destroyed.

Margaret Mead, *Cooperation and Conflict among Primitive Peoples,* McGraw-Hill Book Company, New York, 1937, p. 460.

Far from being two mutually distinct processes, competition and cooperation overlap in various ways, while both may go on simultaneously, as is true of the group whose members cooperate with one another while the group competes with another group.

Competition in American Society. In its competitive emphasis, the United States is probably closer to the Kwakiutl than to the Zuñi, yet this competition is sharply limited by many factors. Enactment of minimum-wage laws works toward a situation in which men are not competing for a bare existence, and a growing emphasis on seniority as a basis of promotion means that many occupational goals cannot be reached by direct competitive efforts. In fact, the following description of the control of the competitive impulse in an American factory setting comes close to the Zuñi practice:

> Worker: "There's another thing; you know the fellows give the fast workers the raspberry all the time. Work hard, try to do your best, and they don't appreciate it at all. They don't seem to figure that they are gaining anything by it. It's not only the wiremen, the soldermen don't like it either. . . . The fellows who loaf along are liked better than anybody else. Some of them take pride in turning out as little work as they can and making the boss think they're turning out a whole lot. They think it's smart. I think a lot of them have the idea that if you work fast the rate will be cut. That would mean that they would have to work faster for the same money. I've never seen our rate cut yet, so I don't know whether it would happen or not. I have heard that it has happened in some cases though."

F. J. Roethlisberger and William J. Dickson, *Management and the Worker*, Harvard University Press, Cambridge, Mass., 1939, p. 418.

Such practices modify but still do not eliminate the generally competitive pattern of American life. Athletics, politics, and business offer many competitive spectacles such as the World Series, the national presidential campaigns, and the struggle of the "independents" against the giants of the automobile industry. American men are encouraged to "make good," and neither the advantage of wealthy parents nor the drawback of being reared on the wrong side of the tracks absolves them from the pressure to get into the race for success. Women cannot rely on matchmaking parents to find a husband, and the sexual competition does not entirely cease when they are married. The possibility of divorce means that the matron feels the need to be always at her best, since other women are still potential rivals. Even religion, often held to be the integrating force in society, functions on a competitive basis as numerous denominations compete for converts. In spite of efforts to moderate or limit the struggle, the average American is enmeshed in competitive activities from the time his mother purchases his first layette until he is buried in an expensive casket under an impressive headstone.

Functions of Competition. Competition functions as one method of allocating scarce things. Other methods are possible. We might ration goods on some basis such as need, age, or social status. We might distribute scarce goods by lottery, or even divide them equally among all people. But each of these methods creates some difficulties. Needs are highly debatable; any system of priorities will be disputed, for no group is likely to feel that another group is more deserving. Equal rewards to people who are unequal in needs, effort, or ability are hard to justify. Competition may be an imperfect rationing device, but it works, and it eliminates a lot of arguments.

Another function of competition is to shape the attitudes of competitors. When persons or groups compete, they normally develop unfriendly and unfavorable attitudes toward one another. Experiments have shown that when the situation is structured so that persons or groups cooperate in pursuit of a common goal, friendly attitudes are encouraged. When they meet under conditions that they consider competitive and frustrating, unfavorable attitudes and unflattering stereotypes appear [Sherif, 1958]. It has often been observed that when racial or religious groups compete, racial and religious prejudices appear and flourish [Berry, 1958, pp. 378–380]. Competition and cooperation differ sharply in the social attitudes they foster in the individual.

Competition is widely praised as a means of ensuring that each person will be stimulated to his greatest achievement. This belief is confirmed by many studies that show that wherever competition is culturally encouraged, it usually increases productivity although it sometimes lowers quality [Murphy et al., 1937, pp. 476–495]. This generalization seems to apply to institutions as well as to individuals. It is often noted that while the competition of many different religious denominations in the United States may have produced many denominations and congregations too small to support their programs efficiently, this competition has also promoted a greater alertness and aggressiveness in American religious institutions. Visitors to Europe often comment on Europe's impressive but empty churches, and evidence shows that Americans attend church and share in church activities in far higher proportion than do Europeans [Vella, 1954; Frakes, 1958; McMahon, 1950]. In universities, too, competition seems beneficial. A recent study of medical education concludes that competition has stimulated scientific productivity [Ben-David, 1960]. This study compares the universities of France and England, where university education was highly centralized, with those of Germany, where the development of independent regional universities led to an intense competition for scientific prestige which favored the rapid development of new discoveries. This finding is consistent with the experience of the Russians who claim that competition between factories has increased production even though all the factories are part of the total communist system.

The stimulus of competition is, however, limited in at least three respects. First, people may decline to compete. Since competition requires that some must lose while all remain somewhat anxious and insecure, people try to protect themselves from its rigors. Businessmen develop monopolistic practices, set quotas, and engage in collusive bidding; unions set work quotas, enforce promotion through seniority, and limit union membership; farmers want price protection; practically every group promotes many competition-limiting arrangements.

Furthermore, many persons simply withdraw from competition whenever they lose too regularly. In singing the praises of competition, many people overlook the important fact that although competition stimulates those who win fairly often, it discourages those who nearly always lose. The slow learner in the classroom, the athletic "dub" on the playground, the adolescent who fails to draw the interest of the opposite sex—such persons usually quit trying, for the pain of repeated failure becomes unendurable. They withdraw from competition in these areas, having decided that the activity is not worthwhile. There is even experimental evidence that repeated failures not only dampen one's willingness to compete but may even impair one's actual ability to compete [Hurlock, 1927; Vaughn, 1936; Winslow, 1944]. It appears that repeated failures will so fill a man with a sense of his incompetence and an overwhelming expectation of failure that he is unable to use his abilities to good advantage. His failure becomes self-perpetuating. It may be that for every genius whom competition has stimulated to great achievement, there are a hundred or a thousand shiftless failures whom competition has demoralized.

A second limitation is that competition seems to be stimulating in only some kinds of activity. Where the task is simple and routine, competition is followed by the greatest output gains; as the task becomes more intricate, and the quality of work more important, competition is less helpful. In intellectual tasks, not only is the production of the cooperative group greater but their work is of higher quality than the group whose members are competing with one another [Deutsch, 1949]. The growing popularity of group medical practice is based on the fact that group practice is not only more profitable, but it also encourages a higher level of professional excellence [New York Academy of Medicine, 1947, p. 137]. The nature of work in today's world is steadily shifting away from the kinds of work where competition between individuals is most beneficial. Competition between groups in technical or intellectual tasks seems to be stimulating, but within the group, cooperation appears to be more stimulating than competition.

A third limitation on competition is its tendency to turn into conflict. To accede peacefully while a coveted reward is claimed by a more skillful competitor is not easy, and the rules of competition are often breached by a resort to conflict.

Conflict

The conflict process is little praised but widely practiced. It develops whenever a person or group seeks to gain a reward not by surpassing other competitors but by preventing them from effectively competing. It is formally defined as the process of *seeking to monopolize rewards by eliminating or weakening the competitors.* A murder or beating, a threat, a law passed to injure a competing group, a restrictive racial covenant (agreeing to allow no nonwhites to buy property)—these are a few of many conflict devices. In its most extreme form, conflict leads to the total annihilation of opponents as when the Romans destroyed Carthage and exterminated its inhabitants, or as when American settlers annihilated many tribes of American Indians. In less violent forms, conflict may be directed toward displacing an opponent from effective competition by getting him fired, getting the building inspector to condemn his place of business, smearing his reputation, or any one of many devices men use to get their competitors out of the way.

Eliminating or weakening the competitors.

Conflict between individuals may involve intense personal animosities; group conflict, on the other hand, the type of greatest interest to sociologists, is highly impersonal, the reason being that group loyalties and needs take precedence over individual feelings. Failure to understand this distinction often leads to the mistaken assumption that peace between groups is simply the result of good feeling between the individuals who compose the groups. Many Norwegians were shocked to see that many German children whom they cared for as refugees during World War I repaid their generosity by returning as German conquerors in World War II. Actually, this show of ingratitude should not have been a surprise, since the German invasion of Norway was the result of conflict between nations in which individual feelings were irrelevant. This observation is borne out by the frequent shifts in power alignments in international conflict. Germans and Italians were enemies in World War I and allies in World War II not because personal feelings had changed but because the national interest was differently defined. Group interests rather than personal relationships determine conflict alignments, as shown by the speed with which our German and Japanese enemies in World War II became our allies when the "cold war" with Russia began. Friendships across boundary lines may help promote joint activities, but it is a mistake to regard personal relationships as the solution to problems of world peace. Individuals usually find their role in group conflict by ref-

Group interest and not personal relationships determine conflict alignments.

erence to the groups to which they belong. When conflict breaks out—a war, a strike, a boycott, a legislative battle—the individual either fights for his group or becomes branded a traitor. The individual physician who supports national health insurance becomes *persona non grata* to the rest of the profession, and when the American Nursing Association failed to support the American Medical Association in its opposition to Medicare in 1962, it incurred the bitter displeasure of the medical association.

The Cumulative Nature of Conflict. Once begun, the conflict process is hard to stop. Since each aggressive act inspires a still more hostile retaliation, the conflict process tends to grow more bitter as it proceeds. Within each group, grievances are repeated and hostile attitudes are intensified. Each group develops a set of moral sanctions that justify a chain of even more savage retaliations.

The atrocities in conflict are often attributed to the sadism or brutality of the individuals who commit them. Yet most of the atrocities in group conflict are committed by ordinary people in an extraordinary situation. The conflict process often places people in roles where they *must* be brutal. Steinbeck's *The Moon Is Down* [1942] pictures an intelligent, humane German commander of forces occupying a Norwegian town who is forced to brutal acts of reprisal to keep the town under control. Under some battle conditions, prisoners who cannot be cared for must be slaughtered. During a strike, union members may be forced to punish a strikebreaker, and management may be forced to punish strikers. Each, in fulfilling his role, is forced into acts of brutality and violence.

But the extremes of conflict cannot be understood unless we recognize that the individual, committing the most indescribable acts of brutality, is supported by his group. He sees his act not as wanton inhumanity but as a moral necessity. During the range wars of the American West the cattlemen who harassed, threatened, burned out, and in some cases murdered the settlers did not see themselves as greedy tyrants withholding land from its legal claimants; they saw themselves as embattled patriots who had fought Indians, drought, and plague to build up a country and a way of life that a horde of greedy scum and conniving politicians wished to steal from them [Dale, 1930, chap. 9; Wellman, 1939, chaps. 35 and 36]. To understand why normal people can commit gruesome atrocities in conflict, we must understand how the group provides the sense of righteousness and sanction for such actions.

Conflict Defines Issues. Until the Supreme Court outlawed racial segregation in the public schools, there was much talk about brotherhood but no real decision as to whether Negroes were to have equal rights in American society. Since the Supreme Court decision, conflict has developed in many formerly peaceful areas and has increased social distance between whites and Negroes. The issue can no longer be buried under platitudinous talk; conflict forces us to face issues and make decisions. The immediate effect of the conflict unleashed by the court decision may have been to shatter many peaceful relationships. The long-run effect, sociologists suspect, will be to reduce discrimination and prejudice and eventually increase cooperative relationships between whites and Negroes in our society.

In this respect group conflict may be compared to the effect of fever in the human body—costly and dangerous, but calling attention to deep-seated tensions that must be relieved if health is to be maintained. Just as the treatment of fever goes beyond symptoms to the cause of the difficulty, so the effective handling of conflict goes beyond merely maintaining order and seeks to treat the basic disturbance. Any tendency to ignore controversial issues or to seek a moderate position might be compared to the tendency to ignore symptoms of ill health.

Conflict forces a facing of social issues and polarizes our attitudes toward them. The moderates are pushed, distrusted, and attacked by both sides and eventually forced to make a choice. The end result of the conflict is that the issues are resolved, at least for a time, in a fairly definite fashion. The fact that the moderate is forced to take a more definite position means he has to assume responsibility instead of simply standing aside and deploring violence. At the end of the Middle Ages when men were being slaughtered because of religious differences, the moderates who were simply inclined to deplore fanaticism were driven to a definite program—the separation of church and state—so that religious differences might be tolerated. In present American racial controversies the moderate is pushed into support of integration as a result of his commitment to the maintenance of law and order.

In spite of the bad publicity and the damage to our prestige abroad, I should also like to comment on Little Rock. A distinguished religious leader from the community said to me this summer, "You know, while it was bad, maybe it was not a total loss." There is much more intelligent understanding of the responsibility of citizenship now. People of the moderate or middle group have come to realize that they do not have the privilege of sitting on the sidelines and letting the radicals at the two ends determine the outcomes. They had to learn that ultimately they had to get in there and get their hands dirty with the problem. They had to see that they were being made the testing place for the whole South, and that when the chips were down they had to choose between law and chaos. "Maybe," he said, "we had to learn that, and it took the crisis to teach it to us."

Dan W. Dodson, "The Creative Role of Conflict Re-examined," *Journal of Intergroup Relations*, 1:5–12, Winter, 1959–1960.

The Disintegrative Effects of Conflict. *Conflict Disrupts Social Unity.* Conflict is a highly disturbing way of settling issues. Strikes may idle thousands of men and acres of costly machinery; marital conflicts may wreck countless families; racial and religious conflicts may prevent communities from facing their problems in a united spirit; atomic wars now threaten the total destruction of humanity. Even when conflict achieves a new equilibrium, the price may be very great. The Thirty Years' War, 1618–1648, established the principle of religious toleration among German states, but it also reduced the German population by at least a third, and much of the cultivated lands became a wilderness.

Internal Conflict Disrupts Group Unity. Conflict within a group makes it hard for members to agree on group goals or to cooperate in pursuit of them. At any moment in several of our states one of the major political parties is split into warring factions, giving the other party a fine chance to win the next election. It was often claimed that France fell to Germany so easily in 1940 because the French people were so divided into conflicting factions that they were unable to unite against the enemy. Hitler confidently expected that the United States, with its heterogeneous population, would also be so riven with internal conflicts as to be unable to wage a united battle. This was one of his more costly misjudgments!

The Integrative Effects of Conflict. *Internal Conflicts Are Sometimes Ultimately Integrative.* A limited amount of internal conflict may indirectly contribute to group interaction. Interests and viewpoints within a group shift from time to time; new policies and new leadership may be needed. An occasional contest within a group may keep its leadership alert and its policies up to date, whereas a suppression of internal conflicts may allow disastrous lags and explosive discontents to accumulate.

External Conflict Tends to Integrate the Group. Conflict with another group provides the members with an external outlet for their hostilities and resentments, and thus siphons off a lot of internal tensions. External conflict compels each member either to cooperate loyally or get out.

Simmel, a very perceptive early analyst of social conflict, defines the alternatives in these words:

> The group in a state of peace can permit antagonistic members within it to live with one another in an undecided situation because each of them can go his own way and avoid collisions. A state of conflict, however, pulls the members so tightly together and subjects them to such a uniform impulse that they must completely get along with or completely repel one another. This is the reason why war with the outside is sometimes the last chance for a state ridden with inner antagonisms to overcome these antagonisms, or else to break up definitely.

George Simmel, *Conflict*, tr. by Reinhard Bendix, The Free Press of Glencoe, New York, 1955, pp. 92–93.

External conflict also unifies the group through the imposition and acceptance of tighter controls than are normally accepted. The nation at war allows its business life to be completely directed toward national objectives in a way that would be unendurable in time of peace. The labor union gives no-strike pledges and accepts work rules it would resist in peacetime. All groups tend to build bureaucratic structures and to centralize authority when faced by the need to organize resistance to an enemy.

While external conflict separates a group from its enemies, it also promotes federations or alliances with other groups. The phrase "politics makes strange bed fellows" expresses the tendency to seek out allies in time of conflict that might be unacceptable in time of peace. Our disdain for communism did not keep us from being effective allies with Russia in World War II; when the cold war developed, our rapid rapprochement with Germany and Japan showed that alliance is based on mutual interest, not mutual affection. Wars and threats of war have unquestionably encouraged the growth of political states and governmental institutions from the earliest tribal alliance to the United Nations. War forces a nation into coordinated activity, stimulates inventions, and inspires heroic sacrifices. Wars have settled issues: The Mexican War ended controversy over American colonization of the Southwest; World War II appears to have ended efforts for the territorial expansion of Japan and Germany; through war the Italian peninsula became a unified nation. By settling issues, wars often clear the way for cooperative action. Conflict thus performs an associative as well as a divisive function and may be considered in some ways an integrative factor in social life.

Alternatives to Conflict

The conflict process may fulfill useful functions, but at so great a cost that man often seeks to avoid it. Conflict is often avoided through some form of two other processes, *accommodation* and *assimilation*.

Accommodation

> It really threw me when my folks got a divorce right after I was graduated.
> I never thought much about my parent's love life; I guess I just took them for
> granted. Our home always seemed to me about like most others. At graduation,
> they came and beamed, gave me graduation gifts, met my friends, and all that.
> Then Dad took me aside and said that he and Mom were calling it quits. He
> said that they had bugged each other for years but had stuck it out to give
> me a proper home. Now that I would be on my own, they were going to
> separate.
> Looking back on it now, I can remember little things that they let slip, but
> at the time I never noticed anything. They kept it pretty well covered up.

This story, adapted from a student's life history in the author's files,
is an example of accommodation, a *process of developing temporary
working agreements between conflicting individuals or groups*. It develops when persons or groups find it necessary to work together despite
their hostilities and differences. Accommodation may be short-lived, or
it may persist for centuries. No real settlement of issues is reached; each
group retains its own goals and viewpoints, but arrives at an "agreement
to disagree" without fighting and perhaps to resume peaceful interaction.
It is what Sumner [1940] called "antagonistic cooperation."

Accommodation replaces conflict with peaceful interaction without
fully settling basic issues, but it allows hostilities to subside while more
friendly attitudes may grow from this peaceful interaction. This fortunate
tendency is illustrated in a Gallup poll [1] showing that whereas in 1942
the adjectives Americans most frequently picked to describe Germans
were "warlike," "hard-working," "cruel," "treacherous," and "intelligent,"
by 1961 the list had changed to "hard-working," "intelligent," "progressive," "practical," and "brave"—a much more favorable list. The accommodation process obviously affects people's attitudes and behavior. Accommodation takes a number of forms. Some are deliberately planned
and formally negotiated; others arise as unplanned products of group
interaction.

Displacement. Displacement is the process of ending one conflict by
replacing it with another. A classic example is the use of war or the
threat of war to end internal conflicts and bring national unity. It is a
standard stratagem of dictators and not unknown among democracies.

Finding a scapegoat is a favorite displacement technique. The term
refers to an ancient Hebrew ceremony in which the sins of the people
were symbolically heaped upon a goat that was driven into the wilderness. Unpopular minorities often become scapegoats. Anti-Semitism has
long been used to deflect criticism and to unite conflicting groups in

[1] Associated Press, Apr. 26, 1961.

blaming Jews for all the ills of the society. In the newly independent countries, all the nation's problems may be blamed on the remaining "colonial influences." The actual behavior of the scapegoat is of little consequence; what matters is that a ruling group may be able to avert a possible attack on itself by diverting popular hostility on the scapegoat.

Institutionalized Release of Hostility. In many societies there are some institutionalized provisions for release of hostilities and tensions. Some primitive tribes regulated combat in a manner designed to express aggression, maintain "honor," and yet avoid destructive warfare. Warner [1931] describes an elaborate pattern of ritualistic warfare wherein Murngin tribes went through involved ceremonial combat in which nobody actually got hurt, yet a lot of hostility could be worked off. Then these rituals closed with a joint ceremonial dance expressing the renewed union and solidarity of the tribes. The Royal Copenhagen Porcelain Works, instead of junking the imperfect pieces, takes them to the Tivoli amusement park, where it collects a fee from people who are willing to pay for the privilege of smashing the rejects. It seems that "busting things up" serves to release hostility and tension.

Perhaps our spectator sports, especially the contact sports like football, hockey, boxing, and wrestling, would be examples of opportunities for the institutionalized release of hostility in our society. Ceremonials and feast days and orgies and religious experiences of various kinds may also serve to release tensions or provide catharsis for hostilities and thus ease the pressures toward conflict. Karl Marx was quite correct in holding that believers in a biblical devil, heaven, and Christian forgiveness would be slow to join in class warfare.

Superordination. In some families one member totally and ruthlessly dominates the others. Some group conflicts end in the total defeat and submission of one group to the other. A war may "end" with the defeated people continuing resistance through guerrilla warfare, assassination, sabotage, and noncooperation, thus continuing the conflict. Or they may accept defeat, submit, and make the best of it, as did Germany and Japan after World War II.

Superordination is likely to be accepted only when the parties are so unequal in power that resistance seems useless or impossible. When the subordinate group gains more power, the superordinate group must either relax its rule or risk a revolt. As Germany and Japan recovered from wartime devastation, the United States relaxed its rule rather than face growing resistance, while Russia's stern rule over conquered peoples provoked revolts in East Berlin, Hungary, and Poland and seething resentment throughout her "colonies."

Conflict between two parties may sometimes be ended by their forced submission to a third party. History is crowded with instances. After Athens and Sparta had exhausted themselves, Macedonia conquered both, and only English rule brought peace between the Scottish clans. Most empires grew by picking off neighbors who were fighting among themselves.

Today the collapse of empires and the end of colonial rule in many areas is followed by the reappearance of local conflicts. The Near East peoples resumed ancient conflicts following the disintegration of the Ottoman (Turkish) Empire. At this writing the Congo and several other African areas are precariously poised on the brink of tribal warfare. Whether stable national governments are possible for such areas is not yet certain.

Compromise. When all the parties are so powerful that none of them relishes the prospect of conflict, they may compromise their differences. Compromise is a form of accommodation in which each accepts less than its full goal in order to avoid or end the conflict. Each party normally makes concessions according to its relative power, with the more powerful party making the fewer concessions.

Since a compromise leaves all parties somewhat dissatisfied, compromise agreements are likely to be honored only as long as the respective power balances remain unchanged. As soon as either group gains in respective power, it is likely to press for a revision of the compromise, threatening renewed conflict if its demands are refused. During prosperous times, when the employer can scarcely fill his orders, the union will press for a more favorable contract; during a recession, when orders are fewer and stockrooms are full, the employer seizes the strategic moment to seek the revisions he desires. Politics may be seen as a continual round of shifting power positions and changing compromises. Politicians are often accused of dishonesty because of their compromising; yet without such compromises between the conflicting demands of many voting groups, democracy would become chaos.

Frequently the conflict has been so bitter and feelings so hostile that the parties are unable to reach a compromise. Several third-party techniques are often helpful in breaking such deadlocks.

Third-party roles in compromise. The techniques of conciliation, mediation, and arbitration use the services of a third party to help reach a settlement. In *conciliation* the third party functions by encouraging the disputants to keep talking; in *mediation* he suggests solutions and uses his personal influence and powers of persuasion; in *arbitration* he hears their arguments and makes a decision the contestants have already agreed to accept. The third party may offer suggestions the disputants could not offer without losing face, and he may be able to find new approaches to end a deadlock. Even if he is given the power of arbitration, his success depends mainly on his ability to gauge their relative power positions and suggest settlements fairly close to what might be obtained through all-out conflict.

Toleration. In some conflicts victory is either impossible or unbearably costly, and compromise is unendurable. Some values may be too deeply cherished to compromise. In these circumstances the participants sometimes discover that agreement may not be absolutely necessary. In toleration, people accept each other's differences without insisting on a settlement. Religious conflict is a classic example. In Europe at the time of the Reformation, both Protestants and Catholics were positive that they had the "true" version of the Christian faith which should be accepted by all men. Neither group was willing to compromise, and in spite of severe conflict, neither group could destroy the other. Adjustment has been made on the basis of toleration; each church ceases to persecute other churches while continuing to hold that these other churches are in error.

Why was religious toleration so long in developing? Partly because toleration requires a frame of mind in which people are willing to grant others the right to be different. Ethnocentrism is the enemy of toleration. Furthermore, toleration is possible only in matters where agreement is not absolutely necessary. As long as church and state were combined, rejection of the established church automatically became treason to the state. Not until their separation could one worship as he pleased and still be a loyal citizen. Catholic and Protestant neighbors may disagree on many religious questions without the disagreement impairing their interaction as neighbors, friends, or fellow workers. If they intermarry, some religious differences may still be open to toleration, but their interaction as husband and wife will absolutely require agreement on a number of issues. Our rather wide use of toleration today rests not only on a considerable readiness to tolerate differences but also on a social structure in which many areas of peaceful interaction are open to groups who differ bitterly on other matters.

Assimilation. Whenever groups meet, some mutual interchange or diffusion of culture takes place. Even groups who strenuously seek to prevent such diffusion, such as the modern Amish or the ancient Hebrews, do not fully succeed in protecting their culture from all cultural interchange. The Old Testament is filled with exhortations to avoid contact with the "heathen" peoples, and of their failure to heed this warning. The story of Samson is an object lesson on the folly of involvement with foreign women.

This process of *mutual cultural diffusion through which persons and groups become culturally alike,* is called *assimilation.* It is always a two-way process, with each group contributing varying proportions of the eventual blend, depending upon respective group size, prestige, and other factors.

The assimilation process is nicely illustrated in the Americanization of our European immigrants. Arriving in great numbers between 1850 and 1913, most of them settled in immigrant colonies in the Northern cities. Within these "ethnic colonies"—Little Italy, Little Poland, and so on—they practiced much of their native European culture while absorbing some of the American culture. The immigrant parents often sought to transmit their European culture to their children, while the children generally sought to become American as rapidly as possible. This conflict often caused parental anguish, family disorganization, and loss of parental control, so that many second-generation immigrants became confused, rebellious, and delinquent. With the maturing of the third generation, the assimilation difficulties generally subsided with fairly complete Americanization and with the disappearance of the ethnic colony as the descendants scattered over city and suburb [Thomas and Znaniecki, 1927].

Assimilation reduces group conflicts by blending differing groups into larger, culturally homogenous groups. The bitter riots against the Irish and the discriminations against the Scandinavians in the United States [Higham, 1955] have disappeared as assimilation erased the group differences and blurred the sense of separate group identity. Anything that binds people into a larger group will tend to reduce rivalry and conflict between them. These effects of assimilation are strikingly illustrated by an experiment involving the experimental formation of different groupings at a summer camp [Sherif and Sherif, 1953]. The boys were all from the same community and were similar in religion, social-class status, age, and nationality background. For the first experimental period ("integrative") they were treated as a single group, and they showed no signs of incipient social conflict. In the second experimental ("segregative") period they were divided into two groups who were housed separately and encouraged to develop separate programs of activities. The groups took the names of "Red Devils" and "Bull Dogs." Group antagonisms quickly developed, and physical violence between the groups reached the point where it had to be suppressed by the adult leaders. Personal relationships followed the patterns of group division shown in Table 10.

This experiment shows that even when there are no real differences or issues to fight over, conflict still tends to develop wherever separate group identity is recognized. We can understand, then, why the assimilation of American Negroes or Japanese-Americans has not ended conflict. The Irish, Swedes, and Germans disappeared as separate groups as soon as they were assimilated. The Negroes and Japanese-Americans,

Table 10   CHOICES OF FRIENDS AT END OF INTEGRATIVE PERIOD AND AT END
OF SEGREGATIVE PERIOD

	Choices made by	Choices received by	
		in-group, per cent	out-group, per cent
End of integrative period	Eventual Red Devils	35.1	64.9
	Eventual Bull Dogs	35.0	65.0
		In-group	Out-group
End of segregative period	Red Devils	95.0	5.0
	Bull Dogs	87.7	12.3

SOURCE: Adapted from Muzafer Sherif and Carolyn Sherif, *Groups in Harmony and Tension*, Harper & Row, Publishers, Incorporated, New York, 1953, p. 268.

although quite fully assimilated, remain identifiable as separate groups. For a variety of reasons, including historical tradition, the wish for scapegoats, and the desire for someone to look down upon, these groups have not gained full social acceptability. Assimilation removes some but not all possible pressures toward conflict.

Summary

The basic social processes are found in all societies, although there is great variation in emphasis. *Cooperation* may be personal or impersonal, deliberate or symbiotic in character. Primary groups demand highly personalized cooperation; secondary-group cooperation is found in many organized social groups as well as in a network of economic relationships that use the motive of individual gain to draw men into essentially cooperative activities.

Competition serves the function of allocating scarce rewards among the competitors. It has the additional function of stimulating both individual and group activity in a manner to increase the total productivity of the competitors, but it also discourages the further efforts of those who regularly fail. Experimental studies show that both cooperation and competition are related to the values of the culture. When the culture legitimizes competition, a competitive system often, but not always, increases the rate of productive activity while quality of work often suffers. Competition is unstable and frequently yields either to cooperation or to conflict.

Conflict develops when attention shifts from the contest itself to an effort to eliminate rivals. Group conflict may take place even when the members of the groups involved lack any personal animosity toward members of the opposing factions. Social conflict is frequently costly and disruptive, but it also has integrative functions. Conflict helps to define issues and bring about a new equilibrium of contending forces. It also promotes unity within the group and may lead to expanding alliances with other groups. Conflict may be ended in several ways. Conflicts may be *displaced* and the aggression directed at a new enemy. Conflicts may sometimes be ended or avoided through an *institutionalized release* of hostilities and aggressions through mock combat, festival and orgy, and other emotional outlets. Conflicts may be relieved, at least temporarily, through *accommodation,* which takes several forms. *Superordination* consists in establishing uncontested rule over a weaker group. *Compromise* involves a limited surrender by all groups in order to end or avoid conflict. *Conciliators, mediators,* and *arbitrators* often aid in arranging compromises. Where compromise is unacceptable yet agreement not absolutely necessary, groups may use *toleration* as an alternative to conflict. Finally, when two groups have become *assimilated,* so that they share a common culture and common goals, they normally disappear as separate groups unless some visible identification remains as a focus for conflict.

Questions and Projects

1. Are cooperation, competition, and conflict natural, instinctive, or automatic human responses, or must they be culturally acquired?

2. Why do you think the consumer cooperative has had such limited success in the United States?

3. What examples of impersonal or symbiotic cooperation have you observed in your hometown, on the campus, or in the hospital?

4. Discuss this proposition: "It is man's nature to want more than his fellows, so competition is firmly rooted in human instinct."

5. Under what conditions is competition an encouragement? When does it inhibit effort?

6. Why does competition often turn into conflict? Does social conflict always involve physical violence?

7. To what extent do friendly personal relations and mutual understanding serve to prevent conflict?

8. How is knowledge of the effects of conflict on group solidarity sometimes used in international relations? In labor-management relations?

9. Should the past relationships between osteopaths and doctors of medicine be described as competition or conflict? Today they are beginning to cooperate. Why?

10. When homesteaders invaded the land of the cattlemen, conflict developed. Was there any practical possibility of avoiding that conflict?

11. Do decent and humane people ever take part in atrocities? Did American soldiers commit any atrocities? Why?

12. Why is accommodation always an unstable arrangement? What happens when the power balance shifts?

13. Why could not toleration have

been used to avoid the Civil War, the present integration conflicts, or the cold war?

14. Why does assimilation not always bring social acceptance and the end of conflict?

Suggested Readings

ALLPORT, GORDON W.: *ABC's of Scapegoating*, Anti-Defamation League of B'nai B'rith, New York, 1948. A concise pamphlet describing and analyzing the scapegoating process.

BOGARDUS, EMORY S.: "The Long Trail of Cooperation," *Sociology and Social Research*, 31:54–62, 1946. A natural history of the process of cooperation.

COSER, LEWIS A.: *The Functions of Social Conflict*, The Free Press of Glencoe, New York, 1956. A study of the conflict process by a sociologist who believes it has functional values.

DODSON, DAN W.: "The Creative Role of Conflict Re-examined," *Journal of Intergroup Relations*, 1:5–12, Winter, 1959–1960. A presentation of the thesis that conflict may have useful consequences.

PARK, ROBERT E., AND E. W. BURGESS: *Introduction to the Science of Sociology*, 2d ed., The University of Chicago Press, Chicago, 1924, chaps. 4–6, 8–11. The classic discussion of the social processes.

PARK, ROBERT E., AND H. A. MILLER: *Old World Traits Transplanted*, Harper & Row, Publishers, Incorporated, New York, 1921. A classic treatment of the assimilation process.

SHERIF, MUZAFER, AND CAROLYN SHERIF: *Groups in Harmony and Tension*, Harper & Row, Publishers, Incorporated, New York, 1953. A research study of how different group structures promote cooperation and antagonism at a boys' camp.

YOUNG, PAULINE V.: *The Pilgrims of Russian Town*, The University of Chicago Press, Chicago, 1932. A highly readable account of the assimilation process.

Social
Mobility

When Paul Stanley (upper-lower to lower-middle and still moving) was in high school he played football well enough to gain a reputation which brought him several offers of scholarships . . . and in time received his law degree. Meanwhile, he had supported himself by working in the law office of John Bates (upper-middle).

Mr. Bates was a loyal alumnus of the local high school. He once said to Mr. John Breckenridge (upper-upper) that "Paul Stanley's a good sound boy. Hard worker and knows people. He's a fellow to watch."

Paul's father and mother (upper-lower) had come over from Poland with their respective parents when they were still children. After they had met and married they settled in the Downtown region of Yankee City where Paul, their first child, grew up. They both had worked in the shoe factory and gone to an "Americanization school" to improve their English.

The Stanleys were proud of their home. They owned it outright, and the husband and wife had planted the flower garden. Mr. Stanley had painted the house and the fences with two coats of white paint. He placed cast-off tires in appropriate places in the front yard and had given them a coating of white paint. After Mr. Stanley had spaded the ground inside the tires, his wife had planted petunias. Rows of hollyhocks grew beside the white fences. . . .

On his son, Paul, he lavished the greatest affection. When Mr. Stanley wanted to expand and demonstrate how he had gone up in the world since coming from Poland, he first talked of his son's college education and then spoke of "my beautiful white house." He then made comments about "all these Yankees who have lived here forever and never got anyplace." . . .

When younger, Paul had been proud of the home of his parents. It was the nicest house in their neighborhood. But now he saw it not as the nicest house in the neighborhood but in the larger context of the whole town, and this made it appear just a little ridiculous. . . . The house he bought was over in Newtown. He wanted to raise his family away from everything which would make them think of what he had gone through. He wanted a nice new house— "one of those cute little bungalows with a big lawn in front and a concrete sidewalk on the street with new curves and a high-class name."

He had been flattered after graduating from law school when some members of the Caribous (upper-middle to lower-lower) had invited him to join their organization. There were only a few Poles in the

Caribous and most of the members were Yankees. They were all good fellows.

Before he had left the bank after negotiating with some of the officials for his money, he had been congratulated by several of the bank employees on acquiring the new house. They had kidded him about his coming marriage. A few evenings later one of the bank clerks told a clique mate of his, the manager of a hardware store, that Mr. Breckenridge thought very highly of Paul Stanley. At the moment he was talking, they were enjoying a glass of prohibition beer at the hall of the American Order of Antlers (upper-upper to lower-middle). The Antlers, they felt, had "everyone who counted in Yankee City" as members.

"Paul Stanley's come a long way," he said, "and he's come the hard way. And what's more, he's going a lot further. Nobody who's got what it takes and who's got the backing of Mr. Breckenridge can help but succeed. You know, I think Paul would make a swell member of the Antlers."

"That's a swell idea," his companion replied.

Within the year, Paul was a member in good standing of the Antlers, and he played bridge there several nights a week. He still belonged to the Caribous, but some of the members of the latter organization were beginning to complain that he didn't come around any more.

The Stanleys were now in a clique with Mr. and Mrs. Tim Pinkham, Mr. and Mrs. Dick Jones, and Mr. and Mrs. Jerry Thomas (lower-middle), but people like the Camps, the Frenches, and the Flahertys (upper-middle), whom Paul knew at the Antlers, never invited them to dinner, nor did any of the "nice ladies of Hill Street" ever call on Annie. It is possible that this occasionally worried them, but there is more evidence that their past success was still a pleasant reward and that the present filled them with hope for the future.

"And anyway," they said, "we're going to see to it that our children have every advantage."

Quoted with very slight adaptation from W. Lloyd Warner and Paul S. Lunt, *The Social Life of a Modern Community*, Yale University Press, New Haven, Conn., 1941, pp. 188–193.

The Nature of Social Mobility

Three things stand out in the above sketch of Paul Stanley. He had ability. He had a family from whom he learned ambition and good work habits. He gained the endorsement of some influential persons. Ability, ambition, sponsorship—without these, few men rise much above their social origins.

No doubt talented persons are born into all class levels. If there were no barriers to social advancement, we could expect a great deal of mobility as some persons climbed while others slipped. But obviously barriers of many sorts exist. The grandson of Henry Ford and the grandson of an Alabama sharecropper did not have an equal opportunity to become a corporation executive. It is true, however, that considerable movement goes on up and down the social ladder. This mobility is aided by all the influences that give people a more nearly equal chance to develop and use their talents. Mobility is discouraged by all the influences that tend to hold one in the same class as his parents. *Inherited wealth* makes it easy for upper-class children to remain upper class; its lack makes it inevitable for lower-class children to remain lower class. *Discrimination* of many sorts limits mobility. Many exclusive schools admit students only after a look at the applicant's family background. The high school student is often funneled into curricula according to social class more than ability, with upper-class students taking the college preparatory courses while the lower classes are shunted into the vocational curriculum [Hollingshead, 1949, chap. 8]. In vocational guidance, the class background of the child, rather than his abilities, sometimes guides the counselor's recommendations. For members of racial minorities, discrimination is an even greater barrier to class mobility.

Class discrimination is not always conscious or intentional. When a successful attorney seeks out the bank president at the country club and casually remarks that he has a nephew, graduating in another year, who aspires to a career in banking, he is not intentionally trying to discriminate against some ambitious youth who has no uncle at the country club. He is merely trying to help his nephew to find a good opening. Yet the effect of such favors is to discriminate heavily against those who have no influential family friends or relatives.

The greatest barrier to class mobility, however, springs from the fact that *social classes are subcultures that fit the child for participation in the class subculture in which he is socialized.* The average lower-class child does not have the ambitions and study habits needed for upward mobility because he has had little chance to learn them in his subculture. The middle-class child has this chance; meanwhile, he is denied the chance to learn the habits and values that would be appropriate for a lower-class world. The process of growing up in a class thus sets forces in motion that tend to hold one in the same class position.

Mobility runs both ways—up and down. There are some who fail to maintain their parental status. Loss of wealth or income, acceptance of a lower-status occupation, and settling into a lower-status pattern of life are both the symptoms and the processes of downward mobility.

The Process of Social Mobility

The American dream tells each young person to hope for a higher status and a better life than his parents had. The emphasis seems to be on higher status more than on money, for many a skilled workman takes pride in a son who enters schoolteaching at a salary less than he would earn as a skilled workman. This accent on status is revealed in a study of workers in automobile factories, which described them as prosperous but dissatisfied [Chinoy, 1952]. In terms of income and possessions they had done far better than their parents would have thought possible. In many cases their parents had lived either in slum tenements or in rural shacks, while these men lived in neat suburban cottages with all the usual modern conveniences. The pay was good and supplemented by fringe benefits such as pensions, insurance, and medical-care plans. Their dissatisfaction was not directed at their economic status but grew from a feeling that they had no chance to escape the category of semiskilled workers.

In other words the lower class had been upgraded; but the American dream also implies that one has a chance to rise to higher-class status, and for these men that possibility seemed remote. In another era an intelligent workman who had mastered mechanical skills might be steadily promoted through supervisory levels until he reached a position in top management, or if these roads were blocked he might use his mechanical skills to start a shop of his own. Today's workers find that supervisory positions above the level of foreman are usually filled by college-trained specialists and that routine assembly-line work does not even give them the mechanical skills that may be used elsewhere; in fact, it usually provides no mechanical skill at all. This situation represents a "break in the skill hierarchy," meaning one may move from unskilled to skilled labor and eventually become a foreman, but beyond that point lie barriers that are difficult to pass without the proper educational qualifications. Thus we have not one occupational ladder but two: One stops with foreman; the other begins with a college diploma and a job in the "executive-development program" and ends with the presidency. To leap from the top rung of the first to the bottom rung of the second is rarely possible.

While the break in the skill hierarchy has largely destroyed the stockboy-to-president route, there are other roads to upward mobility. Education is more necessary to occupational mobility than before, but education is also more readily available than ever before in the United States. Scholarships and other institutionalized aids to the talented youth are available in considerable number. While large-scale manufacturing may offer the poor boy few chances for promotion from within, the multiplication of the service industries—sales and service, retail trade, recreation, resort industry, and many others—offers opportunities to persons with talent and ambition.

In some occupations the status of the occupation itself has changed. Farming has historically included a very few upper-class planters or plantation owners, a moderate number of fairly prosperous middle-status farm owners, and a large number of marginal farmers and tenant farmers of low income and low status. Today we have fewer farmers, but the average farm is larger and more prosperous, its owner is better educated, and his status and living standards compare more favorably with those of urban residents. Between 1940 and 1959 the number of tenant-operated farms declined from 39 to 19 per cent of all farms. These tenant farmers have moved to town or city. Those who remain farmers today are likely to have a higher relative status and income than farmers a generation ago, while many of those who have left the farm have found a job of higher status than the one they left. Other occupations have shown a similar change in the nature or grade of work involved and the status of the occupation.

Prospects for Social Mobility. Are class lines growing more rigid and is upward mobility more difficult? Studies of corporate structure made two or three decades ago pointed toward an increasing concentration of wealth and a narrowing of opportunity [Berle and Means, 1932], but more recent studies find no greater concentration of big-business wealth than fifty years ago [Litner, 1959]. Warner and Abegglen's [1955] study of corporation executives finds that the proportion of owners' or top executives' sons who are promoted to top executive positions has actually declined in the past generation. A *Wall Street Journal* study of new millionaires finds that many of them were poorly educated, foreign-born, and from humble families [Editors, *Wall Street Journal*, 1961]. Natalie Rogoff [1953] studied the occupational status of workers and their fathers in the years 1910 and 1940. She found that a high proportion of farmers' sons had become urban factory workers. Her overall conclusion was that it was about as easy to move from a

Social mobility is probably increasing.

low-status to a higher-status occupation in 1940 as in 1910. Goldstein [1955] studied occupational mobility in a Pennsylvania town between 1910 and 1950, finding that both upward and downward mobility increased steadily during that period. Several other studies have reached the same conclusion, that social mobility in American society is not declining and probably is increasing [Sjoberg, 1951; Kolko, 1957; Lenski, 1958].

The prospects for social mobility depend on the total number of openings in higher-status occupations and on the barriers to their attainment by the lowly born. The need for an increasing number of individuals in higher-status occupations depends on changes in society that create more upper-class jobs and on the extent to which the upper-class parents produce enough children to fill these places. The need for personnel in high-status occupations in the United States has been growing. Meanwhile the high-income groups have had a birth rate too low to replace themselves. This makes room for a good deal of upward occupational mobility.

Social mobility includes all movement between social classes, either up or down. Kahl has compiled Table 11 based on data from a nationwide survey of the National Opinion Research Council to show the percentage of people who moved up or down from the occupational status of their parents.

Kahl [1957, p. 263] concludes: "The upper levels have many new recruits from below, the semi-skilled level has recruits from above and below; . . . the unskilled group is recruited primarily from farm owners and laborers and secondarily from unskilled and semi-skilled workers. Thus the bottom level has recruited from itself."

Table 11   UPWARD AND DOWNWARD MOBILITY IN THE UNITED STATES *

| Social-economic group, 1950 | Per cent who have | | | Total |
	Moved up	Moved down	Remained	
Professional persons	77	—	23	100
Proprietors, managers, and officials, non-farm	65	4	31	100
Clerks, salespeople, and kindred	53	32	15	100
Skilled workers and foremen	56	14	30	100
Semiskilled workers	43	38	19	100
Farmers and farm laborers	3	13	84	100
Unskilled workers, nonfarm	—	73	27	100

* National survey showing proportion of persons in each occupational group who have moved up, moved down, or stayed at the same occupational level as their fathers.
SOURCE: Joseph A. Kahl, *The American Class Structure*, Holt, Rinehart and Winston, Inc., New York, 1957, p. 263.

The development of automation is decreasing the demand for unskilled and semiskilled workers and for fine craftsmen, at the same time calling for a greater number of technicians capable of maintaining and coordinating complicated automatic machinery. This development is opening up a still larger number of higher-status positions, while still further decreasing the openings for the man who has little education or training. There will be a rapidly growing number of openings for graduate engineers and specialists of many sorts and for technicians with at least a high school or junior college education plus specialized technical training. Meanwhile the openings for unskilled laborers will continue their long-term decline. The youth who does poorly at school can no longer drop out and easily get a job. Conant [1961, p. 34] has commented on the social dynamite in those slum neighborhoods where as high as 70 per cent of the boys and girls between the ages of sixteen and twenty-one are both out of school and out of work.

Nursing is an excellent mobility ladder for girls, as is shown by studies [Devereaux and Weiner, 1950; Riessman and Rohrer, 1957, p. 88]. One study [Community Studies, Inc., 1956] of the class background of practicing nurses found that 55 per cent had risen above the occupational status of their fathers, 24 per cent were below, and 21 per cent were about the same. This study probably minimizes the actual amount of upward mobility, since those who had "married well" and left nursing practice were excluded from the sample. Nursing offers better opportunities for a good marriage than many female occupations. Furthermore, a girl can attend a hospital school of nursing at very little cost, far below that of most other kinds of professional training. These factors make nursing one of the best of all mobility ladders for women.

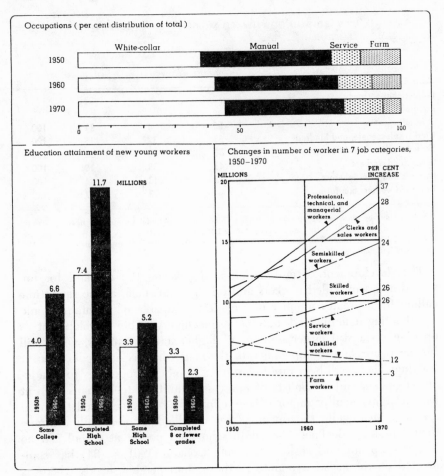

FIGURE 9   Changing Job Opportunities Affect Prospects for Social Mobility.

SOURCE: *Economic Growth in the 1960s*, The National Industrial Conference Board, New York, 1960, p. 11.

The prospects for mobility in American society are considerably brighter than they may appear to the frustrated automobile-assembly-line workers cited a few pages earlier. Direct promotion from laborer to management may be blocked by educational requirements for managerial jobs, but a larger percentage of Americans than ever before are receiving advanced education and anticipating the possibilities for occupational advancement that may follow. While the frontier is gone and the number of farmers is diminishing, the expansion of business and the increase of technical and professional services are giving a chance for upward mobility to millions of Americans. Blind alleys have appeared in some lines and new hurdles to advancement have developed, but new opportunities have opened up along with opportunities for training. The net result of these changes would seem to be about even, indicating that the United States is probably as much an open-class society today as it has been for several decades.

Techniques of Social Climbing. For the boy who wishes to elevate his social-class status, the prime essential is an education and occupation that fit his class ambitions. For the girl, the main problem is to snare the right husband, for her class status will ordinarily follow his. As already indicated, education, occupation, and income are the main factors which, operating over a period of time, will lift one's class status. There are, however, many ways for a skillful climber to speed up the mobility process.

Change in Standard of Living. It is not enough merely to get and spend more money, for *how* one spends it is more important than the amount one spends. To gain acceptance at a new status level one must assume a material standard of living appropriate to that level. This means moving to an appropriate neighborhood, decorating the home in an appropriate manner, driving a car that is neither too humble nor too ostentatious, and so on. The outward appearances must fit. *After* one is solidly established, he may ignore some of the appearances, especially at the upper-class level. The person whose secure upper-class status is beyond question can afford to drive a nondescript car and dress with a casual unconcern for fashion. But those who are on the way up must be careful about conformity to the pattern.

Cultivation of Class-typed Behavior. The mobility-oriented person will not be fully accepted into a higher class until he has absorbed the behavior patterns of that class well enough to follow them without glaring errors. The aspirant can study books on etiquette, read the magazines on home decoration, and consciously watch and copy the manners of those whose acceptance he craves. Patterns of dress, vocabulary and diction, recreational activities, reading interests—these can be overhauled and polished. The children can be given music and dancing lessons and be sent to carefully chosen private schools and summer camps. It is true that not all aspects of a class subculture can be acquired through deliberate study and conscious imitation, but such efforts can speed up the process of acceptance.

Manipulation of Associations. If opportunities for social climbing were removed, many church organizations, civic associations, welfare societies, and other local associations would suffer a calamitous loss of membership. For how is the mobile person to meet and cultivate those who are a notch above him in social status? The very rich can engage a social secretary, part of whose task is to help them in the intricate art of social gameship [Zorbaugh, 1929, pp. 55–56]. The new rich can even engage

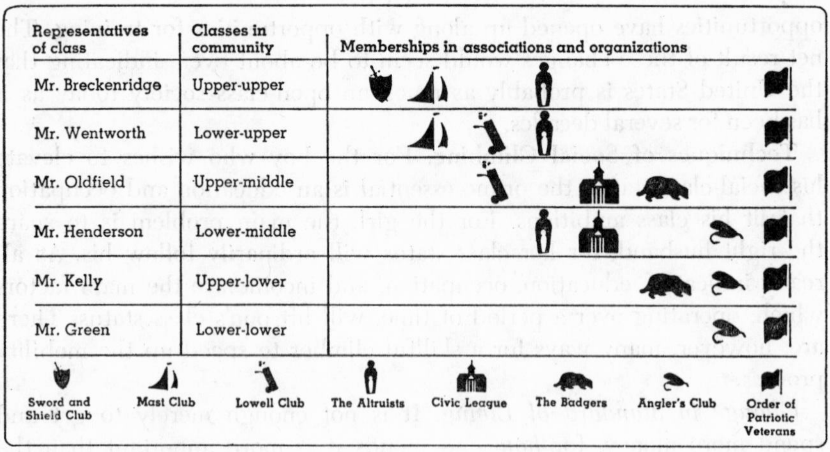

Representatives of class	Classes in community	Memberships in associations and organizations						
Mr. Breckenridge	Upper-upper							
Mr. Wentworth	Lower-upper							
Mr. Oldfield	Upper-middle							
Mr. Henderson	Lower-middle							
Mr. Kelly	Upper-lower							
Mr. Green	Lower-lower							

Sword and Shield Club   Mast Club   Lowell Club   The Altruists   Civic League   The Badgers   Angler's Club   Order of Patriotic Veterans

FIGURE 10 The Community is a Network of Overlapping Associations. *The community is a network of associations or organizations whose membership may include persons at different class levels. Thus the organization helps persons to make social contacts across class lines. For the skillful manipulator, these associations are ladders of upward mobility, but few will climb more than one rung during their lifetime.*

a professional service that is in the business of training the new rich in old-rich behavior [Wakefield, 1961]. But the most useful device for social climbing is the association whose membership overlaps two or more class levels. The mobile person cultivates the highest-status members of an organization. Then he uses these friendships as levers to get himself into other higher-status organizations in which these friends are also members. Thus they climb, dropping out of the lower-status organizations as they gain admission to those of higher-status [Chambers, 1954, pp. 384–406; Meeker, 1949, pp. 130–148].

This, then, is the standard technique of the successful climber—to cultivate the upper-status members of one's cliques and associations and use them to gain entree into status groups in which one is not yet accepted. It takes a good deal of finesse to play this game. One must be socially perceptive, must learn quickly, and probably must have a certain amount of charm. Those who can play the game successfully achieve rapid mobility.

Marriage. People on the way up must be careful whom they marry. At the very least they must choose a mate whose social finesse and learning abilities will not be a drag. At best a "good" marriage is a priceless asset. By marrying into a family a notch or two above his, an ambitious youth gets a better opportunity to use his talents. He may get financial backing to complete an education or launch a business; he gets good connections and valuable introductions; he gets a wife who already fully understands the class culture he must absorb; he gets a powerful motive to "succeed" and prove himself worthy of his wife's confidence in him. A girl who "marries up" is not automatically accepted into her husband's social class, especially if the jump up has been a long one. Such marriages, however, are very rare. The upper-class college boy may romance the tavern maid, but he rarely marries her. Interclass marriages are generally between persons at adjacent class levels. Where the wife has the social finesse and learning ability to absorb the class culture quickly, she is likely to be accepted into her husband's social class with little difficulty.

When a woman "marries down," does she lose her class status? That depends on him. If he soon gains the education, occupation, and income, and absorbs the class culture of her class level, he generally becomes accepted at her class level. But if he retains lower-status education, occupation, income, and behavior, she is likely to find that her old associates are forgetting her.

The Celebrity—A Special Status. How about the famous baseball star or prizefighter who gets more newspaper space than all the nation's scientists combined? How about the singer or actor who zooms to wealth and fame, complete with swimming pool, press agent, and hordes of eager bobby-soxers? What is their social-class status?

Celebrity status is of a special kind, based on spectacular achievement and not on one's total activities and behavior. The celebrity has a national public who follows his actions without ever knowing or interacting with him as a person. His social-class status would be measured by the status of those who would accept him, as a person, as being their social equal, apart from his fame as a celebrity. Thus President Roosevelt was clearly upper class and President Truman just as clearly middle class. Raymond Massey and Sir Cedric Hardwicke were members of the upper class before they became famous actors, and would remain so if they retired; many other famous actors and actresses came from lower-class backgrounds and have never been accepted as upper class, however feted as celebrities.

Since there are many wealthy celebrity chasers, the celebrity meets many upper-class persons at charity balls, house parties, and other occasions. But when he ceases to be a celebrity and becomes a "has been," which people will accept and entertain him as a social equal? This selective treatment tells his true social-class status. Ex-presidents and war-hero generals may always remain celebrities, but many other kinds of celebrities lose their claim to fame and descend to a humble status.

Class and Caste

An *open-class* society is one in which people move up or down in the social structure strictly on the basis of personal effort and ability; a *closed-class* society is one in which position is fixed at birth and cannot be changed by individual achievement. Perfect examples are hard to find, but the frontier society of early America is often regarded as a society in which inherited prestige was of little importance, while the classic representation of the closed society is the caste system of ancient India.

In this caste system, social position was entirely determined by parentage. Since intermarriage between castes was strictly prohibited, the individual was practically helpless to change either his status or that of his children. The barriers between castes were rigid, and exceptions were practically unknown. Caste specified type of occupation, place of worship, use of separate roads for travel, and separation to the greatest possible degree in all social relationships. The Brahmin in the upper caste was likely to be a person of wealth and education, but even if he were bankrupt and illiterate he still retained his caste status. The untouchable whose position was so low that he was outside the framework of the caste system could not raise his status by individual accomplishments. Even if he were able to overcome his handicaps and acquire wealth and fame, he still retained his lowly social status in the eyes of the members of the regular castes [Hocart, 1950; Ryan, 1953; McKim, 1955].

Recent legislation has attacked caste discrimination in India, but it is deeply rooted in the mores and difficult to change. The system is sanctioned by Hindu religious beliefs and regarded as the will of the gods by members of both the higher and the lower castes. The only escape mechanisms are a very limited possibility of changing caste through adoption and the hope that one may have a higher status in his next incarnation. The Hindu believes in a prolonged round of rebirths; if he is unfortunate in his present life, he may be more favored in the next. This religious sanction of caste is not unchallenged, however, for some of the most prominent Hindus, including the late Mahatma Gandhi, have attacked caste barriers as a perversion of the essence of true Hinduism.

The position of the American Negro is sometimes regarded as an example of the caste system, since his position is determined by his racial classification. Even the Negro who is well educated and successful in a profession or business will still be regarded as an inferior by many less-distinguished whites. There is some debate over whether Negroes and whites form true castes in the United States. Critics of the concept point out, for example, that while most whites may feel superior to all Negroes, they do not treat all Negroes alike. Even the most bigoted white is unlikely to treat the Negro university president the same as he treats the Negro sharecropper. Exceptions to the caste barriers are constantly being made for particularly distinguished Negroes. Does this disprove the existence of caste, or merely show that we recognize class differences within the two castes? The latter idea is expressed in the caste-class hypothesis diagramed in Figure 11. The figure describes two castes with a virtually impassible barrier; on each side of the caste barrier is a comparable set of class levels. No Negro will be treated in all respects as though he were white, and vice versa; in some respects Negroes and whites may be treated alike; in others a caste difference is noticeable. Thus Negroes and whites are treated approximately alike when they are buying cars but differently when buying houses. The heart of a caste system, moreover, is the preservation of hereditary distinctions through the prohibition of legal intermarriage. This prohibition is the law in over half the United States, and intermarriage is discouraged by social pressure in the remaining states. Wherever racial intermarriage is prohibited or severely punished, this central feature of a caste system is present.

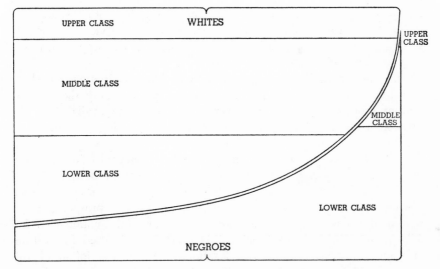

FIGURE 11   The Caste-Class System in the United States. *This figure probably exaggerates the size of the white upper and middle classes, but it aptly illustrates the fact that there are classes within each caste, although the proportion of people in each class differs greatly between castes.*

SOURCE: Reproduced from Allison R. Davis, Burleigh B. Gardner, and Mary R. Gardner, *Deep South,* The University of Chicago Press, Chicago, 1941, p. 10.

The caste-class concept is, in the author's opinion, a valid and useful concept. It describes the fact that certain privileges and duties are assigned to whites and Negroes according to race, while certain other privileges and duties are received by both whites and Negroes according to their social class.

Social Mobility and Deferred Gratification

So many aspects of life are determined by one's attitude toward social mobility that certain attitudes of the middle class, the most mobility-oriented group, have been grouped under the term "deferred gratification pattern" (abbreviated DGP). This is simply the pattern of postponing immediate satisfactions in order to gain some later goal. You readers who are now studying this textbook, instead of playing bridge or "goofing off," are practicing DGP. The DGP may be described as a series of behavior tendencies of one who realizes that social mobility, either upward or downward, is a real probability in his life. Consequently, his attitudes and actions are guided by their supposed effect on his chances for upward social mobility. If the question is raised as to why this should be primarily a middle-class pattern, the answer may be that this is the group that can visualize the most gain from a deferment of present satisfactions for the sake of future gratification. The middle class has both the hope of reaching upper-class status and the fear of slipping into the abyss of lower-class torment. As for the other classes, their view of the life situation does not produce this type of anxiety. The upper class has arrived and feels secure. The lower class has already come close to hitting bottom and, unless converted to middle-class norms, sees little realistic basis for hope of status improvement. Thus both the top and bottom groups can enjoy whatever satisfactions are available in the present, while the middle class must always be planning with an eye to the future.

In this type of planning, any activity today is viewed from the question of its consequences for tomorrow. Marriage may be postponed until one has finished school and secured a good job. Education is considered neither a luxury nor a bore but an investment in future prospects. Thrift will lay the basis for eventual economic power, and emotional control will permit eventual emotional satisfaction. Time is used for self-improvement instead of aimless relaxation. A good description of this pattern has been given by Schneider and Lysgaard.

> Deferred gratification evidently refers to postponement of gratifications or satisfactions. . . . It may be contended that it does indeed fall into a *pattern*, characteristic of the so-called "middle class," members of which tend to delay achievement of economic independence through a relatively elaborate process

A deferment of present satisfactions.

of education, tend to defer sexual gratification through intercourse, show a relatively marked tendency to save money, and the like. . . . [An] important point is the *normative* character of the deferred gratification pattern. Middle class persons feel that they *should* save, postpone, and renounce a variety of gratifications. There are very probably also normative elements in the "lower class" pattern of non-deferment. Thus, Whyte notes that one of the important divergences between the social mobility pattern and the corner-boy activity pattern in Cornerville appears in matters involving expenditure of money. The college boys save money for educational purposes or to launch business or professional careers. But the corner boys must share their money with others and avoid middle class thrift. Should a corner boy have money and his friend not have it, he is expected to spend for both. The corner boy may be thrifty, but, if so, he cannot hope to hold a high position in the corner gang.

Louis Schneider and Sverre Lysgaard, "The Deferred Gratification Pattern: A Preliminary Study," *American Sociological Review*, 18:142–149, 1953.

Evidence that the DGP really exists is found in several research reports [Rosen, 1956; McArthur, 1955; Kluckhohn, 1950; Kahl, 1953]. Thus in a study of 2,500 high school students who classified themselves as "middle class" or "working class," the middle-class students showed many traits of the DGP. For the working-class youth, physical violence both among themselves and in adult associations was more common, occupational goals were lower, more youth expected to leave school before completing high school, and both the youth and their parents gave less emphasis to saving money [Schneider and Lysgaard, 1953]. Other studies have shown a relationship between the postponement of sexual gratification and middle-class status. Kinsey, in his study of the sex life of the American male, came to the conclusion that early sexual intercourse was a routine part of growing up for the lower-class male but a breach of the mores for the males of higher social status. In fact, he concluded that the lower-class boy who had not had sex relations by the age of sixteen was either a physical or mental defective or a middle-class convert "earmarked for moving out of his community and going to college" [Kinsey et al, 1948, p. 381]. Lower-class youth also marry at earlier ages than middle- or upper-class youth [Glick and Landau, 1950]. In all areas of life the lower-class emphasis is on immediate satisfaction rather than waiting for the rewards of a doubtful future.

Why does the lower class so seldom defer gratification? Possibly because the insecurity of the lower-class world places so much pressure for immediate survival that deferring gratification now for the sake of doubtful rewards in the future seems both futile and difficult. Allison Davis describes the pressures of lower-class life.

> The actual daily pressure of 5 to 10 hungry stomachs to fill, backs to clothe, and feet to cover forces the working-class parent to reduce his ambitions to the level of subsistence; to lower his sights as far as long-term planning and studying for better jobs and for finer skills are concerned; to narrow, limit, and shorten his goals with regard to the care, nutrition, education and careers of his children.
>
> This terrible pressure for physical survival means that the child in the average working-class family does not learn the "ambition," the drive for high skills, and for educational achievement that the middle-class child learns in his family. The working-class individual usually does not learn to respond to these strong incentives and to seek these difficult goals, because they have been submerged in his family life by the daily battle for food, shelter, and for the preservation of the family. In this sense, ambition and the drive to attain the higher skills are a kind of luxury. They require a minimum *physical security*; only when one knows where his next week's or next month's food and shelter will come from, can he and his children afford to go in for the long-term education and training, the endless search for opportunities, and the tedious apple polishing that the attainment of higher skills and occupational status require.

Allison Davis, "The Motivation of the Underprivileged Worker," in William F. Whyte (ed.), *Industry and Society*, McGraw-Hill Book Company, New York, 1946, p. 89.

The conditions of lower-class life inspire not an acceptance of the DGP with redoubled efforts for advancement but apathy or revolt. Older people are apt to surrender to a fatalistic view that nothing can be done and that they can only accept their status and take advantage of any opportunities for momentary enjoyment that come their way. Cooperation cushions the shock of insecurity; as long as one's friends or relatives have money, one can eat. Younger people are more apt to revolt. This revolt often takes the form of juvenile delinquency, which through fighting, sexual adventure, and theft provides the excitement and prestige they cannot easily get in any other manner.

These attitudes are hard for middle-class people to understand. They reject fatalism, insisting that the individual can at least to some extent control his own destiny; they reject the notion that one should take care of improvident friends; and they prize the reputation associated with good conduct. For these reasons lower-class conduct seems either immoral or inexplicable. The lower-class convert to middle-class standards who accepts the DGP is considered good, while those who retain a lower-class outlook are thought to be lacking in character and undeserving of sympathy or assistance.

Individual Costs of Social Mobility

The idea that social mobility is good is part of our democratic ethos. We argue that a closed class society thwarts individual personality fulfillment and deprives society of the contributions of many talented individuals.

Whether a society suffers because of limited mobility may depend on its level of complexity. In a somewhat more simple society, such as eighteenth-century Europe or America, very few roles could not be adequately filled by a person of average ability, provided he were identified and prepared for his role from early childhood. Likewise in a stable, unchanging society, the leadership roles, which consist mainly in carrying out the traditional rites and procedures, call for careful training rather than outstanding ability. A closed-class system is probably an asset to the simpler, more stable societies. It guarantees that most roles will be filled adequately, without wasting any talent really needed by the society.

A rapidly changing society, however, requires more of its leaders than an ability to preside over the traditional rituals. And a technologically advanced society requires vast numbers of highly intelligent, highly educated professionals, technicians, and experts. Such a society is less able to afford the waste of any of its brain power. A fairly open-class system may, therefore, be a necessity for "modern" society. Necessary though it may be, the open-class system has its penalties. In several ways it exacts its price from those who compete within it.

Status Insecurity. The medieval cobbler had little chance of rising but little danger of falling. He could be comfortable as a cobbler, free from the prod of ambition or the sting of failure. He could find fulfillment in his work without indignity or shame, and could enjoy his humble possessions and simple comforts without coveting the luxuries he was not encouraged to long for.

An open-class system grants a man a chance to rise but charges him with the fear of failure. He cannot blame society for his low status but must shoulder this responsibility himself. There is no guarantee that he will not drop below his ancestral status, but even if he retains it, this does not mean he has fulfilled his social obligations. His obligation is not merely to maintain his status but to improve it. Other men of low origin have reached high status. Why doesn't he?

Some men in an open-class society respond to the challenge and make rapid advancement; some are so demoralized that they seek escape in drink, narcotics, sex, or other distraction. Many try to protect themselves by supporting institutional arrangements to limit free social mobility. Perhaps the best example of this is seen in trade union, civil service, and business policies which place a premium on seniority as a basis for promotion. As long as one conforms to minimum standards and "keeps his nose clean," he is in line for a gradual advancement that depends less on his own ability than on the health of the man ahead of him and the number of new openings created by the growth of the enterprise. Funeral by funeral, he works his way up the seniority ladder. Some men chafe under the restrictions of the seniority system, but many prefer a slower rate of promotion if it will blunt the rigors of open competition.

Strain of New Role Adjustments. Upward mobility not only carries new privileges; it also carries new responsibilities and restrictions. Occasionally a man declines an offered promotion because he shrinks from the added responsibilities it carries. "Nervous breakdowns" among recently promoted executives are not uncommon.

Occasionally a man declines an offered promotion.

Since social classes are subcultures, upward mobility requires the unlearning and relearning of a great many minor role adjustments. An interminable list of patterns of speech, dress, food preference, table manners, etiquette, recreation, and so on must be revised to fit one's new class status. One study [Hacker, 1962] reports a 50 per cent higher rate of heart symptoms among a group of young executives of working-class origin, as compared with a control group of young executives of middle-class origin. The strain of such adjustments is seldom appreciated by one who has not needed to make them.

Disruption of Primary-group Relationships. Among the student readers of this book will be many mobility-oriented students who are already becoming estranged from their parents. If their parents are working-class people of limited formal education, these students find that they are moving into a different social and intellectual world. On their successive visits home, they are finding fewer and fewer topics on which they can talk comfortably with their parents. Many parents sacrifice to help their children rise above their own position, only to watch sadly as their children become strangers to them. For both, the experience is painful.

Another point of strain comes from the tendency of social mobility to be correlated with geographic mobility, as is suggested in Figure 12. Contrary to the adage that a rolling stone gathers no moss, the person who remains in his hometown is less apt to reach the top of any occupational pinnacle. The life story of ambitious persons usually includes migration to another location for education or apprenticeship, a move to an outlying area to obtain experience, and then a move to the metropolis when he is considered ready to assume major responsibilities. At another level the man on a run-down farm in New England, the laborer in a Puerto Rican village, or the Arkansas hill dweller must move to more industrialized areas if he wishes to improve his opportunities.

This frequent movement means it is difficult to develop roots in the neighborhood and that one is constantly changing the circle of family friends and making new arrangements with schools, churches, and local business establishments. The old family home, the familiar neighborhood, the friends of one's childhood—all these give way to a moving equilibrium of adjustment to new roles, new friends, and new places. The gain is excitement, novelty, and stimulation. The loss is reflected in brittle and temporary relationships often leading to an ultimate loneliness and isolation. Indeed one study [Hollingshead et al., 1954] suggests that mental illness may sometimes be the price for either upward or downward social mobility, and another [Ellis, 1952] finds an abnormally high rate of psychosomatic disorders among a group of upwardly mobile career women.

Even the marriage of the mobile couple is sometimes threatened. Often

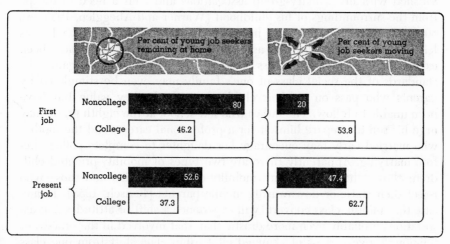

FIGURE 12   Social Mobility Often Requires Geographical Mobility.

SOURCE: Paul H. Landis, "The Territorial and Occupational Mobility of Washington Youth," *Agricultural Experiment Station Bulletin*, no. 499, July, 1944, Pullman, Washington.

the two mates are not equally interested in mobility, or they may differ in their ability to learn the new role adjustments. One mate resents the implied insult of being constantly prodded, polished, and improved; the other resents his mate's lack of cooperation. The successful man who sheds the wife of his youth for a more cultivated partner is a familiar figure among the status seekers.

Other primary-group associates may also be sacrificed. One's easy camaraderie with his friends and fellow workers is threatened when he gains greater authority and income with the prospect of still further promotions. The wife of a major general recently remarked to the author, "I don't know who my friends are any more." Her friendships were now polite and correct, rather than relaxed and genuine. Many enlisted men in the army made no effort to gain officer status for fear it would alienate them from their "buddies" in the ranks; factory workmen sometimes hesitate to become foremen for similar reasons. Friendship under such circumstances may become "status adulterated" in that those beneath one's position are currying favor while those a notch above are in a position to aid or hinder in the continuing process of social advance. In such a setting all motives become suspect, and genuine friendship may be a dim memory of the happier days before one had begun to climb the ladder of occupational success.

The other side of the picture is that upward mobility not only disrupts established social relationships but it may select those most willing to see such relationships disrupted. The person who leaves his hometown, his friends, and his family in pursuit of fortune is often one who is dissatisfied with his primary-group associations and feels a need to escape from the surroundings of his childhood [Warner and Abegglen, 1955, pp. 80–81]. In this sense the boy who makes good is a social deviant who has left behind the attitudes and associations he might normally have been expected to form in the process of growing up. Such a revolt against the standards of the social class of one's family may even be stimulated by parents who pass on to their children standards they value but have been unable to follow. The father who left school at the eighth grade may urge his son to prepare himself for a professional career, and the mother who married early may encourage her daughter to complete college before marrying. Apparently there are two types of mobility-oriented children: those who identify with mobility-oriented parents and those who reject their static or downwardly mobile parents [Reusch, 1953]. In any case the "middle-class convert" will experience a shift of attitudes and associations probably even more drastic than that involved in the process of religious conversion or of changed citizenship. The shift from one class to another is a socially disruptive process that is easier for those who are already disenchanted with their pattern of life and anxious to make a complete break with the past.

Is a high rate of social mobility worth the cost? If a complex, changing society does not permit upward mobility to the talented and ambitious, it runs the risk of turning them into rebels and revolutionaries. The weakness of radical and revolutionary movements in the United States is generally attributed to our open-class system; if one has good prospects of self-advancement within the existing social order, why overthrow it? Thus a high rate of social mobility may tend to stabilize a social order by providing an encouraging outlet to talented persons who are dissatisfied with their social status. At the same time a high rate of social mobility may tend to undermine traditions and develop in the old a cranky conservatism. It may lead to a contempt for "honest toil" and a drive for the "fast buck," and lead to anomie for persons who move rapidly through a succession of statuses and roles [Tumin, 1957]. But the question of whether mobility is good or bad is irrelevant, for a relatively open-class system appears to be necessary and inevitable in a rapidly changing, technologically advanced society.

Summary

Social mobility refers to movement up or down in social status. It usually involves a change in occupation. Differential reproduction rates and expanding industry offer a continuous chance for occupational advancement and social mobility; they are probably at least as great in the United States now as in earlier years. Mobility in the United States has been hampered by a trend toward rigid educational requirements for top jobs, although this hurdle has been countered by an increase in the proportion of youth graduating from high school and college.

While a change in occupation is the crucial step in social mobility, the process may be speeded by (1) revising one's standard of living, (2) cultivating class-typed modes of behavior, (3) manipulating associational memberships, or (4) a strategic marriage. The celebrity enjoys a special kind of status which gains him admittance to upper-class groups while he remains a celebrity.

A society in which people are ranked strictly according to individual ability and performance is known as an *open-class* society; one in which status is theoretically based strictly on heredity is known as a *closed-class* or *caste* society. No class system is entirely open or closed. Modern industrial societies tend toward the open-class system; traditional agricultural societies usually develop caste systems that restrict social mobility. Negro-white relationships in the United States are often cited as a caste situation, although the class differences within each caste make the caste-class concept more useful.

Upward mobility is aided by a time perspective, most often found in the middle class, known as the *deferred gratification pattern*. The lower class tends to reject this pattern in favor of immediate gratification, whereas the upper class has a continuing status security that makes the deferment of gratification seem unnecessary. Lower-class norms are often regarded as immoral or pathological by middle-class critics, but have value in helping individuals adjust to the insecurities of life in the lower-class environment. Mobility brings new opportunities and greater outlets for potential ability, but it also brings emotional strains and threatens patterns of friendship, residence, and family ties. Those not firmly integrated into the social-class setting of their parental home appear to be most adaptable to the changes that make mobility possible. While bringing strain into the life of individuals, a high rate of social mobility may stabilize the social order, since discontented individuals may turn their energies to seeking personal advancement rather than to social revolution.

Questions and Projects

1. Why is it that persons at the very top of the status ladder often spend less freely and put up less "front" than many persons who are a level or two beneath them?

2. Distinguish between caste and class. Is there any caste aspect to stratification in the United States? How does the caste-class concept explain status variations in the United States?

3. What advantages and disadvantages does a closed-class system hold for a society? For the individual? Do you know of any deliberate attempts to decrease competition for status in the United States?

4. What advantages and disadvantages does an open-class system hold for a society? For the individual? What makes absolute "equality of opportunity" impossible?

5. Do you consider yourself to be highly mobility-oriented? What factors do you think explain your own mobility-orientation?

6. Assume that a lower-class and a middle-class person each wins an unexpected $10,000 prize. How would you expect each to use this money? Relate your answer to the concept of the deferred gratification pattern.

7. Assume that higher education became completely free of all costs and that all jobs were filled strictly on merit without regard to family connections. Would you expect the same proportion of lower-class and middle-class youth to reach high-status positions? Why or why not?

8. Why do upwardly-mobile persons usually drift away from their relatives and old friends? Is the tendency due to snobbishness?

9. Is marriage while in college an aid or a threat to the student's prospects for social mobility? Will his social mobility become a threat to his marriage?

10. One study [Shuval, 1963] finds that lower-class girls are more often attracted to nursing by its affective role components (such as opportunity to help people), whereas middle-class girls are more often attracted by its tech-nical-scientific components. Why would you guess this might be true?

11. Are you now engaged in upward, stationary, or downward mobility? What makes you think so?

12. Read *A Tree Grows in Brooklyn* by Betty Smith. What factors account for Francie's rejection of the slum subculture and her desire to escape it? Did she escape through luck or through her own efforts?

Suggested Readings

BENDIX, REINHARD, AND SEYMOUR MARTIN LIPSET: *Social Mobility in Industrial Society,* University of California Press, Berkeley, Calif., 1959. Pulls together and analyzes material from a large number of empirical studies.

CHINOY, ELY: *Automobile Workers and the American Dream,* Doubleday & Company, Inc., Garden City, N.Y., 1955. A treatment of aspirations toward social mobility among auto-mobile-factory employees.

DEVEREAUX, GEORGE, AND FLORENCE WEINER: "The Occupational Status of Nurses," *American Sociological Review,* 15:628–634, 1950. A sur-vey of the development and present status of nursing as a profession.

ELLIS, EVELYN: "Upward Social Mo-bility among Unmarried Career Women," *American Sociological Re-view,* 17:558–563, 1952. A discus-sion of some of the effects of social mobility on personality.

HOLLINGSHEAD, A. B., R. ELLIS, AND E. KIRBY: "Social Mobility and Men-tal Illness," *American Sociological Review,* 19:577–584, 1954. Analy-sis of the strains of social mobility and their effect on mental health.

SCHNEIDER, LOUIS, AND SVERRE LYS-GAARD: "The Deferred Gratification Pattern: A Preliminary Study," *American Sociological Review,* 18:142–149, 1953. A comprehen-sive periodical treatment of this topic.

SJOBERG, GIDEON: "Are Social Classes in America Becoming More Rigid?" *American Sociological Review,* 16:775–783, 1951. Contends that mobility is increasing in American society.

TUMIN, MELVIN M.: "Some Unap-plauded Consequences of Social Mobility in a Mass Society," *Social Forces,* 36:21–37, 1957. Argues that social mobility imposes many personal and social costs on a so-ciety.

WARNER, W. LLOYD, AND PAUL S. LUNT: *The Social Life of a Modern Com-munity,* Yale University Press, New Haven, Conn., 1941. Description of social class and social mobility in a New England factory town. Chap. 7, "Profiles of Yankee City," is again especially recommended.

WILENSKY, HAROLD, AND HUGH ED-WARDS: "The Skidder," *American Sociological Review,* 24:215–231, 1959. Analysis of the social attitudes of the downwardly mobile.

Race and
Ethnic Relations

It all happened in an army camp in occupied Germany after World War II. She was a strikingly beautiful French girl who danced in an act in one of the local night clubs, and he was a sergeant in the U.S. Army. The sergeant and the girl wanted to get married, and I was one of several officers who had to interview them and pass on a report before headquarters would eventually give its approval or disapproval of the marriage. The couple had known each other for six months, a long period under wartime circumstances. The girl looked attractive and intelligent, and the local police had no unfavorable reports in her file. The sergeant had a good army record. He expected to be discharged soon and return to a job in a Pennsylvania factory. All marriages present hazards, and the GI–foreign bride combination has more than the average, but this couple both had good records, and ordinarily approval would have been routine except for one factor, and this one the army didn't officially recognize; he was Negro and she was white.

After the initial introduction I interviewed the girl alone. With a rather brutal directness I probed for her awareness of racial prejudices and discrimination. It was not my assignment to stop the marriage, but I was afraid she might not realize how different the status of a wife in an interracial marriage in the United States might be as compared to the status of the girl friend of a member of the occupying army in a district where most of the troops were Negro.

For some time my questions got exactly nowhere. Her answers were in carefully guarded monosyllables which showed no realization that either her courtship or her marriage would be any different from those of thousands of other French-American couples. Finally, in typically feminine fashion, her composure gave way and she burst into tears.

"I know what you mean," she said. "It's already happened to us here."

As I was transferred shortly afterward, I never learned the final outcome. Possibly the slow procedure of unraveling army red tape found the sergeant back in the states before he could marry. Then again perhaps the marriage took place. If so it may have foundered on the rocks of prejudice and racial discrimination, or the couple may have found the understanding to handle these problems. The outcome of their romance depends on many variables. But in her pathetic confession, "I know what you mean," she revealed that she had discovered the barriers that they could never remove.

From the army experience of a colleague of the author's.

Giddings [1913, p. 17], an early American sociologist, built up a whole system of thought around the concept "consciousness of kind." His thesis was that social groups tend to be made up of those who recognize their similarities and that the people in these groups then classify others as "different"—members of the out-group. The basis of similarity may include any one or any combination of such traits as kinship, religion, regional background, nationality, language usage, economic status, physical appearance, and perhaps others.

Sociologists today attribute less importance to "consciousness of kind" as a basis for grouping than Giddings did. Many of the most important groupings in modern society, such as labor unions, political parties, trade associations, and pressure groups, are not based on "consciousness of kind" at all but include most dissimilar types of persons. It remains true, however, that many important groupings are based on similarities of some kind.

Divisions along racial lines are so important today that sometimes "race relations" is considered a subject by itself. *Races* are defined as groups with distinctive combinations of physical traits that set them off from other races. Skin color is the principal trait used in classifying races, although hair color, hair texture, amount of body hair, eye fold, shape of nose and lips, head contour, and body build are also used.

How many races are there? No objectively correct number can be given. Whether there are three, six, or fifty races depends on which physical features we consider significant and on the degree of similarity in physical appearance we demand of the members of a race. It is conventional to divide the human species into three main racial stocks—the Mongoloid (yellow and brown), the Negroid (black), and the Caucasoid (white). Most groups can be placed in one of these three categories, as is shown in Figure 13. This figure also shows that there are some groups whose racial placement is uncertain because their physical characteristics overlap. For example the Asian Indians have Mongoloid skin color but Caucasoid facial features; the Ainu of northern Japan have Caucasoid skin color and hair and Mongoloid facial features. A further complication arises from the fact that the races have been so busily interbreeding for thousands of years that nearly all racial groups are considerably intermixed. Some groups, like the Jews, are not properly racial at all yet form a definite social entity and are often treated as though they were a race.

The Scientific View of Race Differences

It is clear that the races differ in their inherited physical characteristics. May they also vary in their inborn intellectual and emotional characteristics? This is a reasonable and logical possibility. Is is a fact?

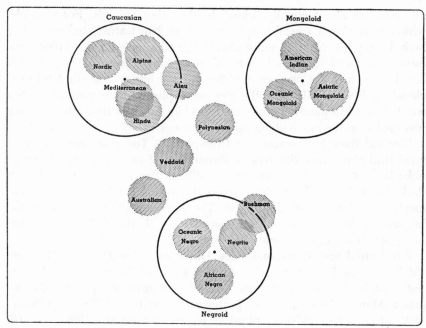

FIGURE 13 **The Races of Mankind.** *Distances between the centers of circles are representative of the degree of relationship.*

SOURCE: A. L. Kroeber, *Anthropology*, Harcourt, Brace & World, Inc., New York, 1948, p. 10.

Some Historic Theories of Race. The ancient world was not much bothered by the question of race differences, for it was not a highly race-conscious world. Slavery was not based on color in the ancient world, and the slave in pagan Rome had far brighter prospects than a slave in the American South. Intense race consciousness among European peoples did not develop until the colonial expansion, when white men needed a handy rationalization to justify their rule over nonwhite peoples. Then a succession of ingenious theories arose, all of which confirmed the white man's superiority and sanctified his rule.

One such theory, still widely held, is the theory of the Hamitic curse, holding that the Negroes are the sons of Ham, cursed by God to be servants [Genesis 9:18–25]. The Bible does not state that the Negroes are descendants of Ham, an oversight that believers in this theory are happy to correct. When the work of Darwin popularized evolutionary theories, it was not long before such theories were applied to racial origins. These held that Negroes were products of a separate evolution or were an intermediate offshoot, and therefore were a primitive, half-animal form of human being [Carroll, 1900]. Scientists, however, are agreed that all men are of one species, product of a single evolution, and all races are about equally "close" to the other animals. For example, whites more closely resemble apes in lip form, hair texture, and amount of body hair, while Negroes more closely resemble apes in skin color, nose form, and facial slant. A variety of geographic theories were given a racial twist, with the superior qualities of the white race attributed to the climate it lives in. All these theories accomplished their purpose, which was to provide a plausible rationale for white rule at a time when science was unable to say much about race differences.

Physical Race Differences Are Unimportant. Today science can say a good deal about race differences. Physically, all races are approximately alike in everything that is important. With a few exceptions (such as a dark skin being useful under a tropical sun), the differences are ornamental, not functionally important. The physical differences within the human species are very modest compared with the differences within many species—dogs or horses, for example.

Intellectual and Emotional Race Differences Are Hard to Measure. Intellectual and emotional characteristics cannot be measured directly but must be inferred from some kind of performance. Here a difficulty arises. Many things can affect performance—native ability, experience, motivation, self-confidence, physical health, testing situation, and still others. The importance of any one of these factors can be measured accurately only if all others are held absolutely constant. How can comparative racial ability be measured? Only by comparing the performance of two racial groups where *all* these other factors are held constant. Does the evidence usually offered meet this test? Two kinds of evidence of racial inequality are usually offered: differential racial achievement and intelligence-test scores.

Differential Racial Achievements. If all races have equal innate abilities, why haven't they made equal achievements? This question is deceptively ethnocentric. We ask, "If they are as smart as we are, why don't they do what we do as well as we do it?" Meanwhile another people may be asking the same question about us. Obviously, if we define achievement purely in terms of our culture's values, we can't lose.

Suppose achievement is defined as the building of a great civilization. Does this feat identify the superior races? Superior at what moment in history? By this test the superior "races" 5,000 years ago would be the Egyptians and the Semitic peoples of Asia Minor; 3,000 years ago, these plus the Indians and the Chinese; 2,500 years ago, the Greeks and the Persians; 2,000 years ago, the Romans; and so it goes. Why, then, did the Nordic whites spend four-fifths of human history hovering about campfires and wiping their greasy fingers on their thighs? The cultural-achievement test of racial superiority works out most nicely if it is confined to the last thousand years of history.

But, one may ask, when have the Negroes built a great civilization? Doesn't their uncreativity show inferiority? It is true that the Negroes built no impressive civilization in the tropical jungles or arid grasslands where most Negroes lived. Neither did anybody else. It is also true that the Negroid peoples in Nubia and Ethiopia created states by 1,000 B.C. surpassing anything the northwestern Europeans built until almost 2,000 years later. But the leading early civilizations were river-valley civilizations. Not until the development of modern technology was it possible to plant civilization in the tropical jungle, where it is still uncertain how well it will flourish. Negroes did, however, contribute to several civilizations that developed on the fringes of Africa, notably those of Carthage and Egypt.

Cultural achievement is a product of many variables—geography and climate, contacts with other peoples, dominant values of the culture, level of preexisting technology, and perhaps racial ability. Since we have no satisfactory way to hold these variables constant, we have no scientific way to measure the factor of racial ability in cultural achievement.

A different sort of cultural achievement is a group's success in absorbing and using an advanced culture with which it comes in contact. By this test the Nordic whites came off rather poorly. Falling heir to Roman civilization, they kicked it to pieces and sat on the remnants for hundreds of years. The nonwhite races of the world today, by comparison, are doing rather well.

Intelligence-test Findings Are Inconclusive. Almost the only scientific attempts to measure comparative racial abilities have been through intelligence testing. There have been dozens, almost hundreds, of comparative studies of racial intelligence, usually Negro-white comparisons. Almost without exception they show a comforting degree of white superiority. The first large-scale test was run during World War I when all servicemen took intelligence tests as part of army-induction procedures. The average scores of whites were consistently higher than those of Negroes. Two qualifications, however, are important: Many individual Negroes had higher scores than many individual whites; and when the scores were broken down by states, Negroes in the top three Northern states had higher average scores than whites in the bottom three Southern states.

Why should Northern Negroes have made higher scores than Southern whites? Selective migration—a tendency for the superior Negroes to migrate northward—is a possible answer, but the evidence for the tendency is not very convincing and certainly would not provide a complete explanation [Klineberg, 1935; Shuey, 1958, chap. 9]. A more probable explanation is that these Negro groups came from a more favorable environment and that this advantage was reflected in their performance

Table 12 SOUTHERN WHITES AND NORTHERN NEGROES BY STATES:
Army Recruits, World War I

Whites		Negroes	
State	Median score	State	Median score
Mississippi	41.25	New York	45.02
Kentucky	41.50	Illinois	47.35
Arkansas	41.55	Ohio	49.50

SOURCE: Otto Klineberg, "What Psychological Tests Show," in Bernard J. Stern and Allain Locke (eds.), *When Peoples Meet*, Progressive Education Association, New York, 1942, p. 449.

on intelligence tests. The average white man in these Southern states lived a poverty-stricken life in an area with poor schools and little social stimulation of any kind. The Northern Negroes, although subject to many types of discrimination, probably had better schools and a more intellectually stimulating environment than many of the Southern whites. Several other studies have shown similar reversals of the usual relation between race and intelligence-test scores.

> Clark, for example, gave the National Intelligence Test to 500 Negro elementary children in Los Angeles and obtained a median IQ of 104.7 which is slightly above the white children with whom they were compared. Peterson and Lanier gave a series of tests to twelve year old white and Negro boys in different cities. They found, in general, that whereas in Nashville there was a marked superiority of white over Negro boys, in Chicago it was not so great and in New York it disappeared altogether.

Otto Klineberg, *Negro Intelligence and Selective Migration*, Columbia University Press, New York, 1935, p. 450.

Nearly all intelligence-test studies that compare *unselected* groups of whites and Negroes show the whites to be superior; but when Eells [1951, p. 61–62] controlled for social class, comparing Negroes with whites at the same class level, he found no significant difference in average test scores. When carefully analyzed, intelligence tests provide stronger evidence for the *equality* than the inequality of races in native abilities.

Other kinds of groups differ in test scores, without any conclusions about innate inferiority being inferred. Almost all heavily Catholic groups make rather low average scores [Klineberg, 1944, p. 35]. Does this mean that Catholics have less native intelligence than Protestants? The heavily Catholic groups tested were from urban slum areas, densely populated by immigrants of southern European background; thus these children were a disadvantaged group. The lowest test scores of all have been made by the isolated mountain people of the southern highlands, the hillbillies, who are entirely Protestant and the most nearly pure Anglo-Saxons in the country. It is clear that we cannot predict a group's test score from its religion or racial origin, but we can make a quite accurate prediction of a group's intelligence-test score if we know its cultural environment.

This relationship of score to environment should be no surprise once we recognize that the intelligence test is misnamed. *Intelligence tests do not measure intelligence; they measure intellectual performance.* The two vary widely; intelligence is inherited, but intellectual performance is affected by many variables of experience. When the intelligence test is used to compare two persons of similar background, motivation, learning experience, health, and familiarity with tests and test situations, it will quite reliably select the one with greater inborn intelligence. When it is used to compare the intelligence of persons or groups who differ in these other respects, the intelligence test is worse than useless, for it gives false measurements. Most Negroes are from a lower-class background. Among the factors that keep their test scores low are poor health, parental disinterest in tests and learning, an educationally impoverished home background, and often a poor school adjustment—the same factors that handicap most lower-class white children. Added to these are some special handicaps imposed by race—a drummed-in sense of racial inferiority and, frequently, an uncertain rapport with a white teacher or test administrator.

We cannot say how white and Negro achievements would compare under conditions of equal opportunity and reward, for nowhere are they fully equal. Not until white and Negro have competed under conditions that are equal in all respects—and for two or three generations of time so that the legacy of past discrimination and failure is forgotten—only then can we make a final judgment as to their respective racial abilities. Meanwhile, practically all social scientists are prepared to assume the equal abilities of all races, as is indicated in this resolution of the American Anthropological Association.

> The American Anthropological Association repudiates statements now appearing in the United States that Negroes are biologically and in innate mental ability inferior to whites, and reaffirms the fact that there is no scientifically established evidence to justify the exclusion of any race from the rights guaranteed by the Constitution of the United States. The basic principle of equality of opportunity and equality before the law are compatible with all that is known about human biology. All races possess the abilities needed to participate fully in the democratic way of life and in modern technological civilization.

Resolution unanimously adopted by the Council of Fellows of the American Anthropological Association, Nov. 17, 1961.

But not all are prepared to accept this conclusion of science. For example, Alabama's Governor John Patterson recently allocated $3,000 from his emergency funds to prove "scientifically" that the Negro is mentally inferior.[1]

Group Differences in Behavior Are Learned. Sometimes the "all men are alike" theme is distorted into a caricature of the facts. It is true that all groups apear to be alike in their inherited abilities. It is also true that groups differ greatly in their learned behavior. It is a fact that, as compared with whites in the United States, Negroes *average* lower in income, education, and stability of work habits; Negroes have higher rates of crime and delinquency, venereal disease, illegitimacy, desertion, and practically every other unflattering index. The bitter Southern resistance to school integration is based in part on the fact that a large proportion of Southern Negro children are dirty, ill-clad, unwashed, vermin-ridden, and uncouth in speech and manner.

How should we interpret such facts? To some, they serve as an excuse for a continued denial of equal opportunity to Negroes. The more perceptive observer sees that these unflattering facts are the *products* of unequal opportunity and will continue as long as opportunities and rewards are unequal. The perceptive observer also notes that averages do not apply to individuals; many Negroes rank far above many whites in achievement.

The social scientist recognizes that there are many *very real* group differences in personality, behavior, and achievement. There is no convincing evidence that any of these differences are rooted in anything inborn; in fact the evidence strongly indicates that all or nearly all *major group differences in personality, behavior, and achievement are entirely learned,* for they are rooted not in heredity but in group tradition, opportunity, and reward. Why, then, do Negroes excel in music, dancing, and athletics? Not because of any special ability but because these fields are more open to Negroes. Why do Jews pursue trade and avoid farming? For over a thousand years, trade was the only occupation Gentiles would let them engage in. If scientists wish to understand special behavior traits of any group, they do not study the group's heredity; they study the conditions under which the group has lived and worked and interacted with other groups throughout its history.

Group Averages Tell Nothing about Individuals. On almost any *uncontrolled* comparison of whites and Negroes in the United States, the Negroes will show a definite inferiority. Many Negroes, however, will rank above many whites. This fact raises some interesting policy questions. For example, when Dallas, Texas, gave a "readiness for learning" test to its first-grade pupils, it found this distribution:

[1] Reported in *Civil Liberties,* monthly newsletter of the American Civil Liberties Union, February, 1962.

READINESS FOR LEARNING

Per cent	Negro	White
In below-average grouping	74	31
In average grouping	18	32
In above-average grouping	8	37

SOURCE: A. D. Albright, "What Are Standards?" *Southern School News*, June, 1958, p. 1.

The above table and many similar pupil comparisons clearly show the average academic superiority of white pupils. They also show that many Negroes were above many whites, since 31 per cent of the whites were placed below-average, while 26 per cent of the Negroes were average or above. If these children are divided according to race for school experience, nearly one-third of the whites will receive certain experiences denied to the one-fourth of the Negroes whose abilities are greater. Racial discrimination involves not only "the unequal treatment of equals"; it always goes beyond this to deny to the superior Negro the privileges enjoyed by the inferior white. Just how to reconcile this practice with the democratic ethos is a persistent problem for the supporters of a caste society.

Most Race Differences in America Are Basically Class Differences. Negroes in the United States live seven years fewer than whites. Negroes have higher rates of venereal disease, tuberculosis, and most infectious diseases, but lower rates of heart disorder, cancer, arthritis, and other degenerative disease. These differences are sometimes attributed to some racial difference in susceptibility. With few exceptions, there is no scientific evidence to support this belief. Similar differences are found when lower-class whites are compared with middle- and upper-class whites.

Most Negroes, Puerto Ricans, and Mexican-Americans are in the lower class. They suffer more infectious disease because of poor diet, poor housing, poor health habits, and lack of medical care. They suffer fewer degenerative diseases mainly because they don't live long enough to develop them. Like lower-class whites, they suffer more mental illness. The Negro illegitimacy rate is about twelve times the white rate. This difference is due partly to social class and partly to the special structure of the Negro family in the United States [Frazier, 1948]. Under slavery, Negroes were not legally entitled to a stable family life; sexual responsibility was not expected of them. The family, such as it was, was mother-centered, with the father an unimportant figure. The lower-class Negro family continues to be mother-centered, for jobs are more available to Negro women than to men. Not until job opportunities permit the lower-class Negro male to be the true *economic* head of the family can we expect him to develop any strong sense of sexual discipline and filial responsibility. The middle- and upper-class Negro family, however, is highly stable and rigidly puritanical, more so than its white counterpart [Frazier, 1957]. Thus are economic and familial institutions interrelated.

To summarize the scientific facts about race differences, we may say that all theories of *inborn* race differences in ability, personality, or behavior are unsubstantiated by scientific evidence. While these characteristics cannot be exactly measured, it appears that all major groups are alike in their average inheritance of everything that is important for behavior or learning. If there are any average differences in innate abilities, they are very small, are clouded by great overlapping, and are insignificant in effect when compared to differences in learning opportunity. There are, however, great differences in the present average behavior and personality of racial and other groups; but these differences are due largely or entirely to group differences in tradition, opportunity, and reward. Wherever the total behavior conditions are alike, behavior eventually becomes alike.

Patterns of Ethnic Relationships

We often hear people speak of the "Jewish race" or the "German race." In doing so they misuse the term. These peoples are not races; yet they are often thought of and treated as races. Sociologists use the term *ethnic group* to refer to any kind of group, racial or otherwise, that is socially differentiated to an important degree. In other words an ethnic group is one which is recognized by society and by itself as a definite group. Although the distinction is associated with a particular set of ancestors, its identifying marks may be language, religion, relationship to a geographic locale, nationality, physical appearance, or any combination of these. The term is properly applied whenever the group differences are considered socially significant enough to set off the group clearly from others. Thus in the United States the term "Catholic" by itself would not be considered an ethnic label, but "French Canadian Catholic" would call up an image of a group with a definite character both in its own eyes and in those of the rest of society.

When the prospective French war bride said she knew what the interviewer meant, her admission was a way of saying she realized society was patterned on ethnic lines. Although we find some pattern of ethnic arrangements in every complex society, there is a great variety in the way different groups have arranged to live together. We shall look at these briefly under the headings "Racist Patterns" and "Equalitarian Patterns." The term *racist* refers to a society that is frankly dominated by one group; *equalitarian* refers to a society in which an effort is made to treat all groups more equally. The following analysis is taken in part from Berry [1958, chaps. 7–12].

Some Racist Patterns of Ethnic Relationship. In spite of some moves toward equalitarian intergroup living, the main trend of the twentieth century has been toward racist solutions of intergroup problems. Never in the world's history has there been so much mass slaughter, expulsion of minorities, and division of territory along ethnic lines as in the period of the last fifty years.

Annihilation. Looking at the most grim of the racist solutions, we find that history's greatest annihilation was carried out by a highly civilized Christian nation. Between 1933 and 1945, the Nazis marched more than 5 million European Jews into the gas chambers with a systematic efficiency. Other cataclysms of history may have taken more lives, but we have no parallel example of such deliberate, premeditated mass slaughter carried out as a calculated government policy. Another recent instance of mass slaughter occurred in the Hindu-Moslem dispute in India in 1948, a conflict that involved practically all the techniques of racist procedure.

Until recent years annihilation or near-annihilation was the price primitive peoples paid for their contact with those from an advanced technological culture. To some extent the annihilation occurred through deliberate slaughter, following the American pioneer philosophy that "the only good Indian is a dead Indian." Usually, though, group decline was a result of more indirect effects of culture contact. These included the greater deadliness of tribal wars with the introduction of firearms, the spread of disease such as tuberculosis, syphilis, and smallpox, limitations of the food supply through the loss of lands, and the disorganization of society through the ravages of alcohol and the weakening of tribal authority. Sometimes disease was deliberately used to decimate a native people. A native would be caught and held in a white settlement until he developed measles, whooping cough, or some such disease. Then he would be released to join his people, who were highly susceptible to the new disease. Often one-half or three-fourths of them would die within a few weeks.

The prospects of native peoples are now changing. The reduction of disease through mass immunization promises to swell their numbers higher than before contact with the white man. This new demographic development is a mixed blessing, since it may be impossible for a society with a traditional culture to sustain an unchecked population increase in the limited territory available.

Efforts to eliminate an ethnic group either through slaughter or through attempts to destroy its culture are classed as *genocide,* a practice now outlawed by the United Nations *Convention on Genocide.* This agreement is a significant step in intergroup relations, but its force is considerably weakened by the fact that at this writing neither the United States nor Russia has ratified the convention.

Expulsion and Partition. The idea that a nation should be composed of those who share a similar ethnic background has been especially popular in recent years. A mass shifting of population has resulted from an effort to make political boundary lines coincide with ethnic groupings— a shift that has frequently upset the patterns of centuries. People whose families had lived in areas for hundreds of years suddenly find themselves declared undesirable aliens and are forced to move to a land which, though it may be populated by persons of the same race, nationality, or creed, to them is new, strange, and terrifying.

During World War II both Russia and the United States forced ethnic groups to move from one part of the country to other areas. The Russians broke up the semiautonomous Volga German Republic and transported its inhabitants to Siberia; the United States placed thousands of West Coast Japanese in detention camps located hundreds of miles from their homes. Little is known of the ultimate fate of these Volga Germans whose ancestors had been invited to Russia by Peter the Great. The United States eventually reversed its policy and allowed the Japanese to live where they wished. Incidentally, although we justified the Japanese detention on the grounds of national security, a far larger concentration of Japanese in Hawaii seems to have been entirely loyal to the United States, and American soldiers of Japanese ancestry gave a good account of themselves in the final years of the war.

Segregation and Discrimination. Another type of racist solution, though less brutal than those just described, is more widespread. In a great many countries the attitude toward the members of subordinate groups is that they should be allowed to function only in a way that serves the interest of the dominant group; in other words, *discrimination.* The essence of discrimination in this sense is *a practice that treats equal people unequally* in that members of different ethnic groups do not have the same opportunities to compete for social rewards. Discrimination means that the duty of the subordinates is simply to do the work the dominants are either unable or unwilling to perform.

The practice of *segregation* implies that contacts between the subordinates and the dominant group will be confined to those essential for the direction of the subordinates in their labors. Subordinates may come into intimate contact with the dominant group as household servants or as laborers in farm and industry. However, purely social contacts are greatly restricted, or if possible, altogether eliminated. If people eat together or sit down together, the association implies equality and tends to undermine the basic assumptions that underlie the system of discrimination. Thus intimacy but not equality of contact is permitted; dominant and subordinate may meet in bed as master and concubine but not as husband and wife.

The segregation-discrimination pattern is probably most perfectly developed in the traditional caste society of India, in which the occupations that people may perform are carefully defined, intermarriage is taboo, and separation is the rule in most social relations. The United States has applied the segregation-discrimination pattern to the relationship of Negroes and whites. Some aspects of this system imply that white men should never work under the direction of colored men, that colored men should receive less money than white men when employed in the same capacity, and that service and educational facilities for colored people should be separate from those used by white people.

Colonialism and Discrimination. At one time nearly half the world's population and territory was included in the colonial empires of a few great powers. When this situation was at its height, the social, political, and economic dominance of the white man was frankly recognized. Perhaps a few native puppets might be kept in luxurious impotence; the rest of the native inhabitants could serve in menial positions or minor clerical occupations but could never hope to be given important executive posts. They might live in or near the houses of whites as servants, but strictly residential dwellings were usually segregated, the Europeans living in a compound cut off from the rest of the population. Native women might serve as mistresses for white men, but legal marriage was rare. The system was somewhat modified in practice by the need to use native personnel in the development of the country. This led to the limited training of a number of natives and to the opening of opportunities in higher education for a few. Eventually, as colonialism began to retreat, the social barriers of discrimination and segregation also tended to be eased; greater political power was granted to the native populations and social relationships reached more of a level of equality. This process has culminated in many countries in the end of foreign rule and the creation of independent governments.

With the coming of independence the tendency is to reverse the process of segregation and discrimination. Thus the Europeans who once were dominant were in some cases forced out of the country. Most of the Dutch were compelled to leave Indonesia, while those who remained soon found that their activities were definitely restricted and their status changed from that of dominance to one of bare toleration. Europeans were shut out of many lines of business activity, and even missionaries and educators now find that their work takes place under the critical supervision of native governments.

Some Equalitarian Patterns of Ethnic Relationship. *Integration.* Perhaps the classic example of the integration of the disparate groups into a common society is seen in the assimilation of European immigrants in the United States. Such immigrants came from a number of national cultures with a variety of languages, customs, dietary habits, family patterns, and general attitudes toward life. The first reaction of immigrants was usually to settle in ethnic colonies, either in small towns which were sometimes given a European name or in urban neighborhoods which became known as "little" Poland, Greece, or Italy. Often they viewed the United States as a temporary haven where they might stay until an unfriendly political regime in their European homeland had disappeared or until they had accumulated enough money to retire in comfort in their homelands. Many immigrants did spend their entire period in ethnic colonies surrounded by fellow nationals, and a considerable number were able to return to Europe as they had planned [Saloutos, 1956]. The majority of immigrants, however, remained in the United States, and either they or their descendants moved out of the ethnic colonies as their assimilation progressed to such an extent that their European background became only a faint memory.

While European immigrants quickly became integrated in a common society, Americans whose racial features set them off from the Caucasians have not found assimilation so easy. The prevailing pattern in America has been the integration of Caucasian ethnics and the segregation of other groups.

In actual practice most colored Americans are still living under conditions of discrimination and segregation. The trend toward integration should be seen against a general pattern in which privileges taken for granted by whites are often denied to other citizens. Housing and employment are unequally available to ethnic groups, and in spite of some change, most Negro children are still attending segregated schools. Even the elementary privilege of voting is often denied to colored citizens, and an attempt to exercise the franchise may involve them in economic penalties or even physical violence in some areas. Colored citizens are never sure of being accepted in hotels and restaurants supposedly catering to the general public and may even find that medical-care facilities are for whites only. Finally, in the matter of informal and recreational contacts, the colored citizen is usually in great difficulty if any of his actions can be interpreted as a demand for social equality. The trend toward integration is undeniable, but many further changes will be required if the integration of colored citizens is to be accepted as the standard pattern of American life.

Cultural Pluralism. The standard example of cultural pluralism is Switzerland, a country that maintains a high degree of national unity although it has no national language and is religiously divided. In Switzerland, Protestants and Catholics have been able to live agreeably under the same government, while speaking either German, French, or Italian. Since the Swiss citizen does not feel that either his religious loyalty or his ethnic identification is threatened by other Swiss, he is free to give a complete allegiance to the Swiss nation as a common government that allows for the tolerance of distinctly different cultural groups. Canada, with a division between the French and the English, and Belgium, with a division between the French and the Flemish-speaking populace, are other examples of cultural pluralism. The different groups that make up a pluralistic society in these nations frequently engage in a struggle for influence, but the essential ideal is that national patriotism does not require cultural uniformity and that differences of nationality, religion, language, or even race do not preclude loyalty to a common national government.

The United States has been cool toward the concept of cultural pluralism, and most Americans have preferred either integration or dis-crimination and segregation as the solution to intergroup differences. Indians comprise practically the only large group in the United States that has expressed some desire for treatment along the lines of cultural pluralism. This preference may be explained by the fact that Indians were here before the arrival of Europeans and in spite of considerable pressure have been able to maintain some degree of cultural integrity.

Amalgamation. While assimilation refers to a blending of two cultures, the term *amalgamation* means a biological interbreeding of two peoples of distinct physical appearance until they become one stock. Although distinct physical types have seldom entirely disappeared, enough inter-breeding has taken place so that it is difficult to find any large group of individuals who form a "pure" racial type.

The Saxon invasion of the sixth century soon pro-duced the Anglo-Saxon type.

England has practiced amalgamation on a grand scale. The Saxon invasion of the sixth century soon produced the Anglo-Saxon type, to be blended again with the Normans in the eleventh century. Hawaii in-cludes the descendants of the original inhabitants of the islands, plus a large number of Caucasian settlers, even larger numbers of Chinese, Japanese, and Filipinos, along with a sizable group of Koreans. All these have intermarried quite freely, with the highest rates in groups having more males than females. White and colored intermarriage is common, and many of the leading families of the islands trace back their ancestry to a union of early European or American traders with the Hawaiian nobility.

In the United States the conditions of slavery favored the amalgamation of white and Negro. Although intermarriage was illegal in the Southern states, concubinage was widespread. Sexual access by white males to Negro females was usually regarded as one of the privileges of the caste system. The system emphasized the dominant position of the white male, since he was in a position to possess Negro females at will and to prohibit such relationships between Negro males and white females. Mere association with white females, however willing, would subject a Negro male to charges of rape, and hundreds of Negro men have been lynched or legally executed on this charge. No white man has been lynched for a similar offense against a Negro woman, and only in recent years have white men been legally prosecuted for raping Negro women.

Amalgamation in the United States has greatly declined during the past century, for a variety of reasons: the end of slavery, the decline of the plantation, fewer white households with Negro servants, the rising status of Negroes, and a growing white disapproval of interracial sex contacts. But while extramarital amalgamation has declined, has interracial marriage increased? We have no reliable recent data on this question. Whether there will eventually be a blending of the races that will produce a light-brown American is by no means certain. At present it is estimated that 21 per cent of the Americans classified as white have some American Negro ancestry, with about 155,000 Negroes moving into the white category between 1941 and 1950; nearly three-fourths of our Negroes have some white ancestry [Stuckert, 1958; Burma, 1946]. In all societies the choice of mates is affected by forces working for endogamy and by counterforces working for exogamy. Legal equality along with increased contact between members of different races may bring a high rate of intermarriage. It is possible that our great-great-great-grand-children may be bound by our preferences in mate selection about as tightly as we are bound by those of our great-great-great-grandfathers. No one can predict the marital choices of future generations.

Minority Reactions to Dominant Groups

The patterns of ethnic relations a society follows are mainly those the dominant group imposes. Yet the minority groups are not entirely passive. Each group plays a role in the interaction. What are some of the minority responses?

Submissive Manipulation. Flattery is the historic weapon of the weak. Harriet Beecher Stowe's *Uncle Tom's Cabin* shows a submissive Negro slave whose adjustment was characterized by faithfulness to his master and deference to white people in general. Through dogged loyalty, flattery, and submissiveness he assumed that he would gain his white master's favor and protection. To many whites, such a Negro is a "good nigger"; that is, he accepts his caste position. But other Negroes may contemptuously call him an "Uncle Tom." In a period when discriminatory patterns are completely dominant, the Uncle Tom posture will help the subordinates to gain the favor of the dominants and also enable them to become acquainted with the culture of a technologically advanced group. As acculturation proceeds to reduce the cultural differences between the two groups, the Uncle Tom posture fades. The subordinates become less willing to assume the role, while the dominants grow less powerful in their ability to dispense penalties and rewards.

Marginal Adaptation. This adaptation is an effort to cultivate fields where there is the least resistance from the majority. Booker T. Washington, a prominent Negro leader in the period between 1880 and 1910, urged Negroes to seek to develop their skills in agriculture and craftsmanship. He promoted vocational education as a step in this direction. The success of his program, however, has been limited by technological trends and white resistance. Mechanization of agriculture and industry restricted the number of people who could make a livelihood as artisans, while both farmers and craftsmen were hostile to Negro competition. Negroes were welcomed as unskilled laborers or field hands but found resistance when they attempted to become independent farmers or highly skilled artisans.

In general the effort of a minority to find an outlet in fields neglected by the majority group is successful only when the field is highly specialized and the minority group is small in numbers. Thus a small number of American Chinese have found a role in hand laundries and in the souvenir shops and restaurants of Chinatowns, and Gypsies have been successful as fortune tellers and carnival operators; but no large ethnic group has been able to find an economic niche where it could escape discrimination.

Withdrawal and Self-segregation. This adjustment has been most characteristic of small religious groups such as the Amish who deliberately limit their interaction with the rest of society; but it may be found to some extent in other types of groups as well. One mark of this tendency is the development of ethnic colonies in which an ethnic group develops schools, churches, social agencies, and recreational establishments catering primarily to an ethnic clientele. While particular institutions of this type such as nationality or racial churches may persist for many years, it is difficult for the group to maintain the cohesion needed to resist the impact of the larger society. Over a period of time, members of such groups find themselves increasingly involved with outsiders and tend to become absorbed in the general community. As they become aware of the opportunities in the society, they discover that often the best economic openings are in businesses serving the general community, the most attractive houses are outside the ethnic area, and the education best adapted to social mobility is found in schools not dominated by the ethnic group. Unless the ethnic colony is held together by a strong religious tie and is either replenished by a constant supply of new members or bitterly ostracized by the rest of society, it does not last very long.

The Oppression Psychosis.When a person is treated in a special manner because of his ethnic identity he cannot easily separate the reason for this treatment from the things that happen for other reasons. A member of a minority group may develop a tendency to impute discrimination even when it is absent. The personal antagonisms normal to any type of social life thus become group antagonisms, and every failure or frustration is attributed to discrimination regardless of the real facts of the situation. Since an inability to distinguish a real from an imaginary environment is a part of many mental illnesses, this behavior in its extreme form may be considered a type of psychosis. Kardiner and Oversey [1951] traced the patterns of behavior discovered in Negroes under psychoanalytic treatment and concluded that ethnic discrimination is often a factor in serious mental illness, since it produces tensions which some individuals are unable to resolve.

Reactions to ethnic status that do not actually lead to mental illness may still prevent the individual from becoming fully socialized. Juvenile delinquency, excessive gambling, drug addiction, alcoholism, and sexual indulgence may also represent a flight from ethnic discrimination into activities that offer temporary escape from the confines of a segregated existence. Ethnic barriers are usually less rigid in the underworld, and narcotics and alcohol offer a temporary release from problems. The amount of such activity in any minority group may be either higher or lower than the general average, depending on a variety of circumstances, but individuals in such groups sometimes find that antisocial behavior is an easy type of reaction to a society they feel has rejected them.

Group Self-hatred. This kind of hatred is another reaction that militates against the maintenance of mental equilibrium. Since the subordinates are a part of the total society, it is difficult for them to reject the unfavorable stereotypes that are a part of the general culture. When the Negro infers from almost everything he reads, sees, hears, and experiences that he is inferior, he can hardly resist believing that he is. The phenomenon of Jewish anti-Semitism is well known, and some degree of similar feeling is hard for members of any minority group to escape. Since society rejects the individual because of the alleged shortcomings of his group, he naturally concludes that the cause of his trouble is not the dominant group enforcing discrimination but the subordinates whose alleged unfavorable traits apparently justify this dicrimination. Some people who have internalized this reaction are able to escape by "passing." The light-complexioned Negro may become "white"; the Jew or the immigrant may change his name and associate only with members of the dominant group.

For most people marks of physical identification or close ties with the group make "passing" impossible. Enforced identification with a group he considers inferior makes it difficult for the individual to accept himself. Just as respect for parents aids the individual in establishing self-respect, so respect for the group with which he is identified helps to establish the self-esteem necessary if he is to become a secure personality. A rather striking example of this process was recounted to the author by a social worker in Hawaii in connection with the local Filipino population. Filipinos were the last group to enter Hawaii in large numbers and held the poorest-paying jobs. Their status difficulties found expression in an attempt by Filipino children to deny their national origin and identify themselves as Japanese or Chinese, since these groups held a higher status in Hawaii. With the coming of independence for the Philippines in 1946 their attitude changed. Now they were identified with one of the first Asian countries to gain independence, and their homeland occupied a prominent place in world affairs. They began to identify themselves as Filipino and, having reason to be proud of their ancestry, could accept it and enter the process of assimilation without anxiety.

Nativism. A quite opposite type of reaction is found in the rejection of the culture of the dominant group and a zealous dedication to minority cultural patterns. Nativist reactions have appeared in many parts of the world. The American Indians in the period around 1888 developed a ghost dance that symbolized the rejection of the white man's world and the futile attempt to revolt against those who had been forcing the Indians into subjection [Berry, 1958, pp. 501–502]. In 1918 Marcus Garvey organized the Universal Negro Improvement Association whose aim was to lead American Negroes back to Africa. He attracted many followers, but his schemes foundered and eventually he was sent to prison on a charge of using the mails to defraud [Cronon, 1955]. Currently a nativist Negro group called the Black Muslims is preaching black supremacy and race hatred to American Negroes [Lincoln, 1961].

A very different type of group, the racist Southern whites, might also be classed as nativist, since their attempts to block national efforts toward racial integration led to a states-rights movement with a vigorous rejection of all non-Southern influence. Nativist movements elsewhere would include the emphasis on "negritude" in central Africa [Balandier, 1955], the Dar Ul Islam movement in Indonesia which strives to reject all Western influences and make Indonesia into a Moslem state [*Economist*, 1956], and a great variety of similar movements in many countries.

Nativist movements often arouse a strong emotional response, but the conditions of life in the modern world make their chances of success rather dubious. In a time when the process of industrialization is forcing all groups to certain common cultural adjustments, any group will find it impossible to turn its back on the rest of the world. Isolation and a return to the past will not solve the problems of today.

Movements of Reform and Revolt. While the nativist movements attempt to reestablish the supremacy of a dying culture, most of the current minority protest movements are an effort to secure for the minority group an acceptable status in the modern world. The National Association for the Advancement of Colored People and several other organizations, largely Negro but with considerable white support, are energetically promoting integration. Techniques include political pressure, publicity, court tests, voter registration drives, boycotts, and mass demonstrations. Negroes will be satisfied with nothing less than complete equality of opportunity and reward. As Myrdal [1944] pointed out two decades ago in his *An American Dilemma*, the practice of discrimination is inconsistent with the ideals of democracy and Christianity which most Americans profess. This inconsistency makes Negroes dissatisfied and whites uncomfortable. It is today being resolved by a rapid though painful march toward integration which, in the opinion of this author, will continue until it is complete.

How Do Ethnic Patterns Change?

Individual Attitudes and Community Behavior. Since ethnic patterns are based on prejudices, is it not useless to attack patterns of segregation and discrimination before prejudices are first reduced? Until quite recently, even the social scientists shared the popular belief that "you can't legislate against prejudice." Like other people, we believed that those who wish to change ethnic relations must rely on education and persuasion; then when persons have formed more tolerant attitudes, their actions will change and discrimination will disappear.

Social scientists now realize that these beliefs are based on unsound theories. First, prejudice is not the cause of discrimination; it is far more nearly true to say that discrimination is the cause of prejudice. Discrimination separates groups so that they have only the inequality type of contacts that create and feed prejudice. Second, we now know that our actions are not primarily determined by our individual attitudes. Current research indicates that probably the reverse is true—that our actions are determined by the pressures of groups of which we are a part and that our attitudes are largely determined by our group actions. This is to say that over a period of time our attitudes conform to the kind of action required by the community in which we live.

An example of this process is found in the experience of Washington, D.C., in connection with the desegregation of swimming pools in 1948. These swimming pools had been operated by the Department of the Interior on a segregated basis. The department had been criticized for allowing segregation and asked several experts their opinions about a change of policy. The conventional answer was that a separation of activities of this type was deeply embedded in the mores of the Southern whites and Negroes of Washington, D.C., and that an attempt to change to integrated swimming pools would lead to disaster. One expert differed. He pointed out that the individual attitudes of Washingtonians were less important than the group pressures they faced. The individuals who followed discriminatory patterns believed that in so doing they were conforming to what was expected of a good citizen. If this pattern could be changed, he believed that integration would proceed without disorder. He reasoned that in this case the essential focus was simply the attitude of the Department of the Interior and the actions of the police department. If the Department of the Interior indicated firmly and definitely that a policy had been decided on and if the police refused to allow any gangs or mobs to form and threaten the swimmers, he felt that integration would succeed. In the implementation of this policy he stressed to the police the fact that they were a professional group charged with preserving the law rather than a collection of individuals acting out their own attitudes. When the swimming pools were opened, a few gangs of white youths gathered in a threatening manner but were quickly dispersed, and after a few days integrated swimming became an accepted pattern [Lohman and Reitzes, 1952].

Some of the implications of this approach may be seen in another example found in a recent study of an integrated teamsters' local union [Rose, 1952]. The union had strongly stressed the idea of integration and had insisted that equal opportunities be given to the drivers regardless of race. Interviewers found that the great majority of white teamsters recognized and supported the policy of employment integration. But when they were asked their opinion about integrated housing, the white teamsters expressed a high degree of opposition. Judged by the standard of racial tolerance, these two attitudes seem to be inconsistent. Looked at from the standpoint of group patterns, however, the inconsistency disappears. The teamsters were members of a union that felt that following a policy of employment integration was vital to the success of the union; as union members they had been indoctrinated with this policy and supported it. They were also residents of neighborhoods that supported the practice of housing segregation, and as conventional members of the community they accepted community values. In both cases the teamsters were responding to the patterns of group expectations, and in neither case could their actions be attributed to purely personal attitudes.

Important as personal attitudes are, they do not exist in isolation. A campaign designed to diminish prejudice is more effective when tied to a definite attack on discrimination, just as a campaign of racial intolerance is more effective when linked to a specific pattern of segregation. The community patterns of ethnic behavior are somewhat influenced by personal attitudes, but they are more directly shaped by public and private groups able to control crucial decisions. The real estate board deciding whether or not it is "ethical" to promote integrated housing, the labor union seeking either to exclude or to integrate, the corporation setting its promotion "ceiling" for Negroes, the school board drawing school-district boundaries and hiring teachers, the courts in reaching decisions, and the legislative bodies passing laws that treat different ethnic groups in either an equal or discriminatory fashion—these and countless other groups set the pattern of the community. If individuals who feel strongly on the topic of ethnic relations are able to influence group policy, their attitudes will have some effect. Otherwise their individual feelings will have little influence on the development of ethnic relationships [Blumer, 1956].

Hospital staffs today are becoming increasingly integrated. Many a patient is startled to find that his nurse is a Negro. Often this person is the first educated, professionally skilled Negro he has ever met. It may take him a while to discover she does not fit the stereotype of shiftless incompetence he has in mind. But as she proceeds with calm efficiency to fill her professional role, he soon stops seeing her as a Negro and sees her as a nurse. Also, she is his assigned nurse; he has no choice but to accept her services, so he does. Integration of nursing staffs is taking place with little difficulty [Goldstein, 1960].

An Example of Institutional Integration. The experience of the United States armed forces provides a case study of the impact of individual attitudes as compared to organized patterns of relationships. Until the end of World War II the army assumed that since soldiers came to military service with the attitudes they had acquired in a segregated civilian society, the armed forces had no choice but to follow a similar policy. By the end of the war there had been some experimentation in mixing Negro platoons in white companies, and by 1953 complete integration was the announced policy of all branches of the armed forces.

In addition to a feeling that segregation was inconsistent with equal treatment of citizens, the change was stimulated by military considerations. When replacements had to be made on a racial basis it was difficult to supply all-Negro units with men who had the training to fill out the needs of the unit. In addition, since the average educational background of the Negro soldiers was poorer than that of the whites, it was difficult to get the distribution of ability in Negro units the army felt was essential. After much hesitation the military authorities decided that integration should be the official policy, and this policy met the test of combat conditions in Korea. A team of social scientists was sent to Korea to assess the effects of integration. They found that Negroes performed better in integrated than in segregated units, that most whites who served in integrated units came to accept integration, and that most of the expected trouble did not materialize [Foreman, 1955].

The fact that the shift to integration in the armed forces was made with unexpectedly little difficulty does not prove it can be accomplished with equal ease in other social situations. Groups without the authoritarian power structure of the armed forces might have greater difficulty in making and implementing such a policy decision. It does indicate that once a firm group decision has been made and it is clear that it will be decisively carried out, individuals will tend to fall in line regardless of personal opinions. Rather than being decided on the basis of either individual attitudes or of some overall principle, the pattern of ethnic relationships is set by the action of the power structure which is able to operate effectively in a particular group. This does not necessarily mean that any particular pattern of ethnic relations is inevitable in the future. What it does indicate is that patterns of ethnic relationships can be deliberately chosen and imposed to a far greater degree than many people realize.

Technology Undermines a Caste System. Today all patterns of intergroup relationship are subject to controversy. While many persons and groups share in the debate, the real causes of change in intergroup relations may be the social changes—in population, in technology, in cultural values—that set the stage for our intergroup relations. For example, the invention of the cotton gin made large-scale cotton plantations profitable and created a need for a large supply of cheap, docile labor. The cotton gin ended all Southern discussion of whether slavery was desirable. More recently, the mechanization of Southern agriculture has replaced unskilled labor with mechanical slaves. Many of the rural Negroes moved to the city or to the North; they escaped from the paternalistic supervision of the planter as well as from some of the patterns of discrimination that could only be rigidly enforced in a rural setting where the white master knew everything his colored hands were doing.

A caste society is best perfected in a static, unchanging system of relationships, sanctified by universally understood traditions. A growing, rapidly changing, dynamic society makes ancient caste rules quite unworkable; for example, a Brahmin in Calcutta today would soon starve if he ate only food upon which the shadow of no untouchable had fallen. A rapidly changing society tends either to reshuffle or to bypass crusty aristocracies and assign the important new tasks and rewards according to individual merit rather than inherited privilege.

Summary

Race differences are biologically trivial but culturally most important. Scientists are agreed that all racial groups probably inherit the same amounts and kinds of abilities, and that all differences in group personality, behavior, or achievements seem to be due to differences in learning situations.

Ethnic relationships involve cooperation and conflict between distinctive social groups which often exist inside the same national boundaries. Bloody persecution, violent revolution, rigid and exploitive segregation, and a fragmenting of political units along ethnic lines have been the principal trends of ethnic relationships in the twentieth century. Other trends include cultural pluralism, which emphasizes the rights of societies rather than of individuals, and integration, which ignores group identification in favor of individual rights. Minority reactions to domination include submissive adjustment, marginal adaptation, withdrawal and self-segregation, the oppression psychosis, group self-hatred, nativism, protest movements, escape through antisocial conduct, and "passing" into the majority group.

Although great emotion may accompany ethnic attitudes, the actual pattern of behavior is found to be dependent on group pressure, while individual behavior usually conforms to community pressures. Community behavior patterns are not always consistent with widespread ethnic attitudes, and the community that supports integrated behavior in one sphere such as employment may support segregated practices in another such as housing. Amalgamation has been practiced on a large scale in the past but seems to be decreasing at the present time.

Questions and Projects

1. Why is the term *ethnic* used in preference to *race* throughout most of this discussion?
2. Is the world tending toward greater contact and cooperation between members of different ethnic groups or toward segregation and conflict?
3. Why do Negroes and Indians differ in the treatment they wish to receive in the United States?
4. Is education the best way to change racial patterns?
5. Which occupational group has done more to change the pattern of ethnic relations—engineers or government officials?
6. If all ethnic discrimination were ended, would all groups produce equal proportions of highly successful men?
7. Many criticisms, some of them justified, were made of the conduct of Negro units in World War II. Is this an argument for or against integration in the armed forces?
8. Has amalgamation been greatest under discriminatory or equalitarian conditions?
9. What is meant by the statement, "Most whites soon come to interact with individual Negroes in terms of the roles each fills rather than in terms of race attitudes"? How does this attitude apply to doctor-patient, nurse-patient, and doctor-nurse relationships?
10. Some Negro patients prefer to be treated by white doctors and nurses. Why?
11. Suppose a white patient objects when a Negro patient is moved into the ward. Which of the following would you do?
   a. Say that you would try to have the Negro patient moved out as soon as possible
   b. Try to persuade him that he should not feel this way
   c. Simply explain that hospital policy is nondiscriminatory
   d. State that the hospital is crowded and that the ward arrangement makes it necessary
12. If both Negroes and whites attend your school, how are they housed —separate dormitories, separate dormitory sections, or integrated? Are roommates assigned at random or are Negroes paired as roommates? What can be said for and against each arrangement?
13. Read Richard Wright's *Black Boy,* Harper & Row, Publishers, Incorporated, New York, 1945. How do you think Richard's socialization was affected by race? Why did he become intensely ambitious?
14. Write a brief essay on what you would expect to happen if you were a Negro traveling through the American South. Then compare this estimate with the account of John H. Griffin, *Black Like Me,* Houghton Mifflin Company, Boston, 1961.

Suggested Readings

GOLDSTEIN, RHODA L.: "Negro Nurses in Hospitals," *American Journal of Nursing,* 60:215–217, 1960. A brief account of the integration of

Negro nurses into the hospital staff.

HALBERSTAM, DAVID: "The White Citizens' Councils," *Commentary*, 22:293–302, 1956. Describes an organized attempt to preserve segregation in the South.

KARDINER, ABRAM, AND LIONEL OVERSEY: *The Mark of Oppression: A Psychosocial Study of the American Negro*, W. W. Norton and Company, Inc., New York, 1951. Portrays the psychic consequences of discrimination.

LOHMAN, JOSEPH D., AND DELBERT C. REITZES: "Notes on Race Relations in a Mass Society," *American Journal of Sociology*, 58:240–246, 1952. A classic presentation of the view that situational pressures rather than attitudes determine ethnic patterns.

M'CCABE, GRACIA S.: "Cultural Influences on Patient Behavior," *American Journal of Nursing*, 60:1101–1104, 1960. Tells how rural, lower-class Negroes adjust to the hospital situation.

NICHOLS, LEE: *Breakthrough on the Color Front*, Random House, Inc., New York, 1954. A popular discussion of the successful integration of the armed services.

REITZES, DELBERT C.: *Negroes and Medicine*, Harvard University Press, Cambridge, Mass., 1958. A study of the status and problems of Negroes in medicine and nursing.

ROSTOW, EUGENE V.: "Our Worst Wartime Mistake," *Harper's Magazine*, September, 1954, pp. 193–201. Discusses our wartime treatment of Japanese Americans.

WOODWARD, C. VANN: *The Strange Career of Jim Crow*, Oxford University Press, Fair Lawn, N.J., 1957. Students who take it for granted that segregation has always been a Southern tradition will be surprised to learn that it was not firmly established until after 1900.

Collective Behavior

We drove around for a long time. We saw a lot of colored people but they were in bunches. We didn't want any of that. We wanted some guy all by himself. We saw one on Mack Avenue.

Aldo drove past him and then said, "Gimme that gun." I handed it over to him and he turned around and come back. We were about 15 feet from the man when Aldo pulled up, almost stopped and shot. The man fell and we blew.

We didn't know him. He wasn't bothering us. But other people were fighting and killing and we felt like it, too.

Alfred M. Lee and Norman D. Humphrey, *Race Riot*, Holt, Rinehart and Winston, Inc., New York, 1943, p. 38.

No topic in sociology is more fascinating than the behavior of crowds and publics. Unfortunately, it is not easy to study scientifically. Mobs, riots, and panics do not often occur under the calm gaze of a visiting sociologist. Deliberately to provoke one, however studious our intent, would put us in jail. Besides, just how would a sociologist conduct an interview in the midst of a mob or a panic? We are limited to eyewitness accounts by observers and participants, to police records, newspaper accounts, and other scattered data. Seldom can we locate a statistically adequate sample of participants for systematic study. A number of ingenious research attempts have been made to duplicate crowd conditions of behavior in a laboratory, but relatively few types of crowd behavior can be so reproduced. Even with these limitations we have a good deal of descriptive information, together with some empirical research, from which we have developed certain insights into the various forms of collective behavior.

Crowd Behavior

A crowd is a *temporary collection of people reacting together to stimuli.* A busload of passengers, each intent on his own interests, is not a crowd; let the driver announce he wishes to stop for a few drinks, and they may promptly become a crowd.

Unlike most other groups, a crowd is temporary. Its members rarely know one another. Crowd behavior is "unstructured," meaning it has no rules, no traditions, no formal controls, no designated leaders, no established patterns for the members to follow. Crowd behavior may appear to be spontaneous and utterly unpredictable, but as we shall see, crowd behavior is not purely a matter of chance or impulse. Crowd behavior is a part of the culture. The kinds of crowds that form and the things a crowd will do and will not do differ from one culture to another. Crowd behavior can be analyzed and understood, and to some extent predicted and controlled.

Some Characteristics of Crowd Behavior. *Anonymity.* Crowds are anonymous, both because they are large and because they are temporary. The size of the group and the nature of the interaction remove the sense of individuality from the members, even when they recognize acquaint-

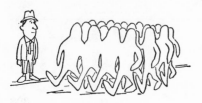

Crowds are anonymous.

ances. They do not pay attention to other members as individuals and do not feel that they themselves are being singled out as individuals. Thus the restraints of a member of a crowd are reduced, and he is free to indulge in behavior he would ordinarily control, because moral responsibility has been shifted from him to the group. At least one study [Festinger et al., 1952] claims to have confirmed these mechanisms through laboratory experimentation. Members of crowds seldom confess to any feeling of guilt after sharing in even the most outrageous atrocities, and this shift of moral responsibility to the group is part of the explanation.

Impersonality. Group behavior is typically impersonal. The soldier bears no personal grudge against the enemy soldier he shoots, nor does it matter that the opposing football player is a personal friend. The impersonality of crowd behavior is revealed in race riots where one member of the enemy race is as good as another, as is shown in the quotation that opens this chapter.

It should be no surprise that peaceful passersby are attacked in race riots. If the other *group* is the enemy, then *any* member of the group is automatically a victim. When FLN terrorists in Algeria tossed a grenade, killing a guest in a hotel, Europeans surged into the streets and lynched the first two Moslems they found [*Time*, 1961]. But if the group setting for behavior is destroyed, then the behavior changes. For example, in the Chicago race riot, one Negro outdistanced all but one of his assailants so that the two became separated from their groups and began to interact as individuals, whereupon they quit fighting [Chicago Commission, 1922, p. 22]. Removed from their groups, fighting seemed pointless. Group behavior is impersonal; when interaction becomes personal, it ceases to be group behavior and changes in nature.

Suggestibility. Since crowd situations are normally unstructured, they have no designated leaders and no recognized behavior patterns for the members to carry out. Furthermore their individual responsibility has been shifted to the group. Often the situation itself is a confused and chaotic one. In such a state of affairs, people act readily and uncritically upon suggestion, especially if the suggestion is stated in a decisive and authoritative manner. The "unpredictability" of crowds is just another way of saying that crowds are highly suggestible [Lang and Lang, 1961, pp. 221–225].

Social Contagion. The most dramatic feature of crowd behavior is the emotional build-up that crowd members give to one another. This communication of feeling is most impressive in mobs and riots but is found in orderly crowds as well. The first one or two cheers at a pep rally normally fall flat; not until we hear the deep swell of voices around us will we cheer very lustily. Every profesisonal speaker or entertainer knows that an audience thinly scattered over a large auditorium will be unresponsive. A smaller hall which they will fill is far better. Above all, they must be seated closely together, without many empty seats separating them. Every revivalist tries to move the audience down front so that they are close to him, and solidly packed, before he starts. The phenomenon he seeks has sometimes been called by the cumbersome title *interactional amplification,* although the term *social contagion* is simpler. This is the process whereby the members of a crowd stimulate and respond to one another and thereby increase their emotional intensity and responsiveness. This process helps to explain why crowd behavior sometimes goes farther than most of the members intended. A panty raid starts out as a lark; the girls protest prettily; there is a good deal of hooting, calling, and risque kidding; matrons and administrators fuss and stew; police may try to intervene, usually without enough force to be effective; everyone gets steadily more excited as each member both stimulates and responds to each other member. Persons who came intending to be only onlookers get caught up in the process and find themselves joining in. Sometimes the interaction reaches the riot level, complete with injuries and destruction of property.

Social contagion helps explain the great suggestibility of a crowd, once it is tuned up for action. A person reading in solitude a hilarious scene from a popular comedy will not find it nearly so funny as when he sees it as a member of an audience. The "claque," a small organized group that starts and leads the applause for a star at the right moment, is a familiar fixture in the European opera house. Since our own actions are reinforced by the actions of others, it takes only a few to start a wave of laughter or applause.

When a crowd becomes emotionally aroused, it needs emotional release, and may act upon the first suggested action that is in line with its impulses. Lynching mobs are not always concerned about which Negro they lynch; if the intended victim escapes, they may lynch any Negro who is handy. In Omaha in 1919, when the mayor refused to surrender a lynch victim, the mob attempted to lynch the mayor and very nearly succeeded [*Literary Digest,* 1919]. In a Texas town in 1930 the victim was hidden in the vault of the courthouse; the mob burned the courthouse, then followed by wrecking the Negro part of town [Cantril, 1941, pp. 97–110]. The Civil War draft riots in New York City began as protests against the draft, but soon became full-fledged anti-Negro riots. Any suggested action, if it is in line with the established impulses and antagonisms of the members, is likely to be acted on by an emotionally aroused crowd [Lang and Lang, 1961, chap. 8].

These characteristics of crowd behavior explain why the crowd is more than a collection of individuals. Each individual member is to some degree a different person in the crowd than he is when alone. As Allport [Lindzey, 1954, p. 28] remarks, "It used to be said in Germany that there is no such thing as a 'single Nazi.' Only with the support of a group does the peculiar subservience to the leader and his ideology take possession of the individual." We can never fully undertsand crowd behavior unless we understand that the crowd, like all groups, is more than merely a collection of individuals.

A crowd in action can be a terrifying thing. A factual account of everything said and done by an aggressive mob would be unprintable. To cite just one example, lynching victims were frequently burned alive, or slowly strangled, and sometimes emasculated as well as being subjected to other inexpressible tortures [Raper, 1933, pp. 6–7, 144]. People will apparently do anything when caught up in the crowd. Is this true?

Limitations on Crowd Behavior. However seemingly irrational and unrestrained, crowd behavior is limited by at least four considerations: (1) the emotional needs of the members; (2) the mores of the members; (3) the leadership of the crowd; (4) the external controls over the crowd.

Emotional Needs of Members. Crowd behavior expresses the emotional needs, resentments, and prejudices of the members. In a crowd situation people may do things they ordinarily would not do, but a crowd does only those things that most of its members *would like to do*. The emotional stimulus and protection of the crowd enables its members to express the impulses, hostilities, aggressions, and rages they are restrained from expressing in calmer moments. Many of us, for example, like to break things, but we restrain the impulse. In a riot, men shed their restraints and can tear things up without guilt feelings. If blocked from its first objective, a mob generally shifts to another. The substitute, however, still represents the hated victim, or fulfills the frustrated wish.

Analysis of members of race riots (based on eyewitness accounts and on police records of arrested members) shows that the active participants tend to be young, unmarried, lower-class, and economically insecure [Wada and Davies, 1957]. A great many of them already had police records for other offenses [Lee and Humphrey, 1943, pp. 80–88]. Hence the participants are likely to be persons with few responsibilities, many frustrations, and violent race prejudices. They have bitter class hostilities, reject middle-class values, and resent being lectured at and pushed around by authorities representing the middle-class world. They happily join in any riot available, and a race riot is especially satisfying.

Mores of Members. Crowd behavior is limited by the mores of its members. The crowd rarely if ever does anything that does not claim a measure of moral approval. Lynchings do not occur in areas where the mores of most people strongly condemn them. Lynchings occur (or used to occur) only where a large proportion of the people felt that a lynching

A crowd does only those things that most of its members would like to do.

was morally justified, even necessary, under certain circumstances. The members of the lynching party normally viewed themselves as public benefactors, not as guilty lawbreakers. Thus even the lynching party is expressing rather than violating the mores of the members and probably the dominant mores of the region. Note, furthermore, that while the victim may be killed, burned, and mutilated, he is never crucified, nor is his body ever eaten. The mores do not support these actions.

It is true that a crowd member may confess later that he shared in acts he realizes were morally wrong. Each person, like each group, holds a number of mutually inconsistent moral views, and at a given moment, one or another of them is operative. At the time it may seem like a very good idea that a self-appointed delegation of students should revenge past insults by painting indelicate epigrams on the walls of a rival institution; later, in the dean's office, it is equally clear that the act was destructive, illegal, and ungentlemanly. Our mores teach us that we should be loyal to family, friends, and fellow workers and do nothing that injures other people. When a strike is called in a vital industry, such as railway transportation or telephone communications, should the worker loyally support his striking fellows and thereby inconvenience and possibly injure the public, or should he stay on the job and thereby injure his fellows? Rarely in a behavior situation does the individual have only *one* applicable moral judgment. Which of one's several sets of mores will operate in a particular situation will depend largely on the group pressures surrounding him in that situation.

The function of the crowd is not to paralyze the moral judgments of its members; the function of the crowd is to isolate and neutralize some of one's moral judgments so that certain others can find unrestrained expression. Thus a crowd is doing only those things for which the mores of the participants give considerable approval.

Crowd Leadership. The leadership profoundly affects the intensity and direction of crowd behavior. Given a collection of frustrated, resentful people, a skillful demagogue can convert them into a vengeful mob and direct their aggression at any "enemy" who is included among their antagonisms. Likewise a leader can sometimes calm or divert a crowd by a strategic suggestion or command.

Since most crowd behavior is unstructured, with no designated leaders, leadership is evidently "up for grabs." Anyone may be able to assume leadership by simply calling out suggestions and commands. The most unlikely persons sometimes assume leadership. In the panic of the *Lusitania* ship disaster, it was an eighteen-year-old boy under whose directions a few lifeboats were successfully filled and launched [LaPiere, 1938, p. 459]. In many crowd situations, the members, frustrated by confusion and uncertainty, *want* to be directed, and the first person who starts giving clear orders in an authoritative manner is likely to be followed. An impressive appearance is helpful, but the assured manner of one who knows what he is doing is essential. Let us see specifically what the crowd leader does.

1. *The leader must establish rapport.* By *rapport* we mean a responsive, trusting attentiveness such as any really successful speaker gets with his audience. The author recalls observing a war-bond rally of workers in a large factory. A visiting dignitary gave a speech that was a model of good speech construction and delivery, spoken in Harvard accents. It was received with polite applause. He was followed by the plant manager who began by holding out two hamlike paws and saying, "You guys see these hands? They didn't get that way pushing a pencil. They pushed a wheelbarrow for four years, and then they operated a drill press and a turret lathe and just about every damn machine in this place." With these few words, he established rapport. He spoke their language. Rapport is most easily established by a leader who has the same background as the members. He senses their wants, recognizes their antagonisms, speaks their language, and can predict their reactions.

2. *The leader builds emotional tensions.* For some types of crowds (mobs, riots, some audiences) the leader builds up their emotional tensions by an impassioned reminder of their problems and grievances. The revivalist convicts the sinners of their sins; the leader of the lynching mob arouses the men to defend the purity of their wives and daughters; the cheerleader focuses all of history on the outcome of tomorrow's game. In some kinds of crowds (the panic, some audiences) the leader need not arouse emotional tension, for it already exists; he passes directly to the next function.

3. *The leader suggests action to release the tension.* The revivalist calls for repentance; the cheerleader demands victory and lights the bonfire; the lynch leader calls "Let's get him!"

4. *The leader justifies the suggested action.* Seldom does a crowd respond instantly to suggestion (except perhaps in panic behavior). Generally the leader makes some effort to justify the suggestion. The re-

vivalist pictures the new life of release from sin; the lynch leader warns, "It'll be your daughter next!" The repetition of the suggestion and its justifications permits social contagion to continue to operate, so that tension continues to mount and the need for release of tension continues to grow.

Leadership can function either to stimulate or to restrain a crowd, or to direct crowd activity from one objective to another. Leadership is, therefore, one of the limiting factors in crowd behavior.

External Controls. Most mob behavior occurs in the summertime when people are normally standing around and gathering in large outdoor assemblies. Cold weather discourages mobs; so do hard thundershowers. Mob behavior is rare on army posts, where military discipline can be invoked to maintain order. Servicemen must release their tensions off the post—and do so at frequent intervals!

The principal external controls on crowd behavior, however, are those exerted by the police. There are practically no instances of persons being lynched in spite of a really determined effort of law-enforcement officials to prevent the lynching. Most lynchings were preceded either by the open connivance of law-enforcement officials or by their merely token resistance. The virtual disappearance of lynching in recent years stems in large part not from any lack of persons who would enjoy a lynching but from the determination of law-enforcement officials to prevent lynchings.

Within recent years, police have learned a great deal about handling crowds. A sociologist, Joseph D. Lohman [1947], has prepared a widely used handbook on the handling of potential riot situations, which summarizes in simple language what social science has learned about directing crowd behavior. Among the procedures used in preventing small incidents from developing into riots are (1) preventing crowd formation by promptly arresting and carrying off noisy troublemakers and ordering the onlookers to move on; (2) meeting threatened disorder with an impressive *show of force*, bringing enough police and equipment into the area so that a *use* of force is unnecessary; (3) isolating a riot area by throwing a police cordon around it, allowing people to leave but not to enter the area; (4) peeling down a crowd by directing the persons on the fringes to "break up and go home," thus stripping the crowd down to its core and depriving the core of its mass support; (5) emphasis in police training on the officer's duty to maintain the peace, so that the officer's own prejudices do not lead him into the fatal error of ignoring attacks on those he doesn't like.

With very few exceptions, serious rioting is evidence of police failure. Recent school-integration disorders are an example. Where local police and public officials let it be known that no disorders would be tolerated, practically no disorders occurred. Where officials showed no such determination, or even invited violence by prophesying it, as did Governor Faubus of Arkansas, violence developed [Blossom, 1959].

Some exceptions must be made to the proposition that police can control crowds if they wish. Small cities have no police reserves that can be shifted from place to place in an emergency. Police in a college town, outnumbered a hundred to one, may be unable to handle a student body on a rampage. A local festival or celebration may bring people into a locality beyond the capacity of the police to control. Under most circumstances, however, mobs and riots in American society are symptoms of police failure.

Some Forms of Crowd Behavior. *The Audience.* An audience is a crowd with interest centered on stimuli outside themselves. The stimuli are mainly one-way. With the movie, radio, or TV audience, the stimuli are entirely one-way. Every instructor, however, realizes that any performer before a "live" audience is affected by the audience reaction. Dollard tells how he was stimulated by the responsive audience in a lower-class Southern Negro church that he was invited to address.

> It was all I had expected and more too. Not familiar enough with the Bible to choose an opportune text, I talked about my own state, described the country through which I had passed in coming south, spoke of the beauty of their land, and expressed my pleasure at being allowed to participate in their exercises. Helped by appreciative murmurs which began slowly and softly and became louder and fuller as I went on, I felt a great sense of elation, an increased fluency, and a vastly expanded confidence in speaking. There was no doubt that the audience was with me, was determined to aid me in every way. I went on. . . .
>
> The crowd had enabled me to talk to them much more sincerely than I thought I knew how to do; the continuous surge of affirmation was a highly elating experience. For once I did not feel that I was merely beating a sodden audience with words or striving for cold intellectual communication. . . .
>
> Mine was a miserable performance compared to the many Negro preachers I have seen striding the platform like confident panthers; but it was exactly the intensive collective participation that I had imagined it might be. No less with the speaker than with the audience there is a sense of losing the limitations of self and of unconscious powers rising to meet the unbound, unconscious forces of the group.

John Dollard, *Caste and Class in a Southern Town*, Yale University Press, New Haven, Conn., 1937, pp. 242–243.

Within an audience, then, there may be significant two-way stimulus and response, even though the audience situation discourages the communication. There is also a certain amount of communication between members as they cheer, applaud, boo, whisper, mutter, doze, or snore.

Social contagion still operates, although at a more subdued level than in other crowds—highly subdued at a sedate church service, more freely expressive at a political rally or a sports event.

The Mob. A mob is an emotionally aroused crowd taking aggressive action. There are several types of mobs, differing in important respects.

1. *The lynching mob* was once popular in the South and West, although lynchings have occurred in all parts of the country. Although riots occur in most countries, lynching is a peculiarly American institution, rare in other parts of the world. It is a part of the vigilante tradition wherein a self-appointed group of citizens seeks to preserve public order by punishing deserving culprits. The nineteenth-century victims were both white and Negro; twentieth-century victims became predominantly Negro, with 1,795 American Negroes and 195 whites lynched since 1900.

Lynchings were not all alike. Raper [1933, pp. 55ff.] and Cantril [1941, pp. 93–110] have distinguished between what they call the Bourbon and the proletarian lynching. The Bourbon lynching took place in Deep South areas of heavy Negro population. Rigid segregation prevented direct competition between whites and Negroes, and the "poor whites" were less likely to see the Negroes as a threat or to harbor a general bitterness toward Negroes than in some other areas. A lynching was seen as a deserved punishment of a specific person for a specific offense. It was carried out by leading citizens, or with their encouragement, and without serious interference from law-enforcement officials. The mob was small and orderly, as though conducting a legal execution. Other Negroes were not molested, nor was Negro property destroyed.

The proletarian lynching took place where Negroes were less numerous and their status less exactly defined. There was more direct competition between Negroes and poor whites and much more poor-white hostility against Negroes in general. The lynching was an outburst of white antagonism against the Negro group; its object was to punish the race, not just an individual. The lynching mob was large and emotional, made up mainly of poor whites who were unconcerned with whether the victim was guilty or whether they had the right person. The lynching was generally accompanied by torture and mutilation and often followed by mistreatment of other Negroes and destruction of Negro property. Community reaction tended to vary with social class; upper-class members and community leaders disapproved; lower-class members justified the lynching as necessary to keep the Negroes in "their place." A lynching, then, may be pseudolegal execution by community leaders, an impassioned emotional outburst of deprived whites against the Negro race, or some combination of both. In either case the individual is supported by the crowd in taking an action basically in accord with his mores.

Lynching today has virtually ceased, with only six persons (one white and five Negroes) lynched since 1950. Although now presumably ended, lynching remains of interest to social scientists as a dramatic form of group behavior.

2. *The riot.* A riot is a violently aggressive and destructive mob. It may be a race riot in which members of two races indiscriminately hunt down and beat or kill one another, as in Chicago in 1919 [Chicago Commission, 1922] or in Detroit in 1941 [Lee and Humphrey, 1943]. It may be a religious riot, as that between the Hindus and the Moslems in India in 1947 [Duncan, 1947, McGinty, 1947]. It may be a nationality riot, as between American servicemen and Mexicans in Los Angeles in 1943, the so-called zoot-suit riot [Turner and Surace, 1956], or the many mob actions against European immigrants in the United States during the nineteenth and early twentieth centuries [Higham, 1955]. Race, religion, or nationality—no matter what the cause, the crowd behavior is much the same. A group is disliked because it is different, or it serves as a convenient scapegoat, or it is hated because it is a competitive threat. With suitable stimulating incidents and without effective police discouragement, persons who are individually frustrated and insecure start action; it builds and grows; the attacked group strikes back; and the riot is under way.

There are other kinds of riots. The protest riot, common in colonial countries, has with the object of dramatizing grievances and wringing concessions from the governing powers. The acquisitive riot is an orgy of looting and stealing. The destructive riot is an orgy of wrecking and burning of property. In practice most riots contain elements of all these types. In the race riot in Springfield, Illinois (Lincoln's home town), in 1908, a mob of several thousand whites assaulted every Negro they could lay hands on; they looted their homes and stores and then burned the buildings [Walling, 1908]. Any riot provides the individual with the support of the crowd and a release from moral responsibility so that he may express any impulse that seizes him. Most riots include all these elements—flaunting of authority, attack on disliked groups, and looting and wrecking of property.

3. *The orgy.* Like other mobs the orgy serves to release tensions; unlike the others, it releases tension not through an attack on anything or anybody but through revelry. One cannot have an orgy by oneself; revelry must be shared or it falls flat. But a very creditable orgy may be promoted by anywhere from a handful of persons to a crowd of thousands. Exactly where "decent recreation" leaves off and the orgy begins is perhaps a value judgment. But to be effective in the release of tension, the orgy must involve behavior that exceeds the ordinary daily restraints and inhibitions.

In the orgy, we see the factors that operate in all crowd behavior—

leadership, social contagion, suggestibility, and transfer of moral responsibility to the group. Since it takes time for these forces to begin to operate, the party takes a while to get going. Before long, inhibitions are diluted and interaction becomes less restrained. Thus many a party, after-the-game celebration, and convention get-together winds up as an orgy.

All societies create frustrations in their members, and all societies provide in some way for the release of tensions. In many societies the orgy is an institutionalized way for members to release their accumulated tensions. A great many primitive societies had periodic festivals or holidays in which ceremonial and orgiastic behavior were combined. Games, feasting, drinking, orgiastic dancing, and the suspension of some of the sex taboos were common features of primitive festivals. Among the Incas, for example,

> Holidays might last for a day or for a week; there might be public dancing, such as when hundreds of radiantly clothed "Chosen Women" danced with Huascar's chain; there could be games and sports; there was always drinking, of a sort one writer calls "approved license." For the Indian [Inca] was expected to get drunk, which he did, quaffing immense quantities of fermented chicha; for ritual drunkenness was as essential to a good festival as agricultural discipline to a good harvest.
>
> Games at the festivals differed from those played by the Indian boy. . . . On the day fixed for the [December] feast, men and girls came to a predetermined place among the ripened fruit gardens, whose ripening they were to celebrate. Men and women were completely naked. At a given signal they started on a race, upon which bets were placed, toward some hill at a distance. Each man that overtook any woman in the race "enjoyed her on the spot."
>
> Victor W. VonHagen, *Realm of the Incas*, Mentor Books, New American Library of World Books, Inc., New York, 1957, pp. 96–97. From the series, *The Ancient Sun Kingdoms of the Americas*, The World Publishing Company, Cleveland.

Students of revelry have assumed that the greater the accumulated tensions, the greater the temptation to find release through orgy. Casual observation would seem to support this thesis. Wherever men are isolated from female company and subjected to harsh discipline, monotonous work, and unsatisfactory living conditions for long periods of time, most of them promptly go on a spree at the first opportunity. Army camps, naval crews, construction camps, lumber camps, and mining camps are classic examples. Presumably the greater the frustrations and tensions, the more riotous the release. Ernie Pyle [1943, p. 3], the perceptive war correspondent, observed that infantrymen often endured mud, rain, and dirt and continuous chaos and uncertainty even as to where they would eat and sleep, whereas sailors ordinarily had clean clothes, good food, and a ship to call home. He then remarked that ". . . sailors didn't cuss as much or as foully as soldiers. They didn't bust loose as riotously when they hit town." One writer describes the emotional needs and outlets of the men who built Hoover Dam during the early 1930s.

> To men who have pushed concrete fifteen days, or nights, with no more emotional outlet than a pool table can absorb, Las Vegas becomes a natural and compelling magnet. The liquor is vile and no one trusts the wheels; but all drink and play furiously. It is pay-day, and it matters not what the night of the week. Where Sunday and Christmas are days like any others, traditional Saturday-night revels lose all significance. By ten-thirty things are well under way. By two everyone is drunk and begging for more. Rooms, as large as small auditoriums, are packed to bursting with sweating inebriates fighting for the edge of the gambling tables.

Theo White, "Building the Big Dam," *Harper's Magazine,* June, 1935, p. 118.

Today the automobile and the mobile home have largely destroyed the isolation of the construction camp, lumber camp, or mining camp, and the orgy has largely faded from their fringes. What no amount of moralizing could do, changing technology has accomplished. The armed services have attempted to make military life more comfortable and less frustrating, and the row of taverns, gambling places, and houses of prostitution in the nearest town may have shortened but not entirely disappeared.

American society has many approved forms of recreation—dancing, moviegoing, participation sports, spectator sports, and many others—that doubtless serve to release tensions. Our society has not, however, institutionalized the orgy as an outlet. In primitive societies the orgy is a relatively safe outlet. In a nonmechanical society, drunkenness that is limited to an occasional socially designated experience is comparatively harmless. In a society with a consanguine family system, collective property ownership, and a serene unconcern for exact biological paternity, an occasional period of sexual license creates no problems. But in our society the price of an orgy may be a painful accident, a costly fire, or a scandalous pregnancy. Our society's inability to provide safe, harmless orgies, however, also carries a price tag. In a society that produces a great many tensions within individuals, these tensions must find release in one way or another. Blocking one dangerous outlet does not guarantee that the substitute outlet will be less offensive. LaPiere comments:

> That the cause of the drunken spree lies in social circumstances which demand an occasional escape, rather than, as moralists assume, in the commercial provision of opportunities for such indulgence, is illustrated by the history of an attempt to check the week-end sprees of English industrial workers. Motivated, no doubt, by the best of intentions, the stringent closing of the "pubs" in the depressing East End of London some years ago had, however, such unanticipated consequences that it was soon found advisable to remove the

harsh restrictions. **Withholding alcohol from workers who were accustomed to a week-end drunk reduced drunkenness and disorderly conduct, but it caused a striking increase in the frequency of wife beating, murder, and suicide.**

Richard LaPiere, *Collective Behavior*, McGraw-Hill Book Company, New York, 1938, p. 484.

The persistent question of how to reconcile our appetite for revelry with our need for individual safety and social order is not likely to be settled in the foreseeable future.

4. *The panic.* A panic involves the same elements of crowd behavior, blossoming suddenly under the stress of crisis. We have done little empirical research on panic, since we dare not produce panics to order for study. There are many descriptive accounts and theoretical formulations [Strauss, 1944; Foreman, 1953]. Panic appears to be most likely to seize a group that is fatigued by prolonged stress, although many panics have spread through perfectly relaxed groups. Whenever they occur, a preliminary crisis produces fear, uncertainty, confusion, and a lack of decisive leadership. The role of leadership is crucial in panic prevention, for panic spreads when members lose faith in organized, cooperative effort and each takes individual defensive action [Mintz, 1951]. In a burning building, one person shouting "Fire!" or "Let me out!" may be enough to start a panic. When a crowd is leaving in orderly manner, if there is any interruption—if someone stumbles and momentarily blocks the aisle— somebody may break out of line in a dash and touch off a panic.

In panic prevention, a leader does at least two things: He organizes the crowd so that cooperative activity can proceed, and he relieves uncertainty by specific directions and reassurances. Marshall [1947, p. 130] has pointed out that when an army unit is under heavy fire, if the unit leader says "Let's get out of here!" panic is likely; but if he says "Follow me to that fence," panic is improbable. Once panic has spread, it generally continues until the crisis is past or the members are exhausted (or dead). Panic prevention depends upon a leader assuming authoritative direction *quickly enough* to organize cooperative action before some individual panics and touches off mass panic.

Some Other Forms of Crowdlike Behavior. *The Rumor.* Much of our casual conversation consists of rumor mongering. Every topic, from our neighbor's morals to the fate of the nation, attracts interesting and disturbing rumors. Whenever there is social strain, rumors flourish. Wherever accurate and complete facts on a matter of public concern are not available, or are not believed, rumors abound. Since rumors can ruin reputations, discredit causes, and undermine morale, the manipulation of rumor is a common propaganda device.

In the definitive work on rumor, Allport and Postman [1945, p. 46] point out that a great amount of rumor mongering springs from nothing more complicated than the desire for interesting conversation and the enjoyment of a salacious or unusual tidbit. A person is most likely, however, to remember and spread a rumor *if it will relieve, justify, and explain his emotional tensions.* People who dislike Republicans, hate Negroes, or fear Communists will remember and repeat damaging rumors about these groups. The rumor changes continuously as it spreads, for people unconsciously distort it into the form that most perfectly supports their antagonisms. People uncritically accept and believe a rumor if it fits in with their pattern of beliefs and antagonisms, or if it provides an emotionally satisfying explanation of phenomena. Thus many bitter critics of the Roosevelt administration readily believed and repeated rumors to the effect that wartime rationing was unnecessary (rumors that warehouses and gasoline storage tanks were overflowing, that the government was wasting or destroying vast quantities, etc.). Such rumors were emotionally satisfying to critics of the rationing program and justified the black-marketing of the many people who violated rationing restrictions [Clinard, 1952].

The health field abounds with unfounded rumors. A common one is that the American Medical Association has suppressed a miraculous new cure for selfish reasons. To disprove such a rumor calls for a detailed history of laboratory tests and inadequately controlled experiments, and rumor believers are seldom interested in detailed explanations.

Fads and Fashion. The fad apparently originates in the desire to gain and maintain status by being different, by being a leader, and dies out when it is no longer novel. Bogardus [1950, pp. 305–309] studied 2,702 fads over many years, finding that most of them deal with superficial accessories and gewgaws. Typically, they grow rapidly, have a two- or three-month plateau, and then decline, although some last longer and a few become permanent parts of the culture.

Fashions are like fads but change more slowly and are less trivial. Fashions reflect the dominant interests and motives of a society at a particular time. In the eighteenth century, elaborate clothing reflected an ornate and decorative upper-class culture, and the confining styles of the Victorian era reflected Victorian prudishness [Flugel, 1930]. Today's trend toward informality of dress harmonizes with our increasingly informal patterns of social life.

Fashion choices and changes are not entirely irrational but meet various social needs as defined by social class, age and sex group, and other group affiliation. Fashion consciousness aids the middle-class social climber, and a distinct mode of dress fills the early teen-ager's need to "belong" in a private world not run by adults [Barber and Tobel, 1953]. Fashion changes are deliberately manipulated by the apparel industry, but only to a limited degree, for there is evidence that consumers will not passively accept everything labeled "fashionable" [Jack and Schiffer,

1948; Lang and Lang, 1961, chap. 15].

The Craze. The craze differs from the fad in that it becomes an obsession for its followers. Many crazes involve some kind of get-rich-quick scheme. The Holland tulip craze of 1634 bid up the price of tulip bulbs until their value exceeded their weight in gold. The Florida land boom of the 1920s pushed land prices to levels fantastically beyond any sound economic valuation. In the craze, the individual gets caught up in a crowdlike hysteria and loses his caution. Speculators sell to one another at climbing prices until some bad news pricks the bubble or until all the susceptible persons have joined so that no new money is entering the market; then confidence falters and the market collapses in a frenzy to unload holdings [Mackay, 1932].

Many crazes revolve around trivial behavior. Flagpole sitting, dance marathons, monopoly, jigsaw puzzles, canasta, chain letters, and many others have had their moment. Since the craze is taken over by only a small fraction of the population and is a time-consuming preoccupation, it inevitably wears itself out quite quickly, soon to be replaced by another for those who are susceptible.

Mass Hysteria. We could cite many examples of mass hysteria in which some form of irrational, compulsive behavior or anxiety afflicts a number of people. In one town, dozens of people reported being attacked by a "phantom anesthetist" who sprayed them with an unknown drug that caused temporary paralysis and various other symptoms [Johnson, 1945]. A wave of uncontrollable twitching spread through a Louisiana high school [Schuler and Parenton, 1943]. The *New York Times* [Sept. 14, 1952] reported that at a Mississippi football game, 165 teen-age girls in a cheering section became excited and "fainted like flies." The Salem witchcraft trials are an interesting historical example of mass hysteria [Starkey, 1949]. The waves of flying-saucer reports, together with an elaborate pseudoscientific literature on flying saucers, are a more modern example of mass hysteria [Hackett, 1948; Gardner, 1957, chap. 5]. From an analysis of the reports, it can be concluded that flying-saucer reports were the main cause of flying-saucer reports; that is, publicity about flying saucers was dependably followed by a series of new "sightings." While such mass delusions are interesting phenomena, we have not studied them sufficiently closely to permit more than educated guesses as to why some people succumb while others resist.

Publics and Public Opinion

A *public is a scattered group of people who share an interest in a particular topic.* Many publics exist in a complex society. We have a baseball public, a theater public, an opera public, a movie public, a foreign-trade public, an investments public, a political-affairs public, and so on. Wherever there is an issue or activity about which a number of persons have become interested, have developed opinions, and perhaps have argued, we have a public. The term *the public* is a favorite of the journalist or politician. Since no topic actually interests everyone, the term may be technically incorrect. When used, it is a synonym for "the people" or for "practically everybody."

The members of a public are not gathered together like the members of a crowd. Each member of a public can communicate directly with only a handful of the other members. A public is reached mainly through the mass media. The titles of many magazines reveal the public for which each is published—*House and Garden, Field and Stream, Guns and Ammo, Western Horsemen, Cats' Magazine, U.S. Camera, Stamps, Motor Trend, The Theater, Workbench, Audio, National Geographic, Holiday, Pacific Affairs,* and hundreds more. Since the members of a public can communicate effectively only through such mass media, it follows that those who control these media have considerable power to influence the opinions of the public.

Publics are created by cultural complexity. In a simple culture there would be few if any publics. A complex culture produces many interest groups with rival axes to grind. For example, one interest group wishes to keep our national parks in their unspoiled condition with a minimum of development; another group wants to develop them into recreation centers with resorts, airstrips, and ski lifts; still other groups wish to hunt the game, log the timber, mine the minerals, graze the grassland, or dam the streams in the parks. Such interest clashes multiply as a culture becomes more complex.

Few issues arise in a simple, stable culture; that is, few situations develop that cannot be handled by following the traditional customs and mores of the society. But in a complex, changing culture, issues are constantly arising. In other words, situations are constantly developing which our traditional customs and mores either will not handle at all or will do so only in a way that leaves some groups dissatisfied. For example, "Should atomic tests, necessary for atomic development, be continued at the risk of possible injury to the health of the world's people?" Tradition gives no clear answer. Or, "Who should pay the costs when workers are displaced through automation?" The traditional answer is, "The worker himself"; but since many people reject this solution as too cruel, an issue of "What shall we do about technological unemployment?" is created.

In these ways a complex, changing culture creates a great many publics, each concerned with an activity, interest, or issue. As the members of a public consider the issue, and form opinions concerning it, *public opinion* is developed.

Public opinion refers to the opinions held by a public on an issue. Strictly speaking, the term should perhaps be "public opinions," since several opinions are normally held by the members of a public; but the term public opinion is commonly used to refer to all the differing opinions held by the members of a public. The term is also often used to refer to the opinions of *the* public—of everybody—including those who have no interest and no definite opinions on the issue. These various connotations leave the exact meaning of the term a little confused; its meaning must be inferred from its context.

Dimensions of Public Opinion. *Direction.* An opinion may be for or against a proposed course of action. A count of the "yes" and "no" or the "approve" and "disapprove" opinions measures the direction of opinion. *Intensity* refers to how strongly an opinion is held. "Yes" may mean "Yes, absolutely, whatever the costs," or it may mean, "Yes, I guess so." *Integration* refers to how an opinion is tied in with one's total set of beliefs and values. Is this opinion an expression of a man's general outlook, or an exception to it? For example, Mr. Smith favors national health insurance (sometimes called "socialized medicine") because he favors a welfare state wherein the government provides many social services to its citizens. Mr. Jones, less enthusiastic about the welfare state, supports national health insurance because after some study he believes it is the only practical way to organize health services. Mr. Brown, strongly opposed to the welfare state, supports national health insurance because he dislikes physicians and wants to see them get their heads knocked together. Mr. Black supports it because his union tells him it is good. While identical in direction and perhaps intensity, these four opinions are basically quite different because of the way they relate to the rest of the mental context of their holders. The opinion that is well integrated with one's total mental context is less susceptible to being changed than the one that is divorced from or inconsistent with one's general mental outlook.

Measurement of Public Opinion. The leaders of a group or a nation cannot lead wisely unless they know which way the people are willing to be led. The public-opinion poll is a recent invention for finding out what people are thinking. A poll is simple in concept but difficult in execution because, as we saw earlier, an opinion is a rather complicated phenomenon. The pollsters prepare a set of questions on an issue, seeking to phrase the questions in such a way that the wording does not prejudice the informant's answer. Then these questions are offered to a small number of people (from a few hundred to a few thousand) so that each group or class in the total population is represented in the sample in its correct proportion. If all these preliminary arrangements are made without serious error, opinion is measured quite accurately. The Gallup poll, for example, has predicted the vote on recent elections with an average error of less than 2 per cent [Gallup, 1957]. But many pitfalls in public-opinion polling are encountered that a pollster must guard against if he is to attain this level of accuracy. One of the greatest is the tendency of people to state firm opinions on issues they know nothing about, have not thought about, and really have no firm opinion on. In 1959 a Los Angeles newspaperman asked a number of people, "Do you think the Mann Act deters or helps the cause of organized labor?" About one person in eight knew what the Mann act was (it forbids the interstate transportation of women for immoral purposes) and realized that the question was unanswerable. But of the remainder who admitted they knew nothing of the Mann Act, about one-half expressed decided opinions about its effects. If the "opinions" of people who know nothing about an issue are included, a poll is not very accurate. Other pitfalls surround the wording of questions, the selection of the sample, and the weighing or interpreting of responses [Parten, 1950; Selltiz et al, 1959, chap. 7]. Polling is no job for amateurs!

Manipulation of Public Opinion. The main emphasis in public-opinion research has been on ways of manipulating public opinion [Albig, 1957]. *Propaganda* includes all efforts to persuade people to a point of view on an issue; everything from Sunday-school lessons to billboards are examples of propaganda. The usual distinction between education and propaganda is that education seeks to cultivate one's ability to make discriminating judgments, while propaganda seeks to persuade one to the undiscriminating acceptance of a ready-made judgment. In practice, education often includes a good deal of propaganda. Teachers sometimes propagandize for their own opinions; interest groups seek to get their own propaganda, disguised as educational materials, into the school; society virtually forces the school to propagandize for the approved moral and patriotic values. To draw a clear distinction between education and propaganda is not always possible.

Most students, beginning perhaps with a ninth-grade course in civics, have seen descriptions of the techniques of propaganda in textbook after textbook. We shall not repeat them here. Good descriptions of propaganda techniques are easily available, should the student wish to consult them [Lee and Lee, 1939; Doob, 1948; Lasswell, 1933, 1951].

Limits of Propaganda. If the powers of propaganda were unlimited, the side with the most money and the best public relations agency would always win. Since this does not always happen, the power of propaganda must be limited in various ways.

1. *Competing propagandas* are probably the greatest limitation. Where the state has a monopoly of propaganda, as in totalitarian states, it is

Competing propaganda exerts a restraining influence.

difficult for a citizen to find any facts to use in arriving at opinions other than the officially approved ones. With a monopoly of propaganda, a propagandist can suppress and manufacture facts, and no effective rebuttal is possible. The mere existence of competing propaganda in a democratic state exerts a restraining influence both on the propagandist and on the recipient.

2. *The sophistication of the recipient* limits the effects of propaganda. In general, those who are well educated or well informed on the issue are less affected by propaganda than the poorly educated and the poorly informed.

3. *The beliefs and values of the recipient* limit the propaganda he will believe. Many people are fond of picturing themselves as open-minded and discriminating analysts of competing propagandas, but in most cases they probably are reacting mechanically to slogans and catchwords. Most people apparently accept uncritically any propaganda that fits in with their established attitudes and values and reject, equally uncritically, any that conflicts. For example, most American physicians appear to have accepted uncritically the American Medical Association propaganda depicting the National Health Service in England as a miserable failure, although the facts are that it has been quite successful [Cook, 1959; Lindsey, 1962; Robinson, 1962]. For this reason, a propagandist rarely tries to change the basic attitudes of his recipients; instead he tries to get them to accept his definition of the issue in terms of their attitudes. A propagandist for civil-rights legislation, for example, would not try to change white attitudes toward Negroes; instead he would try to identify civil-rights legislation with their belief in democracy and fair play and with their desire for a favorable world image of the United States. The propagandist against civil-rights legislation rarely attacks democracy or fair play, or even attacks Negroes; he pictures civil-rights legislation as a Communist-inspired scheme to stir up trouble, or as a bureaucratic assault on states' rights and local liberties. Communist propaganda has been ineffective in the United States because its pictures of the villainous businessman, the "oppressive" church, and a "proletariat" middle class simply struck no responsive note in the basic images, attitudes, and values of the American people. To be effective, propaganda must fit in with established habits, values, and images.

4. *Cultural trends* limit the effectiveness of propaganda. An existing cultural trend has almost never been successfully opposed by propaganda in a democratic society. Propaganda that conflicts with the existing trends and values of the culture is likely to attract only a handful of beatnik eccentrics. For this reason, probably all "back to the simple life," "away with the materialism," and "women's place is in the home" propagandas are doomed to futility. Propaganda may accelerate or retard a cultural trend, reinforce or weaken a value; but it is doubtful if propaganda in a democratic society can either initiate or halt a cultural trend, either destroy a well-established value or instill a new value culture is not already developing.

Psychological Warfare. There is nothing new in the use of propaganda as a military weapon; only the great modern emphasis on psychological warfare is new. Entirely too much was expected of psychological warfare in World War II. Propaganda that was intended to undermine the morale of the enemy had little effect either on enemy civilians or military units so long as their primary-group structures remained intact. Not until disruption of primary-group life through separation, loss of communication, loss of leadership, interruptions of food and medical supplies, and other disruptions—not until then did morale and organized resistance crumble. Apparently psychological warfare has little effect on an efficiently operating enemy; its main effect is to hasten the disintegration of the enemy after superior military force has begun his defeat [Shils and Janowitz, 1948].

The United States and the Soviet Union are both engaged in worldwide propaganda programs whose effects cannot be accurately predicted. The short-run effects of such propaganda campaigns seem to lie in ". . . providing people with a rationale for their existing convictions rather than in changing their attitudes" [Bogart, 1957]. The long-run effects of a sustained propaganda program may be greater, since it may gradually build up a body of factual information among its recipients and thus effect gradual changes of attitude and opinion. This, at least, is the hope that motivates our "Voice of America" broadcasts.

Summary

Crowd behavior is a characteristic of complex cultures and is usually absent in simple societies. A crowd is a temporary gathering of people who are acting together. Crowd behavior is characterized by (1) anonymity—the individual loses his customary restraints and sense of personal responsibility; (2) impersonality—only the group affiliation of the person is important; (3) suggestibility—crowd members act uncritically upon suggestions; (4) social contagion—crowd members build up one another's emotional involvement. Crowd behavior is limited, however, by (1) the emotional needs and attitudes of the members; (2) the mores of the members, who rarely do anything that is not condoned by certain of their mores; (3) its leaders, who must establish rapport, build emotional tensions, suggest action to relieve these tensions and justify this action; (4) external controls, mainly the police, who can usually control crowd behavior if they wish to and are properly trained.

Crowd behavior takes many forms. The *audience* is largely, but not entirely, a one-way crowd responding to a single stimulus. The *mob* is a crowd in violent action. The *lynching mob* is an extralegal device for the enforcement of local mores, and takes different forms according to the local setting. The *riot* is a violently aggressive mob whose members are generally releasing accumulated hostilities against other groups. The *orgy* is a good-natured mob enjoying itself through uninhibited indulgence. The *panic* is a mob in sudden, disorganized flight from danger. Some other forms of group behavior are crowdlike in nature, including *rumors, fads and fashions, crazes,* and outbreaks of *mass hysteria.*

A complex, rapidly changing society creates many *publics,* each of which is a group of people who share a particular interest. The various opinions of the members of the public concerned with an issue, together with the more casual views of those persons who are not much concerned with the issue, are loosely lumped together under the term *public opinion.* Individual opinions differ in direction, intensity, and integration or in the way they tie in with the rest of one's thinking. Consequently it is difficult to "add up" individual opinions and measure the sum of public opinion, but professional pollsters have developed techniques that can measure opinion with considerable accuracy.

Practically every interest group today is trying to manipulate public opinion so that propaganda, often called "public relations," is one of our largest businesses. Propaganda may be less powerful than it sometimes appears to be, for its effects are limited by competing propagandas, by the sophistication of its recipients, by the established beliefs and values of the recipients, and by the existing trends within the culture. Psychological warfare attempts to use propaganda to weaken an enemy and to project a favorable image of one's own country on the world's people.

Questions and Projects

1. When we say that crowd behavior is "unstructured," what do we mean? Of what importance is its unstructured character?

2. Why do mob members seldom feel guilty about their mob actions?

3. Are there any situations in our

culture that contain elements of the institutionalized orgy?

4. Should we fully institutionalize the orgy in American society? What benefits might accrue? What difficulties would arise?

5. What causes the "panty raids" on girls' dormitories? Why do they occur in the spring rather than the fall? Why is the news of one often followed by several more?

6. Do you think you are immune to panic? To crazes? To mass hysteria? What makes you think so?

7. Can you think of any propaganda efforts or causes that have failed in the United States because they conflicted with our cultural values? With prevailing cultural trends?

8. Write up a description of a campus pep rally as an example of crowd behavior.

9. Try an experiment in rumor. Select a rumor (consult with your instructor in finding a harmless rumor) and set it going by a specified number of tellings. Then record the time, frequency, and form in which it "comes back" to you as it spreads over the campus.

10. How do you account for the huge popularity of books like Jarvis's *Arthritis and Folk Medicine*, Tal-

ler's *Calories Don't Count*, and Hauser's *Look Younger, Live Longer* which have not been accepted by the medical profession?

11. Recall and describe a crowd situation in which the behavior lagged dispiritedly for a time. Show how each of the characteristics of crowd behavior came into operation and kindled a proper enthusiasm in the members.

12. Why have so many American physicians accepted highly inaccurate descriptions of the National Health Service in England, although more accurate descriptions are easily available?

13. Prepare a list of aggressive actions you think you might be capable of performing if placed in a suitably encouraging crowd situation. Prepare a list of actions in which you think you could not possibly share no matter what the crowd situation. Give your reasons for each listing.

14. Run a campus public-opinion poll on a fictitious proposition such as "Do you favor or oppose the Hill-Wallerton proposal for Federal scholarships to college students?" See how many will admit they do not know of the proposal, and how many state firm opinions on it.

Suggested Readings

ALLPORT, GORDON W., AND LEO POSTMAN: *The Psychology of Rumor*, Holt, Rinehart and Winston, New York, 1947; or "The Basic Psychology of Rumor," in Wilbur Schramm (ed.), *The Process and Effects of Mass Communication*, The University of Illinois Press, Urbana, Ill., 1955, pp. 141–155. How and why rumors appear and circulate.

CANTRIL, HADLEY: *The Psychology of Social Movements*, John Wiley & Sons, Inc., New York, 1941, chap. 4, "The Lynching Mob." A vivid description of two lynchings, analyzed in terms of the people who performed them.

LANG, KURT, AND GLADYS ENGEL LANG: *Collective Dynamics,* Thomas Y. Crowell Company, New York, 1961. A textbook in collective behavior, with interesting chapters on rumor, panic, crowd behavior, fashion, public opinion, and other topics covered in this chapter.

LEE, ALFRED MCCLUNG, AND NORMAN D. HUMPHREY: *Race Riot,* Holt, Rinehart and Winston, Inc., New York, 1943. A description and analysis of the Detroit race riot of 1941.

TURNER, RALPH H., AND LEWIS M. KILLIAN: *Collective Behavior,* Prentice-Hall, Inc., Englewood Cliffs, N.J., 1957, chaps. 3–13. An interestingly written textbook, about half of which is devoted to the topics covered in this chapter.

WHITE, THEO: "Building the Big Dam," *Harper's Magazine,* June, 1935, pp. 112–121. An entertaining explanation of how and why construction camp workers used to go on payday sprees.

CHAPTER
15

Population

Since the end of World War II the rate of population increase has continued to accelerate and has reached a level of about 1.7 per cent per year. . . . At the rate of world population increase for the period 1800–1850, for example, the present population would double in 135 years; at the 1900–1950 rate, in 67 years; at the postwar rate, in only 42 years.

Projection of the post-World War II rate of increase gives a population of one person per square foot of the land surface of the earth in less than 800 years.

Philip M. Hauser, *Population Perspectives*, Rutgers University Press, New Brunswick, N.J., 1960, p. 7.

Human ecology is the study of man in relation to his physical environment. More simply, it is the study of how people and institutions are located in space. It includes both the study of population (demography) and the study of community and regional organization.

Demographers are interested in both the size and the composition of a population. A small population, in relation to natural resources and the size of the territory, will limit economic growth and urban development. A dense population with limited natural resources will have difficulty in maintaining a high standard of living. On the other hand a growing population offers increasing markets for housing, food, and similar commodities, whereas a declining population may reduce market demand. Sometimes a population will vary from the usual sex and age distribution with certain predictable social consequences. A population with a large number of children and old people leaves a smaller proportion of people in productive labor to support them. If the sex ratio is markedly unequal, then many people will be unable to marry and may seek companionship outside the normal family relationships. In many ways population statistics are reflected in the social life of a people.

Population has been relatively stable throughout most of history. In the first 1,650 years since the birth of Christ, world population a little more than doubled. In the next 125 years it doubled again. By the year 2000, it is expected to double in only 27 years. World population now

One person per square foot of land surface in less than 800 years.

grows in about 6 years by as many persons as it grew in the first 1,650 years following the birth of Christ. The earth could support a population somewhere between 7.5 billion and 50 billion, depending on whose estimate we accept; the higher figure, however, assumes that our technology will be able to produce the "things" we need from rocks, sea, and air and that we will be willing to live on food from algae farms and yeast factories. At present rates of growth, we shall reach this figure in less than 200 years.

One demographer [Knibbs, 1928, p. 49] has estimated that if the offspring from a single couple were to grow at the rate of 1 per cent a year for 10,000 years, it would take 248,293,000,000,000,000 earths to hold the bodies of all these people. Yet our present rate of world population increase is 1.7 per cent, and is expected to go as high as 2.6 per cent by the year 2000 [United Nations, 1958]. Even now, India is growing at an annual rate of 2 per cent, while Ceylon, Taiwan, and some other areas are growing at 3 per cent. Obviously, such rates of population growth are a recent phenomenon and are certain, *one way or another*, to be temporary. Birth rates, however, have seldom responded to large-scale efforts at change either up or down, and the success of such efforts in the underdeveloped countries is by no means certain. So far only the Japanese have been measurably successful in deliberate national efforts to reduce the birth rate.

Social and Cultural Aspects of Population Change

What causes a change in the rate of population growth? There is no evidence that groups differ in their biological capacity to reproduce and survive, or that this capacity changes from time to time. One scholar [de Castro, 1952] has advanced the theory that hunger and poor diet produce a rise in the reproductive capacity as the species struggles to survive. Critics have noted that his evidence is contradictory and inconclusive and that he confuses the actual birth rate with biological capacity to reproduce and survive [Fairchild, 1952]. Since our biological capacity to reproduce appears to be constant, social and cultural factors must explain most variations in birth and death rates.

Changes in Death Rates. Throughout most of history, both birth and death rates have been high, with only a small rate of natural increase. In the Bronze Age of ancient Greece, expectation of life at birth was an estimated 18 years. By the opening of the nineteenth century it had doubled to about 36 years. A century and a half later it has doubled again, now standing at 70 years in the United States. Between 1900 and 1961, our death rate fell by almost one-half, from 17.2 to 9.3 deaths per thousand people. What has caused such a sharp decline?

A great many factors, stretching backwards for hundreds of years, have shared in the drop in the death rate. Improved transportation made it possible to transport a food surplus and alleviate a local famine. Improvements in food preservation made it possible to preserve a food surplus. Modern political institutions are able to organize the collection and distribution of a food surplus and avert starvation. But medicine, sanitary engineering, and public-health measures were mainly responsible for the dramatic drops of the past century. After Pasteur and the germ theory of disease, many epidemic diseases quickly yielded to preventive measures. Pure food and water supply routed others. In the Western countries today, the great killers of the past—smallpox, cholera, diphtheria, typhoid, and scarlet fever—have become so rare that it is hard to find cases for medical students to observe.

The decline in the death rate began about 1750 in England and France and generally preceded any decline in the birth rate. A country with a falling death rate and a stationary birth rate will show an explosive rate of population increase. This is what explains the rapid population growth of recent centuries.

Age at Marriage and the Marriage Rate. One factor in the birth rate is the proportion of people who get married and the ages at which they marry. A study of fertility in Indianapolis finds that women married under the age of seventeen have twice as many children as women married at the age of twenty-six to twenty-eight, as seen in Table 13.

Table 13   WIFE'S AGE AT MARRIAGE AND FERTILITY

Children per 100 wives by age 44	Age at marriage							
	Under 17	17–19	20–22	23–25	26–28	29–31	32–34	35+
Catholic couples	394	351	331	227	191	165	—*	—*
Protestant couples	366	276	207	169	129	69	72	34

* Too few cases to be reliable.

SOURCE: Data from Pascal K. Whelpton and Clyde V. Kiser, "Social and Psychological Factors Affecting Fertility," *Milbank Memorial Fund Quarterly,* 21:232, 233, 1943. This study covers a sample of white families in Indianapolis, Ind.

The recent American increase in the number of marriages in general and in early marriage in particular has been one of the unexpected developments of the last half century. People had often assumed that while marriage was a practical necessity in the rural setting, the city encouraged bachelorhood. It was also assumed that in an agricultural society men could and should marry early, whereas in an urban society marriage would have to be postponed in order to gain an education. Again, the rural society was associated with a system in which the work of women was largely restricted to the home, and it was assumed that as women became "emancipated" from restriction to a domestic life, they would postpone or avoid marriage for the sake of a career.

None of these assumptions has been borne out. Feminine emancipation, urbanization, and increased education have all been accompanied by a rush to the altar. It remains true that urban people and college-educated people still marry later than rural and less-educated people.

Table 14 PROPORTION OF PERSONS MARRIED AND MEDIAN AGE AT FIRST
MARRIAGE IN THE UNITED STATES, 1890 TO 1960

Year	Proportion married 14 years old and older, standardized for age		Median age at first marriage	
	Male, per cent	Female, per cent	Male	Female
1890	61.2	59.4	26.1	22.0
1900	59.9	58.7	25.9	21.9
1910	60.4	60.1	25.1	21.6
1920	61.3	60.4	24.6	21.2
1930	62.1	61.2	24.3	21.3
1940	62.8	61.0	24.3	21.6
1950	68.0	66.1	22.8	20.3
1955	69.3	67.4	22.6	20.2
1960	70.0	67.8	22.8	20.3

SOURCE: Department of Commerce, Bureau of the Census, *U.S. Census of Population,* vol. 2, part 1, *Current Population Reports,* series P–20, nos. 96 and 105.

But *every* group is marrying earlier than formerly. This general tendency toward earlier marriage has more than canceled the effects of increasing urbanization and education. Why, in the face of so many "logical" reasons for postponing marriage, has the age at marriage fallen so sharply? We are uncertain. Perhaps it is a natural consequence of the fact that parents permit and often encourage children to start "dating" and "going steady" at earlier ages than formerly. Perhaps it shows a growing unwillingness to follow the deferred gratification pattern and is an expression of the buy-now-pay-later attitude that characterizes so much of our society. At any rate the fact of earlier marriage is indisputable, and one consequence is accelerated population growth.

Cultural Norms and Family Limitation. Since both governments and churches are often concerned about the birth rate, one might assume that the controlling cultural norms are political or religious. Rulers of expanding countries usually oppose birth control and urge a high birth rate as the basis of military strength. On different grounds, the Roman Catholic clergy condemn the use of contraceptives and tend to minimize the pressures of overpopulation. On the other hand the Protestant clergy tend to accept contraception as a legitimate aspect of social adjustment. The governments of some overpopulated countries encourage birth control as necessary for population stabilization.

The evidence to date indicates that, with the exception of Japan, neither governments nor churches have had much effect on the birth rate. Hitler and Mussolini had little success in the effort to stimulate a

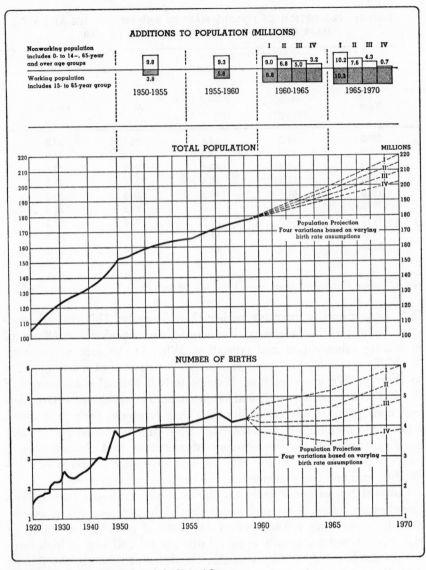

FIGURE 14   Future Population of the United States.

SOURCE: *Economic Growth in the 1960s,* The National Industrial Conference Board, New York, 1960, p. 7.

higher birth rate, and most of the current governmental efforts to reduce population increases have had disappointing results. Likewise, the endorsement of birth control by the Protestant clergy has had little effect in areas where the general social milieu favors large families, and the strictures of the Catholic clergy have not prevented a falling birth rate among urban Catholics. The Catholic Church forbids its members to use any means of contraception except the rhythm method, which is less effective than most other techniques. But as Table 15 shows,

Table 15   RELIGION AND BIRTHS, SELECTED CITIES, 1950

City	Percentage of population Catholic	Children per 100 women 15 to 49 years old, standardized for age, 1950
San Francisco	67	302
Atlanta	6	318
Boston	59	338
Denver	35	367
New Orleans	73	373
Birmingham	8	374

SOURCE: Wilson H. Grabill, Clyde V. Kiser, and Pascal K. Whelpton, *The Fertility of American Women*, John Wiley & Sons, Inc., New York, 1958, pp. 93–94.

many heavily Catholic areas have lower birth rates than many Protestant areas. Apparently Catholics react to urban and materialistic pressures in the same way as other people. That these pressures are effective is shown by a study of Hamtramck, a municipality entirely surrounded by the city of Detroit. Hamtramck, from the period 1920 to 1955, was about 90 per cent Polish Catholic in population. In 1920 when most of the residents were recent immigrants of rural peasant background, the birth rate was 97 per cent above that of surrounding Detroit which has about a 50:50 Catholic-Protestant ratio. The Polish immigrants, however, quickly changed their family patterns. In 1930 the Hamtramck birth rate was only 18 per cent higher than that of Detroit, in 1940 it was 3 per cent lower, and by 1950 it was 13 per cent lower. The authors of the report [Mayer and Marx, 1957] conclude, after interviewing a sample of the residents, that this change in the birth rate was accomplished by the widespread use of contraception.

To be seen in its true perspective, religion would have to be viewed as one of many parts of a cultural complex that determines whether or not families adopt birth-control practices. It is difficult to establish the relative influence of religious teaching, since even with the most rigorous controls it is hard to find groups of people entirely comparable except in their religious affiliation. Two careful attempts to determine the role of religion, one in Indianapolis and the other in Puerto Rico, have given contradictory results.

The Indianapolis study [Whelpton and Kiser, 1943] excluded both Negroes and foreign-born and sought to compare the birth rate of white

Protestants and Catholics of comparable economic status. The results indicated a higher birth rate for Catholics. A later study [Freedman et al., 1961], which again controlled other socioeconomic variables, concluded that Catholics have a substantially higher birth rate than *similarly situated* Protestant Americans. True, the *overall* Catholic birth rate is very close to that of non-Catholics, as is shown in Table 16, and

Table 16   NUMBER OF CHILDREN EVER BORN PER 1,000 WOMEN, MARRIED AND HUSBAND PRESENT, BY RELIGION, 1957

| Religion | Women 15 to 44 years old | | Women 45 years old and over | Ratio to nation | |
	Per 1,000 women	Per 1,000 women standardized for age		Women 15–44 standardized for age	Women 45 years old and over
Total U.S.	2,218	2,188	2,798	1.00	1.00
Protestant	2,220	2,206	2,753	1.01	.98
Baptist	2,359	2,381	3,275	1.09	1.11
Lutheran	2,013	1,967	2,382	.90	.85
Methodist	2,155	2,115	2,638	.97	.94
Presbyterian	2,001	1,922	2,188	.88	.78
Other Prot.	2,237	2,234	2,702	1.02	.97
Roman Catholic	2,282	2,210	3,056	1.01	1.09
Jewish	1,749	*	2,218	.79	.79
Other, none, and not reported	2,069	2,075	2,674	.95	.96

* Standardized rate not computed where there are fewer than 150,000 women in several component 5-year age groups.

SOURCE: Department of Commerce, Bureau of the Census, *Current Population Reports*, series P–20. Table as presented in Donald J. Bogue, *The Population of the United States*, The Free Press of Glencoe, New York, 1959, p. 696.

this is partly because ". . . young Catholic women appear to have adopted the family planning practices of the general population to such an extent that their age-standardized fertility measure in 1957 was only one per cent above that of the nation" [Bogue, 1959, p. 696]. But it is also partly due to the fact that Catholics are heavily concentrated in urban areas where birth rates are normally lower.

In Puerto Rico a survey [Hill et al., 1959] made to evaluate the efforts of public-health clinics to spread contraceptive practice did not find that religious objections were a significant barrier. In fact Catholics who regularly attended mass were more apt to use contraceptives consistently than either Protestants or the less faithful Catholics. The Puerto

Rican Catholics and Protestants were somewhat comparable groups, since they were similar in education and in rural and urban residence and shared a fairly homogeneous cultural background.

Perhaps American Catholicism exercises greater control than Puerto Rican Catholicism; we do not yet have really conclusive evidence. A few religious groups whose faith is closely related to their general culture, such as the Mormons and the Hutterites, show a consistently high birth rate. For large groups whose members are not knit in a closely controlled culture, such as Protestants and Catholics, one can only say that their birth rates tend to follow general social trends and that the religious factor is difficult to isolate from other variables.

Social Status and the Birth Rate. The folk proverb that the "rich get richer and the poor get babies" describes fairly correctly the relationship between social status and the birth rate. In general, a low birth rate is more characteristic of urbanized, well-educated, high-income groups, and a high birth rate is more apt to be found among rural, poorly educated, low-income groups.

The Planning Attitude and Family Limitation. In rural areas a large family has labor value. In the modern city, child labor is prohibited, and each additional child adds to the family expenses without increasing its income. Supposedly, in the city only the wealthier couples could afford large families, whereas the poor would find a large family a difficult burden. Such reasoning assumes that both the poor and the more prosperous have the same tendency to plan their lives. In the discussion of the deferred gratification pattern in the chapter on social mobility, we found that planning was not a typical lower-class pattern. Instead of trying to control his environment, the lower-class person is apt to consider himself a creature of fate, subject to forces beyond his control. He does not budget his income, pursue long-term educational goals, or take advantage of occupational opportunities. If the rest of his life is subject to chance, why, then, should he take pains to control the number of his children? Conversely, the middle-class person is quite well aware that the cost of a large family may make his financial goals unreachable, and he uses contraception to control the number of offspring.

Family limitation was known among the upper-class families of Greece, Rome, and some other classical civilizations and in some primitive societies, but only recently has family limitation become common in the Western world. It arose as an urbanized middle class saw a chance for economic advancement through the control of its environment and gradually shifted from a fatalistic to a planning approach. As time passed, the planned family pattern has gradually diffused to lower-income groups and rural areas. While the process has been accompanied by controversy, the spread of birth control seems due rather to cultural changes that prompted the adoption of the planning process than to the success of birth-control propaganda.

Future Population Pressure. Urbanization and industrialization in Western countries have had twin effects on population growth. The development of urbanization and industrialization was accompanied by changes in medicine and sanitation that produced a rapid drop in death rates and a great population growth. But urbanization and industrialization also unleashed forces that eventually led to a reduction of the birth rate. We have thus shifted from a society with high birth and death rates to a society with low death rates and medium birth rates, but with a higher rate of population growth than can possibly be sustained over any great period of time.

The non-Western world is now in the earlier stages of this cycle. Death rates have been plunging precipitously as non-Western lands gained epidemic control in the post-World War II years. For example the death rate in Ceylon fell by one-half in a single decade [Morgan, 1956]. In such countries, a rapidly falling death rate and an approximately stationary birth rate give a rate of population growth that soon becomes unmanageable. The pressure of numbers may lead to effective means of population restraint or to an aggressively expansionist military policy. More than thirty years ago Thompson [1929] stated that population pressure was encouraging Japan's march toward war, and suggested ways of averting this eventuality. His suggestions were not followed, and we all know the outcome. Will China and India repeat this story? Possibly so. Only they might be less likely to lose [Organski and Organski, 1962].

The argument about population pressure still swirls around the ideas of the Rev. Thomas R. Malthus, the English clergyman whose *Essay on Population* in 1798 attracted the world's attention. Malthus believed the essential reason for poverty was the pressure of population growth on the world's resources. He reasoned that the effects of natural fertility were held in check only by such negative forces as famine, war, and pestilence. Thus whenever an improvement in the arts yielded an economic surplus, these products would soon be consumed by an expanding population. Malthus did not deny the possibility of increasing industrial and agricultural production, but he believed the increase would be unable to keep up with the population growth, and expressed his belief that population tends to multiply in a geometric ratio (2, 4, 8, 16, etc.) while production can only increase in an arithmetic ratio (1, 2, 3, 4, etc.). Each increase in population becomes a basis for a further increase in the next generation, but each increase in the yield from an acre of land is not a basis for a still further increase the following season. Instead, having boosted the yield this year makes it harder, not easier, to boost the yield still higher next year. Thus people increase through multiplication, whereas the food supply increases only by addition and is constantly being outrun by the growth of population. Malthus urged later marriage as a means of keeping down the birth rate, but he was pessimistic about the chances of this policy being followed. He saw no practical possibility of averting hunger, famine, and pestilence. Organized charity and relief would only enable a few more to survive today so they might starve tomorrow. Because of these gloomy predictions of Malthus, economics became known as the "dismal science."

In the 1920s it was popular to believe that the events of the preceding century had disproved the Malthusian hypotheses. The world had seen the greatest population growth in its history, and at the same time the standard of living had improved rather than declined. Why did Malthus's gloomy predictions fail to materialize? One reason is that Malthus failed to foresee the widespread use of improved methods of contraception. The contraceptive devices of his day were so crude and inefficient that Malthus and other writers paid little or no attention to them. Another reason was that Malthus could not be expected to foresee the magnitude of the industrial and agricultural revolution of the nineteenth and twentieth centuries. Great new land areas in North and South America and Australia were brought under cultivation. Improvements in agriculture rapidly boosted output per acre. For a time, birth rates in the Western world were falling so rapidly and production was rising so rapidly that Malthus began to sound like a gloomy scold instead of a gifted thinker.

Recently, however, Malthus has been restored to fashion by scholars known as "neo-Malthusians." The Western nations, while using family planning, now seem to be planning and raising families much larger than can possibly be maintained for very many generations. Pressure on our water resources is already acute in some parts of the United States, and further pressures may be anticipated as our population figures continue to soar. Granted that the United States can provide a high standard of living for 250 million people, can we provide it for 400 million, or a billion, or 10 billion?

But it is the underdeveloped areas of the world that offer the best illustrations of Malthus's chilling predictions. Here the "revolution of rising expectations" meets the population explosion. In these areas death control has been sensationally effective, birth control is difficult to popularize, and the expansion of agricultural and industrial production is a slow and complex process. In spite of considerable improvement, production in these areas has done little more than keep up with the population increase, and in some areas has actually fallen behind population growth. In spite of herculean efforts, the gap between the per capita income of the industrialized and the underdeveloped areas continues to increase [Myrdal, 1957, pp. 4–5].

Whether an unchecked population growth can take place in even the next fifty years without a deterioration in living standards is still debatable. Possibly economic developments in Asia and Africa will speed up, once the basic equipment of a modern society has been established. Possibly new scientific developments may multiply our productivity. But even if we might escape a Malthusian doom, some people are asking if this kind of struggle is really worthwhile. Rapid population growth carries a price tag of many kinds. One scholar [A. Miller, 1960] claims evidence that rapid population growth requires an increase in governmental controls of many kinds, promotes the bureaucratization of society, and reduces the range of individual liberties. Already in England, that historic citadel of individual liberty, the state will take away a farmer's land (with compensation) if he does not farm it efficiently; the national interest cannot allow a landowner the luxury of inefficient land use. In the Netherlands, one is not permitted to build a one-story house; the land cannot be spared. Individual liberty is a luxury that is gradually sacrificed as population pressure grows intense. How much of it should be sacrificed in order to feed more people?

Migration

People in the United States are especially conscious of immigration since, except for the American Indians, they are all the descendants of immigrants. From the time of the Pilgrim fathers some 30 million immigrants, mostly from Europe, settled in this country and changed it from a wilderness of food gatherers and hunters to the flourishing nation we

Except for the American Indians, they are all the descendants of immigrants.

know today. International immigration is now less important than in previous years, but a tremendous movement within the country leads to a constant redistribution of population.

Push, Pull, and Channels. The forces affecting migration may be grouped under the three headings push, pull, and channels. *Push* relates to unfavorable factors in the homeland that make people want to leave. In the 1840s a potato famine made the United States seem attractive to many Irishmen, and the failure of the Revolution of 1848 caused many Germans to seek their fortunes in a land that asked no questions about political beliefs. Sometimes the push comes from a catastrophe, sometimes from economic stagnation and lack of opportunity, sometimes from political or religious persecution. Today the shifts of national boundary lines after World War II and the rise of intolerant political movements, especially communism, have made life in their native lands intolerable for many people. At the time of the International Refugee Year, 1960, it was estimated that 15 million people had been forced to leave their ancestral homes and had not yet found a permanent place of residence [*New York Times,* Jan. 26, 1959, p. 5].

Pull refers to the attractive features in the country receiving immigrants. Immigration proceeds toward the area of greater opportunities, as these are perceived by the individual. This perception is a cultural definition rather than a necessarily valid objective judgment. It is not the overall opportunity for economic development that is decisive but the ease with which the individual can move into a situation with relatively little cultural adjustment. Alaska, for instance, is much more sparsely settled than California or New York and may have greater undeveloped economic opportunities. Yet dozens of immigrants move to these states for every one who enters Alaska simply because they seek an opportunity to make a living in an area where they believe they will be comfortable. Very few people seem to want the hardy life of the raw frontier. Indonesians continue to move into heavily populated Java, while sparsely peopled Sumatra beckons for settlers. Filipinos continue to flock to Luzon, while the government pleads for people to occupy idle land in Mindanao. Possibly this picture may be changed by the growth of industrialization which brings both jobs and cultural amenities to the more isolated areas. Likewise extraordinary opportunity for gain such as a gold discovery or the presence of rich agricultural land with easy access to markets may exert a powerful pull. Frequently, though, the migration to areas of supposedly rich potential is slow until "social overhead"—towns, schools, medical resources, roads, and stable governments—has been provided. An area becomes attractive when the handicaps of a different environment seem less significant than the opportunity for more rapid social mobility in a direction that does not seem to threaten traditional cultural standards.

Channels refer to the means of movement from one area to another. They include the availability of transportation, information, and help in overcoming financial obstacles and the presence or absence of barriers in both the homeland and the receiving country. The twentieth century has seen the development of marvelous means of transport accompanied by severe restrictions on immigration. Physically it was never easier to move from one country to another.

Socially or politically, people find it harder to make such a move now than they did in the nineteenth century. Then they could ordinarily move about without restrictions of any kind. Even passports were seldom required. Today we take it for granted that countries will select the type and number of immigrants they wish to receive and that individuals will be unable to move unless some governmental body has given permission. Among the early immigrants to America were prostitutes, prisoners from penal colonies, illiterates, adherents of radical political movements, and the diseased and physically deformed, none of whom would be admitted today. Indeed, it is certain that many of the early migrants whose memory is now enshrined by the Daughters of the American Revolution and similar organizations would not be able to qualify for entry under our present laws.

International Migration. Increasing population and a developing nationalism have combined to make governments wish to restrict immigration to the types of immigrant they feel the national culture can most easily assimilate and to the number the nation can easily absorb into its economy. In the United States we exclude those with physical defects and certain other personal disqualifications. We also set a quota for each country, based on our population composition in 1920 and designed to favor the Northwestern European nations. We will normally admit no more than 156,387 immigrants. Actually, we never admit that many because the (Northwestern European) countries with the larger quotas do not fill them. While some additional immigration was allowed as an emergency measure to help displaced persons after World War II, the net effect of the United States immigration policy since 1921 has been to make immigration relatively unimportant as far as the size and composition of the American population is concerned.

Most of the world has followed immigration policies similar to those of the United States. The countries friendliest to immigration are those such as Brazil, Canada, and Australia that are considered underpopulated and welcome additional immigrants as a means of developing their resources. Since Australia and Canada restrict Oriental and African immigration, even those countries cannot be described as having a completely open immigration policy.

Internal Migration. Although international migration is subject to increasing restrictions, a considerable shift of people is constantly going on within nations. One American family in five will move in a normal year. In times past the American industrial labor force was recruited from European migrants and the agricultural force from African slaves. Now that slavery has been ended and immigration reduced, the need for labor is met by shifts of the American population and by the recruitment of temporary agricultural laborers from Mexico. The past forty years have seen millions of people moving to the cities of the West and the East from the agricultural areas of the South and the Middle West, as well as a considerable movement of Puerto Ricans to the mainland.

CHARACTERISTICS OF IMMIGRANTS TO THE UNITED STATES

Before 1890, were predominantly	After 1890, were predominantly
From Northwestern Europe	From Central, Southern, and Eastern Europe
Protestant	Catholic
Literate	Illiterate
Skilled or semiskilled	Unskilled or peasant
Accustomed to democracy	Accustomed to authoritarian government
Scattered in settlement	Bunched in urban areas
Easily assimilated	Uneasily accommodated

Does the above table suggest some reasons why immigration came to be viewed as a "problem" after the turn of the century?

While this internal migration is different from that crossing international boundary lines, the processes of the two shifts are much the same. The movement into a new region changes the population composition, provides new labor, and introduces a group of people ignorant of the prevailing folkways, who have to make their adjustment to a strange cultural setting. Southern whites and Negroes along with Puerto Ricans and others thus make many of the same contributions and experience many of the same problems as the European immigrants of an earlier day.

Changing Population Composition

The composition of a population affects its social life. Washington, D.C., with its droves of female clerical workers, St. Petersburg with its retired people, and Columbus, Georgia, with nearby Fort Benning— these cities are different, in part, because of differences in the age, sex, and occupational composition of the population whose needs they fill.

As shown in Table 17, the age composition of the United States has been constantly changing. A high birth rate means that children will compose a large fraction of the total population and old people a relatively small fraction. The long-term decline in our birth rate, lasting until the 1930s, reduced the children's share of our population and increased the proportion of the aged. Meanwhile a very slight extension of the life span further increased the proportion of the aged. Then in the 1930s the birth rate started back up, climbing from 16 births per 1,000 in

Table 17   THE CHANGING AGE COMPOSITION OF THE AMERICAN POPULATION

| | Dependents per 100 persons of working age (20–64) | | |
Year	Young and old	Young only (under 20)	Old only (over 64)
Census			
1820	153	146	7
1850	123	117	6
1900	94	86	8
1940	71	59	12
Estimate			
1950	72	58	14
Projection			
1960	91	74	17
1970	98	80	18
1980	104	85	19

SOURCE: Slightly adapted from Philip M. Hauser, *Population Perspectives*, Rutgers University Press, New Brunswick, N.J., 1960, p. 71.

1933 to 26.5 in 1947, then falling to 21.8 in 1963. This overall gain has increased the proportion of children, but not greatly enough to prevent the proportion of aged from continuing to rise. People over sixty-five made up 5.4 per cent of the population in 1930, but 9.3 per cent in 1962. It is expected to remain at about 9 or 10 per cent through 1980.

We must remember that changes primarily in the birth rate, not in the death rate, have changed the proportion of the aged in our population. This point is widely misunderstood by people who confuse *life span* with *life expectancy*. The life span measures the time fortunate people live until carried off by "old age"; life expectancy is the mean number of years of life remaining at any given age. Life expectancy at birth has doubled in the last century and a half; life expectancy at age sixty has shown very little change. In other words, infants today are far more likely to reach the age of sixty than infants a century ago, but people who have reached sixty today have scarcely any more years of life remaining than those who reached sixty a century ago. Stated still differently, more people live to be old today, but old people today do not live much longer than old people used to live.

So life span and death rates have had only a minor part in the increasing proportion of the aged. But if the number of children in a population is increased, the *proportion* of the aged in the population is reduced. The recent rapid growth in the proportion of the aged is due to the fact that those recently approaching old age were born during the period of high birth rates, while those now approaching middle age were born during a period of lower birth rates. If the birth rate should remain stable over a long period of time, the proportion of the people at each age level would stabilize, and we should then have what demographers call a "normal" population distribution.

Changes in population composition have many social consequences. A change in the ratio of dependents to workers has great economic impact. It affects employment, living standards, and price levels. The proportion of the aged has important economic and political consequences such as the drive for more generous pension plans and health and welfare services for the aged and experimentation with retirement communities, recreational programs, and other services for the aged. Possibly the greater influence of the aged may reinforce a conservative trend as the older people try to slow the course of social change.

The scientific study of the aged is claiming increased attention. *Geriatrics* is a branch of medicine that studies old age and its diseases; *gerontology* is a more inclusive field embracing the entire study of the aged and their problems. In a society with a higher proportion of old people living in a society that is less comfortable for the aged than a rural society used to be, gerontology is a rapidly growing discipline. One fact alone—the fact that men by 1975 can expect three times as many years of retirement as men at the turn of this century (Figure 15) makes gerontology an important field of study.

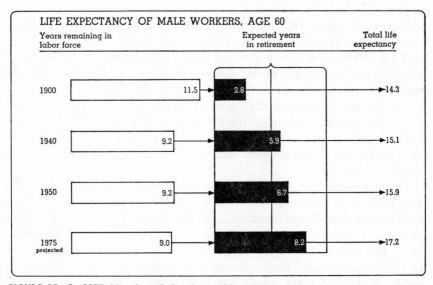

FIGURE 15   By 1975, Men Age 60 Can Expect Three Times as Many Years of Retirement as in 1900.

SOURCE: *1961 White House Conference on Aging, Chart Book,* Federal Council on Aging, Government Printing Office, Washington, D.C., 1961, p. 50.

Population Quality

Because the lower classes have higher birth rates than the middle and upper classes, many people conclude that the human race is breeding itself into mediocrity. This conclusion assumes, of course, that the lower classes are inferior in hereditary capacities. Is this assumption correct?

The question is difficult to answer. The differential birth rate has existed for thousands of years. Ancient Greece and Rome were worried about the low birth rate among their "better" families. If the differential birth rate were *highly* dysgenic, the human race would already have bred itself into stupidity.

About the only real evidence on the comparative innate abilities of different social classes is that found in comparative test scores. But intelligence tests and aptitude tests are notoriously misleading when used to compare groups of differing cultural background. Such tests have a strong class bias [Davis, 1948; Eells, 1951]. The words used and the material covered are more familiar to middle- and upper-class children than to lower-class children. The class difference in average scores was far greater on the verbal parts of the tests than on the nonverbal parts, again showing how class background affects test performance [Eells, 1951]. That the social classes differ markedly in inherited abilities is an unproved hypothesis, not a fact.

One recent study [Bajema, 1963] finds that people of high IQ have more children than those of lower IQ. People in the 69 to 79 IQ range had 1.5 children each, rising to 2.6 children for people with IQs over 120. This tendency of the more intelligent to reproduce themselves would tend to counteract the class differential in reproduction.

A different argument is that modern society promotes the deterioration of the race by preventing the elimination of the unfit. Medical care, public health measures, and social welfare services, it is argued, prevent the elimination of the dullards and weaklings, preserving them to reproduce their kind.

This argument assumes that earlier societies did eliminate the unfit. The truth is that natural selection has never operated at the human level; culture has always interfered with the elimination of the unfit. Most primitive societies practiced some form of food sharing, so that the entire group fattened or starved together regardless of their individual abilities. In both primitive and medieval societies, most work was performed in rigidly traditional ways which left little room to display superior ingenuity or penalize mediocrity. Some societies gave exceptional reproductive opportunities to epileptics and others whom we would recognize as less fit. In some societies celibacy for the clergy has removed many of the presumably superior persons from legitimate reproduction. The belief that earlier societies dependably eliminated the unfit is not historically true.

Is modern society preserving the unfit? Epidemic diseases formerly removed many people, while others, presumably stronger, escaped or recovered. Was their survival due to anything hereditary? We cannot say, for we know nothing definite about hereditary immunities to most illnesses. The great reductions in death rates have come in the infectious diseases, where it has not been definitely established that any hereditary factors are involved. In clearly inherited disorders like congenital malformations, the death rate remains as high as ever. Until it has been shown that the disease susceptibilities are inherited, the belief that medical science has dysgenic consequences is an unproved hypothesis.

What can be proven is that the average level of performance was never so high as it is today. The average person today lives longer, grows larger, and loses less time in illness than ever before. Any dysgenic consequences of modern life that may be in force are more than canceled by our better use of the people we have.

Summary

In the past three centuries a nearly stable world population has exploded into fantastic growth. Effective death control has cut the death rate in nearly all areas of the world, while only in some areas has the birth rate fallen appreciably, and in scarcely any has it fallen enough to restore a historic stability of population.

A society's birth rate is largely a result of the average age at marriage, the proportion of people who marry, and their use or nonuse of birth control. Malthus dismissed the idea of the effectiveness of contraception and predicted inevitable overpopulation and misery unless people controlled population growth by postponing marriage. The rapid colonial expansion and the industrial and agricultural development of the nineteenth century delayed the fulfillment of Malthus's predictions, but they now appear likely to be fulfilled in at least some parts of the world.

Migration is affected by the *push* given to people by unsatisfactory conditions at home, by the *pull* of attractive opportunities elsewhere, and by the *channels* or means through which they are able to migrate. The United States received a constant stream of immigrants until the enactment of restrictive legislation in 1921. Since then immigration has been restricted not only by the United States but also by many other countries. Most migration today is internal, especially from farm to city within a country. Political dislocations are producing record numbers of refugees today, but although transportation is easy, social restrictions make refuge resettlement more difficult than ever before.

The composition of a population affects its social life in many ways. Changes in age composition are due mainly to changes in the birth rate, and are presently increasing the proportions both of the children and the aged in our population. The permanent presence of a rather large group of old people in our population has prompted the rise of *gerontology,* a discipline devoted to the problems of the aged.

The class differential in birth rates and the health and welfare services of modern society are sometimes accused of having damaging effects on the quality of the population, but these are unproved hypotheses, doubted by most social scientists.

Questions and Projects

1. What has been the rate of population growth throughout most of history? Why have world rates of population changed recently? How long will present rates of growth continue?

2. What factors other than birth control affect the rate of reproduction?

3. At the present time the prosperity of some areas of the world might be favorably affected by population increase. Evaluate the prospects of migration from overpopulated areas to those considered underpopulated.

4. What were the ideas of Malthus? Do you feel that the passage of time has outdated or confirmed these ideas? Why or why not?

5. What are the factors that limit the ability of governmental or religious institutions to influence the birth rate?

6. How would you explain the tendency in the United States toward an excess of females in the cities and an excess of males in the rural districts?

7. What is meant by "push," "pull," and "channels" in connection with immigration?

8. How are changes in our age distribution related to the political demand for Medicare?

9. Account for the fact that while medical science (and other factors) has succeeded in greatly extending the expectation of life at birth, it has had little effect on the span of life.

10. Suppose we discovered the means to control the aging process and lengthen the span of life by 50 or 100 per cent. What might be some social consequences?

11. In recent years the United States has had an increase in the proportion of both children and aged. What effects would you expect this change in population to have in social and economic relationships?

Suggested Readings

CHANDRASEKHAR, S.: "Family Planning in Rural India," *Antioch Review,* 19:399–410, 1959. A report on efforts to introduce the use of contraceptives in an Indian village.

FREEDMAN, RONALD: "Planned Family and American Population Growth," *Antioch Review,* 17:31–44, 1957. Treats the paradoxical combination of widespread family planning and rapid population growth.

GRABILL, WILSON H., CLYDE V. KISER, AND PASCAL K. WHELPTON: *The Fertility of American Women,* John Wiley & Sons, Inc., New York, 1958. A detailed study of American fertility.

HANDLIN, OSCAR: *The Newcomers,* Harvard University Press, Cambridge, Mass., 1959. A comparison of Puerto Rican adjustment in New York City with that of previous immigrants.

HAUSER, PHILIP M.: *Population Perspectives,* Rutgers University Press, New Brunswick, N.J., 1960. A scholarly popularization of consequences of rapid population growth.

LANDIS, PAUL H.: "Is There Room for the Next 1,000,000,000 People?" *Clearing House,* 18:140–141, 1953. A popularly written article taking a neo-Malthusian viewpoint.

MAYER, ALBERT J., AND SUE MARX: "Social Change, Religion and the Birth Rate," *American Journal of Sociology,* 62:383–390, 1957. A discussion of the trend toward the adoption of birth control in Hamtramck, Michigan.

CHAPTER 16 **The Community**

America the Beautiful is relentlessly becoming America the Mess. . . . The question we face is: "Is it possible to be motorized and urbanized, yet civilized?"

To date, the resounding answer has been no. Ninety per cent of Americans now live in metropolitan areas, but their use of the family automobile has produced civic and suburban blight, cretinizing commuting and poisoned air. [The correct figure here is 63 per cent, although it is probably correct that 90 per cent live in or near a metropolitan area.] It has brought the cities that produce our wealth to the edge of ruin. . . .

The basic problem is that cities and automobiles serve opposite purposes. Cities enable people to live together; automobiles enable people to move apart. So far, when we have tried to reconcile these opposites, we have left people out of the equation. Thus, our efforts usually take the form of trying to make the city a better place for automobiles rather than for people. This way lies madness, because every improvement in traffic flow simply results in more traffic.

Similarly, when we try to take advantage of the automobile's mobility or move business and people out of clogged cities, the result is to pull tax props out from under the towns, and ruinous blight corrodes the civic heart. Worse, we blight the area into which we move. Natural beauty and productive land is "thrown to the bulldozers" at a rate of more than a million acres a year . . . in order to "mass-produce the mess that is to take their place."

John Keats, reviewing Wilfred Owen, *Cities in the Motor Age,* in *New York Times Book Review,* Mar. 1, 1959, p. 7.

The community is as old as man—or even older, for our subhuman ancestors probably shared a community life. A community is a territorial grouping within which people carry out a full round of life activities. More formally defined [Jonassen, 1959, p. 20; Hillery, 1955], a community includes (1) a grouping of people, (2) within a geographic area, (3) with a division of labor into specialized and interdependent functions, (4) with a common culture and a social system that organizes their activities, (5) whose members are conscious of their unity and of belonging to the community, and (6) who can act collectively in an organized manner The community is a relatively self-sufficient local area within which all or nearly all aspects of the culture can be experienced. The term is sometimes loosely used to describe other groups or subcultures—the "community of scholars," the "artistic community," or the "community of nations," for example—but these are nonsociological uses of the term.

It has been traditional to classify communities as rural or urban, depending on whether their populations were small and agricultural or large and industrial or commercial. The classification was never entirely satisfactory, for it made no provision for such communities as the fishing village, the mining camp, or the trading post. Today the growth of the suburb and the urbanization of rural life make the rural-urban dichotomy still less perfect, but the terms continue to be used for lack of better ones.

The Rural Community

The physical and social conditions of urban and rural life are different. Consequently there are differences in the personality and behavior of urban and rural people. These differences have provided endless source material for the novelist and the playwright, and continue to interest the sociologist.

Traditional Characteristics of Rural Life. Rural communities are not all alike. Edwards [1959] distinguishes at least five types of rural communities: the town-country community with farms scattered about a village center; the open-country community without any village center; the village community whose subtypes include the fishing village, the mining village, and the mill village; the line village, with farm homes strung along the road at the ends of long, narrow farms; and the plantation. Yet certain characteristics are common to nearly all kinds of rural communities.

Isolation. Perhaps the most conspicuous feature of American rural life was its isolation. Throughout much of the world, rural people are clustered in villages. In the United States, for reasons not entirely clear, the isolated homestead became the usual pattern of rural settlement, a pattern productively more efficient but socially isolating. Not only was the local group isolated from other groups, but each family was isolated from other families. With a thinly scattered population, personal contacts were few. Each contact involved the perception of an individual as a complete person, not simply as a functionary. Impersonal contacts in rural societies were few—no anonymous bus drivers, ticket sellers, grocery clerks, or policemen. Nearly every contact was with an acquaintance who must be treated, not only in terms of his economic function, but also in terms of his total personality and all the many facets of his status in the community.

The hospitality pattern of the American frontier, wherein the traveler was welcome to spend the night at almost any farmhouse, was a practical response both to frontier needs—where else would the traveler stay? —and to frontier loneliness. The traveler brought news, contact with the outside world, and a break in monotony. He was almost always welcome. Even today the hospitality pattern survives under conditions of extreme isolation. On the Alaska Highway the mores of the region require that one offer assistance to any stranded motorist; he may actually die if assistance is not given. The hospitality pattern is a perfect illustration of how customs and mores arise in response to social needs and change as these needs change.

Homogeneity. Taken as a whole, American settlers were a quite heterogeneous lot. But within a given locality, the settlers were likely to be quite homogeneous in ethnic and cultural background. They showed a strong tendency to follow earlier migrants from their home communities, so that the migrants from a particular country and district tended to be clustered into rather homogeneous settlements. This homogeneity, together with the comparative isolation of settlements from one another, helped to encourage the conservatism, traditionalism, and ethnocentrism of American rural communities.

Agricultural Employment. Nearly all were engaged in agriculture; even the minister, doctor, teacher, and storekeeper were deeply involved in an agricultural way of life. The agricultural practices were highly traditional, allowing very little experimentation or trial-and-error methods. All faced common problems, performed common tasks, and shared a common helplessness before the awesome natural forces that man cannot control. Rural people are often said to be more religious than city dwellers, possibly because of this closeness to overpowering natural forces. The city dweller, surrounded by man-made buildings, streets, elevators, and automobiles, operating smoothly on a man-made schedule, may have a less compelling sense of his utter dependence upon God than the farmer who watches the tender green shoots shrivel in drought or wash away in flood. In any event, all shared common tasks and common fears, and developed those common reactions that made the rural locality a true community.

Subsistence Economy. The traditional American homestead sought to produce nearly everything it consumed. The bulging smokehouse, the well-stocked fruit cellar, and the shelves sagging with home-canned goods were a source of pride to the farm family. In a rapidly expanding economy with a chronic shortage of money and credit, a subsistence-and-barter economy was a socially useful adaptation. Thrift was an honored value, and conspicuous consumption was mainly an urban vice. A farmer's status was measured by his lands, his herds, his barns, his crops, and the inheritance he could pass on to his children—and not by the name of his tailor or interior decorator.

Living within a subsistence rather than a market economy, rural people were inclined to be suspicious of intellectuality and "booklearning." The farmer was most likely to see a piece of paper when some "city slicker" was trying to do him out of something. Distrust of city people and disapproval of urban life were a predictable rural attitude.

These are some of the influences that shaped American rural personality. Hospitable and cooperative, conservative and religious, hardworking and thrifty, ethnocentric and intolerant—these characteristics were products of the physical and social conditions of rural life in America. Today these conditions have vastly changed. And so has the social behavior of rural people.

The Rural Revolution. *Reduced Isolation.* Two generations ago the isolation of rural life could be measured by the contrast between the styles shown in the Sears, Roebuck catalogue and those on the pages of a metropolitan newspaper. Today the styles are the same. The automobile and good roads have wrought a transformation of rural and village life that is difficult for the present generation of students to appreciate. Thousands of small villages have ceased to be true communities, as good roads have carried their trade, their storekeepers, and their professional men to a nearby city. If close enough to the city, they have become suburbs; if too distant, they have become the half-empty shells of decaying houses and aging people, as are so many of the villages of America today. Transportation plus the press, movies, radio, and television have ended the social isolation of rural America. Indeed the true provincial today may be the urban slum dweller who may spend years without venturing beyond his own set of canyons.

Commercialization and Rationalization of Agriculture. Without a revolution in agricultural productivity, there could have been little urban growth. In 1790 it required the surplus of nine farm families to support one urban family; today ten nonfarm families are supported by each farm

The true provincial today may be the urban slum dweller.

family. Farming used to be a way of life calling for no special knowledge beyond that which one absorbed unavoidably as he grew up. Today farming is a highly complex operation calling for substantial capital, specialized knowledge, rapid changes in productive technology, and continuous market analysis. Today's successful farm has become a roofless factory calling for a variety of managerial skills comparable to those needed for many another business.

As farming has grown more demanding, the number of farm families has fallen precipitously—from 6.7 million and 22 per cent of all American families in 1935 to 4.2 million and 9.2 per cent of all families in 1962. The tenant farmer and sharecropper have been rapidly fading away, falling from 2,770,000 in 1930 to 735,000 in 1959. Meanwhile the average size of farms has steadily increased from 174 acres in 1940 to 303 acres in 1959. These trends are still continuing at a rapid rate and would proceed even faster if they were not retarded by political programs intended to aid marginal farmers. Fewer than half our farms produce 85 per cent of our farm produce and could easily produce the remaining 15 per cent if farm production were not deliberately restricted.

Because of changes in agricultural technology, the farm population is rapidly shrinking. In 1790 the rural (farm and nonfarm) residents comprised 94.8 per cent of the population. By 1920, when "farm" and "rural nonfarm" people were first separated in the census, farm people com-

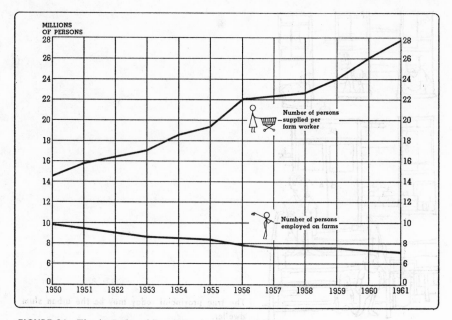

FIGURE 16   The Agricultural Revolution in the United States.

SOURCE: The Conference Board, *Road Maps of Industry*, no. 1408, Dec. 21, 1962.

prised 30.1 per cent of the population; in 1963 only 7.1 per cent, and they are still diminishing in number. We were once a nation of farmers. Today farmers are becoming one of the smallest of our major occupational groups. At present 2 million of our farm families are unnecessary and could leave the farm tomorrow without ever being missed, were there other jobs to absorb them. It is likely that one way or another most of this farm surplus will leave the farm.

As the farm has become part of a market economy, the attitudes appropriate to a subsistence economy have languished. Thrift as an absolute value, good in and of itself, was a useful practice in a subsistence economy. In a market economy it becomes an anachronism. Farm people today appear to have as avid an appetite for new cars and color television sets as urbanites. After all, values grow out of the experience of the group. In a subsistence economy of limited productivity, where there was rarely enough of anything, especially money, the elevation of thrift to an absolute value was practical and sensible. With the development of a highly productive market economy, thrift becomes pointless as an end in itself. Instead, reasonable thrift becomes a means to an end, for example the saving of money on inessentials in order to afford the major purchase of a home or a new car. This and many other value changes have accompanied the technological revolution in American agriculture.

Urbanization of Rural Life. It is no longer possible to identify a rural rustic by his outmoded dress or bucolic manner. All the historic rural-urban differences are shrinking. To a substantial degree, rural life is becoming urbanized, as historically urban patterns spread into rural areas.

There are many examples of urbanization. The electric pump and the septic tank have brought urban plumbing to the rural home. The rural birth rate has been dropping closer to the urban birth rate—77 per cent higher in 1940, 40 per cent higher in 1950, and 34 per cent higher in 1960. Our population in 1960 was classified as 69.8 per cent urban (living in communities of over 2,500), 8.7 per cent rural farm, and 21.5 per cent rural nonfarm. Many of these rural nonfarm people are urban commuters, who become a powerful urbanizing influence on rural life. In many urban fringe areas, people are divided between farm and nonfarm employment, and any classification of such areas as either rural or urban is arbitrary. Recently the rather clumsy term "rurban" was coined for these mixed areas that are neither urban nor rural. The term has not become very popular; but the phenomenon of the mixed urban-rural area is important, for this is a rapidly growing form of community in America.

The Urban Community

The Development of Cities. The city is a recent invention of man. In order for the primitive Stone Age village to overshoot its few dozen households and expand to a size of several hundred thousand, it was necessary to have a food surplus, a water supply, and a transportation system. Since a river valley provided all three, the first large cities arose six or seven thousand years ago in the valleys of the Nile, the Tigris, and the Euphrates. Surplus food to support an urban population was provided by the fertile valley, and the slow-flowing rivers provided simple transportation. Although most ancient cities remained tiny by modern standards, a few reached a size of several hundred thousand, complete with problems of water supply, sewage disposal, and traffic congestion.

The growth of cities unleashed revolutionary changes. The primitive village was organized on a kinship basis and guided by customary procedures. The large city brought (1) a division of labor into many specialized occupations, (2) social organization based on occupation and social class rather than kinship, (3) formal governmental institutions based on territory rather than family, (4) a system of trade and commerce, (5) means of communication and record keeping, and (6) a rational technology. Obviously the large city could not arise until the culture had made a number of necessary inventions; at the same time the development of the city proved a great stimulus to the making and improving of such inventions as carts and barges, ditches and aqueducts, writing, number systems, governmental bureaucracies, and many others.

Cities are of many kinds—temple cities, political capitals, resort cities, industrial cities, trading centers, and others. Most large cities are diversified, carrying on all these functions. An early sociologist, Cooley [1894], noted that cities tend to grow wherever a "break" in transportation causes goods to be unloaded and reloaded for transshipment. Port cities like London, Montreal, and New Orleans are located up a navigable river at the point where large ocean vessels can go no further. Denver lies at the foot of a mountain grange, Pittsburgh at the confluence of two rivers. Modern resort cities like Las Vegas may violate this rule, but the break-in-transportation theory still serves to explain the location of most cities.

The Structure of Cities. Cities may look as though they just happened

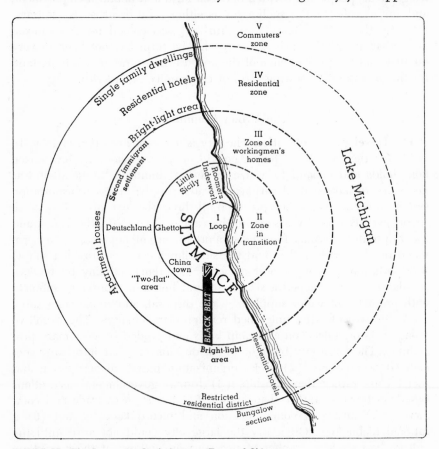

FIGURE 17 The Concentric Circle Pattern: Zones of Chicago.

SOURCE: R. E. Park and E. W. Burgess, *The City*, The University of Chicago Press, Chicago, 1925, p. 55

—grew without plan or design. It is true that urban growth does not proceed according to a prearranged design; but neither is the growth entirely haphazard. Cities have structure; that is, there is some reason for the arrangement of their parts. Several sociologists have sought to discover the underlying pattern according to which a city develops.

Patterns of Urban Design. Burgess's *concentric zone pattern,* shown in Figure 17, is one such attempt. Based on his studies of Chicago in the early 1920s, it shows a central business district at the center, surrounded by a slum consisting of old buildings that are gradually being replaced by the expansion of the business district. This in turn is surrounded by zones of successively better-class residences.

Do real cities resemble the Burgess pattern? Each American city has a central business district, partly or entirely surrounded by a slum. This surrounding zone contains the oldest building in the city, where decay, dirt, and congestion make them undesirable. Housing quality tends to improve as one moves outward from this slum, and much of the choice residential area is located in the suburbs. However, these zones are not unbroken bands surrounding the city; nor are they circular in shape. Instead, the various grades of residence are rather irregularly distributed and often concentrated on one side of the city. This observation led Hoyt [1933] to frame his *sector theory of city growth,* holding that a particular kind of land use tends to locate and remain in a particular sector of the city. Figure 18 shows how this theory is borne out in several American cities over several decades. Thus industry tends to locate in one sector, upper-class housing in an opposite sector, and working-class housing in intermediate sectors; then as time passes, each of these sectors simply expands outward until some change in topography breaks up the pattern.

The *multinuclear theory* [Harris and Ullman, 1945] holds that a number of centers—business, shopping, manufacturing—and residential areas become located early in a city's history. Topography, cost, and historical accident all enter into these early choices. These concentrations tend to survive and fix the pattern of later city growth. Larger cities, which usually represent the growing together of once separate villages or communities, provide multiple nuclei. These three patterns are shown in comparison in Figure 19.

Still another pattern can be recognized—one so simple that it has not been dignified by being called a theory. It relates topography to land use. Railroads tend to follow the river bottom, heavy industry locates along the railroad, upper-class residence seeks the highlands, and the intermediate levels of housing are scattered in between.

The existence of alternative theories shows that none of them are entirely satisfactory. None of them are perfectly illustrated by any

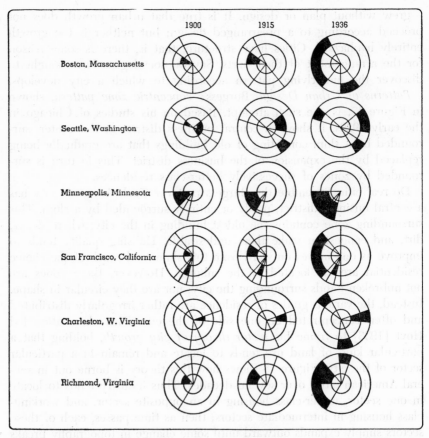

FIGURE 18 Changes in the Location of Fashionable Residences. *This graph illustrates Hoyt's sector theory. The solid black spaces show shifts in the fashionable residential areas between 1900 and 1936.*

SOURCE: Homer Hoyt, *The Structure and Growth of Residential Neighborhoods in American Cities,* Federal Housing Administration, Washington, D.C., 1939, p. 115.

American city, and cities outside the United States will fit still less perfectly. Each is a theoretical pattern that real cities more or less perfectly resemble. Since most American cities do show some resemblance to one of these patterns, the theories are helpful in revealing their prevailing structure.

City structure today is being revolutionized by transportation. In most cities the central business district has ceased to expand, as the commercial growth leapfrogs to the suburban shopping centers. A growing ring of decay is left surrounding the business district, as it no longer razes its fringe as it expands. An aging and decaying central city is soon trapped by declining tax sources and mounting tax expenditures.

This is the basic reason why nearly every city in the country is busily engaged in urban renewal programs.

Metropolitan Areas and Suburbs. Modern transportation is responsible for the suburb and the metropolitan area. Suburbs are defined as "urbanized, residential communities which are outside the corporate limits of a large central city, but are culturally and economically dependent upon the central city" [Dobriner, 1958, p. xvii]. A "standard metropolitan statistical area" is defined by the census as a county or group of counties containing at least one city or a pair of "twin cities" with over 50,000 people. Adjacent counties are included if they are metropolitan in char-

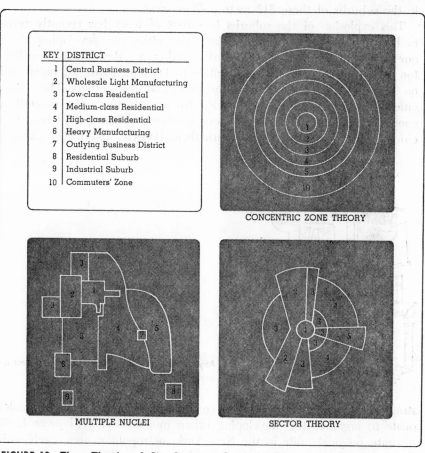

KEY	DISTRICT
1	Central Business District
2	Wholesale Light Manufacturing
3	Low-class Residential
4	Medium-class Residential
5	High-class Residential
6	Heavy Manufacturing
7	Outlying Business District
8	Residential Suburb
9	Industrial Suburb
10	Commuters' Zone

CONCENTRIC ZONE THEORY

MULTIPLE NUCLEI

SECTOR THEORY

FIGURE 19 Three Theories of City Structure. *Generalizations of internal structure of cities. The concentric-zone theory is a generalization for all cities. The arrangement of the sectors in the sector theory varies from city to city. The diagram for multiple nuclei represents one possible pattern among innumerable variations.*

SOURCE: C. D. Harris and E. L. Ullman, "The Nature of Cities," *Annals of the American Academy of Political & Social Science,* 242:13, November, 1945.

acter, as measured by certain criteria. In 1960, 63 per cent of the nation's population lived in our 212 metropolitan areas, and this figure is expected to rise to at least 70 per cent by 1975.

The suburb is the fastest growing part of America. Between 1950 and 1960, the suburbs of our metropolitan areas grew by 49.0 per cent, while our rural population was shrinking 0.8 per cent and the central cities were growing by only 10.6 per cent. In 58 of the metropolitan areas, the central city actually *lost* population between 1950 and 1960, and a comparable loss was experienced by nearly all the major cities. Nearly two-thirds of the entire nation's growth for the decade took place in the suburbs of these 212 metropolitan areas.

This explosion of the suburbs is a part of what has recently come to be known as *urban sprawl*. Vast strip cities are developing along our superhighways. A continuous urbanized area is developing from Boston to Baltimore, another from Buffalo to Detroit, across Michigan and on through Chicago around to Milwaukee, and many others. These strip cities fit no traditional pattern of city structure. In time, new theoretical constructs will be developed to describe them. Urban sprawl and strip cities bring a host of problems with them [Whyte, 1958]. The existing

Any coherent overall planning becomes almost an impossibility.

structures of township, city, and county government are quite inadequate to organize this developing urban monstrosity. With over 1,400 separate political units in the New York metropolitan area, each with its vested interests to defend, any coherent overall planning becomes almost an impossibility. Some observers believe that the problems of these metropolitan areas are so difficult that they will not be solved, and that the largest metropolitan areas will go into a relative decline [Vernon,

1960]. Urban sprawl is certain to be an interesting topic to sociologists and a headache for city planners for many years.

Changing Racial Structure. In every large American city the white people are fleeing to the suburbs while Negroes fill up the spaces they leave. Negroes are effectively excluded from the suburbs of most American cities. Wherever statistics show Negro suburban growth, it is generally found to be in industrial satellite towns, or occasionally in segregated Negro suburbs, not in typical residential suburbs. Between 1940 and 1950, while the white population of all central cities was increasing by 3.7 per cent, the Negro population grew by 67.8 per cent. In Chicago, Negroes comprised 8 per cent of the population in 1940, 19 per cent in 1957, and are expected to reach 33 per cent by 1970. Nonwhites in New York City composed 6 per cent in 1940 and 13 per cent in 1957, while by 1970, Negroes and Puerto Ricans are expected to make up 45 per cent of the population of Manhattan and nearly one-third of the entire city. Washington, D.C., already has an actual majority of Negroes [Grodzins, 1958, pp. 1–3].

Such population shifts have many consequences. Negroes have lower average incomes but generally must pay higher prices than whites for comparable housing [Laurenti, 1960]. This discrimination brings overcrowding, congestion, and neighborhood deterioration to Negro areas, even though individual Negroes take as good or better care of property than *comparable class levels* of whites. But the sheer pressure of numbers ensures that the changing racial composition of the central city will bring a spreading of slums and its associated problems. The prospective political consequences of a Negro-dominated central city and a white suburb are interesting. Perhaps the traditional suburban dislike for annexation may change, as white suburbs annex themselves to the city in order to prevent city domination by Negroes. Or, conversely, perhaps the suburbs will resist annexation in order to remain politically separate from Negroes. Of course the elimination of housing segregation would end these problems, for then Negroes would be distributed over the area according to their income and preference. While housing segregation is under spirited attack, it may not decline quickly enough to avert these problems.

Urban Ecological Processes. Change is continuous in the American city. The means through which the distribution of people and institutions change are known as *ecological processes.* To understand them we must begin with the *natural area,* a collection of people and activities drawn together in mutual interdependence within a limited area. The single-men's district of flophouses and cheap hotels, cheap restaurants, pawn shops, burlesque shows, taverns and missions, all catering to the

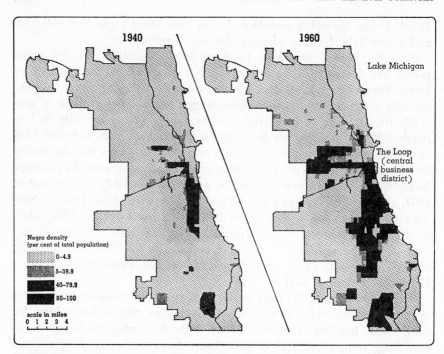

FIGURE 20   The Changing Face of Chicago. *Chicago has the second-largest Negro popu-lation of any city in the United States—813,000 at the 1960 census count, or three times as many as it had in 1940. Negroes now represent about 23 per cent of the city's total population. The pattern of change in Chicago typifies that of most Northern cities that have had a large Negro influx. In 1940, when Chicago had only 277,700 Negroes (8 per cent of total population), the great bulk lived in a long, narrow ghetto south of the Loop, the city's central business district. There were very few Negroes (i.e., fewer than 5 per cent) in 814 of the city's 935 census tracts. The 66 tracts that were 80 per cent or more Negro contained 86 per cent of the city's total Negro popu-lation. Chicago has remained a highly segregated city, despite the enormous increase in Negro population. Census tracts with 80 per cent or more Negroes now contain 80 per cent of the city's Negro population (tracts with 40 to 80 per cent Negroes hold another 12 per cent), while tracts with fewer than 5 per cent Negroes hold 89 per cent of the city's white population. But now there are 152 tracts that are 80 to 100 per cent Negro, compared to 66 in 1940.*

The growth in Negro residence has occurred largely by the expansion of the old Negro ghetto into the adjoining areas rather than by the settling of new areas. (See right-hand map.) The expansion of the Negro ghetto has produced some improvement in the quality of Negro housing; however, conditions that white middle-class people call "blight" represent to Negroes a great improvement in housing standards.

SOURCE: Charles E. Silberman, "The City and the Negro," *Fortune*, March, 1962, p. 91.

needs of low-income homeless men, is an example of a natural area. Other natural areas include the department-store section, the entertainment area, the communities of recent immigrants, the rooming-house district, the college students' residential area, the warehouse district, and many others. Natural areas are unplanned. They arise from the free choices of individuals. Persons having similar desires and preferences are drawn together into an area where these needs are most easily fulfilled, and their association creates a natural area.

The *neighborhood*, unlike the natural area, may be either planned or unplanned. A neighborhood is an area where people neighbor. There is very little neighboring in some areas, such as the rooming-house district, and more neighboring in the ethnic communities and family-residence areas. Some urban neighborhoods are consciously planned, with housing, communication, shopping, and recreation facilities deliberately arranged to encourage neighboring. More often the neighborhood is an unplanned product of people's need for social relations. Neighboring is greatest in family-residence areas where people face common problems of child rearing and crabgrass fighting. Neighborhoods and natural areas are constantly being formed, dissolved, and relocated through the urban ecological processes of *concentration, centralization, decentralization, segregation,* and *invasion* [Lee, 1955].

Concentration is the tendency for people and institutions to gather where conditions are favorable. It produces the growth of cities. *Centralization* is the clustering together of the economic and service functions in the city. People come together to work, to play, to shop, then return to other areas to live. The shopping district, the factory district, and the entertainment district are empty of people for a part of each day or night. The central business district is a prime example of centralization. *Decentralization* describes the tendency of people and organizations to desert the center of the city for outlying areas where congestion is less and land values are lower. The automobile and motor truck and electric power have greatly encouraged residential, commercial, and industrial decentralization, which greatly complicates the task of anyone seeking to diagram the structure of the city.

Segregation refers to the concentration of certain types of people or organizations within a particular area. The "Gold Coast," the ghetto, and the black belt are examples along with the hotel and banking districts, the theater district, and "used-car row." Segregation may be either voluntary or involuntary. Most immigrant groups voluntarily segregated themselves, for life was more comfortable that way. The ghetto in the large American cities was partly voluntary and partly involuntary [Wirth, 1928]. The black belt is an example of involuntary segregation as realtor practices, the threat of violence, and "neighborhood-improvement associations" limit Negro residence to a restricted Negro area [Abrams, 1955; Grier and Grier, 1960].

Invasion takes place when a new kind of people, organization, or activity enters an area. Residential areas may be invaded by business; a business area may be invaded by a new kind of business; residents of a different class level or ethnic group may move into a residential area. Generally invasion is of a higher-status area by a lower-status group or institution. This direction of invasion is a normal outcome of the process of city growth and aging. A once-exclusive residential area of no-longer-fashionable homes is invaded by people a class level below the present occupants. A generation later the same area may be invaded by persons still another level lower, or by Negroes, or by secondhand stores and other business houses. Occasionally the direction is reversed. Nearly every large city today contains areas where dilapidated housing is being renovated or rebuilt into an upper-class residential area. Many upper-income people have fled to the suburbs because the attractive new housing is located there. Many would like to remain close to the city's center if satisfactory housing is available. Some areas have therefore traveled the complete cycle of upper-class residence to slum to upper-class residence. In all likelihood the cycle will now be repeated.

Stages in the invasion cycle. Several sociologists have sought to define the several stages of an invasion cycle [McKenzie, 1925, p. 25; Gibbard, 1938, pp. 206–207; Lee, 1955, pp. 257–260]. The *initial* stage brings a small number of people into the area and may not even be noticed for a time. When the old occupants become aware of an invasion, a *reaction* stage begins whose intensity depends on the cultural and racial characteristics of the invaders, the attitudes of the old residents, and the neighborhood solidarity of the old residents. Opposition is most likely when the invaders are Negroes. A common device is the "civic," "protective," or "neighborhood-improvement" association. This organization seeks to prevent residents from selling or renting to the invaders, and to discourage the invaders from seeking to buy or rent in the area. Such associations are most effective when most of the homes are owned by their occupants. If the reaction fails to stop the invaders, then the *general-influx* stage soon follows. When there are enough newcomers to make the old residents unwilling to remain, the "tip point" has been reached, and the old residents rapidly abandon the area to the newcomers. The *climax* is reached with the complete replacement of the old residents with newcomers or with commercial or institutional land use. The final stage is *succession,* in which the area may remain in a disorganized and chaotic state, or may become well-organized around its new residents or land use.

This invasion cycle is continuously in operation in every American city. The processes of growth and aging make it inevitable. It is a costly process—costly in terms of human frustration and economic waste—but no one has suggested a practical alternative. Zoning is not an alternative —it is simply a technique for making invasion and succession more deliberate and orderly.

Incidentally, the Negro invasion is a perfect illustration of how the culture creates social conflicts. The Negro population of our major cities has been exploding, largely through the urban migration of Negroes. Since Negroes are excluded from most new housing developments, they can find room to live only by invading white residential areas. If there were no discrimination, Negroes would scatter themselves over the community according to income and preference, as other ethnic groups have eventually done. But because there *is* discrimination, Negroes are continuously desperate for a place to live. Many whites would not object to a sprinkling of Negroes in their neighborhood, but will not live in a predominantly Negro district. Fearing a mass Negro invasion, they try to keep out all Negroes. Their effort restricts Negro housing and makes it more likely that a mass invasion will soon follow an initial influx. Thus whites' effort to keep Negroes out ensures that when they do come to many neighborhoods, they will come in an overwhelming tide. This is another example of the self-fulfilling prophecy. The prediction that the first Negro family will bring a flood of Negroes causes white people to act in ways that guarantee exactly this result [Wolf, 1957]. Of all possible ways of providing housing for a growing urban Negro population, we seem to have hit upon the most inefficient and painful.

It is through these ecological processes that the city continues to change. How do they shape urban life and personality?

Urban Life and Personality

Speed and Tension. The city is always in a hurry. Work and play are timed by the clock as we proceed from deadline to deadline. Lunches become business appointments, or the busy executive eats lunch at his desk, barking commands between bites. Genuine relaxation is impossible for many urbanites, and a vacation is merely a change of scene for equally tightly scheduled activities.

Anonymity. The sheer pressure of numbers makes for anonymity. Of course there are groups within which the urbanite is known as a person, but much of his routine life is spent in the anonymous crowd—the *Lonely Crowd* of David Riesman [1950]. The heterogeneity of city life with its mixture of people of all races, creeds, classes, occupations, and ethnic origins heightens this sense of anonymity. Different interests sepa-

A vacation is merely a change of scene for
equally tightly scheduled activities.

rate people from any intimate acquaintance with others whom they meet
in passing. Lee remarks:

> Anonymity is a loss of identity in a city teeming with millions. Many urban-
> ites live in a social void, or vacuum in which institutional norms are not effec-
> tive in controlling or regulating their social behavior. Although they are aware
> of the existence of many institutional organizations and many people around
> them, they do not feel a sense of belongingness to any one group or commu-
> nity. Socially, they are poor in the midst of plenty.

Rose Hum Lee, *The City*, J. B. Lippincott Company, Philadelphia, 1955, p. 454.

In the rooming-house areas and "skid rows" are the extremes of urban
anonymity—the forgotten men and women of obscure past and uncertain
future. They exist outside the pale of organized conventional living, with
their life centered in the rooming house or flophouse, the cheap tavern,
and perhaps the rescue mission. They are the defeated refuse of our social system, resigned and often contented with a social role that demands
little and offers little.

Social Distance. City people are physically crowded but socially distant. Social distance is a product of anonymity, impersonality, and heterogeneity. Ethnic differences are one form of heterogeneity, dividing
people into groups that often dislike or feel disdain of one another.
But occupational differences may be even more important sources of
social distance. Unlike the agricultural community, the city has no common occupational focus to serve as a common interest. Workers may
follow any one of thousands of different occupations and have little
understanding of or interest in other lines of work. The varieties of
work attract men with a great range of education, skills, training, and
temperament. This diversity of interests, backgrounds, and economic
levels is such that men learn to reveal only that side of their personality
the other person would be expected to understand. This constant masking of one's true feelings adds up to a great lack of understanding.
Thus the great city which multiplies contacts also produces loneliness.
From this loneliness a man often flees into a frantic effort to accommodate himself to changing popular tastes in order to prove to his blasé
neighbors that he really "belongs" and thus merits at least a segment of
their attention. The city is a place of outward conformity and inner

reservations, of "front" and conspicuous consumption, of "keeping up with the Joneses." When people cannot know us for what we are, they must judge us by what they see. Hence the great importance of the well-tailored appearance, the impressive car, the occupational title, and the "good" address.

Most routine social contacts in the city are impersonal, segmented, and correct. Formal politeness takes the place of genuine friendliness. The telephone and the printed checklist make it possible to contact people impersonally when necessary while keeping them at a distance. Urbanites become nigh-dwellers, not neighbors. Apartment dwellers may live for years without any acquaintance with many of the other occupants. In the absence of spontaneous, informal social interaction, a sort of social cleavage serves to restrict social interaction to that which is formal and correct. The ability of urbanites to look past or through people without seeing them is quite disconcerting to many rural visitors.

Regimentation. The pressure of numbers requires that urban life be highly regimented. Traffic lights control the flow of traffic; elevators and escalators move on schedule. The city dweller learns to work by the clock, under close supervision, often following the letter of his instructions without any effort to understand what he is doing or why. Changes in his routine are decreed from above and must be coordinated by the electronic computer which places each human robot in the right spot at the right time performing the right function. Even recreation for children is organized, and the harried housewife races to get Junior to his club at 4:15 so that he will be on time for the period of "free play." Such control is sometimes irksome, but the true city dweller has learned to accept the idea that most of life is according to plan and to justify his subservience to regulation on the ground of efficiency.

What results do these conditions of urban life have on personality? Very little actual research has been done on this question, although it has attracted a great deal of sociological speculation. Sociologists suspect that urban life produces greater emotional tension and insecurity, and some empirical evidence supports this conclusion. The rates of mental illness are higher in the city than in rural areas. It is, however, not clear whether the city causes more mental disorder, attracts the maladjusted person to the city, or merely locates and diagnoses more of the mental illness in the population. One well-controlled study, however, finds that farm and small-town children show a higher level of personal adjustment than urban children, with greater self-reliance, a greater sense of personal worth, and fewer feelings of nonbelonging [Mangus, 1948]. Although insecurity and rejection are entirely possible in a rural setting, the heterogeneous and anonymous nature of the city probably increases insecurity and nonbelonging.

Segmentation of personality is a necessary technique for coping with the multiple human contacts of an urban area. Most routine urban contacts are of a secondary-group rather than primary-group nature. Most contacts are instrumental; that is, we use another person as a necessary functionary to fulfill our purposes. We do not ordinarily interact with entire persons but with people as mailmen, bus drivers, elevator operators, salespersons, and other functionaries. We thus interact with only a segment of the person, not with the whole person. Such casual, superficial, short-lived relations with segments of people constitute a large part of the urbanite's social relations, in contrast to the rural dweller who has relatively fewer contacts with anyone whom he does not know well or with whom he fails to interact as a complete person [Sorokin and Zimmerman, 1929, pp. 48–58]. Even the superficial camaraderie with the taxicab driver is not genuine informal social interaction, but is a standardized part of the service [Davis, 1959].

Urban and Rural Convergence

Much of the foregoing discussion is already becoming outdated. We noted the urbanization of rural life and the suburban movement. Urban-rural differences of all sorts are rapidly shrinking in the Western world, and in time this will probably be true of the rest of the world. The suburb is the most rapidly growing part of America, and the suburban family is tending to become the "normal" family as we conceive it. This family is intermediate in size between the rural and urban families, and as compared with the urban family, is more strongly integrated around kinship ties; parental and sibling roles are strengthened, and the family is more active in voluntary organizations and community life [Jaco and Belknap, 1953]. The problems of community organization are increasingly those of the suburb and its relation to the central city. Suburban America *is* America.

The importance of the rural-urban distinction has already become secondary to the occupational distinction [Stewart, 1958; Dewey, 1960]. The distinctive rural pattern of life is more closely linked to an agricultural occupation than to mere residence in a rural area. A recent study of rural-urban differences in interpersonal relations found that farm people differed considerably from urban residents, while there was comparatively little difference between urban and rural nonfarm people [Riess, 1959]. Clearly, occupation has become more important than rural or urban residence as a clue to one's personality and way of life.

Nor should it be assumed that urbanization *necessarily* brings anomie, disorganization, or a lack of informal primary-group relationships. Earlier observers of urbanism were impressed by these features of urban life [Park et al., 1925; Sorokin and Zimmerman, 1929]. But either the observers exaggerated these characteristics or urbanites have changed. Some recent studies have found that anomie is no more widespread in highly urbanized than in less highly urbanized areas [Greer and Kube, 1959]. As urbanism increases, neighboring and participation in formal organizations decline, but primary-group relationships within kinship and friendship groups increase. When rural people migrate to the city, they do not enter a social vacuum but rely heavily on relatives for social interaction [Blumberg and Bell, 1959]. Instead of the extended family declining in importance with urbanization, research finds that the extended family is an even more important unit in large cities than in rural areas [Key, 1961]. Apparently as urbanism increases and people become more anonymous as members of the community, they rely more heavily on close friends and relatives for intimate response, identity, and a sense of belonging. The rise of the proportion of secondary contacts with urbanism implies no absolute weakening of primary-group life.

Community Integration and Planning. To some observers the American community has ceased to be a true community. Stein [1960] argues that our loss of craft satisfactions, of ethnic identity, of local autonomy, and of significant local ceremonial has destroyed the community of American towns and cities. He is highly critical of the striving for status and the *kaffeeklatsching* of the suburb, and longs for the lost humanizing virtues of a past he assumes offered fuller opportunities for personal fulfillment.

Whether it is necessary to the good life that communities be integrated in the traditional manner can be argued. Today all American communities—urban, rural, or suburban—are more nearly alike than ever before. Locality has ceased to be an effective basis for grouping. Special interest has largely replaced locality as the basis for grouping. Locality groups are too diversified to have very much in common. But special interests of all kinds—occupational, recreational, religious, promotional—unite people who may have little in common except this special interest. As one enthusiast testifies, "The friendships and pleasures I owe to collecting! The people you get to know! Book collectors are nocturnal people; they love to sit up and talk, and they're always good fun." [1] Such unity as survives in the modern community comes largely from the interlocking membership of many such special-interest groups.

In rural America, where locality and occupation once converged to give a common way of life to most people, it was not difficult to maintain an integrated community and an effective system of social control. Today it is more difficult. While the primary group survives in the

[1] Donald F. Hyde, quoted in *The New Yorker*, Mar. 22, 1958, p. 25.

city, it no longer functions as a very effective community control. Whether it is possible for the primary group to be an effective social control in the modern city is debatable [Tannenbaum, 1948; Riemer, 1959]. Angell [1947; 1951] in his study of the integration of American cities took a low crime rate and a high proportion of contributors to the community chest as indexes of community integration. He concluded that cities with an ethnically homogeneous population and a low rate of geographic mobility had a higher degree of moral integration. While geographic mobility will probably continue, ethnic heterogeneity will decline as present immigrant groups become fully assimilated. There is therefore some prospect that community integration may grow somewhat more attainable as time passes.

City planning is today the recommended antidote for urban problems. Practically every city has a city planning board, although often it does little but decide on the location of highways and public buildings. Any comprehensive planning is certain to meet opposition from many vested interests. Yet without comprehensive planning and execution of these plans, the American city faces accelerating decay. Slums are spreading faster than they are being cleared. Uncoordinated, piecemeal development of the urban fringe and of the "strip" cities is certain to mean great waste and agonizing future problems. Sewers, water mains, and expressways built *after* many homes and buildings are constructed will require expensive demolition. One suburb will wind up with lots of children to educate; another suburb will have the industrial properties that make up the tax base needed to finance good schools. Certain areas will begin to have costly floods when the development of adjacent areas alters the watershed. Quiet residential areas will become noisy thoroughfares because of developments in adjacent areas. Problems like these are the fruits of uncoordinated, unplanned regional development. There are as yet few planning authorities with power to make, let alone enforce execution of, plans for an entire metropolitan area. Eventually, after the problems have become intolerable and most of the mistakes have already been made, we shall probably create the plans.

Summary

A community is an area within which all a group's life activities can be carried on. Rural and urban people are different because the physical and social conditions of life are different in urban and rural communities. The traditional rural community tended to be a folk society. Its isolation, homogeneity, agricultural occupation, and subsistence economy all tended to develop people who were thrifty, hardworking, conservative, and ethnocentric. Changing technology has brought a rural revolution, with reduced isolation, commercialized large-scale farming, and in many respects a way of life very similar to urban patterns.

Cities are possible because of an agricultural surplus together with means of transportation, and tend to develop at "breaks" in transportation. Attempts to explain the structural arrangement of American cities have produced the concentric-zone, sector, and multiple-nuclei theories, none of which any city perfectly fits but which all cities somewhat corroborate. The most significant current developments in city structure are the suburb and the metropolitan area, which now account for most of our current population growth. As whites flee to the suburbs, the central city becomes increasingly Negro, thereby aggravating certain racial and political problems of the city.

The city is a conglomeration of natural areas, constantly forming and shifting through the ecological processes of concentration, centralization, decentralization, segregation, and invasion. The invasion cycle has several stages: the initial influx, reaction, general influx, climax, and succession.

Urban life and personality are affected by the physical and social conditions of urban living—speed and tension, anonymity, social distance, and regimentation. These conditions produce impersonality, insecurity, and segmentation of personality. Today, however, urban and rural differences are rapidly shrinking. The rural-urban distinction is already less important than occupational classification as a clue to our personality and way of life. Yet our increasingly urban world is beset by problems of community integration and organization, and community planning is a growing concern.

Questions and Projects

1. Why are cities such recent inventions in man's long history?
2. How are the personality characteristics of rural and urban people a product of their physical and social conditions of life? What sort of problems are faced by rural migrants to the city?
3. What has produced the rural revolution? What has this done to rural-urban differences?
4. Are there rural slums? What produces them? How do they resemble and differ from urban slums?
5. Why has "conspicuous consumption" been more of an urban than a rural pattern? Is this relation changing today? How or why?
6. Is urban life better or less satisfying than rural life? Is your answer influenced by ethnocentrism?
7. A few sociologists have objected to the phrase "urbanization of rural life" to describe current changes. Are there any respects in which urban life is being "ruralized"? Contrast the relative amounts of diffusion in each direction.
8. Why has it been easier to integrate the small rural community than the large city? Is there any

reasonable prospect of greater community integration for urban areas?

9. Many hospitals, built several decades ago, now find themselves in deteriorating areas. What problems does this create? What can be done about it?

10. Read Edward T. Chase, "Jam on the Côte d'Azur," *Reporter*, Sept. 28, 1961, pp. 44–46, or Wilfred Owen, *Cities in the Motor Age*, The Viking Press, Inc., New York, 1959. Then prepare your answer

to the question: Are automobiles an asset or a blight upon the modern city?

11. To the city you know best, apply each of the three theories of city structure. Which fits it best? How well does the theory describe the actual arrangement of this city?

12. Trace the stages of the invasion cycle for an area of the city you know best. Try to date each stage. How long did each stage last and how long did the entire cycle require? Was it a happy period?

Suggested Readings

ALLEN, FREDRICK LEWIS: "The Big Change in Suburbia," *Harper's Magazine*, June, 1954, pp. 21–28; July, 1954, pp. 47–53. Some social effects of the mass-produced suburbs.

BELL, WENDELL, AND MARION D. BOAT: "Urban Neighborhoods and Informal Social Relations," *American Journal of Sociology*, 62:391–398, 1957. Research data on the extent and intimacy of neighborhood contacts in the urban milieu.

CHASE, EDWARD T.: "Jam on the Côte d'Azur," *Reporter*, Sept. 28, 1961, pp. 44–46. A popularly written article on traffic problems in European and American cities.

CONANT, JAMES BRYANT: *Slums and Suburbs*, McGraw-Hill Book Company, New York, 1961. Contrasts the effects of slum and suburb on the functioning of the school.

EDITORS OF *Fortune*: *The Exploding Metropolis*, Doubleday & Company, Inc., Garden City, N.Y., 1958. A brief, readable treatment of urban problems.

LEE, ROSE HUM: *The City: Urbanism and Urbanization in Major World Regions*, J. B. Lippincott Company, Philadelphia, 1955. A textbook in urban sociology, with emphasis on urbanization in different areas of the world.

ROGERS, EVERETT M.: *Social Changes in Rural Society*, Appleton-Century-Crofts, Inc., New York, 1960. A textbook in rural sociology, with emphasis on rural social change.

SUSSMAN, MARVIN B. (ED.): *Community Structure and Analysis*, Thomas Y. Crowell Company, New York, 1959. A series of articles summarizing recent research and its relation to community problems.

Social and
Cultural Change

*Homouda Awadan's nights have been restless recently, mainly be-
cause his cow no longer sleeps in the same room with him.*

*Awadan is one of 2,000 peasants moved last summer from over-
populated mud-hut villages into Ibis, a modern village with brick
houses, electric lighting, running water and special pens for cattle.*

*The operation is sponsored by the U.S. Point Four program and
the Egyptian Agriculture Department.*

*Life in the modern village has posed many problems to the fella-
heen (peasants), many of whom came from villages that have seen
little change since the days of the pharaohs.*

*All his life Awadan has slept with his cow, his chief work animal
and provider of milk, yogurt and white cheese. Keeping the animal
inside the house kept his floor littered with animal refuse, but
Awadan could not take a chance on the beast being stolen.*

*"For the past three nights I have been waking in the middle of
the night to check on my cow down in the village," said Awadan,
still not used to the separation from his most treasured possession.*

*Awadan often yearns for the uncomplicated life of the mud
village, but he remembers the five acres of land the government
gave him and decides to stay. He never owned land before. He had
to rent it from a big landowner.*

*Sheikh Rashad, director of the co-operative union at Ibis village,
said it took much convincing to move the fellaheen into the model
village. They are not inclined to move, no matter how crowded, he
said.*

*In spite of all preparations, unexpected situations arose, Rashad
said. Stacks of dry wood soon began appearing on top of the houses,
similar to the mud villages, he added. At Ibis they had special
storage rooms for wood, but the fellaheen would not use them.*

Associated Press, Nov. 9, 1959.

All cultures are constantly changing—some rapidly and some very slowly. Even when it tries to do so, no society succeeds in exactly copying and transmitting the culture of its ancestors. This fluidity is most easily illustrated by language changes. English has changed so greatly that most students have their troubles with Shakespeare and are hopelessly lost in Chaucer. Samuel Johnson published his dictionary in the hope that it would stabilize word meanings and stop language changes, but soon he confessed he had failed. Social change is continuous and irresistible. Only its speed and direction vary.

Some sociologists distinguish between *social change,* changes in the social structure and social relationships of a society, and *cultural change,* changes in the culture of a society. In practice, these two types of change are so closely interwoven that the distinction is not very useful. Most sociologists use the terms interchangeably or simply lump both under the term social change.

There is an important distinction between social change and progress. The term "progress" carries a value judgment. Progress means change in a desirable direction. Desirable as measured by whose values? Are faster automobiles, increased leisure, rising standards of living, and growing acceptance of divorce and birth control desirable or not? Not even all Americans are agreed, while the Pakistani or Masai will be still more skeptical. Since "progress" is an evaluative term, social scientists prefer the neutrally descriptive term "social change."

Processes of Social Change

Discovery. A discovery is *a human perception of a fact or relationship that already exists.* Man discovered the principle of the lever, the circulation of the blood, and the conditioned reflex. A discovery is an addition to mankind's store of verified knowledge.

A discovery becomes a factor in social change only when it is put to use. A discovery may become part of the background of knowledge that people use in evaluating their present practices. Thus the recent discoveries of physiology and psychology that males and females are very much alike in their intellectual capacities did not *compel* men to alter the status of women; but the discoveries made the nineteenth-century patriarch look ridiculous and certainly diluted men's determination to preserve traditional male dominance.

When new knowledge is used to develop new technology, vast changes generally follow. The ancient Greeks knew about the power of steam, and before A.D. 100 Hero of Alexandria had built a small steam engine as a toy, but steam power produced no social changes until it was put to serious use two thousand years later. Discoveries become a factor in social change when new knowledge is put to new uses.

Invention. An invention is often defined as *a new use of old elements* of the culture. Thus George Selden in 1895 combined a liquid gas engine, a liquid gas tank, a running-gear mechanism, an intermediate clutch, a driving shaft, and a carriage body and patented this contraption as an automobile. None of these elements were new; the only novelty was the combined use of them. The Selden patent was attacked and eventually revoked by the courts on the grounds that he did not originate the idea.

Inventions may be classified as *material* inventions, such as the bow and arrow, telephone, or airplane, and *social* inventions, such as the alphabet, constitutional government, or contract bridge. In each case old elements are used, combined, and improved for a new application. Invention is thus a continuing process, with each new invention the last in a long series of preceding inventions and discoveries. In a popularly written book, Burlingame [1947] has analyzed a number of familiar inventions, showing how each began hundreds or thousands of years ago and passed through dozens of preliminary inventions and intermediate stages. Invention is not strictly an individual matter; it is a social process involving an endless series of modifications, improvements, and recombinations.

Diffusion. Even the most inventive society invents only a modest proportion of its new elements. Most of the social changes in all known societies have developed through *diffusion, the spread of culture traits from group to group.* Diffusion operates both within societies and between societies. Jazz originated among Negro musicians of New Orleans and became diffused to other groups within the society. Later it spread to other societies and has now been diffused throughout the civilized world.

Diffusion takes place whenever societies come into contact. Societies may seek to prevent diffusion by forbidding contact, as in the case of the Old Testament Hebrews.

> When the Lord thy God shall bring thee into the land whither thou goest to possess it, and hath cast out many nations before thee . . . thou shalt smite them and utterly destroy them; thou shalt make no covenant with them, nor shew mercy unto them; neither shalt thou make marriages with them. . . . For they will turn away thy son from following me, that they may serve other gods. . . . But . . . ye shall destroy their altars and break down their images, and cut down their groves, and burn their graven images with fire [Deuteronomy 7:1–5].

Like most attempts to prevent intercultural contacts, this effort failed. The Old Testament tells how the Hebrews persisted in mingling and intermarrying with the surrounding tribes, adopting bits of their cultures in the process. Whenever cultures come into contact, some exchange of culture traits always takes place.

Most of the content of any complex culture has been diffused from other societies.

Most of the content of any complex culture has been diffused from other societies. Ralph Linton has written a famous passage that tells how the 100 per cent American has actually borrowed most of his culture from other areas.

Our solid American Citizen awakens in a bed built on a pattern which originated in the Near East but which was modified in Northern Europe before it was transmitted to America. He throws back covers made from cotton, domesticated in India, or linen, domesticated in the Near East, or silk, the use of which was discovered in China. All of these materials have been spun and woven by processes invented in the Near East. He slips into his moccasins, invented by the Indians of the Eastern woodlands, and goes to the bathroom, whose fixtures are a mixture of European and American inventions, both of recent date. He takes off his pajamas, a garment invented in India, and washes with soap invented by the ancient Gauls. He then shaves, a masochistic rite which seems to have been derived from either Sumer or Ancient Egypt.

Returning to the bedroom, he removes his clothes from a chair of southern European type and proceeds to dress. He puts on garments whose form originally derived from the skin clothing of the nomads of the Asiatic steppes, puts on shoes made from skins tanned by a process invented in ancient Egypt and cut to a pattern derived from the classical civilizations of the Mediterranean, and ties around his neck a strip of bright-colored cloth which is a vestigial survival of the shoulder shawls worn by seventeenth century Croatians. Before going out for breakfast he glances through the window, made of glass invented in Egypt, and if it is raining puts on overshoes made of rubber discovered by the Central American Indians and takes an umbrella, invented in southeastern Asia. Upon his head he puts a hat made of felt, a material invented in the Asiatic steppes.

On his way to breakfast he stops to buy a paper, paying for it with coins, an ancient Lydian invention. At the restaurant a whole new series of borrowed elements confronts him. His plate is made of a form of pottery invented in China. His knife is of steel, an alloy first made in southern India, his fork a medieval Italian invention, and his spoon a derivative of a Roman original. He begins breakfast with an orange, from the eastern Mediterranean, a cantelope from Persia, or perhaps a piece of African watermelon. With this he has coffee, an Abyssinian plant, with cream and sugar. Both the domestication of cows and the idea of milking them originated in the Near East, while sugar was first made in India. After his fruit and first coffee he goes on to waffles, cakes made by a Scandinavian technique from wheat domesticated in Asia Minor. Over these he pours maple syrup, invented by the Indians of the Eastern woodlands. As a side dish he may have the egg of a species of bird domesticated in Indo-China, or thin strips of the flesh of an animal domesticated in Eastern Asia which have been salted and smoked by a process developed in Northern Europe.

When our friend has finished eating he settles back to smoke, an American Indian habit, consuming a plant domesticated in Brazil in either a pipe, derived from the Indians of Virginia, or a cigarette, derived from Mexico. If he is hardy enough he may even attempt a cigar, transmitted to us from the Antilles by way of Spain. While smoking he reads the news of the day, imprinted in characters invented by the ancient Semites upon a material invented in China by a process invented in Germany. As he absorbs the accounts of foreign troubles he will, if he is a good conservative citizen, thank a Hebrew deity in an Indo-European language that he is a 100 per cent American.

Ralph Linton, *The Study of Man*, Appleton-Century-Crofts, Inc., New York, 1936, pp. 326–327. Copyright 1936, D. Appleton-Century Company, Inc.

Diffusion is always a two-way process. Europeans gave horses, firearms, Christianity, and whisky to the Indians, in exchange for corn, potatoes, tobacco, and the canoe. Yet the exchange is often a lopsided one. When two cultures come into contact, the simpler one generally borrows more traits than the more complex one, and low-status groups generally borrow more than high-status groups. Slave groups generally absorb the culture of their masters, their own culture being largely forgotten.

Diffusion is a selective process. A group accepts some culture traits from a neighbor, at the same time rejecting others. We accepted much of the Indian's food but rejected his religion. Indians quickly accepted the white man's horse but long rejected the white man's cow.

Diffusion generally involves some modification of the borrowed element. Each cultural trait has *form, function,* and *meaning.* Any or all of these may change when a trait is diffused. When Europeans adopted Indian tobacco, they smoked it in a pipe somewhat like the Indian pipe, thus preserving the form, although they also added other forms—cigarettes, chewing tobacco, and snuff. But they changed function and meaning completely. Indians smoked tobacco as a ceremonial ritual; Europeans used it first as a medicine, and later for personal gratification and sociability. The outward forms of Christianity have been diffused more readily than the functions and meanings. In missionary areas many converts have accepted the forms of Christian worship while retaining many of their traditional supernatural beliefs and practices. Non-Western peoples have put tin cans and other Western artifacts to a variety of uses, both utilitarian and aesthetic. American colonists accepted maize (corn) from the Indians unchanged; it traveled to Europe, where it was used as food for animals but not for people; it was then diffused to West Africa where it became a favorite food and even an offering to the gods. Endless examples could be cited to show how traits are nearly always modified as they are diffused.

Many useful traits fail to be diffused to other societies. The abacus, thousands of years old, is nearly as efficient as a modern calculating machine (and far cheaper), yet it was never adopted by Western societies. Over two thousand years ago, Chinese physicians immunized for smallpox and knew the use of ephedrine [Thorwald, 1963], but these medical secrets had to be rediscovered in the West. Why some useful traits failed to be diffused is a continuing puzzle to social scientists.

Factors in the Rate of Change

Discovery, invention, and diffusion are processes of change, but what causes them to happen? We cannot answer this question without first examining the meaning of the term "cause." A cause is sometimes defined as a condition that is *both necessary and sufficient* to produce a predictable effect. It is necessary in that we never have this effect without this cause, and sufficient in that this cause, alone, always produces this effect. Thus defined, very few causes have been established in social science. Does drunkenness cause divorce? Many long-suffering souls put up with a drunken mate, while others divorce mates who are bone dry. Obviously drunkenness is neither a necessary nor a sufficient condition to produce a divorce. Most causation in social science is multiple; that is, a number of factors interact in producing a result. What factors interact in producing a social change?

First of all, we note that the factors in social change are predominantly *social* and *cultural*, not biological or geographical. Not everyone accepts this view. Some people would attribute the rise and fall of great civilizations to changes in the biological characteristics of nations. Often these theories have a racial twist; a great civilization is said to arise from a vigorous, creative race, and falls when the race mixes with lesser breeds and dilutes its genius. According to an opposite version, a great burst of creativity follows a fortunate intermixture of races and dies out as this hybrid strain runs out. Most scientists reject all such theories. There is no convincing scientific evidence that any race differs from any other race in its biological basis for human learning, or that man's biology has changed during the last twenty-five years or so. During the period of recorded history, man's biological attributes appear to have been a constant, not a variable, in his behavior.

Changes in physical environment are an occasional factor in social change. For example the north coast of Africa was somewhat less arid in classical times than it is today. Many ancient port cities are now miles up the river delta. Climates change, soil erodes, and lakes gradually turn into swamps and finally plains. Although social life is affected by these changes, they come so very slowly that they are a minor factor. True, man may speed up these changes through his land use; he can accelerate or retard soil erosion through conservation practices. But the causes are still social and cultural, for it is the actions of men that set these environmental changes in motion.

Much more common in human history is a change of physical environment through migration. Especially with primitive societies, whose members are very directly dependent upon their physical environment, migration to a different environment brings major changes in culture. Civilized man can more easily transport and practice his culture in a new and different environment. The British colonial in the jungle outpost often persisted in taking afternoon tea and dressing for dinner. Yet no one would suggest that he was unaffected by the jungle environment; even civilized man's culture is affected by a change of physical environment.

Population Changes. Any major change in size or distribution of a people always produces major social changes. When a thinly settled frontier fills up with people, the hospitality pattern declines, secondary-group relations multiply, institutional structures grow more elaborate, and many other changes occur. A rapidly growing population must either migrate or improve its productive techniques. Great historic migrations and conquests—the Huns, the Vikings, and many others—have arisen from the pressure of a growing population upon limited resources. Migration itself encourages change, for it brings a group into a new environment, subjects it to new social contacts, and confronts it with new problems. No major population change leaves the culture unchanged.

Structure of the Society. The structure of a society affects its rate of change in subtle ways that are not immediately apparent. A society that vests great authority in the very old people, as classical China did for centuries, is likely to be conservative and stable. A society that stresses conformity and trains the individual to be highly responsive to the group, such as the Zuñi, is less receptive to change than a society like the Ileo who are highly individualistic and tolerate considerable cultural variability [Ottenberg, 1959]. When a culture is so highly integrated that each element is tightly interwoven with all the others in a mutually interdependent system, change is difficult and costly. Among a number of Nilotic African peoples such as the Pakot, Masai, and Kipsizis, the culture is highly integrated around the cattle complex.

Cattle are not only a means of subsistence; they are also a necessity for bride purchase, a measure of status, and an object of intense affection [Schneider, 1959]. Such a system is strongly resistant to social change. But when the culture is less highly integrated, so that work, play, family, religion, and other activities are less dependent on one another, change is easier and more frequent. A tightly structured society wherein every person's roles, duties, privileges, and obligations are precisely and rigidly defined is less given to changes than a more loosely structured society wherein roles, lines of authority, privileges, and obligations are more open to individual rearrangement.

The structure of American society is highly conducive to social change. Our individualism, our lack of rigid social stratification, our relatively high proportion of achieved statuses, and our institutionalization of research all encourage rapid social change. Today tens of thousands of workers are systematically employed in finding new discoveries and inventions. This explanation is something new in the world's history. Our dazzling and upsetting rate of change is one consequence.

Isolation and Contact. Societies located at world crossroads have always been centers of change. Since most new traits come through diffusion, those societies in closest contact with other societies are likely to change most rapidly. In ancient times of overland transport, the land bridge connecting Asia, Africa, and Europe was the center of civilizing change. Later with sailing vessels, it shifted to the fringes of the Mediterranean Sea, and still later to the northwest coast of Europe. Areas of highest intercultural contact are the centers of change.

Conversely, isolated areas are centers of stability, conservatism, or backwardness. Almost without exception, the most primitive tribes have been those who were the most isolated, like the polar Eskimos or the Aranda of central Australia. Even among civilized peoples, isolation brings cultural stability. The most "backward" American groups have, at least until recently, been found in the inaccessible hills and valleys of the Appalachians [Sherman and Henry, 1933].

Leyburn [1935] has shown how European groups who migrated to remote, isolated frontiers often retained many elements of their native culture long after they had been discarded by their parent society. Thus by the nineteenth century, the social life of the Boers in the Transvaal resembled the life of the late seventeenth-century Holland Dutch more than that of their contemporaries in the Netherlands. Isolation invariably retards social change.

Since contact promotes diffusion, highly ethnocentric groups have sometimes sought to preserve their culture from change by preventing social contacts with other societies. The early Hebrews felt themselves commanded by God to exterminate the Philistines and destroy all their

artifacts; the Pilgrims migrated repeatedly, and finally sought total isolation in America; the Amish avoid all but the absolutely necessary
economic contacts with out-groups. But unless a group is physically isolated, it is difficult to prevent social contact, and such efforts have generally failed.

Attitudes and Values. To us, change seems normal, and most West-
erners pride themselves on being progressive and up to date. By contrast, the Trobriand islanders off the coast of New Guinea have no
concept of change, and do not even have any words in their language
to express or describe change [Lee, 1959a, pp. 89–104]. When West-
erners tried to explain the concept of change, the islanders could not
understand what we were talking about. Societies obviously differ greatly
in their general attitude toward change. A people who revere the past,
worship their ancestors, honor and obey their elders, and are preoccupied
with traditions and rituals will change slowly and unwillingly. When
a culture has been relatively static for a long time, the people are likely
to assume it should remain so indefinitely. They are intensely and unconsciously ethnocentric; they assume that their customs and techniques
are correct and everlasting. A possible change is unlikely even to be
seriously considered.

A changing society has a different attitude toward change, and this
attitude is both cause and effect of the changes already taking place.
Changing societies are aware of social change. They are somewhat
skeptical and critical of some parts of their traditional culture and will
consider and experiment with innovations. Such attitudes powerfully
stimulate both the proposal and acceptance of changes.

Attitudes and values affect both the amount and the direction of social
change. The ancient Greeks made great contributions to art and learning but little to technology. Work was done by slaves; to concern oneself with a slave's work was no proper task for a Greek scholar. No
society has been equally dynamic in all aspects, and its values determine
in which area—art, music, warfare, technology, philosophy, religion—it
will be inventive.

The Cultural Base. The cave man could make exceedingly few material inventions, for he had very little to work with. Even the bow and
arrow combines a number of inventions and techniques—notching the
bow ends, tying the bowstring, hafting and pointing the arrow, plus the
idea and technique of shooting it. Not until these components were invented was it possible to invent the bow and arrow. By the *cultural base,*
we mean *the accumulation of knowledge and technique* available to the
inventor. As the cultural base grows, an increasing number of inventions
and discoveries become possible. The invention of the geared wheel
provided an element that has been used in hundreds of inventions. The

It is highly probable that imaginative persons will put these items together.

discovery of electromagnetism and the invention of the vacuum tube provided necessary elements for hundreds of more recent inventions.

Unless the cultural base provides the necessary preceding inventions and discoveries, an invention cannot be completed. Leonardo da Vinci in the late fifteenth century sketched many machines that were entirely workable in principle and detail, but the technology of his day was incapable of building them. His drawings for the aerial bomb, hydraulic pump, air-conditioning unit, helicopter, machine gun, military tank, and many others were clear and workable, but the fifteenth century lacked the advanced metals, fuels, lubricants, and technical skills necessary to carry his brilliant ideas into practical reality. Many inventive ideas have had to wait until the supporting gaps in knowledge and technique were filled in.

When all the supporting knowledge has been developed, the appearance of an invention or discovery becomes almost a certainty. In fact, it is quite common for an invention or discovery to be made independently by several persons at about the same time. Ogburn [1922, pp. 90–102], a sociologist who specialized in the study of social change, listed 148 such inventions and discoveries, ranging from the discovery of sunspots, independently discovered by Galileo, Fabricius, Scheiner, and Harriott, all in 1611, to the invention of the airplane by Langley (1892–1897), Wright (1895–1901), and perhaps others. When the cultural base provides all the supporting items of knowledge, it is very probable that one or more imaginative persons will put these items together for a new invention or discovery.

The great importance of the cultural base is seen in the principle of *cross-fertilization* and the *exponential principle*. By *cross-fertilization* we mean that discoveries and inventions in one field became useful in an entirely different field. Pasteur's germ theory of disease grew out of his efforts to tell France's vintners why their wine turned sour. The vacuum tube, developed for radio, made possible the electronic computer, which now airs research in nearly everything from astronomy to zoology. Certain radioactive materials, by-products of the search for more deadly weapons, are now invaluable in medical diagnosis, therapy, and research.

We cannot predict in what remote fields of knowledge a new discovery or invention may prove useful.

The exponential principle simply states that as the cultural base grows, its possible uses tend to grow in a geometric ratio. To illustrate: If we have only two chemicals in a laboratory, only one combination (of two or more) is possible; with three chemicals, four combinations are possible (A-B-C, A-B, A-C, and B-C); with four chemicals, ten combinations; with five chemicals, twenty-five; and so on. As the size of the cultural base grows by addition, the possible combinations of these elements grows by multiplication. This helps to explain today's high rate of discovery and invention. A vast accumulation of scientific technical knowledge is shared by all the civilized societies, and from this base, new inventions and discoveries flow in a rising tide.

Needs and Crises. A society's rate of change is powerfully affected by the needs it recognizes. An unrecognized need is of no consequence. According to our values, half the world needs to discard ancient systems of land holdings and consolidate tiny, scattered parcels into more practical units. But unless a society feels such a need, nothing changes; only the felt needs of a society count.

Some workable inventions languish until the society discovers or develops a need for them. The zipper fastener was invented in 1891 but was ignored for a quarter century. The pneumatic tire was invented and patented by Thompson in 1845 but was ignored until the popularity of the bicycle created a need for it; then it was reinvented by Dunlop in 1888.

Crises create new needs and bring a sharper recognition of existing needs. Nearly every modern safety regulation was preceded by a dramatic catastrophe—the sinking of the *Titanic*, Chicago's Iroquois Theater fire, and many others. Throughout history, wars and threats of war have been a stimulus to political organization, from the Delian League of Greek city-states, through the Five Nations of the Iroquois, to the United Nations of today. During World War II, the United States' efforts at weapons development led to great discoveries in nuclear physics; our efforts to protect our troops' health led to many medical discoveries, especially in tropical medicine; our productive effort called for greatly increased governmental controls over the economy and greatly accelerated the employment of married women; the war ended American isolationism and left us with sweeping world commitments. Of all crises, war and war dangers are probably the most productive of social changes.

Necessity, however, is no guarantee that the needed invention or discovery will be made. At present we need a cure for cancer, a reliable missile defense, and an effective protection against radioactivity. There is no certainty that we shall develop any of these. Necessity may be the mother of invention, but invention also needs a father—a cultural base to provide the necessary supporting knowledge and technique.

Resistance to and Acceptance of Social Change

Not all proposed innovations are accepted by the society. A process of *selective acceptance* operates as some innovations are accepted instantly and some only after long delay, some are rejected entirely and others are accepted in part. Thus we accepted completely the Indian's corn, accepted and modified his tobacco, accepted in a very small, highly modified way his totemic clans (Boy Scout "beaver" and "wolverine" patrols), and totally rejected his religion. Acceptance of innovations is never automatic and is always selective according to a number of considerations.

Specific Attitudes and Values. Aside from its general attitude toward change, each society has many specific attitudes and values that cling to its objects and activities. When government agents introduced hybrid corn to the Spanish-American farmers of the Rio Grande Valley a few years ago, they readily adopted it because of its superior yield, but within three years they all returned to the old corn. They didn't like the hybrid corn because it didn't make good tortillas [Apodaca, 1952]. People's established likes and dislikes are important factors in social change.

If an object has a purely utilitarian value—that is, if it is valued because of what it will *do*—change may be accepted quite readily when a better model is offered. If something is valued intrinsically—valued for itself, aside from what it will do—change is less readily accepted. To the American farmer, cattle are a source of income, to be bred, culled, and butchered whenever most profitable. But to many of the Nilotic peoples of Africa, cattle represent intrinsic values. The owner recognizes and loves each cow. To slaughter one would be like killing one of the family. A Pakot with a hundred cattle is rich and respected; the one with only a dozen is poor; the one with none at all is ignored as though he were dead. Efforts of colonial officials to get such peoples to manage their herds "rationally"—to cull their herds, breed only the best, and stop overgrazing their lands—have generally failed.

The average American, who usually takes a coldly rational, thoroughly unsentimental view of economic activities, finds it hard to appreciate the sentiments and values of non-Western peoples. He is irritated by the Biaga of Central India, who refused to give up their primitive digging sticks for the far superior moldboard plow. Why? The Biaga loved the earth as a kindly and generous mother; they would gently help her with the digging stick to bring forth her yield, but could not bring themselves to cut her "with knives" [Elwin, 1939, pp. 106–107]. The American is annoyed by the Ettwah Indians' unwillingness to adopt green manuring (plowing under a crop of green sanhemp as fertilizer). But to this Indian, "green manuring involves a very cruel act of plowing under the sanhemp leaf and stalk before they are ripe. This act involves violence" [Mayer, 1958, p. 209]. Yet is there any basic difference between these illustrations and an American's refusal to eat horse meat because it conflicts with his values? What is the basic difference between the Cambodian farmer who rejects fertilizer because it is an interference with nature and the many Americans who reject contraception because it is an interference with nature? How about those American groups who reject divorce, or alcoholic beverages, or movies, or card playing because these would conflict with their values? To each of us, it seems entirely logical and right to reject any innovation that conflicts with our mores or values; when another group does likewise, their refusal often impresses us as stubborn ignorance. Such is ethnocentrism!

Medical history is filled with examples of resistance to new medical discoveries. Pasteur was ridiculed and vilified for many years. In the fourteenth century, Theodoric and Henry de Mondeville argued that suppuration of wounds, contrary to Galen, was not a natural healing process and could be avoided by cleanliness; but after their death their improved aseptic methods were abandoned. Harvey was denounced because he challenged Galen's authority. Semmelweiss was dismissed from his hospital because he insisted on asepsis. Stern [1941, chap. 9] describes many such rejections. Such blind opposition to medical discoveries has now largely disappeared from the medical profession, but a somewhat undiscriminating resistance to changes in medical economics continues.

Medical and nursing practice today are both rapidly changing. Physicians are turning to group practice and resisting proposals for national health insurance. Professional nurses are becoming administrators, and much of the bedside nursing is being assumed by practical nurses and nurses' aides. These changes meet considerable resistance from nurses, who find their greatest satisfaction in bedside nursing [Saunders, 1954a; Riessman and Rohrer, 1957, pp. 11–17; Pearlin, 1962]. Nurses often resist changes in nursing procedures recommended by physicians and administrators, feeling that they know the patient's needs best [Riessman and Rohrer, 1957, pp. 200–205; MacAndrew and Elliott, 1959]. Even in a so highly technical field as nursing, attitudes and values can retard change.

Demonstrability of Innovations. An innovation is most quickly accepted when its usefulness can be easily demonstrated. The American Indians eagerly accepted the white man's gun, but still have not fully accepted the white man's medicine, whose superiority is less easily demonstrated. Many inventions are so inefficient in their earlier stages that general acceptance is delayed until they are perfected. During the automobile's first three decades of development, public reception was expressed by the derisive advice to "get a horse!" Early imperfections delay, but rarely prevent, the eventual acceptance of workable inventions.

Some innovations can be demonstrated quite easily on a small scale. Others cannot be demonstrated without costly, large-scale trials. Most mechanical inventions can usually be tested in a few hours or days and at modest cost. Most social inventions such as universal suffrage, free love, socialized medicine, or world government are not easily tried out in the laboratory or testing bureau. Many social inventions can be tested only through a long-term trial involving at least an entire society. We hesitate to adopt an innovation until we have been shown how it works; yet we can discover the practical value of most social inventions only by adopting them. This dilemma slows their acceptance.

Compatibility with Existing Culture. Innovations are most readily accepted when they fit in nicely with the existing culture. The horse fitted easily into the hunting culture of the Apache, as it enabled them to do better what they were already doing. Not all innovations mesh so nicely. Innovations may be incompatible with the existing culture in at least three ways.

First, *the innovation may conflict with existing patterns.* In some parts of Asia and Africa, Islam now appears to be spreading faster than Christianity, perhaps because Christianity conflicts with native polygamy while Islam does not. We have already seen how difficult it would be for American society to institutionalize premarital sex experience. It conflicts not only with some of our mores and sentiments but also with our family structure and property institutions, neither of which makes any very satisfactory provision for children born out of wedlock.

When an innovation conflicts with existing culture patterns, at least three outcomes are possible: (1) It may be rejected, just as most Americans have rejected communism; (2) it may be accepted and the conflicting cultural traits may be adjusted to it, as we have altered our child-labor practices to permit compulsory public education; (3) it may be accepted, and its conflict with the existing culture may be concealed and evaded by rationalization, as in those areas (including France and five of the United States) where the sale of contraceptives is forbidden by law, yet they are sold for "prevention of disease." While not always decisive, conflict with the existing culture discourages acceptance of an innovation.

Second, *the innovation may call for new patterns not present in the culture.* The American Indians had no patterns of animal husbandry into which the cow could be fitted. When they were first given cows by government agents, they hunted them as game animals. A society generally tries to use an innovation in old, familiar ways. When this fails, the society must develop new ways of making effective use of the new element. Thus we have disguised each new building material to make it look like an old, familiar material. Early concrete blocks were faced like rough-finished stone; asphalt and asbestos shingles were finished to look like brick or wood; aluminum siding was made to look like wood. Then, after some years, each of these materials begins to be used in designs and ways that make full use of its own properties and possibilities. Most innovations call for some new patterns in the culture, and it takes time to develop them.

Third, *some innovations are substitutive, not additive,* and are less readily accepted. It is easier to accept innovations that can be added to the culture without requiring the immediate discard of some familiar trait. American baseball, jazz, and the western movie have been diffused throughout most of the world. Each could be added to almost any kind of culture without requiring the surrender of any native traits. But the approximate equality of the sexes, democracy, and rational business enterprise have been diffused more slowly; each requires the surrender of traditional values and practices. Wherever the nature of the choice is such that one cannot have *both* the new and the old, the acceptance of the new is usually delayed.

Costs of Change. Change is nearly always costly. Not only does change disrupt the existing culture and destroy cherished sentiments and values, but it also involves some specific costs.

Technical Difficulties of Change. Very few innovations can simply be added to the existing culture; most innovations require that the existing culture be modified in some way. England's monetary system (pence, shillings, and pounds) is a clumsy nuisance as compared with a decimal monetary system like ours, while the American system of weights and measures is clearly inferior to the European metric system. Why not change? Because the process of changeover is so painful. Learning the metric system would be comparatively simple, but the task of making and stocking everything from window frames to nuts and bolts in both size ranges for a half century or so is overwhelming. Railroads would be more efficient if the tracks were a foot or two farther apart to permit wider cars, but the cost of rebuilding the tracks and replacing the rolling stock is prohibitive. Our city streets are far too narrow for today's traffic, but street widening is unbearably costly after the streets are lined with skyscrapers. New inventions and improved machines often make present machinery obsolete and destroy the market for technical skills workmen have spent years in developing.

Vested Interests and Social Change. The costs of social change are never evenly distributed. The industry that is made obsolete and the workmen whose skill is made unmarketable are forced to bear the costs of technical progress, while others enjoy the improved products. Those to whom the *status quo* is profitable are called *vested interests*. The most determined and effective opposition to a proposed change generally comes from the vested interests whom it would injure. Examples are almost endless. In 1579 the Council of Danzig, acting in response to pressure from weavers, ordered the strangulation of the inventor of an improved weaving machine, and the spinsters of Blackburn, England, invaded Hargreave's home to destroy his spinning jennies [Stern, 1937]. The early railroads were opposed by landowners who didn't want their lands cut up and by canal owners and toll-road companies, and then in turn the railroads became vigorous opponents of the automobile and helped to block construction of the St. Lawrence Seaway. In 1922 the major automobile manufacturers launched a massive advertising campaign against four-wheel brakes, claiming they would injure passengers, damage tires, and cause cars to overturn. Employer opposition to the organization of labor unions was long and bitter, and still continues in the Deep South and on the factory farms of the Southwest [Bendiner, 1961], while many unions resort to "featherbedding" in the effort to retain jobs made unnecessary by technical change. The radio industry bottled up FM radio as long as possible, and more recently the television industry and the motion-picture-theater operators have done their best to block pay television. Each group is an ardent advocate of "progress" in general, but seldom at the expense of its own vested interests.

Vested interests, however, appear as promoters of change whenever they believe the proposed change will be profitable to them. American corporations spend billions of dollars each year to develop new products that they can sell profitably. Many business groups in the Great Lakes area energetically supported the St. Lawrence Seaway proposal. Such governmental enterprises are normally denounced as socialism by vested interests that are not enriched thereby, while those vested interests whom the proposal benefits will find other terms to describe it. (Apparently "socialism" operates when the government spends money to benefit *you*, not me!) Business interests have sought and obtained many kinds of government regulation and "interference" when it seemed in their interest to do so. Labor unions have been most eloquent supporters of laws to limit child labor. The great Chicago fire of 1871 showed the weakness of competing private fire-fighting companies, and, more important, imposed such heavy losses on fire insurance companies that they threw their support behind the proposal for tax-supported municipal fire departments. The American Medical Association opposed voluntary group-health insurance until it discovered that Blue Cross got their bills paid [Hyde and Wolff, 1954]. Many social reforms have finally been secured, after long agitation, because powerful vested interests came to redefine their interests and decided that the reform would benefit them.

Role of the Change Agent. Who proposes a change and how does he go about it? The identity of the initiator affects acceptance or rejection. Any proposal of the Communist party in the United States is doomed to certain defeat. Opponents of all sorts of proposals often label them Communist in order to defeat them. Innovations that are first adopted by persons at the top of the prestige scale and power system are likely to filter downward quite rapidly; those first adopted by low-status persons are likely to percolate upward more slowly, if at all.

Successful change agents often seek to make the change appear innocuous by identifying it with familiar cultural elements. King Ibn Saud introduced radio and telephone to Saudi Arabia by quoting the Koran over them. Franklin D. Roosevelt's leadership rested partly on his ability to describe significant reforms in terms of homespun American sentiments and values.

The change agent must know the culture in which he works. When American officials sought to combat communism through posters contrasting pictures of great religious leaders with those of Communist leaders, the campaign failed among the Moslem Indonesians, who felt it irreverent and offensive to display a picture of Mohammed. Government attempts to settle Navajo Indians as individual families on irrigated land were unsuccessful, for the Navajo were accustomed to work land cooperatively along extended kinship lines. An amusing illustration of how ignorance and ethnocentrism handicapped a change agent is found in Micronesia, where an American labor relations expert sought to recruit Palauan workers for a mining operation. He first demanded to see the "chief," which posed a problem since they had no chief in their social structure. Finally they produced a person with whom the American expert sought to establish rapport by throwing an arm around his shoulders and laughingly tousling his hair. In Palauan culture this was an indignity roughly equivalent, in our culture, to opening a man's fly in public [Useem, 1952]. Needless to add, this expert was not very successful.

Sometimes a change agent succeeds in promoting a change, only to find that the results are an unhappy surprise. In one South African area the Western workers noticed that the native mothers were exhausted by nursing their babies for two years, so they successfully introduced bottle feeding. The innovation had the effect of evading the native taboo on sexual relations during lactation, so that instead of bearing a child every three or four years, they now bore a child every year or so, and were more exhausted than ever [Lee, 1959b]. Change agents must thoroughly understand the interrelations of the culture if they are to be able to predict the consequences of a particular change. At this moment, when thousands of American representatives are functioning as change agents in nearly every underdeveloped country of the world, we might remind ourselves of the necessity for change agents to be observant students of the society they wish to help, if they are to avoid the unhappy consequences so aptly pictured in the popular novel *The Ugly American* [Lederer and Burdick, 1958].

The efforts of the change agent are not always appreciated. The inventor is often ridiculed, the missionary may be eaten, and the agitator or reformer is usually persecuted. Radicals are likely to be popular only after they are dead, and organizations (like the DAR) dedicated to the memory of dead revolutionists have no fondness for live ones. Those seeking to change the segregated racial patterns of the American South may become heroes tomorrow, but they must be prepared to face jail and physical violence today. The recent record of a prominent Negro minister is revealing.

> Christmas, 1956, Shuttleworth home bombed and completely demolished; winter 1957, Bethel Baptist Church dynamited by racists; late 1957, Shuttleworth and wife mobbed, beaten, and stabbed; jailed eight times—four times during the Freedom Rides; sued for three million dollars by state officials of Alabama; automobile and personal property sold at public auction; driver's license revoked for a whole year; three Shuttleworth children illegally arrested and beaten in Gadsden (Alabama) . . . is currently involved in twenty-seven criminal and civil actions.

SCLC *Newsletter* (Southern Christian Leadership Conference), September, 1961.

Change agents are often hated and despised, especially when they attack attitudes and values other people cherish.

Social and Personal Disorganization

Social Effects of Discovery and Invention. No social change leaves the rest of the culture entirely unaffected. Even an "additive" innovation draws time and interest away from other elements of the culture. Some innovations are shattering in their impact on a culture. When the missionaries passed out steel axes to the Yir Yoront of Australia, the gift appeared to be an innocuous gesture, but the stone ax was so tightly integrated into the culture that a chain reaction of disruption spread through their social structure [Sharp, 1952]. The stone ax was a symbol of adult masculinity. It might be lent to women and to youths, and the lines of ax borrowing were very important features of their social organization. When superior steel axes were passed out indiscriminately, and owned by women and youths, the symbol of authority was so undermined that authority itself became clouded, relations confused, and reciprocal obligations uncertain. The stone for the axes was quarried far to the south and traded northward along trade routes through an established system of trading partners, who also shared in important ceremonials. With the substitution of the steel ax, trading relationships languished, and this rich ceremonial sharing was lost. Deep and serious disturbance of Yir Yoront culture is traced to the single innovation of the steel ax. The illustration is dramatic; but have the effects of the automobile or the radio on American culture been less far-reaching? Ogburn [1933, pp. 153–156] has compiled a list of 150 social changes that he attributes to the radio; and television has brought still more.

Much has been written about the social effects of invention. It does not matter whether the new element has been invented within the society or diffused into it; the social effects are equally great. Explosives, invented by the Chinese and used only for fireworks, were diffused to the West and led to the invention of firearms. Guns "made all men the same size" and ended the power advantage of the horsed knight in armor; cannons ended the relative impregnability of the medieval castle and strengthened the king at the expense of the provincial nobility. A diffused element often finds a society quite unable to cope with it successfully. For example, primitive societies that brew their own alcoholic beverages generally have cultural controls over their use, but primitive societies that received alcohol from white men had no such controls, and the effects were generally devastating [Horton, 1943]. To cite one instance, the Eskimo of St. Lawrence Island, when first introduced to alcohol, promptly went on a month-long drunk and missed the annual walrus migration; the following winter most of them died of starvation [Nelson, 1899]. Innovations, whether invented or diffused, can be equally disruptive.

Unequal Rates of Change. Since a culture is interrelated, changes in one aspect of the culture invariably affect other aspects of the culture. Eventually the affected traits will be adapted to this change, but only after some time has passed. This time interval between the arrival of a change and the completion of the adaptations it prompts is called *cultural lag,* a concept developed by Ogburn [1922, pp. 200–213]. As an illustration, he pointed out that about 1870, workers in large numbers began entering factories where they were often injured in unavoidable accidents. But not until another half century had passed did most states get around to enacting Workmen's Compensation laws. In this instance the cultural lag was about fifty years.

A cultural lag exists wherever any aspect of the culture lags behind another aspect to which it is related. Probably the most pervasive form of cultural lag in present Western societies is the lag of institutions behind changing technology. For example, in most states the size of a county was based on the distance one could travel to the county seat and return in the same day; despite improved transportation, the county unit still remains at its old size, inefficient for many of its functions. The metropolitan city sprawls over a hodgepodge of many different state, county, city, and township units, so that efficient area planning, government, and law enforcement become an impossibility. At least a half century ago, advancing technology had tied the civilized world into an interdependent whole, but it took a second world war to jolt the United States out of its complacent isolationism. For a full century, urbanization and industrialization were destroying the possibility for the individual worker to ensure the security of his family by depending on himself, his relatives, and his neighbors; yet only after the Great Depression of the 1930s dramatized this fact did we establish social security, unemployment insurance, and other welfare measures.

Some cultural lags involve the lag of one part of the material culture behind a related part of the material culture. A quarter century after cars are built to cruise at high speeds, we get started on a superhighway system. Most airports are too small to accommodate the latest types of aircraft. For a quarter century after we replaced the horse with the automobile, we continued to build the garage out behind the house, back where the smelly stables used to go. Sometimes the material culture lags behind changes in the nonmaterial culture. For example, educational research has long since discovered that movable classroom furniture aids in organizing learning activities, yet thousands of classrooms still have inflexible rows of desks screwed to the floor. Finally, one aspect of the nonmaterial culture may lag behind other related aspects of nonmaterial culture. For example, millions of dollars are spent on quack practitioners and patent medicines that medical science has repeatedly shown to be useless, while dozens of communities reject measures like fluoridation that science has shown to be effective and harmless. Hughes et al. [1958, p. 270] have shown how the nursing profession is outgrowing its legal definition. Nurses are taking over more of the physician's functions, and sometimes must break the law in doing so. Thus the law lags behind good nursing practice.

Cultural lags are numerous in any rapidly changing culture. They are symptoms not of a backward society but of a highly dynamic and increasingly complex society. But even if all people were wise, objective, and adaptable, time would still be needed to discover what adaptations a new change would require, and more time to work out and complete those adaptations. Most of us, however, are pretty ignorant about matters outside our specialty, are prejudiced and swayed by our vested interests, and are not nearly so adaptable as we like to imagine. Cultural lags are numerous and persistent.

Social and Personal Disorganization. As has been repeatedly suggested in this chapter, all new elements disrupt the existing culture to some extent. If a culture is well organized, with all of its traits and institutions fitting nicely together, change in any one of them will disorganize this arrangement.

When a culture becomes highly disorganized, the people's sense of security, morale, and purpose in life are damaged. When people are confused and uncertain, so that their behavior is also inconsistent, hesitant, and contradictory, they are described as *personally disorganized*. If their disorganization proceeds until they lose their sense of purpose in life and become resigned and apathetic, we describe them as *demoralized*. A demoralized people is likely to suffer population decline through a lowered birth rate or a higher death rate, or both. The capacity of a thoroughly demoralized people simply to die out has attracted the attention of a number of anthropologists [Rivers, 1922; Maher, 1961].

The extermination of the buffalo had such effects on the American Indians of the Great Plains [Lesser, 1933; Wissler, 1938; Sandoz, 1954, chap. 15]. The buffalo provided food, clothing, and shelter; in all, over fifty separate parts of the buffalo carcass were used by the Indians. The buffalo hunt provided the principal object of the Indian's religious ceremonials, the goal of his maturing, and a road to status and recognition. His other avenue to status—warfare—was also dependent on an ample supply of dried buffalo meat. When the government exterminated the buffalo in order to pacify the Indians, it demoralized them as well. The integrating and status-giving functions of the war party and the buffalo hunt were lost. Religious ceremonials were now empty and meaningless. The hunting economy was totally destroyed, and the Indians lived, and sometimes starved, on government handouts. The traditional goals and values that gave zest and meaning to life were now unavailable, and to substitute the white man's goals and values was an almost impossible learning task. In the few instances where Indians did successfully adopt the white man's economy, this, too, was soon destroyed by the white man's hunger for the Indians' land [Foreman, 1932; Collier, 1947, pp. 199–219]. Suffering from the destruction of their own culture, denied access to the white man's culture, ravaged by his diseases, and corrupted by his alcohol, it is not surprising that many Indian tribes became deeply demoralized. Depopulation was almost universal, and only in recent decades has Indian population begun to rebuild. This story of devastatingly disruptive social change, disorganization of the culture, and personal disorganization and demoralization of the people has been repeated hundreds of times in the world's history.

Not all native peoples, however, have been demoralized by their contacts with Western societies. The Palauans of Micronesia have worked out an interdependent blend of traditional culture and Western commercialism. They happily drive trucks and pound typewriters to earn money to buy the traditional clan gifts, and use motor launches to carry their sweet potatoes to traditional festivals [Mead, 1955, p. 128]. Whether change disrupts a society to the point of demoralization depends on the nature of the changes, the way they are introduced, and the structure of the society on which they impinge.

Is change least painful when it comes slowly? Not necessarily. Since culture is interrelated, it is generally easier to accept a cluster of related changes than to accept them one at a time. For example, if a primitive people is given cotton clothes without soap, then filth and disease are predictable; if given clothes without irons and sewing machines, then they will be clothed in tatters. With mud floors to sit on and no place to store clothing and these other artifacts, filth and clutter are a certainty. But if all these elements—clothes, soap, irons, sewing machines, and floored houses with shelves and closets—are adopted together within a single generation, these changes can be made far more easily than if spaced over several generations.

Western cultural diffusion generally converts the native village into a depressing slum, not because the people adopt too many new elements but because they adopt too few. It may even be psychologically easier to make a lot of changes than a few. As Margaret Mead has observed, "A people who choose to practice a new technology or enter into drastically new kinds of economic relationships will do this more easily if they live in different houses, wear different clothes and eat different, or differently cooked, food" [1956, pp. 445–446]. Much of the social disorganization accompanying social change stems from the fact that a people who are willing to adopt new elements are blocked from doing so. Sometimes they are blocked by their own limited resources and sometimes by the unwillingness of the dominant white to admit them into full participation in Western civilization. The Mau Mau terrorism in Kenya was largely attributable to the frustration of the Kikuyu's intense desire to share in Western civilization [Bascom and Herskovitz (eds.), 1959, p. 4].

We need, therefore, to revise the notion that slow change is necessarily more comfortable than rapid change. In some situations the rapid wholesale change of a way of life may be infinitely less disturbing than piecemeal changes, as Mead [1956, chap. 18] has shown in her study of the Manus, who have moved from the Stone Age into Western civilization in a single generation. The reason may be that slow change allows cultural lags to accumulate, not to be corrected until they become painful. Rapid change may actually produce fewer lags, because many of the related items of the culture may be changed at the same time.

Change has come with dazzling speed upon contemporary Western societies. Within a few short generations, the Western peoples have shifted from life in rural, agricultural, folk societies to life in an immensely complex urban, industrial, impersonal mass society. Are contemporary Western societies disorganized? Certainly! Cultural lags are numerous at every point. The school strains constantly to prepare children for a society that changes even before they become adult. The church carries a doctrine stated largely in the language and context of an agricultural society; much of it is irrelevant to the needs and problems of our impersonal secondary-group world, yet the effort to restate its message in modern terms has riven the church into warring factions. A century ago husband and wife had a quite clearly defined role for each to assume; today no bride can be at all sure what she will be expected to be and do in her marriage. Every level of government is struggling with tasks few of our grandfathers would have guessed it would ever assume. Disputes over the privileges and responsibilities of corporations, unions, and other economic groups now occupy the heart of the political arena. In this impersonal urban world of ours, although the traditional informal controls of the folk society are failing to regulate the behavior of individuals, we are still hunting for effective substitutes.

These are symptoms of social disorganization—failure of traditional controls, role confusions and uncertainties, conflicting moral codes, and experimentation and change in institutional functions. In such a disorganized society, people are affected. Many fail to internalize a coherent system of values and behavior controls. A smaller number become seriously disorganized, and grow so erratic and contradictory in behavior that they are diagnosed as mentally ill and in need of psychotherapy.

If our society is so badly disorganized, why are we not all mentally ill? Despite our accelerating rate of social change during the past century, we find no conclusive evidence that the amount of mental illness has significantly increased [Goldhamer and Marshall, 1953]. True, mental-hospital patients have multiplied, but this proves only that more persons receive hospital treatment, not that more are ill. The answer may be that a changing society may be able to develop personalities that are more resistant to the strain of social change [Mead, 1947]. Children in our society are socialized to anticipate and appreciate change. The strain of change may be considerably reduced by a socialization that seeks to prepare persons to adapt themselves to change. Since adult roles are uncertain, we seek to socialize and educate children to function successfully in several roles, not just in one. Finally, we have developed social case work and psychiatry for persons who cannot work out an effective life pattern by themselves. All over the world today, the rate of social change is accelerating. Whether man can adapt himself and his social life to

Children in our society are socialized to anticipate and appreciate change.

changed needs as rapidly as his needs are changing is still a moot question.

Social Planning: Can Change be Directed? It is possible to control and direct social changes so they will be less painful and costly? Social scientists are disagreed. Some feel that social change is caused by social forces beyond man's effective control. For example, when the necessary supporting knowledge is developed, an invention will be made by someone, even if this invention is most troublesome to man. The atom bomb is an illustration. We fear it may destroy us, yet go on advancing it because others will do so anyway. Could the Indian wars possibly have been avoided? The Indians had land we needed for our growing population, and our advance was certain to destroy the Indian's way of life. The many unnecessary brutal episodes were merely the symptoms, not the cause, of a conflict that was unavoidable, given these groups with their respective needs and cultural backgrounds. Practically any great social change can be thus described in terms of blind social forces, so that what *did* happen was about the only thing that *could* happen in that situation.

Some other social scientists think we can exert *some* influence over the course of social change. They believe some degree of social planning is possible. *Social planning* is defined as "a conscious interactional process combining investigation, discussion, agreement, and action in order to achieve those conditions, relationships, and values that are regarded as desirable" [Himes, 1954, p. 18]. More simply, social planning is an attempt at the intelligent direction of social change [Adams, 1950; Riemer, 1947]. Advocates point out that social planning is an old American tradition. When the framers of our Constitution rejected primogeniture (the European provision that the lands pass intact to the eldest son) and entail (the provision that prevents him from selling them), these American planners were seeking to construct a society of small land-owning farmers instead of a society of landed estates. This purpose was reinforced by the Homestead Act of 1862, which gave public lands in small parcels to individual farmers instead of selling them in large blocs to the highest bidders. Zoning ordinances, building codes, public education, and compulsory school-attendance laws are examples of social planning. Nearly every city now has its city-planning commission, and regional-planning commissions are a next step that many are advocating.

A critic of planning would contend that such planning efforts do not really change anything but are merely a slightly more orderly way of carrying out the changes that are inevitable anyway. The comment perhaps sums up the matter. Certainly no social planning will prevent or reverse a change that present knowledge and long-time trends are creating. There is, for example, no way of returning to the "simple life"; nor is it possible by planning to steer social change in a direction contrary to most people's wishes and values. The major social changes are probably uncontrollable, but social planning may be able to reduce the delays and costs of integrating them into the culture.

Summary

All societies change continuously. New traits appear either through *discovery* and *invention* or through *diffusion* from other societies.

The rate of social change varies enormously from society to society and from time to time. Changes in population size or distribution always produce other social changes. The structure of the society affects change; a highly integrated, authoritarian, conformist society is less prone to change than a less highly integrated, individualistic society. Since isolation retards change and cultural contacts promote change, physically or socially isolated groups are relatively unchanging. A society's attitudes and values toward change greatly encourage or retard change. The *cultural base* provides the foundation of knowledge and skill necessary to develop new elements; as the cultural base expands, the possibilities of new combinations multiply in an exponential manner, while knowledge in one area often cross-fertilizes other areas of development. Finally, the felt needs of a society are a powerful stimulus, and a crisis dramatizes the needs of a society.

Not all innovations are accepted. The attitudes and values of a group determine what kind of innovations a group is likely to accept. If an innovation's usefulness can be demonstrated easily and cheaply, the proof is helpful; but many social inventions cannot be tested except through a complete acceptance. New and compatible elements are more readily accepted than those which clash with important elements of the existing culture. Technical difficulties of fitting a changed element into the existing culture often cause great economic cost and personal inconvenience. Vested interests normally oppose change, but they occasionally discover that a proposed change is to their advantage. The change agent's ingenuity and social position affect his success in introducing changes. Unless the change agent knows the culture very well, he generally miscalculates the consequences of his changes.

Social and personal disorganization are costs of social change. Discoveries and inventions, as well as diffused new elements, often set off a chain reaction of change disrupting to many aspects of the culture. The different elements of the culture, interrelated and interdependent though they are, do not change at the same rate of speed. The time interval between the appearance of a new element and the completion of the adaptations it forces is called *cultural lag*. All rapidly changing societies have many cultural lags and are said to be somewhat disorganized. In a disorganized society, persons who may have greater difficulty in finding a comfortable behavior system become themselves disorganized. When they lose hope of finding a rewarding behavior system and cease trying, they have become demoralized and may actually die out as a group. In an effort to speed and simplify this process and reduce the costs and wastes of social change, social planning is increasingly being attempted. Social scientists are not agreed on the degree of success to be expected from the direction of social change by social planning.

Questions and Projects

1. Why are social scientists hesitant to use the term "progress"?
2. Is knowledge of the diffusion process likely to reduce ethnocentrism?
3. Have there been any recent American attempts to prevent diffusion or to limit contacts of Americans with other cultures?
4. What are some of the change-promoting features of American society? What are some of its change-resisting features?
5. Is the rate of invention likely to continue rising, or to fall off? Why?
6. Why will a person who insists on the latest cars, fashions, and gadgets often be entirely satisfied with nineteenth-century social philosophies?
7. How many of those persons we now consider "great" were noncontroversial during their lives? How many achieved greatness by promoting changes and how many by preventing changes?
8. Is it possible for a change agent to promote a major change without arousing violent hostilities?
9. Can you think of any cultural lags in our social attitudes—widely held attitudes that are no longer consistent with scientific knowl-

edge or with the needs of modern society? How about attitudes concerning race, male and female relations, war and international relations, local and national government?

10. Why has American medicine readily accepted changes in medical technology but resisted most changes in medical economics?

11. In what respects has medical "progress" proved disorganizing?

12. Can social planning ever change "human nature"? Must it, in order to succeed?

13. Evaluate this statement: "The more successfully we progress, the fewer cultural lags and social problems we shall have."

Suggested Readings

ABRAHAMSON, JULIA: A Neighborhood Finds Itself, Harper & Row, Publishers, Incorporated, New York, 1959. An account of urban-renewal planning for a deteriorating Chicago neighborhood.

ADAMS, E. M.: "The Logic of Planning," Social Forces, 28:419–423, 1950. A brief outline of the principles of social planning in a democracy.

BASCOM, WILLIAM R., AND MELVILLE J. HERSKOVITS (EDS.): Continuity and Change in African Cultures, The University of Chicago Press, Chicago, 1959. Two essays—Simon Ottenberg, "Ileo Receptivity to Change" (pp. 130–143), and Harold K. Schneider, "Pakot Resistance to Change" (pp. 144–167)—seek to explain the opposite reactions of two societies to social change.

GILLIN, JOHN P.: The Ways of Men, Appleton-Century-Crofts, Inc., New York, 1948, chap. 25, "Conditions and Processes of Culture Change." A well-illustrated, systematic treatment of the factors involved in change and in its acceptance or rejection.

LEE, DOROTHY: "The Cultural Cur-

tain," Annals of the American Academy of Political and Social Science, 323:120–128, 1959. An interesting article showing, with many illustrations, the need for change agents to understand the culture in which they promote change.

MEAD, MARGARET: Cultural Patterns and Technical Change, UNESCO, 1955; Mentor Books, New American Library of World Literature, Inc., New York, 1955. Studies the impact of modern technology on five traditional societies with discussion of how to proceed in bringing modern technology to traditional societies.

SPICER, EDWARD H. (ED.): Human Problems in Technological Change, Russell Sage Foundation, New York, 1952. A casebook describing a number of societies where important changes were introduced, showing the process of adoption and the social consequences of these changes.

STERN, BERNHARD J.: Society and Medical Progress, Princeton University Press, Princeton, N.J., 1941, chap. 9. A history of the resistance to medical change.

Social Problems and
Social Policy

At 14 Carol bears a grievous burden. Her mother, Mrs. Virginia M., 31, suffers from cancer and doctors say that she has less than a year to live. Her father, Leon, 34, is a chronic alcoholic who is unable to hold a steady job. There are three younger children—Betty, 10; Janie, 5; and Joey, 2—and all are largely supported by the small salary Mrs. M. earns as a building superintendent.

Carol tries anxiously to ease her mother's tasks. Before and after school she helps with the cleaning and the marketing. But she lives in mounting fear of her mother's death and she knows the day is not far off when she and the other children will have to be separated and brought up by relatives. Mrs. M. is so frightened herself that she is unable to comfort Carol. Recently, when Carol began failing her studies and flying into unmanageable rages, school authorities called in the agency.

Sympathetic counseling has lessened Carol's tensions. Mrs. M., who had given up going to the clinic, has been persuaded to resume medical care. But Mr. M. is unchanged and the future of his family remains in doubt. In the dark months ahead, Carol and her mother must have the continued support of the counselor, upon whom so much depends.

New York Times, Dec. 15, 1963, II, p. 1.

Personal hardships are usually symptoms of unsolved social problems. Any complex, rapidly changing society will have many unsolved social problems. We are able to take a brief look at only a few of them.

Origin of Social Problems

Value Conflicts. A condition is not a social problem unless people feel that it is undesirable and that something can be done about it. Child labor was not a social problem as long as people considered it desirable. Poverty was not a social problem in medieval society because people saw no real possibility of relieving it; poverty was accepted as inevitable and unchangeable. A condition becomes a social problem only when a *value judgment* is made that the condition is undesirable and curable.

But seldom are all people in agreement in their value judgments; if they were, the condition would be treated and cease to be a problem. If all whites were agreed that Negroes should be inferiors, they would be uniformly treated as inferiors, would *feel* as inferiors, and the race problem would largely disappear. If all whites felt that Negroes should be treated as equals, discrimination would end, and the race problem would be solved. The problem persists because some whites want to keep the Negro in "his place" while others want to complete his emancipation. Gambling and prostitution remain problems because the community is unable to agree whether to legalize them or to make a really determined effort to suppress them. Social problems grow from the value conflicts within the society.

Social Disorganization. A perfectly organized society would have no social problems. All parts of the culture would harmonize neatly. Any actually injurious conditions like poverty would be rationalized as natural or even as beneficial, and would not be defined as undesirable.

But social change disrupts the established arrangements of a society. Old rules become unworkable, and new conditions arise that the traditional procedures do not handle properly. Values may so change as to define old conditions as no longer tolerable. Social problems grow out of the disorganization of traditional society by social change.

For example, changing technology transformed us from a nation of rural farmers to a nation of large cities where the patterns and social controls of the rural village are not very effective; the result is increased problems of crime, juvenile delinquency, family disorganization, urban planning, and others. Increased scientific knowledge about inherited racial attributes has undermined the earlier assumption of an innate Negro inferiority and encouraged changed value judgments about race discrimination. The increased complexity of society creates a need for more education; this poses the problem both of providing the educa-

tion and of curtailing the child labor that would interfere with education. Social change disorganizes traditional arrangements, undermines
traditional rules, and creates social problems.

Personal Deviation. Most people internalize the norms of the culture
and behave in the expected manner. But some do not. Those who fail to
do so are *deviants*. Some kinds of deviants—beatniks, eccentrics, religious
fanatics, hermits—are relatively harmless. Others, such as revolutionaries,
alcoholics, drug addicts, sex deviants, and criminals—are serious problems.

Why has the deviant failed to internalize the conventional norms?
Actual deviants more or less closely resemble one of two ideal types.
One is the *conforming member of a deviant subculture*. An example
would be the member of the delinquent street gang in the slum. Since
delinquent behavior is a normal part of the slum subculture surrounding
him, he becomes delinquent through internalizing the norms of this
subculture. By contrast, some deviants are *deviant members of a conforming subculture*. The delinquent boy from a "good" family and
neighborhood is an example. He has rejected the norms that are prevalent
and approved in his subculture; some emotional difficulty, probably
rooted in the family, has prevented him from absorbing the approved
norms he is surrounded by. In his case personal counseling and perhaps
psychotherapy are indicated. But with the slum delinquent, only a transformation of his subculture is likely to be effective.

Some Personal Pathologies

Because space forbids discussion of all the major social problems, we
shall limit ourselves to two that especially impinge on nursing practice.

Alcoholism as a Social Problem. About two-thirds of all American
adults drink in some degree, and an estimated 4 to 5 million of these are
problem drinkers. This drinking pattern makes alcoholism one of our
most prevalent diseases. About one out of sixteen drinkers becomes an
alcoholic, and we have some evidence that the others could not become
alcoholic even if they tried [Golin, 1958]. Apparently some persons are
immune to alcoholism and others are susceptible. Possibly some constitutional susceptibility is involved. Considerable research has sought the
causes of alcoholism in endocrine disorders, vitamin deficiencies, hormonal
imbalances, and other physiological conditions, but the studies have
found nothing very convincing. The research effort to find personality
factors associated with alcoholism has also been rather unsuccessful
[Syme, 1957]. The majority opinion, however, holds that the causes of
alcoholism probably lie in an inadequate personality, unable to face the
problems of life without a crutch or an escape. Successful treatment for

alcoholics often includes psychotherapy to help the alcoholic reorganize his personal and emotional life in a more satisfying manner.

Alcoholics Anonymous, an organization of former alcoholics who seek to help other alcoholics to rehabilitate themselves, has proved to be a fairly successful form of group therapy. The alcoholic finds a sympathetic group of people who really understand his difficulties. He gains emotional support from the group and maintains status by staying in sobriety. Meanwhile the older members are strengthened by their need to set a good example; the process of assisting others into sobriety helps them, themselves, to remain sober. Of course many alcoholics do not seriously want to be cured; their alcoholism permits them to evade responsibility and assume the "sick" role. To become cured means they must assume responsibility and face life. An alcoholic cannot be cured until he wants to be cured. Among those who do, Alcoholics Anonymous is probably more successful than any other approach [Alcoholics Anonymous Comes of Age, 1957].

Drug Addiction. No one knows how many drug addicts there are in the United States. Various estimates place the number from 45,000 to a little over 100,000. Most authorities agree that their number is probably decreasing and that the lurid popular articles about teen-age drug and sex orgies are wildly exaggerated [Chein, 1956].

Popular misconceptions about drug addicts abound. Addicts are not violent sex maniacs; most of them are sexually quite passive. They play no part in organized crime, for an addict is untrustworthy; the police need only shut him up for a few hours and he will tell all he knows in exchange for a "fix." Addicts are calm and passive as long as they get their regular dosage; when denied it, they become frantic. A great deal of our petty crime is committed by addicts who need the money to buy a fix. Illegally purchased narcotics are expensive, costing from twenty-five to one hundred dollars a day to keep in supply; many female addicts become prostitutes for this reason. Our crime rates would drop sharply if the problem of drug addiction were solved. Many addicts deteriorate physically, but their decline is due less to the effects of the drugs than to the poor diet and living conditions that so often accompany addiction.

In earlier days many people became addicted through medication. This is less likely today, since physicians are more cautious about prescribing narcotics and can choose from a far greater variety of analgesics. Even when a patient has become habituated to narcotics through medication, he is unlikely to become a true addict unless personality factors make him susceptible. The typical addicts are "nervous, tense individuals with a great deal of anxiety and many somatic complaints . . . irresponsible, selfish, immature, thrill-seeking individuals who are constantly in trouble" [Isbell, 1958, p. 2]. One medical study of atypical reactions to narcotics drugs found the atypical reactors to be aimless, drifting, irresponsible types who had overprotective mothers and harsh, demanding fathers [von Felsinger, 1955]. As with alcohol addiction, the drug addict seems to be an inadequate personality, unable to cope successfully with life.

While estimates vary so widely as to be almost useless, most authorities agree that very few drug addicts are permanently cured. Most addicts do not really want to be cured. They may be committed for treatment against their will, or, if they seek treatment, it is usually for the purpose of scaling their needs down to a figure they can afford. At present, the main hope of a higher rate of cure lies in getting addicts for treatment earlier in their addiction.

Present laws and procedures for handling addiction are becoming increasingly criticized. Under existing laws and judicial decisions, drug addiction is a crime, not a disease. A physician may not legally prescribe narcotics for the relief of withdrawal symptoms; narcotics may be prescribed only for other illnesses. The addict must depend on illegal sources of supply, at fantastically high prices.

A growing number of authorities believe it would be better for the law to define addiction as an illness [Stevens, 1952]. A joint committee of the American Medical Association and the American Bar Association has recommended that the addict be legally permitted to purchase, under prescription and at legal prices, narcotics as he needs them [Joint Committee, 1961]. This sanction would destroy the illegal narcotics traffic. It would cut the daily cost to a few cents so that the addict would not need to engage in crime to pay the high cost of illegal narcotics. It would bring the addict to medical attention early in his addiction so that the possibility of treatment could be explored. It seems likely that this early detection would reduce the amount of addiction and greatly reduce the social destructiveness of those addicts who are incurable. In England, where such a program is followed, the addiction rate is far lower than in the United States [Schur, 1962].

The Problem of Medical Care

While the United States is the wealthiest nation in the world, it is not clear it is the healthiest. In the last few years, for example, we slipped from sixth to eleventh place among the nations in maternal mortality. Our infant death rate per 1,000 live births is 25.3 compared with 15.3 for Sweden and the Netherlands. Yet we know that, except among the aged, *most ill health is unnecessary*. Five orphanages in North Carolina found that only 1.4 per cent of their 1,138 former students called in the draft had been rejected, while the rejection rate for the entire state was 56.8 per cent. This contrast was attributed to "sound nutrition and reasonably adequate medical care" [Poe, in Malmberg, 1947, p. 27]. Yet despite our patchwork of free health services and health agencies, many people simply do not receive the medical care they need. Who are these medically disadvantaged groups?

People in understaffed areas. Medical facilities are so concentrated in the wealthier regions and urban areas as to leave many of the poorer, more isolated areas woefully understaffed. Of the 757 "medical service areas" into which the AMA divides the country, the number of physicians varied in 1950 from 1 for each 380 persons to 1 for each 5,100 persons [Dickinson, 1954]. Such data help explain why Alabama and South Carolina have diphtheria rates eighteen times as high as New York or Michigan [*Public Health Reports,* 1957].

Low-income groups. Medical care is costly. Americans spent an average of $119 each for health care in 1962, but this expenditure is unevenly distributed. A survey in a New York town a few years ago found that, as compared with upper-income groups, although the low-income group had over twice as many illnesses lasting over twice as long, they were only three-fifths as likely to be fully treated by a physician [Koos, 1954]. This low-income group was less than one-half as likely to have a family doctor, only one-third as likely to have any health insurance, and only one-sixth as likely to have a family dentist. Low-income people need more medical care, but get less, than more prosperous people.

It is true that a great deal of free medical care is available to low-income people, but the provisions are spotty and poorly organized. Where the poor live in the shadow of a teaching hospital, excellent treatment of some kinds is readily available; at other places, they are in difficulty. Free clinics are available, but they are often inconveniently located, entail long waits, and sometimes offer only brusk, cursory examination. If, in order to attend a maternity clinic, a working mother must take a day off work, arrange for a baby-sitter, travel many miles, then wait and perhaps be told to come back tomorrow, she probably will not repeat the experience.

Most free services are categories; that is, they are available for some kinds of disorders and to some groups of people but not for others. Free care for tuberculosis or polio is readily available, but not for arthritis or heart disorders which are many times more widespread. A thorough general physical examination, such as is recommended annually for all persons who have reached middle age, is totally unavailable to most low-income people.

The aged. People over sixty-five have less than half the average income of adults under sixty-five (in 1960, $2,530 to $5,315 for family units; $1,055 to $2,570 for persons living alone). Although the medical needs of the aged are far greater, only three out of five have any form of health insurance, while four-fifths of the younger people are covered. They are twice as likely to have one or more chronic conditions. Despite their limited resources, they now average 50 per cent more visits to the physician per year and two and one-half times as many hospital days per year.

How can the aged pay for greater medical expenses out of reduced incomes? Many of them can't. Some, fearing exhaustion of their limited resources, deny themselves the services they need. Others exhaust their resources and then become dependent on public expenditure or private philanthropy, which together accounted for about $1½ billion for aged health care in 1960.

The Kerr-Mills Act of 1960 provides Federal grants to the states to share hospital and nursing-home-care costs for the needy aged. State provisions vary. In Michigan, for example, single persons must have less than $1,500 in annual income and less than $1,500 in personal property to be eligible; couples may have up to $2,500 in income and $2,000 in personal property. Supporters of this program, including the AMA, claim it avoids waste of public funds by restricting free services to those of the aged who are really needy. Critics object to the means test as being undignified, claiming that its limits are too low and the services too restricted.

As this is being written (1964) Congress seems likely to adopt a proposal, known as Medicare, to finance hospital and nursing-home care for the aged through social security payments, or possibly through a separate payroll tax. In either case, payments would be raised one-fourth of 1 per cent for both employer and employee. Thus the worker would pay part of the cost of his aged medical care during his working lifetime.

Medicare is strenuously opposed by the AMA, which charges it is socialistic and would be an opening wedge for socialized medicine. The first charge is ironical, since Medicare, a contributory insurance plan, is *less* socialistic than the direct government handouts under the existing Kerr-Mills program that the AMA supports. The second charge has some basis. If Medicare worked well, its success would probably encourage the demand that social security financing of medical care be extended to lower-age groups. The American Nurses' Association supports Medicare in principle, to the intense annoyance of the AMA [O'Neill, 1962].

Migrant workers. Our highly specialized agriculture demands a roving army of about 300,000 migratory workers—men, women, and children. In 1961 they worked an average of 136 days, earning an average of $6.65 per day, or $902 for the season. Minimum-wage and hour laws protecting most other workers do not apply to farm labor. Although some migrant farm workers may earn some income during the rest of the year, they remain in the lowest-income group. Most of them work at some kind of harvesting—picking cherries, beans, tomatoes—staying a few days or weeks at a place, then moving on. Since the grower cannot be expected to provide elaborate housing for only a few weeks' use per year, accommodations range from barely tolerable to unspeakable. Water supply and sanitary facilities are usually primitive.

Low income, poor living conditions, probably poor health habits, and lack of medical care all conspire to bring illness to migrant workers. Since they are not members of the community, they are largely ignored by community agencies. Being nonresidents, they are ineligible for most welfare services, including health services. A dramatic emergency, such as acute appendicitis, may warrant treatment, but anything not requiring immediate attention is generally ignored. At present, not much is being done for the health or welfare of migrant farm workers.

Other groups. Several other groups receive inadequate medical care. Racial minorities suffer not only from all the factors associated with low income but in addition from some discrimination in access to medical facilities. Accordingly, our nonwhite population is only one-half as likely to have any health insurance but has illness and death rates 50 per cent higher. Certain religious groups reject some or all kinds of medical care. Christian Scientists, for instance, a sober, moderately prosperous group that should be well above average in health level and longevity, actually have an expectation of life slightly below average and considerably below what it should be [Wilson, 1956]. For one reason or another, many Americans receive inadequate medical care.

Changing Practices in Medical Care. Medical care is changing. It is steadily becoming more highly specialized. Physicians are gravitating toward group practice, and medical care is becoming more centralized in clinics and hospitals. It is steadily and rapidly becoming more costly. During the years 1952 to 1962 the proportion of personal incomes spent for medical care rose from approximately 4 per cent to almost 6 per cent. The present and proposed changes in the financing of medical care are a subject of much controversy.

Voluntary Health Insurance. Three out of four Americans had some form of voluntary health insurance in 1962. Nearly half of these have Blue Cross–Blue Shield plans, a slightly larger number are covered by insurance company plans, and a very few have independent plans. Most plans exclude routine medical expenses like office and home calls and cover mainly the heavier costs of hospital and surgical care. Of the total national medical bill of $219 billion in 1962, some $7.1 billion was defrayed by health insurance. Thus health insurance covers slightly less than one-third of our national health bill; those carrying health insurance have an average of about two-fifths of their total medical costs covered.

A small handful of comprehensive group medical-care plans are in operation that attempt to cover nearly all medical costs. For example, Group Health Association (Washington, D.C.) provides hospital care with no limit on costs or on number of days of care and covers nearly all other hospital charges, provides unlimited medical and surgical care, including unlimited office calls, specialist services, and home calls ($5 charge for the first home call for any illness), and certain other services. It is a "closed-panel" system; that is, the member can choose only from among those physicians who have contracted to provide services to the members. These services cost (in 1964) from $141 a year for a single person to $359 for a family of five or more. (A lower-cost plan with more limited coverage is also available.)

These comprehensive care plans offer about twice as much service at a not much higher cost than the Blue Cross–Blue Shield premiums. How can they afford to? By encouraging early diagnosis and preventive medicine, so that their members need fewer hospital admissions [Daily, 1959]. General practitioners and sometimes specialists are paid on a salary or capitation basis rather than fee-for-service, which reduces the cost per unit of service. It also reduces unnecessary services, estimated to waste 20 per cent of the Blue Cross dollar [Silverman, 1958]. Some bookkeeping savings are made. Drugs are prescribed under their generic name at far lower cost than when prescribed under brand name. Because group medical practice achieves many cost efficiencies, these comprehensive care groups can give patients more for their money.

Such plans long met bitter opposition from medical societies, largely because of their closed-panel feature. In 1959 the AMA officially dropped its opposition, but its attitude remains unenthusiastic.

No form of voluntary health insurance offers much hope to those groups now receiving inadequate medical care. Most of these persons lack the income to buy health insurance. If their health needs are to be met, it must be through private philanthropy or some tax-supported program.

Compulsory National Health Insurance. About the time of World War I and again during the Truman administration, serious efforts were made to enact national health insurance, sometimes called "socialized medicine." The more recent proposal called for compulsory national health insurance built on the framework of the social security system. A 3 per cent payroll tax would be collected from both employer and employee. Benefits would include all services of dentists and physicians, including specialists, hospital care, home-nursing care, laboratory and related services, appliances, and medicines. All practitioners and other medical personnel would be free to participate if they desired. National administration would be vested in a national board and advisory council that would determine policy and allocate funds; local administration would be handled by local boards of physicians and laymen. Specific guarantees would include

> free choice of doctor, hospital, etc., by the insured persons; freedom of the doctor, dentist, or nurse to practice where he chooses; no intrusion into the management of hospitals; payments to practitioners by methods of their choice, at rates sufficient to yield adequate annual incomes.

I. S. Falk, in President's Commission on the Health Needs of the Nation, *Building America's Health*, Government Printing Office, Washington, D.C., vol. 4, pp. 68–69, 1953.

After a spirited battle, the proposal for national health insurance was defeated and is not now being actively promoted. It is almost certain to be revived, however, especially if Medicare is enacted and proves workable.

The basic issue is not *whether* to socialize medicine, for this has already been done to a substantial degree. About one-fourth of our national health bill is already paid from tax funds under a variety of programs. Most new hospitals are now being aided by Federal grants under the Hill-Burton Act, and medical education is tax-supported. Obviously the issue is not *whether* we socialize medicine but *how much and in what ways!* This distinction makes irrelevant much of the public debate over socialized medicine.

The Fields of Social Work

Social problems may be attacked either through basic social reforms or through social-welfare programs. Social reform seeks so to change the society that the problem itself will be mitigated. For example, the labor legislation of the 1930s sought to change the basic power balance of the society, giving organized workers a greater power to advance their interests. The present civil-rights movement is, among other things, an attempt to reduce Negro poverty by enlarging Negro economic and educational opportunities. Urban renewal is an effort to arrest the spread of urban blight and slum problems.

The social-welfare approach aims to help individuals to get along within our present social system. Without greatly changing the society, social work helps people to adjust to the society in which they live. The two approaches are not incompatible; both can be pursued at the same time. Many social workers are ardent social reformers. This discussion will confine itself to a brief description of some forms of social work.

Social-work agencies are divided into *public agencies,* which are supported by tax funds, and *private agencies,* which are supported by

voluntary contributions. They are further divided into *casework agencies,*
which deal mainly with individuals, and *group-work agencies,* like the
YMCA and YWCA, which are primarily concerned with group activities.

Public-Assistance Agencies. These agencies provide a monthly income
and certain other services to persons with insufficient income. The Social
Security Act of 1935 and its subsequent amendments deal with three
programs: social insurance, public assistance, and maternal- and child-
health and child-welfare services. The Old-Age and Survivors' Disability
Insurance program is the main bulwark against destitution. In addition,
several forms of categorical assistance are given, with the Federal and
state governments sharing the cost and the states defining standards
and handling administration. The provisions are as follows: (1) Old Age
Assistance is provided to all needy aged according to their needs. (2)
Aid to the Blind is provided. (3) Aid to the Permanently and Totally
Disabled is provided. (4) The Aid to Families of Dependent Children
program (ADC-U) provides a monthly income to mother and children
where the father is unemployed, dead, divorced, or otherwise separated
and fails to provide support. Under the aforementioned Kerr-Mills bill,
some medical services are provided to the "medically indigent." For the
needy who are ineligible for the above programs, general assistance or
public relief is provided. The objective is to aid the individual to become
self-supporting if possible, or to provide a minimum of continuing support (and it is *really* minimum!) where rehabilitation is not possible.

Family Social Services. Private family-casework agencies are found
in practically all large- and medium-sized cities. They provide casework
services and do not ordinarily give financial assistance. A staff of professionally trained social workers offer counseling services to families
in the following areas: premarital counseling, marital discord, parent-
child difficulties, in-law troubles, budgeting problems, and others. Where
public assistance is required, the caseworker helps with the referral.
Where prolonged psychiatric diagnosis and treatment are needed, referral is made. Clients come from all class levels; the more prosperous
clients often pay a fee for their services.

Homemaker service is provided by many family-service agencies and
by some public-welfare agencies. Where the mother is absent or sick
and no relative or neighbor is available, the breakup of the family is
averted by providing a temporary housekeeper or "homemaker."

Child-welfare Services. Orphanages are out of date. Present opinion
favors keeping children in some sort of more normal home setting, for
even a mediocre home is better for children than the best orphanage.

Welfare and health services for children are supported by Federal
grants-in-aid to the states. They provide *maternal- and child-health*

services, including prenatal clinics and well-baby clinics; school, dental, and mental-health services; and advisory and consultation services, usually administered by state and local health departments.

Services for crippled children include medical, surgical, corrective, and other services and care as well as facilities for diagnosis, hospitalization, and aftercare. The program is usually administered by state and local health departments. A number of private agencies, supported by fraternal or religious organizations, also offer services for crippled children.

Child-welfare services for homeless, orphaned, neglected, or abandoned children are available through the child-welfare division of state and local public-welfare departments. Services include casework with parents and relatives and help in social and economic difficulties. Adoption, foster-home care, or institutional care are arranged for children born out of wedlock, or for other children who need to be removed from unsatisfactory homes. Informed opinion favors having adoptions be arranged by professional agencies instead of informally by the parties themselves. Adoptive children should be placed with happily married, emotionally stable couples whose intellectual status corresponds to that of the child. Otherwise, the child's record of achievement may disappoint the parents, or the child may so out-distance the parents that rapport is lost as he matures. It should be added that physicians and nurses are no more well equipped to arrange adoptions than social workers are to perform or assist in appendectomies.

Day nurseries and child-care centers are needed by many working mothers. Some of these facilities provide not only day care but also seek to promote parent education through conferences, study groups, and the mothers' participation in nursery-school activities.

Medical Social Work. Most hospitals and many clinics employ medical social workers. The physician, especially the specialist, is not in a position to familiarize himself with the entire life story of his patient. Very often, personal or family problems are connected with illness. Some patients need casework services in order to understand the causes and nature of their illness. Often the patient or his family has difficulty accepting the illness or the limitations on activity it imposes. Sometimes a patient unconsciously prolongs his convalescence because he doubts his ability to resume family responsibilities in his impaired condition. Sometmes the services of several social agences are needed to carry the patient and his family through a major illness to rehabilitation.

The medical social worker helps with these problems. She arranges referrals for any social services that are needed—vocational rehabilitation, public assistance, homemaker service, and so on. She counsels with the patient and his family so that they may understand and accept the illness and any permanent handicaps it may entail. She interprets to patient and family the recommendations of the physician. She seeks to help the family resolve any personal-adjustment problems so that psychosomatic illness may subside. She plays a key role in the shift of medical concern from the *illness* to the *patient,* and is primarily responsible for carrying into fulfillment the concept of "total patient care."

This list by no means comprises a complete catalogue of social-work services. It merely offers a brief description of those most closely related to health.

The Role of the Nurse

Nurses are not social workers, yet they cannot help becoming involved in social problems. One patient worries about her children's care; another worries over her husband's reaction to her radical mastectomy; still another, overwhelmed by her family responsibilities, is in no hurry to get well. What is the nurse to do when she senses a problem?

Some hospitals have a *referral coordinator* who handles referrals of patients for outpatient care or other welfare services. If not, sometimes there is a medical social worker who can act as referral coordinator. In any case the nurse would ordinarily report the case to her nursing supervisor, who would make arrangements for referral. Only in exceptional cases would the nurse attempt to make the referral herself.

If she attempts the referral herself, it usually will not be effective simply to tell the patient whom to call. The patient may be too ill, too unsophisticated, too apathetic, too overwhelmed by her situation to show such initiative. It will usually be necessary that the agency be informed, so that the agency worker can make the contact. Often the nurse will be uncertain which agency to call. In this case, she might call either the local community chest or the Council of Social Agencies, describing the case and asking what agency should handle it. These organizations are clearinghouses for local social-work agencies.

Few professional roles are as challenging, as demanding, and as rewarding as the role of the nurse. She is the key member of the medical team. She has the most contact with the patient, knows him better than anyone else, and bears primary responsibility for his welfare. She must keep the physician fully informed of his condition, and interpret to him the physician's instructions. She must strike a wise balance between subservient obedience and independent responsibility. She must preserve a degree of emotional stability that is demanded of very few people. She must be sensitive to the needs and feelings of others, must feel and show a sympathetic interest in their welfare, yet must at the same time limit her personal involvement. Eventually, she will probably combine this role with her role as wife and mother.

While the demands are great, so are the rewards. Millions of people are trapped in work that is monotonous and uninteresting. Millions suffer a sense of futility at the pointlessness of their lives. Not so the nurse! Nobody in the world does more important work than she. To say this is not maudlin sentimentality; it is objective fact. True, the financial rewards are small; but they will grow as nurses organize for more effective collective bargaining, as they are beginning to do [Kruger, 1961; Carter, 1962]. Meanwhile the personal rewards are great. Few persons who enter nursing ever come to regret their choice.

Questions and Projects

1. A century ago, child labor was not a social problem. Why did it become one? Why has medical care become a social problem?
2. How do value conflicts create social problems? What value conflicts exist with respect to medical care?
3. How does social change disorganize a society and produce social problems?
4. Distinguish the two ideal types of deviants. Can all deviants be classified into one of these two types?
5. What is believed to be the main cause of alcoholism? Is the same true of drug addiction? What would be gained by legally defining drug addiction as an illness?
6. Why are we, the wealthiest nation, not also the healthiest?

7. What groups of people in America fail to get adequate medical care?
8. Considerable free medical care is available. Explain why this provision has not completely solved the problem for low-income groups.
9. Why do migrant workers have greater difficulty getting medical care than other low-income groups?
10. Why can the comprehensive group-health plans offer more service for the money than limited-coverage plans like Blue Cross?
11. Outline the social-work services described in this chapter. Why should the nurse know something about social work?

Suggested Readings

COOK, DON: "Socialized Medicine Ten Years Old," *Harper's Magazine*, May, 1959, pp. 32–37. An appraisal of Britain's National Health Service.

DAILY, EDWIN F.: "Medical Care under the Health Insurance Plan of Greater New York," *Journal of the American Medical Association*, 170:272–276, 1959. A description of one of the comprehensive medical-care plans.

ENGEL, LEONARD: "We Could Save

40,000 Babies a Year," *New York Times Magazine,* Nov. 17, 1963, pp. 31ff. Tells how many unnecessary deaths might be prevented.

FRIEDLANDER, WALTER A.: *Introduction to Social Welfare,* Prentice-Hall, Inc., Englewood Cliffs, N.J., 1961, chaps. 9–12. A detailed outline of those fields of social work most closely touching on health and medical care.

HORTON, PAUL B., AND GERALD R. LESLIE: *The Sociology of Social Problems,* Appleton-Century-Crofts, Inc., New York, 1965. Chap. 2 outlines the origin of social problems; chap. 17 includes a discussion of alcoholism and drug addiction; chap. 18 gives a detailed treatment of the problem of health and medical care.

ROBINSON, KENNETH: "The Case for Britain's Health Service," *New York Times Magazine,* Nov. 18, 1962, pp. 42ff. A factual but sympathetic analysis of socialized medicine in Britain.

STEVENS, ALDEN: "Make Dope Legal," *Harper's Magazine,* November, 1952, pp. 40–47. Presents the case for defining drug addiction as a disease rather than a crime.

WENSLEY, EDITH: *Nursing Service without Walls,* National League for Nursing, New York, 1963. A brief organizational manual showing how referral of patients for outpatient care and other welfare services should be organized.

Glossary

ACCOMMODATION Peaceful adjustment between hostile or competing groups; "antagonistic cooperation."

ACCULTURATION Acquisition by a group or individual of the traits of another culture.

ACHIEVED STATUS Status reached by individual effort.

AGGREGATE A gathering of people without conscious interaction.

AMALGAMATION Biological interbreeding of two or more peoples of distinct physical appearance until they become one stock.

ANOMIE A situation in which a large number of persons lack integration with stable institutions, to the extent that they are left rootless and normless.

ANXIETY Fear that is out of proportion to any objective stimulus.

APPLIED SCIENCE Scientific methodology applied to the search for knowledge that will be useful in solving practical problems.

ASCRIBED ROLE A role based on inherited status and assigned without regard to individual ability or performance.

ASSIMILATION Mutual cultural diffusion through which persons or groups come to share a common culture.

ASSOCIATION A group with its own administrative structure, organized to pursue some common interest of its members.

ATTITUDE A tendency to feel and act in a certain way.

BUREAUCRACY Administration characterized by rules, hierarchy of office, and centralized authority.

CASTE SYSTEM A stratified society in which social position is entirely determined by parentage, with no provision for achieved status.

CHARISMATIC LEADERSHIP Type of leadership in which the personality of the leader appears to embody the values of the group.

CLIQUE A small group of intimates with intense in-group feelings based on common sentiments and interests.

COMPARTMENTALIZATION Process of attempting to isolate parts of the personality from each other so that the individual is unaware of value conflicts.

COMPETITION Process of seeking to monopolize a reward by surpassing all rivals.

CONCEPT An idea or mental image that embodies generalized or common elements found in a number of specific cases.

CONFLICT The effort to monopolize rewards by eliminating or weakening the competitors.

CONJUGAL FAMILY A married couple and their dependent children.

CONSANGUINE FAMILY Extended clan of blood relatives with their mates and children.

COOPERATION Joint activity in pursuit of common goals or shared rewards.

CULTURAL PLURALISM Toleration of cultural differences within a common society; allowing different groups to retain their distinctive cultures.

CULTURAL RELATIVISM Concept that the function, meaning, and "desirability" of a trait depend upon its cultural setting.

CULTURAL TRAIT Smallest unit of culture as perceived by a given observer.

CULTURE Social heritage the individual receives from the group; a system of behavior shared by members of a society.

CULTURE COMPLEX A cluster of related traits organized around a particular activity.

DEFERRED GRATIFICATION PATTERN Postponement of present satisfactions for future rewards.

DEMOGRAPHY Statistical study of population composition, distribution, and trends.

DEVIATION Failure to conform to customary norms of a society.

DISCRIMINATION A practice that treats equal people unequally; limiting opportunity or reward according to race, religion, or ethnic group.

ENDOGAMY Requirement that mates be chosen within some specified group.

ETHNIC GROUP A number of people with a common cultural heritage that sets them apart from others in a variety of social relationships.

ETHNOCENTRISM Tendency of each group to take for granted the superiority of its own culture.

ETHOS Unifying spirit running through various aspects of a culture.

EXOGAMY Requirement that mates be selected outside some specified group.

FERAL MAN Individual supposedly reared apart from human society and hence imperfectly socialized.

FOLK SOCIETY Small, isolated, often nonliterate, homogeneous society characterized by a high degree of group solidarity.

FOLKWAYS Customary, normal, habitual behavior characteristic of the members of the group.

GHETTO Any part of a city in which the population is restricted to a particular ethnic group; most often applied to a Jewish district.

GOALS Attainments our values define as worthy.

HYPOTHESIS Tentative, unverified statement of the relationship of known facts; a reasonable proposition worthy of scientific testing.

IDEOLOGY A system of ideas that sanctions a set of norms.

INSTINCT An inborn behavior pattern characteristic of all members of the species.

INSTITUTION Organized system of social relationships which embodies certain common values and procedures and meets certain basic needs of society.

LATENT FUNCTIONS Unintended effects of a policy or program.

LOOKING-GLASS SELF Perception of the self that one forms by interpreting the reactions of others to him.

MANIFEST FUNCTIONS Professed objectives of institutions or associations.

MARGINAL MAN Individual torn between two or more cultures; partly assimilated into each and fully assimilated into neither; often an immigrant.

MORES Strong ideas of right and wrong which require certain actions and forbid others. Mores have a larger moral component than do folkways.

NORM A standard of behavior. Statistical norm is a measure of actual conduct; cultural norm states the expected behavior of the culture.

POLYANDRY A form of polygamy in which several husbands share one wife.

POLYGAMY A plurality of mates.

POLYGYNY A form of polygamy in which one husband has several wives.

PRIMARY GROUP Small group in which people come to know one another intimately as individual personalities; distinct from the impersonal, formal, utilitarian secondary group.

PRIMITIVE Characteristic of small societies that are culturally homogeneous and relatively isolated, with fairly simple technological and economic organization. Such a society is usually, but not always, preliterate.

PURE SCIENCE Search for knowledge for its own sake without regard to its practical usefulness or consequences.

REFERENCE GROUPS Groups whose norms we respect and generally adopt.

RITE OF PASSAGE Any ritual that marks movement from one life stage to another, such as the ceremonies attending birth, death, puberty, or marriage.

ROLE Behavior of one who holds a certain status.

SACRED SOCIETY A society with a homogeneous set of folkways and unified moral values that are revered as sacred and eternal.

SCIENTIFIC METHODS Methods of study that produce organized, verified knowledge.

SECONDARY GROUP Group in which contacts are impersonal, segmental, and utilitarian, as distinct from the small, intimate, highly personal primary group.

SECULAR SOCIETY Society with a diversity of folkways and mores; also any group in which religious influence is minimized.

SECULARIZATION Movement from a sacred to a rationalistic, utilitarian, experimental viewpoint.

SEGREGATION Separation of two or more groups based on a desire to avoid equal-status social contacts.

SOCIAL CONTROL Means and processes by which society secures its members' conformity to its norms and values.

SOCIAL DISTANCE Degree of closeness to, or acceptance of, members of other groups.

SOCIAL MOBILITY Movement from one class level to another. Synonymous with "vertical" mobility.

SOCIAL PROCESSES Repetitive forms of behavior commonly found in social life in most societies.

SOCIALIZATION Process by which one internalizes the patterns of the group so that a distinct self emerges unique to the individual.

SOCIETY A group of people who share a common culture.

SOCIOLOGY Scientific study of man's social life.

STATUS Position of an individual in a group.

SUBCULTURE A cluster of behavior patterns related to the general culture of a society and yet distinguishable from it; behavior patterns of a distinct group within the general society.

SYMBIOSIS (SOCIAL) Mutual interdependence without conscious decision to cooperate.

SYMBOL That which stands for something beyond its own immediate meaning; especially a specific object representing a more diffused, generalized, or abstract concept. The flag, the cross, and Uncle Sam are examples.

UTOPIA A perfect society.

VALUES Measures of goodness or desirability.

XENOCENTRISM Rejection of the culture of one's own group.

Bibliography

ABRAHAMSEN, DAVID: *Crime and the Human Mind*, Columbia University Press, New York, 1944.

ABRAMS, CHARLES: *Forbidden Neighbors: A Study of Prejudice in Housing*, Harper & Row, Publishers, Incorporated, New York, 1955.

ADAMS, E. M.: "The Logic of Planning," *Social Forces*, 28:419–423, 1950.

ADORNO, T. W., ELSE FRENKEL-BRUNS-WICK, D. J. LEVINSON, AND R. N. SANFORD: *The Authoritarian Personality*, Harper & Row, Publishers, Incorporated, New York, 1950.

ALBIG, WILLIAM: "Two Decades of Opinion Study: 1936–1956," *Public Opinion Quarterly*, 21:14–22, 1957.

Alcoholics Anonymous Comes of Age, by a cofounder, Harper & Row, Publishers, Incorporated, New York, 1957.

ALLPORT, GORDON W., AND LEO POSTMAN: *The Psychology of Rumor*, Holt, Rinehart and Winston, Inc., New York, 1945.

ALMOND, GABRIEL A., ET AL.: *The Appeals of Communism*, Princeton University Press, Princeton, N.J., 1954.

ALT, HERSCHEL, AND EDITH ALT: *Russia's Children*, Bookman Associates, Inc., New York, 1959.

ALTUS, W. D., AND T. T. TABEJIAN: "MPPI Correlates of the California E-F Scale," *Journal of Abnormal and Social Psychology*, 48:145–149, 1953.

America, Aug. 24, 1957, p. 518, "Rome and New Orleans."

ANDERSON, ODIN W.: "Infant Mortality and Social and Cultural Factors; Historical Trends and Current Patterns," in E. Gartly Jaco, *Patients, Physicians and Illness*, Prentice-Hall,

Inc., Englewood Cliffs, N.J., 1958, pp. 10–24.

ANGELL, ROBERT C.: "Social Integration of American Cities," *American Sociological Review*, 12:335–342, 1947.

ANGELL, ROBERT C.: *The Moral Integration of American Cities*, special issue of *American Journal of Sociology*, no. 1, part 2, July, 1951.

APODACA, ANADETO: "Corn and Custom: The Introduction of Hybrid Corn to Spanish-American Farmers in New Mexico," in Edward H. Spicer (ed.), *Human Problems in Technological Change*, Russell Sage Foundation, New York, 1952, pp. 35–39.

ARNOLD, THURMAN: *The Folklore of Capitalism*, Yale University Press, New Haven, Conn., 1937.

ASCH, S. E.: "Effects of Group Pressure upon the Modification and Distortion of Judgments," in Heinz Guetzkow (ed.), *Groups, Leadership, and Men*, U.S. Office of Naval Research, Carnegie Press, Carnegie Institute of Technology, Pittsburgh, Pa., 1951.

AXELROD, MORRIS: "Urban Structure and Social Participation," *American Sociological Review*, 21:13–18, 1956.

BAIN, READ: "The Self- and Other-words of a Child," *American Journal of Sociology*, 41:767–776, May, 1936.

BAJEMA, CARL J.: "Estimation of the Direction and Intensity of Natural Selection in Relation to Human Intelligence by means of the Intrinsic Rate of Natural Increase," *Eugenics Quarterly*, 10:175–187, 1963.

BALANDIER, GEORGE: "Race Relations in West and Central Africa," in

Andrew W. Lind (ed.), *Race Relations in a World Perspective*, University of Hawaii Press, Honolulu, 1955.

BALES, ROBERT F.: "Small-group Theory and Research," in Robert K. Merton, Leonard Broom, and Leonard S. Cottrell, Jr. (eds.), *Sociology Today: Problems and Prospects*, Basic Books, Inc., Publishers, New York, 1959, pp. 293–308.

BARBER, BERNARD: *Social Stratification*, Harcourt, Brace & World, Inc., New York, 1957.

BARBER, BERNARD, AND LYLE S. TOBEL: "Fashion in Women's Clothes and the American Social System," *Social Forces*, 31:124–131, 1953.

BARNES, C. A.: "A Statistical Study of the Freudian Theory of Levels of Psychosexual Development," *Genetic Psychology Monographs*, 45:105–174, 1952.

BASCOM, WILLIAM R., AND MELVILLE J. HERSKOVITZ (EDS.): *Continuity and Change in African Cultures*, The University of Chicago Press, Chicago, 1959.

BAVELAS, ALEX: "Communication Patterns in Task-oriented Groups," in Dorwin Cartwright and Alvin F. Zander (eds.): *Group Dynamics*, Harper & Row, Publishers, Incorporated, New York, 1953, pp. 493–494.

BEARD, CHARLES, AND MARY BEARD: *The Rise of American Civilization*, The Macmillan Company, New York, 1930.

BEAVER, ALMA PERRY: "Personality Factors in Choice of Nursing," *Journal of Applied Psychology*, 37:374–379, 1953.

BELL, WENDELL, AND MARYANNE T. FORCE: "Urban Neighborhood Types and Participation in Voluntary Associations," *American Sociological Review*, 21:19–25, 1956.

BEN-DAVID, JOSEPH: "Scientific Productivity and Academic Organization," *American Sociological Review*, 25:828–843, 1960.

BENDINER, ROBERT: "What's Wrong in the House of Labor?" *Reporter*, 25:41–46, Oct. 12, 1961.

BENEDICT, RUTH: *Patterns of Culture*, Houghton Mifflin Company, Boston, 1934.

BENNE, KENNETH D., AND WARREN BENNIS: "Role Confusion and Conflict in Nursing; the Role of the Professional Nurse," *American Journal of Nursing*, 59:196–198, 1959(a).

BENNE, KENNETH D., AND WARREN BENNIS: "Role Confusion and Conflict in Nursing; What Is Real Nursing?" *American Journal of Nursing*, 59:380–383, 1959(b).

BERLE, ADOLF A., AND GARDINER C. MEANS: *The Modern Corporation and Private Property*, The Macmillan Company, New York, 1932.

BERNSTEIN, MOREY: *The Search for Bridey Murphy*, Doubleday & Company, Inc., Garden City, N.Y., 1956.

BERRY, BREWTON: *Race and Ethnic Relations*, Houghton Mifflin Company, Boston, 1958.

BIDERMAN, ALBERT D.: "Social-Psychological Needs and 'Involuntary' Behavior as Illustrated by Compliance in Interrogation," *Sociometry*, 23:120–147, 1960.

BIERSTEDT, ROBERT: *The Social Order*, McGraw-Hill Book Company, New York, 1957.

BLIVEN, BRUCE: "The Revolution of the Joneses," *New York Times Magazine*, Oct. 9, 1960, pp. 28ff.

BLOOD, ROBERT A., AND DONALD M. WOLFE: *Husbands and Wives*, The

Free Press of Glencoe, New York, 1960.

BLOOM, B. S.: "The Thought Process of Students in Discussion," in Sidney J. French (ed.), *Accent on Teaching*, Harper & Row, Publishers, Incorporated, New York, 1954.

BLOOM, SAMUEL W.: "The Process of Becoming a Physician," *Annals of the American Academy of Political and Social Science*, 346:77–87, 1963.

BLOSSOM, VIRGIL: *It Has Happened Here*, Harper & Row, Publishers, Incorporated, New York, 1959.

BLUMBERG, LEONARD, AND ROBERT R. BELL: "Urban Migration and Kinship Ties," *Social Problems*, 6:328–333, 1959.

BLUMER, HERBERT: "Social Science and the Desegregation Process," *Annals of the American Academy of Political and Social Science*, 304:137–143, 1956.

BOGARDUS, EMORY S.: "The Long Trail of Cooperation," *Sociology and Social Research*, 31:54–62, 1946.

BOGARDUS, EMORY S.: *Sociology*, The Macmillan Company, New York, 1949.

BOGARDUS, EMORY S.: *Fundamentals of Social Psychology*, Appleton-Century-Crofts, Inc., New York, 1950.

BOGARDUS, EMORY S.: "Racial Distance Changes in the United States during the past Thirty Years," *Sociology and Social Research*, 43:127–135, 1958.

BOGARDUS, EMORY S.: "Racial Reactions by Regions," *Sociology and Social Research*, 43:286–290, 1959.

BOGART, LEO: "Measuring the Effectiveness of an Overseas Information Campaign: A Case History,"

Public Opinion Quarterly, 21:475–498, 1957.

BOGART, LEO: *The Age of Television*, Frederick A. Praeger, Inc., New York, 1958.

BOGUE, DONALD J.: *The Population of the United States*, The Free Press of Glencoe, New York, 1959.

BOSSARD, JAMES H. S., AND W. P. SANGER, "The Large Family System," *American Sociological Review*, 17:3–9, 1952.

BOVARD, EVERETT W., JR.: "Group Structure and Perception," *Journal of Abnormal and Social Psychology*, 46:398–405, 1951.

BRADY, THOMAS F.: "French Worker-Priests Must Abandon Politics," *New York Times*, Jan. 31, 1954, sect. 4, p. 7.

BREWSTER, AGNES W., SCOTT J. ALLEN, AND LUCY M. KRAMER: "Experience with a Prepaid Drug Benefit," *Journal of Health and Human Behavior*, 4:14–22, Spring, 1963.

BROWN, ROGER W.: "Determinants of the Relationship between Rigidity and Authoritarianism," *Journal of Abnormal and Social Psychology*, 48:469–475, 1953.

BUERKLE, JACK V.: "Patterns of Socialization, Role Conflict, and Leadership among Nurses," *Sociology and Social Research*, 44:100–105, 1959.

BUREAU OF LABOR STATISTICS: *Summary of the Report on Conditions of Women and Children Wage Earners in the United States*, Bulletin no. 175, Washington, 1916.

BURGESS, ERNEST W., AND LEONARD S. COTTRELL: *Predicting Success or Failure in Marriage*, Prentice-Hall, Inc., Englewood Cliffs, N.J., 1939.

BURGESS, ERNEST W., AND HARVEY J. LOCKE: *The Family: From Institu-*

tion to Companionate, American Book Company, New York, 1953.

BURLINGAME, ROGER: *Inventors behind the Inventor,* Harcourt, Brace & World, Inc., 1947.

BURMA, JOHN H.: "The Measurement of Negro Passing," *American Journal of Sociology,* 52:18–22, 1946.

BURMA, JOHN H.: "Student Attitudes towards and Participation in Voluntary Organizations," *Sociology and Social Research,* 32:625–629, November, 1947.

CADY, JOHN F.: "Religion and Politics in Modern Burma," *Far Eastern Affairs,* 12:149–162, 1953.

CALVIN, A. D., AND WAYNE H. HOLTZMAN: "Adjustment to the Discrepancy between Self Concept and the Inferred Self," *Journal of Consulting Psychiatry,* 17:39–44, 1953.

CAMPBELL, DONALD T., AND THELMA H. MC CORMACK: "Military Experience and Attitudes toward Authority," *American Journal of Sociology,* 62:482–490, 1957.

CANTRIL, HADLEY: *The Psychology of Social Movements,* John Wiley & Sons, Inc., New York, 1941.

CANTRIL, HADLEY: "Identification with Social and Economic Class," *Journal of Abnormal and Social Psychology,* 38:74–80, 1943.

CAPLOW, THEODORE: *The Academic Marketplace,* Basic Books, Inc., Publishers, New York, 1958.

CAROTHERS, J. C.: "A Study of Mental Derangement in Africans, and an Attempt to Explain Its Peculiarities, More Especially in Relation to the African Attitude of Life," *Journal of Mental Science,* 93:548–597, 1947. Summarized in James C. Coleman, *Abnormal Psychology and Modern Life,* Scott, Foresman and Company, Chicago, 1956, pp. 256–259.

CARROLL, CHARLES: *The Negro a Beast, or, in the Image of God,* American Bible and Book House, St. Louis, Mo., 1900.

CARTER, BARBARA: "Medicine's Forgotten Women," *Reporter,* 26:35–37, Mar. 1, 1962.

CARTWRIGHT, DORWIN, AND ALVIN F. ZANDER (EDS.): *Group Dynamics: Theory and Research,* Harper & Row, Publishers, Incorporated, New York, 1953.

CENTERS, RICHARD: *The Psychology of Social Classes,* Princeton University Press, Princeton, N.J., 1949.

CHAMBERS, ROSALIND C.: "A Study of Three Voluntary Organizations," in D. V. Glass (ed.), *Social Mobility in Britain,* The Free Press of Glencoe, New York, 1954, pp. 384–406.

CHANDRASEKHAR, S.: "Mao's War with the Chinese Family," *New York Times Magazine,* May 17, 1959, pp. 21ff.

CHAPIN, F. STUART: "Research Studies of Extra-curricular Activities and Their Significance in Reflecting Social Change," *Journal of Educational Sociology,* 4:491–498, 1931.

CHAPIN, F. STUART, AND JOHN E. TSOUDEROS: "Formalization Observed in Ten Voluntary Associations; Concepts, Morphology, Process," *Social Forces,* 33:306–309, 1955.

CHAPIN, F. STUART, AND JOHN E. TSOUDEROS: "The Formalization in Voluntary Associations: Concepts, Morphology, Process," *Social Forces,* 34:342–344, 1956.

CHEIN, ISIDOR: "Narcotics Use among Juveniles," *Social Work,* 1:50–60, April, 1956.

CHICAGO COMMISSION ON RACE RELATIONS: *The Negro in Chicago,* The

University of Chicago Press, Chicago, 1922.

CHINOY, ELY: "The Tradition of Opportunity and the Aspirations of Automobile Workers," *American Journal of Sociology*, 57:453–459, 1952.

CLAUSEN, CONNIE: *I Love You, Honey, but the Season's Over*, Holt, Rinehart and Winston, Inc., New York, 1961.

CLINARD, MARSHALL B.: *The Black Market: A Study in White Collar Crime*, Holt, Rinehart and Winston, Inc., New York, 1952.

CLINARD, MARSHALL B.: *Sociology of Deviant Behavior*, Holt, Rinehart and Winston, Inc., New York, 1957.

COHEN, ALBERT K.: *Delinquent Boys: The Culture of the Gang*, The Free Press of Glencoe, New York, 1955.

COLEMAN, JAMES S.: *The Adolescent Society*, The Free Press of Glencoe, New York, 1961.

COLLIER, JOHN; *Indians of the Americas*, W. W. Norton & Company, Inc., New York, 1947.

COMMUNITY STUDIES, INC.: *A Survey of the Social and Occupational Characteristics of a Metropolitan Nurse Complement*, Community Studies, Inc., Kansas City, Mo., 1956.

CONANT, JAMES B.: *Slums and Suburbs: A Commentary on Schools in Metropolitan Areas*, McGraw-Hill Book Company, New York, 1961.

COOK, DON: "Socialized Medicine Ten Years Old," *Harper's Magazine*, May, 1959, pp. 32–37.

COOLEY, CHARLES HORTON: "The Theory of Transportation," *Publications of the American Economic Association*, vol. 9, no. 3, 1894.

COOLEY, CHARLES HORTON: *The Nature of Human Nature*, Charles Scribner's Sons, New York, 1902.

COOLEY, CHARLES HORTON: "A Study of the Early Use of Self Words by a Child," *Psychological Review*, 15:339–357, 1908.

CORWIN, RONALD G.: "The Professional Employee: A Study of Conflict in Nursing Roles," *American Journal of Sociology*, 66:604–615, 1961.

CORWIN, RONALD G., AND MARVIN J. TAVES: "Some Concomitants of Bureaucratic and Professional Conceptions of the Nurse Role," *Nursing Research*, 11:223–227, 1962.

CRONON, EDMUND D.: *Black Moses*, The University of Wisconsin Press, Madison, Wis., 1955.

DAI, BINGHAM: "Obsessive-Compulsive Disorders in Chinese Culture," *Social Problems*, 4:313–321, 1957.

DAILY, EDWIN F.: "Medical Care under the Health Insurance Plan of Greater New York," *Journal of the American Medical Association*, 170:272–276, 1959.

DALE, EDWARD EVERETT: *The Range Cattle Industry*, University of Oklahoma Press, Norman, Okla., 1930.

DAVIDSON, BILL: "Combat Soldiers Fail to Shoot," *Colliers*, Nov. 8, 1952, pp. 16–18.

DAVIS, ALLISON: *Social-class Influences on Learning*, Harvard University Press, Cambridge, Mass., 1948, 1952.

DAVIS, ALLISON, AND ROBERT J. HAVIGHURST: "Social Class and Color Differences in Child-rearing," *American Sociological Review*, 11:698–710, 1946.

DAVIS, FRED: "The Cabdriver and His Fare: Facets of a Fleeting Relationship," *American Journal of Sociology*, 65:158–165, 1959.

DAVIS, KINGSLEY: *Human Society*, The

Macmillan Company, New York, 1949.

DAWSON, CARL, AND W. E. GETTYS: *Introduction to Sociology*, The Ronald Press Company, New York, 1948.

DEASY, LEILA CALHOUN: "Socio-economic Status and Participation in the Poliomyelitis Vaccine Trial," *American Sociological Review*, 21:185–191, 1956.

DE CASTRO, JOSUÉ: *The Geography of Hunger*, Little, Brown and Company, Boston, 1952.

DEUTSCH, MORTON: "An Experimental Study of the Effects of Cooperation and Competition upon Group Process," *Human Relations*, 2:199–231, 1949.

DEUTSCHER, IRWIN: *Public Images of the Nurse*, Community Studies, Inc., Kansas City, Mo., 1955.

DEVEREAUX, GEORGE, AND FLORENCE WEINER: "The Occupational Status of Nurses," *American Sociological Review*, 15:628–634, 1950.

DEWEY, RICHARD: "The Rural-Urban Continuum: Real but Relatively Unimportant," *American Journal of Sociology*, 66:60–66, 1960.

DICKINSON, FRANK G.: *How Bad Is the Distribution of Physicians?* Bulletin 94B, American Medical Association, Chicago, 1954.

DITTES, JAMES E., AND HAROLD H. KELLEY: "Effects of Different Conditions of Acceptance upon Conformity to Group Norms," *Journal of Abnormal and Social Psychology*, 53:100–107, 1956.

DOBRINER, WILLIAM M. (ED.): *The Suburban Community*, G. P. Putnam's Sons, New York, 1958.

DOOB, LEONARD: *Propaganda*, Holt, Rinehart and Winston, Inc., New York, 1948.

DRAPER, THEODORE: "The Psychology of Surrender," *Atlantic Monthly*, 176:62–65, 1945.

DRURY, ALLEN: *Advise and Consent*, Doubleday & Company, Inc., Garden City, N.Y., 1959.

DUBOIS, CORA: *The People of Alor*, The University of Minnesota Press, Minneapolis, 1944.

DUNBAR, H. FLANDERS: *Mind & Body: Psychosomatic Medicine*, Random House, Inc., New York, 1955.

DUNCAN, DAVID DOUGLAS: "In the Middle of an Indian Massacre," *Life*, Oct. 6, 1947, pp. 6ff.

DURKHEIM, EMILE (1897): *Le Suicide: étude de Sociologie*, F. Alcon, Paris, tr. by J. A. Spaulding and G. Simpson, The Free Press of Glencoe, New York, 1951.

Economist, 181:59, 1956, "Rebels in Indonesia."

EDITORS OF *Wall Street Journal: The New Millionaires and How They Made Their Fortunes*, Bernard Geis Associates, New York, 1961.

EDWARDS, ALLEN A.: "Types of Rural Communities," in Marvin B. Sussman (ed.), *Community Structure and Analysis*, Thomas Y. Crowell Company, New York, 1959.

EELLS, KENNETH, ET AL.: *Intelligence and Cultural Differences*, The University of Chicago Press, Chicago, 1951.

EGGAN, DOROTHY: "The General Problem of Hopi Adjustment," *American Anthropologist*, 45:357–373, July, 1943.

EHRMANN, WINSTON: *Premarital Dating Behavior*, Holt, Rinehart and Winston, Inc., New York, 1959.

ELLIS, EVELYN: "Social Psychological Correlates of Upward Social Mobility among Unmarried Career Women," *American Sociological Review*, 17:558–563, 1952.

ELWIN, VARRIER: *The Biaga*, John

Murray (Publishers), Ltd., London, 1939.

ELWOOD, ROBERT H.: "The Role of Personality Factors in Selecting a Career," *Journal of Applied Psychology*, 11:199–201, 1927.

ERNST, MORRIS, AND DAVID LOTH: *Report on the American Communist*, Holt, Rinehart and Winston, Inc., New York, 1952.

EULAN, HANS: "Identification with Class and Political Role Behavior," *Public Opinion Quarterly*, 20:515–529, 1956.

FAIRCHILD, HENRY PRATT (ED.): *Dictionary of Sociology*, Philosophical Library, Inc., New York, 1944.

FAIRCHILD, HENRY PRATT: Review of Josué de Castro, *The Geography of Hunger*, in *Social Forces*, 31:82–84, 1952.

FESTINGER, L., A. PIPESTONE, AND T. NEWCOMB: "Some Consequences of Deindividuation in a Group," *Journal of Abnormal and Social Psychology*, 47:382–389, 1952.

FESTINGER, LEON, HENRY W. RIECKEN, AND STANLEY SCHACHTER: *When Prophecy Fails*, The University of Minnesota Press, Minneapolis, 1956.

FLUGEL, J. C.: *The Psychology of Clothes*, The Hogarth Press, Ltd., London, 1930.

FOREMAN, GRANT: *Indian Removal*, University of Oklahoma Press, Norman, Okla., 1932.

FOREMAN, PAUL B.: "Panic Theory," *Sociology and Social Research*, 37:295–304, 1953.

FOREMAN, PAUL B.: "The Implications of Project Clear," *Phylon*, 16:263–274, 1955.

FORTUNE, R. F.: *The Sorcerers of Dobu*, E. P. Dutton & Co., Inc., New York, 1932.

Fortune, February, 1940, p. 21, "The People of the United States—A Self-portrait."

FOSKETT, JOHN M.: "Social Structure and Community Participation," *American Sociological Review*, 20:431–438, 1955.

FOX, RUTH: "The Alcoholic Spouse," in Victor W. Eisenstein (ed.), *Neurotic Interaction in Marriage*, Basic Books, Inc., New York, 1956, pp. 148–167.

FRAKES, MARGARET: "Folk Church in a Welfare State," *Christian Century*, 75:1020, 1958.

FRAZIER, E. FRANKLIN: *The Negro Family in the United States*, Holt, Rinehart and Winston, Inc., New York, 1948.

FRAZIER, E. FRANKLIN: *Black Bourgeoisie*, The Free Press of Glencoe, New York, 1957.

FREEMAN, RONALD, PASCAL K. WHELPTON, AND JOHN W. SMIT: Socio-economic Factors in Religious Differentials in Fertility," *American Sociological Review*, 26:608–614, 1961.

FREEMAN, HOWARD E.: "Attitudes toward Mental Patients among Relatives of Former Patients," *American Sociological Review*, 26:59–66, 1961.

FRIEDLANDER, WALTER A.: *Introduction to Social Welfare*, Prentice-Hall, Inc., Englewood Cliffs, N.J., 1961.

FROMM, ERICH: "Individual and Social Origins of Neurosis," *American Sociological Review*, 9:380–384, 1944.

FROMM, ERICH: *The Art of Loving*, Harper & Row, Publishers, Incorporated, New York, 1956.

GALLUP, GEORGE, AND S. F. RAE: *The Pulse of Democracy*, Simon and Schuster, Inc., New York, 1940.

GALLUP, GEORGE: "The Changing Climate for Public Opinion Research," *Public Opinion Quarterly*, 21:23–28, 1957.

GARDNER. MARTIN: *Fads and Fallacies in the Name of Science*, Dover Publications, Inc., New York, 1957.

GERBNER, GEORGE: "The Social Role of the Confessions Magazine," *Social Problems*, 6:29–40, 1958.

GIBBARD, HAROLD: "Residential Succession: A Study in Human Ecology, unpublished Ph.D. dissertation, University of Michigan, 1938.

GIDDINGS, F. H.: *The Principles of Sociology*, The Macmillan Company, New York, 1913.

GILBERT, DORIS C., AND FRED L. WELLS: "A Ward Socialization Index," *American Journal of Nursing*, 57:59–61, 1957.

GILLIN, JOHN L., AND JOHN P. GILLIN: *Cultural Sociology*, The Macmillan Company, New York, 1948.

GLICK, PAUL C., AND EMANUAL LANDAU: "Age as a Factor in Marriage," *American Sociological Review*, 15:517–529, 1950.

GLICK, PAUL C.: *American Families*, John Wiley & Sons, Inc., New York, 1957.

GLUECK, SHELDON, AND ELEANOR GLUECK: "Working Mothers and Delinquency," *Mental Hygiene*, 41:327–352, 1957.

GLUECK, SHELDON, AND ELEANOR GLUECK: *Predicting Juvenile Delinquency and Crime*, Harvard University Press, Cambridge, Mass., 1959.

GOLDHAMER, HERBERT, AND ANDREW MARSHALL: *Psychosis and Civilization: Two Studies in the Frequency of Mental Illness*, The Free Press of Glencoe, New York, 1953.

GOLDSTEIN, RHODA L.: "Negro Nurses in Hospitals," *American Journal of Nursing*, 60:215–217, 1960.

GOLDSTEIN, SIDNEY: "Migration and Occupational Mobility in Norristown, Pennsylvania," *American Sociological Review*, 20:402–408, 1955.

GOLIN, MILTON: "The Troubled Employee," *Journal of the American Medical Association*, 168:1371–1375, 1958.

GOULD, HAROLD A.: "The Implications of Technological Change for Folk and Scientific Medicine," *American Anthropologist*, 59:507–516, 1957; reprinted in Dorrian Apple (ed.), *Sociological Studies of Health and Sickness*, McGraw-Hill Book Company, New York, 1960, pp. 88–99.

GRAHAM, SAXON, AND ABRAHAM M. LILIENFELD: "Genetic Studies of Gastric Cancer in Humans: An Appraisal," *Cancer*, 11:945–958, 1958.

GREENWALD, HAROLD: *The Call Girl*, Ballantine Books, Inc., New York, 1959.

GREER, SCOTT, AND ELLA KUBE: "Urbanism and Social Structure: A Los Angeles Study," in Marvin B. Sussman (ed.), *Community Structure and Analysis*, Thomas Y. Crowell Company, New York, 1959.

GRIER, EUNICE, AND GEORGE GRIER: *Discrimination in Housing*, Anti-Defamation League, New York, 1960.

GRIFFIN, JOHN H.: *Black Like Me*, Houghton Mifflin Company, Boston, 1961.

GRODZINS, MORTON: *The Metropolitan Area as a Racial Problem*, The University of Pittsburgh Press, Pittsburgh, Pa., 1958.

GROSS, EDWARD: "Some Functional Consequences of Primary Group Controls in Formal Work Organizations," *American Sociological Review*, 18:368–373, 1953.

HACKER, ANDREW: "The Boy Who

Doesn't Go to College," *New York Times Magazine,* June 24, 1962, pp. 11ff.

HACKETT, HERBERT: "The Flying Saucer," *Sociology and Social Research,* 32:869–873, 1948.

HARLOW, HARRY F., AND MARGARET K. HARLOW: "A Study of Animal Affection," *Natural History,* 70:48–55, 1961.

HARRIS, C. D., AND E. L. ULLMAN: "The Nature of Cities," *Annals of the American Academy of Political and Social Science,* 242:7–17, 1945.

HARVEY, JESSE: Unpublished doctoral dissertation, reported in *Science News Letter,* Dec. 5, 1953, p. 360.

HAVIGHURST, ROBERT J., AND ALLISON DAVIS: "A Comparison of the Chicago and Harvard Studies of Social Class Differences in Childrearing," *American Sociological Review,* 20:438–442, 1955.

HENRY, JULES: "The Formal Social Structure of a Psychiatric Hospital," *Psychiatry,* 17:139–151, 1954.

HERTZLER, J. O.: *American Social Institutions,* Allyn and Bacon, Inc., Boston, 1961.

HERZOG, ELIZABETH: *Children of Working Mothers,* Children's Bureau Publication no. 382, U.S. Department of Health, Education, and Welfare, 1960.

HIGHAM, JOHN: *Strangers in the Land: Patterns of American Nativism, 1860–1925,* Rutgers University Press, New Brunswick, N.J., 1955.

HILL, REUBEN, J. MAYONE STYCOS, AND KURT W. BACK: *The Family and Population Control,* The University of North Carolina Press, Chapel Hill, N.C., 1959.

HILLERY, GEORGE A.: "Definitions of Community: Areas of Agreement," *Rural Sociology,* 20:111–123, 1955.

HIMES, JOSEPH S.: *Social Planning in America: A Dynamic Interpretation,* Doubleday & Company, Inc., Garden City, N. Y., 1954.

HOCART, ARTHUR M.: *Caste: A Comparative Study,* Methuen & Co., Ltd., London, 1950.

HOEBEL, E. ADAMSON: *Man in the Primitive World,* McGraw-Hill Book Company, New York, 1949.

HOESS, RUDOLF: *Commandant of Auschwitz,* tr. by Constantine Fitzgibbon, The World Publishing Company, Cleveland, 1960.

HOLLINGSHEAD, AUGUST B.: *Elmtown's Youth,* John Wiley & Sons, Inc., New York, 1949.

HOLLINGSHEAD, AUGUST B., AND FREDRICH C. REDLICH: "Social Stratification and Psychiatric Disorders," *American Sociological Review,* 18:163–169, 1953.

HOLLINGSHEAD, AUGUST B., R. ELLIS, AND E. KIRBY: "Social Mobility and Mental Illness," *American Sociological Review,* 19:577–584, 1954.

HOLLINGSHEAD, AUGUST B., AND FREDRICH C. REDLICH: *Social Class and Mental Illness,* John Wiley & Sons, Inc., New York, 1958.

HOOTON, E. A.: *Crime and the Man,* Harvard University Press, Cambridge, Mass., 1939.

HOOVER, J. EDGAR: *Masters of Deceit,* Holt, Rinehart and Winston, Inc., New York, 1958.

HORNEY, KAREN: *The Neurotic Personality of Our Time,* W. W. Norton & Company, Inc., New York, 1937.

HORTON, DONALD: "The Functions of Alcohol in Primitive Societies," *Quarterly Journal of Studies on Alcohol,* 4:293–303, 1943.

HOYT, HOMER: *One Hundred Years of Land Values in Chicago,* The University of Chicago Press, Chicago, 1933.

HUFF, DARRELL: *How to Lie with Statistics,* W. W. Norton & Company, Inc., New York, 1954.

HUGHES, EVERETT C., HELEN MACGILL HUGHES, AND IRWIN DEUTSCHER: *Twenty Thousand Nurses Tell Their Story,* J. B. Lippincott Co., Philadelphia, 1958.

HURLOCK, ELIZABETH B.: "The Use of Group Rivalry as an Incentive," *Journal of Abnormal and Social Psychology,* 22:278–290, 1927.

HUXLEY, ALDOUS: *Brave New World,* Doubleday & Company, Inc., Garden City, N. Y., 1932.

HUXLEY, ALDOUS: *Brave New World Revisited,* Harper & Row, Publishers, Incorporated, New York, 1958.

HYDE, DAVID R., AND PAYSON WOLFF, WITH ANN GREEN AND ELLIOT LEE HOFFMAN: "The American Medical Association: Power, Purpose, and Politics in Organized Medicine," *Yale Law Review,* 63:938–1022, 1954.

INKELES, ALEX: "Industrial Man: The Relation of Status to Experience, Perception, and Value," *American Journal of Sociology,* 66:1–31, 1960.

ISBELL, HARRIS: *What to Know about Drug Addiction,* Public Health Service Publication no. 94, Washington, 1958.

JACK, NANCY KOPLIN, AND BETTY SCHIFFER: "The Limits of Fashion Control," *American Sociological Review,* 13:730–738, 1948.

JACO, E. GARTLEY, AND IVAN BELKNAP: "Is a New Family Form Emerging in the Urban Fringe?" *American Sociological Review,* 18:551–557, 1953.

JACOB, K. K.: "Are Missionaries 'Western' Agents?" *Catholic World,* 184:449–451, 1957.

JOHNSON, DONALD M.: "The 'Phantom Anesthetist' of Mattoon: A Field Study of Mass Hysteria," *Journal of Abnormal and Social Psychology,* 40:175–186, 1945.

JOINT COMMITTEE OF THE AMERICAN BAR ASSOCIATION AND THE AMERICAN MEDICAL ASSOCIATION: *Drug Addiction: Crime or Disease? Interim and Final Reports,* Indiana University Press, Bloomington, Ind., 1961.

JONASSEN, CHRISTEN T.: "Community Typology," in Marvin B. Sussman (ed.), *Community Structure and Analysis,* Thomas Y. Crowell Company, New York, 1959.

JONES, HOWARD W., AND WILLIAM W. SCOTT: *Hermaphroditism, Genital Abnormalities, and Related Endocrine Disorders,* The Williams & Wilkins Company, Baltimore, 1958.

JOST, HUDSON, AND LESTER W. SONTAG: "The Genetic Factor in Autonomic Nervous-system Function," *Psychosomatic Medicine,* 61:308–310, 1944.

KAHL, JOSEPH A.: "Educational and Occupational Aspirations of 'Common Man' Boys," *Harvard Educational Review,* 23:186–203, 1953.

KAHL, JOSEPH A.: *The American Class Structure,* Holt, Rinehart and Winston, Inc., New York, 1957.

KALLMAN, FRANZ J.: "The Genetic Theory of Schizophrenia," *American Journal of Psychiatry,* 103:309–322, November, 1946.

KAPLAN, BERT: *A Study of Rorschach Responses in Four Cultures,* Papers of the Peabody Museum of American Archeology and Ethnology, 42, no. 2, Harvard University, Cambridge, Mass., 1954.

KAPLAN, BERT, AND THOMAS F. A. PLANT: *Personality in a Communal Society: An Analysis of the Mental Health of the Hutterites,* University of Kansas Press, Lawrence, Kan., 1956.

KARDINER, ABRAM, AND LIONEL OVERSEY: *The Mark of Oppression: A Psychosocial Study of the American Negro*, W. W. Norton & Company, Inc., New York, 1951.

KELLOGG, W. N., AND L. A. KELLOGG: *The Ape and the Child*, McGraw-Hill Book Company, New York, 1933.

KEPHART, W. M.: *Family, Society, and the Individual*, Houghton Mifflin Company, Boston, 1961.

KERCHER, LEONARD, VANT W. KEBKER, AND WILFRED C. LELAND, JR.: *Consumers' Cooperatives in the North Central States*, The University of Minnesota Press, Minneapolis, 1941.

KEY, WILLIAM H.: "Rural-Urban Differences and the Family," *Sociological Quarterly*, 2:49–56, 1961.

KEYS, ANCEL: "Experimental Induction of Neuropsychoses by Starvation," in Milbank Memorial Fund, *Biology of Mental Health and Disease*, Harper & Row, Publishers, Incorporated, New York, 1952, pp. 515–525.

KINKEAD, EUGENE: *In Every War but One*, W. W. Norton & Company, Inc., New York, 1959.

KINSEY, ALFRED C., WARDELL B. POMEROY, AND CLYDE E. MARTIN: *Sexual Behavior in the Human Male*, W. B. Saunders Company, Philadelphia, 1948.

KLINEBERG, OTTO: *Negro Intelligence and Selective Migration*, Columbia University Press, New York, 1935.

KLINEBERG, OTTO: *Characteristics of the American Negro*, Harper & Row, Publishers, Incorporated, New York, 1944.

KLUCKHOHN, FLORENCE: "Dominant and Substitute Profiles of Cultural Orientation: Their Significance for an Analysis of Social Stratification," *Social Forces*, 28:376–393, 1950.

KNIBBS, GEORGE HANDLEY: *The Shadow of the World's Future: Or the Earth's Population Possibilities and Consequences of the Present Rate of Increase of the World's Inhabitants*, Ernest Benn, Ltd., London, 1928.

KOENIG, ROBERT P.: "An American Engineer Looks at British Coal," *Foreign Affairs*, 26:285–286, 1948.

KOLKO, GABRIEL: "Economic Mobility and Social Stratification," *American Journal of Sociology*, 63:30–38, 1957.

KOMAROVSKY, MIRRA: "Cultural Contradictions and Sex Roles," *American Journal of Sociology*, 52:184–189, 1946 (*a*).

KOMAROVSKY, MIRRA: "The Voluntary Associations of Urban Dwellers," *American Sociological Review*, 11:686–698, 1946 (*b*).

KOOS, EARL LOMON: *The Health of Regionville*, Columbia University Press, New York, 1954.

KRETSCHMER, ERNEST: *Physique and Character*, Harcourt, Brace & World, Inc., New York, 1925.

KRON, THORA: *Nursing Team Leadership*, W. B. Saunders Co., Philadelphia, 1961.

KROUT, MAURICE A.: *Introduction to Social Psychology*, Harper & Row, Publishers, Incorporated, New York, 1942.

KRUGER, D. H.: "Bargaining and the Nursing Profession," *Monthly Labor Review*, 84:699–705, 1961.

KUHN, MANFRED H., AND THOMAS S. MC PARTLAND: "An Empirical Investigation of Self-attitudes," *American Sociological Review*, 19:68–75, February, 1954.

KUO, ZING YANG: "Genesis of Cat's Responses in Rats," *Journal of Comparative Psychology*, 11:1–35, 1931.

KUTNER, BERNARD: "Surgeons and Their Patients," in E. Gartly Jaco, *Patients, Physicians and Illness*, The Free Press of Glencoe, New York, 1958.

LAMBERTSEN, ELEANOR C.: *Nursing Team Organization and Function*, Teachers College, Columbia University, New York, 1953.

LANDER, BERNARD: *Toward an Understanding of Juvenile Delinquency*, Columbia University Press, New York, 1954.

LANDIS, PAUL H.: *Social Control*, J. B. Lippincott Company, Philadelphia, 1939, 1956.

LANDIS, PAUL H.: *Making the Most of Marriage*, New York: Appleton-Century-Crofts, Inc., New York, 1960.

LANG, KURT, AND GLADYS ENGEL LANG: *Collective Dynamics*, Thomas Y. Crowell Company, New York, 1961.

LAPIERE, RICHARD T.: *Collective Behavior*, McGraw-Hill Book Company, New York, 1938.

LAPIERE, RICHARD T., AND PAUL R. FARNSWORTH: *Social Psychology*, McGraw-Hill Book Company, New York, 1949.

LAPIERE, RICHARD T.: *A Theory of Social Control*, McGraw-Hill Book Company, New York, 1954.

LASSWELL, HAROLD D.: "Propaganda," *Encyclopaedia of the Social Sciences*, The Macmillan Company, New York, 1933, vol. 12, pp. 521–527.

LASSWELL, HAROLD D.: "The Strategy of Soviet Propaganda," *Proceedings of the Academy of Political Science*, 1951, vol. 24, pp. 214–226.

LAURENTI, L. M.: *Property Values and Race*, University of California Press, Berkeley, Calif., 1960.

LAVA, HORACIO: "The Colonial Structure of the Philippine Economy," *Comment*, 2d quarter, 1958, pp. 42–55.

LEDERER, WILLIAM J., AND E. L. BURDICK: *The Ugly American*, W. W. Norton & Company, Inc., New York, 1958.

LEE, ALFRED M., AND ELIZABETH BRIANT LEE: *The Fine Art of Propaganda*, Harcourt, Brace & World, Inc., and the Institute for Propaganda Analysis, New York, 1939.

LEE, ALFRED M., AND NORMAN D. HUMPHREY: *Race Riot*, Holt, Rinehart and Winston, Inc., New York, 1943.

LEE, DOROTHY: Freedom and Culture, Prentice-Hall, Inc., Englewood Cliffs, N. J., 1959 (*a*).

LEE, DOROTHY: "The Cultural Curtain," *Annals of the American Academy of Political and Social Science*, 323:120–128, 1959 (*b*).

LEE, ROSE HUM: *The City*, J. B. Lippincott Company, Philadelphia, 1955.

LENSKI, GERHARD E.: "Trends in Intergenerational Mobility in the U.S.," *American Sociological Review*, 23:514–523, 1958.

LESSER, ALEXANDER: "Cultural Significance of the Ghost Dance," *American Anthropologist*, 35:108–115, 1933.

LEVY, MARION J.: *The Family Revolution in Modern China*, Harvard University Press, Cambridge, Mass., 1949.

LEWIS, SINCLAIR: *Babbitt*, Harcourt, Brace & World, Inc., New York, 1922.

LEYBURN, JAMES G.: *Frontier Folk-*

ways, Yale University Press, New Haven, Conn., 1935.

LINCOLN, C. ERIC: *The Black Muslims in America,* Beacon Press, Boston, 1961.

LINDESMITH, ALFRED E.: "Social Problems and Sociological Theory," *Social Problems,* 8:98–102, 1960.

LINDSEY, ALMONT: *Socialized Medicine in England and Wales,* The University of North Carolina Press, Chapel Hill, N.C., 1962.

LINDZEY, GARDNER (ED.): *Handbook of Social Psychology,* Addison-Wesley Publishing Company, Inc., Cambridge, Mass., 1954, vol. I.

LINTON, RALPH: *The Study of Man,* Appleton-Century-Crofts, Inc., New York, 1936.

Literary Digest, Oct. 11, 1919, p. 16, "Omaha."

LITNER, JOHN: "The Financing of Corporations," in Edward S. Mason (ed.), *The Corporation in Modern Society,* Harvard University Press, Cambridge, Mass., 1959, chap. 9.

LOHMAN, JOSEPH D.: *The Police and Minority Gorups,* Chicago Park District, Chicago, 1947.

LOHMAN, JOSEPH D., AND DELBERT C. REITZES: "Note on Race Relations in Mass Society," *American Journal of Sociology,* 58:240–246, 1952.

LOMBROSO, CESARE: *Crime, Its Causes and Remedies,* tr. by H. P. Horton, Little, Brown and Company, Boston, 1912.

LORTIE, DAN C.: "Anesthesia: From Nurse's Work to Medical Specialty," in E. Gartly Jaco, *Patients, Physicians and Illness,* The Free Press of Glencoe, New York, 1958, pp. 405–412.

LOUGH, ORPHA M.: "Women Students in Liberal Arts, Nursing, and Teacher Training Curricula and the MMPD," *Journal of Applied Psychology,* 31:437–445, 1947.

LOWIE, ROBERT H.: *Introduction to Cultural Anthropology,* Holt, Rinehart and Winston, Inc., New York, 1940.

LUMLEY, FREDERICK E.: *Means of Social Control,* Appleton-Century-Crofts, Inc., New York, 1925.

LYNCH, FRANK: *Social Class in a Bicol Town,* Philippines Studies Program, University of Chicago, Chicago, 1959.

LYND, ROBERT S., AND HELEN M. LYND: *Middletown,* Harcourt, Brace & World, Inc., New York, 1929.

LYND, ROBERT S., AND HELEN M. LYND: *Middletown in Transition,* Harcourt, Brace & World, Inc., New York, 1937.

MAC ANDREW, CRAIG, AND JO ELEANOR ELLIOTT: "Varying Images of the Professional Nurse: A Case Study," *Nursing Research,* 8:33–35, 1959.

MC ARTHUR, CHARLES: "Personality Differences between Upper-class Harvard Freshmen (private school graduates) and Middle-class Harvard Freshmen (public school graduates)," *Journal of Abnormal and Social Psychology,* 50:247–254, 1955.

MC GINTY, ALICE B.: "India: A House Divided," *Current History,* 13:288–289, 1947.

MACGREGOR, FRANCES COOKE: "Social Sciences and Nursing Education," *American Journal of Nursing,* 57:899–902, 1957.

MACKAY, CHARLES: *Extraordinary Popular Delusions and the Madness of Crowds,* L. C. Page & Company, Boston, 1932.

MC KENZIE, R. D.: "The Ecological Approach to the Study of the Human Community," in Robert E. Park, E. W. Burgess, and R. D. McKenzie (eds.), *The City,* The University of

Chicago Press, Chicago, 1925, pp. 63–79.

MC KIM, MARRIOTT (ED.): *Village India*, The University of Chicago Press, Chicago, 1955.

MC MAHON, FRANCIS E.: "Protestant Disability in Spain," *Commonweal*, 52:177–178, 1950.

MAHER, ROBERT F.: *The New Men of Papua: A Study in Cultural Change*, The University of Wisconsin Press, Madison, Wis., 1961.

MALMBERG, CARL: *140 Million Patients*, Reynal and Company, New York, 1947.

MANGUS, A. R.: "Personality Adjustment of Rural and Urban Children," *American Sociological Review*, 13:566–575, 1948.

MANIS, JEROME G., AND BERNARD N. MELTZER: "Attitude of Textile Workers to Class Structure," *American Journal of Sociology*, 60:30–35, 1954.

MARSHALL, S. L. A.: *Men under Fire*, William Morrow and Company, Inc., New York, 1947.

MAUKSCH, HANS O.: "Becoming a Nurse: A Selective View," *Annals of the American Academy of Political and Social Science*, 346:88–98, 1963.

MAYER, ALBERT J., AND PHILIP HAUSER: "Class Differentials in Expectation of Life at Birth," *La Révue de l'Institute de Statistique*, 18:197–200, 1950; reprinted in Reinhard Bendix and Seymour M. Lipset (eds.), *Class, Status, and Power*, The Free Press of Glencoe, New York, 1953, pp. 281–285.

MAYER, ALBERT J., AND SUE MARX: "Social Change, Religion and the Birth Rate," *American Journal of Sociology*, 62:383–390, 1957.

MAYER, ALBERT J., ET AL.: *Pilot Project: India*, University of California Press, Berkeley, Calif., 1958.

MEAD, GEORGE HERBERT: *Mind, Self and Society*, The University of Chicago Press, Chicago, 1934.

MEAD, MARGARET: "Administrative Contributions to Democratic Character Formation at the Adolescent Level," *Journal of the National Association of Deans of Women*, 4:51–57, January, 1941.

MEAD, MARGARET: "The Implications of Culture Change for Personality Development," *American Journal of Orthopsychiatry*, 17:633–646, 1947.

MEAD, MARGARET: *Cultural Patterns and Technical Change*, UNESCO, Mentor Books, New American Library of World Literature, Inc., New York, 1955.

MEAD, MARGARET: *New Lives for Old*, William Morrow and Company, Inc., New York, 1956.

MEEKER, MARCIA: "Status Aspirations and the Social Club," in W. Lloyd Warner (ed.), *Democracy in Jonesville*, Harper & Row, Publishers, Incorporated, New York, 1949, pp. 130–148.

MENZIES, ISABEL E. P.: "A Case-study in the Functioning of Social Systems as a Defense against Anxiety," *Human Relations*, 13:95–121, 1960.

MERTON, ROBERT K.: "Social Structure and Anomie," *American Sociological Review*, 3:672–682, 1938.

MERTON, ROBERT K.: "Manifest and Latent Functions: Toward a Codification of Functional Analysis in Sociology," in *Social Theory and Social Structure*, The Free Press of Glencoe, New York, 1957, pp. 19–84.

MILLER, ARTHUR S.: "Some Observations on the Political Economy of Population Growth," *Law and Con-*

temporary Problems, 25:614–632, 1960.

MILLER, DANIEL C., GUY E. SWANSON, ET AL.: *Inner Conflict and Defense,* Holt, Rinehart and Winston, Inc., New York, 1960.

MILLER, S. M., AND ELLIOT G. MISHLER: "Social Class, Mental Illness, and American Psychiatry," *Milbank Memorial Fund Quarterly,* 37:174–199, 1959.

MILLER, S. M., AND FRANK RIESSMAN: "The Working Class Subculture: A New View," *Social Problems,* 9:86–97, Summer, 1961.

MINTZ, ALEXANDER: "Non-adaptive Group Behavior," *Journal of Abnormal and Social Psychology,* 46:150–158, 1951.

MONROE, KEITH: "The New Gambling King and the Social Scientists," *Harper's Magazine,* January, 1962, pp. 35–41.

MONTAGUE, ASHLEY: *Man: His First Million Years,* Mentor Books, New American Library of World Literature, Inc., New York, 1958.

MOORE, W. E.: *Industrial Relations and the Social Order,* The Macmillan Company, New York, 1947.

MORENO, J. L.: "Psychodramatic Treatment of Marriage Problems," *Sociometry,* 3:2–23, 1940.

MORGAN, THEODORE: "The Economic Development of Ceylon," *Annals of the American Academy of Political and Social Science,* 305:92–100, 1956.

MURDOCK, GEORGE P.: *Our Primitive Contemporaries,* The Macmillan Company, New York, 1936.

MURDOCK, GEORGE P.: *Social Structure,* The Macmillan Company, New York, 1949.

MURDOCK, GEORGE P.: "Sexual Behavior: A Comparative Anthropo-logical Approach," *Journal of Social Hygiene,* 36:133–138, 1950.

MURPHY, GARDNER, LOIS MURPHY, AND THEODORE M. NEWCOMB: *Experimental Social Psychology,* Harper & Row, Publishers, Incorporated New York, 1937.

MYERSON, ABRAHAM: *Social Psychology,* Prentice-Hall, Inc., Englewood Cliffs, N.J., 1934.

MYRDAL, GUNNAR: *An American Dilemma,* Harper & Row, Publishers, Incorporated, New York, 1944.

MYRDAL, GUNNAR: *Rich Lands and Poor,* Harper & Row, Publishers, Incorporated, New York, 1957.

NATIONAL EDUCATION ASSOCIATION: *Status and Trends of Education,* Washington, August, 1959.

NELSON, EDWARD W.: "The Eskimo about Bering Straits," *18th Annual Report, Bureau of American Ethnology,* Washington, 1899, part 1, pp. 268–270.

NEWCOMB, DOROTHY PERKINS: *The Team Plan,* G. P. Putnam's Sons, New York, 1953.

NEW YORK ACADEMY OF MEDICINE: *Medicine in the Changing Order,* The Commonwealth Fund and Harvard University Press, New York, 1947.

NICHOLS, LEE: *Breakthrough on the Color Front,* Random House, Inc., New York, 1954.

NIMKOFF, MEYER F., AND RUSSELL MIDDLETON: "Types of Family and Types of Economy," *American Journal of Sociology,* 66:215–225, 1960.

NORTHCOTT, WILLIAM C.: "Christianity's Lost Continent," *Spectator,* 202:217, 1959.

O'CONNOR, PATRICIA: "Intolerance of Ambiguity and Abstract Reasoning

Ability," *Journal of Abnormal and Social Psychology*, 47:526–530, 1952.

ODUM, HOWARD W.: *Understanding Society*, The Macmillan Company, New York, 1947.

OGBURN, WILLIAM F.: *Social Change*, The Viking Press, Inc., New York, 1922.

OGBURN, WILLIAM F.: "The Influence of Invention and Discovery," in President's Research Committee on Social Trends, *Recent Social Trends*, McGraw-Hill Book Company, New York, 1933, pp. 122–166.

OGBURN, WILLIAM F.: "The Wolf Boy of Agra," *American Journal of Sociology*, 64:449–454, March, 1959.

O'NEILL, MICHAEL J.: "Siege Tactics of the AMA, *Reporter*, 26:29–32, Apr. 26, 1962.

ORGANSKI, KATHERINE, AND A. F. K. ORGANSKI: *Population and World Power*, Alfred A. Knopf, Inc., New York, 1962.

OTTENBERG, SIMON: "Ileo Receptivity to Change," in William R. Bascom and Melville J. Herskovitz (eds.), *Continuity and Change in African Cultures*, The University of Chicago Press, Chicago, 1959, pp. 130–143.

PARK, ROBERT E., AND ERNEST BURGESS: *Introduction to the Science of Sociology*, The University of Chicago Press, Chicago, 1921.

PARK, ROBERT E., E. W. BURGESS, AND R. D. MC KENZIE: *The City*, The University of Chicago Press, Chicago, 1925.

PARSONS, TALCOTT: "Certain Primary Sources and Patterns of Aggression in the Social Structures of the Western World," *Psychiatry*, 10:167–181, 1947.

PARSONS, TALCOTT: *Essays in Socio-logical Theory*, The Free Press of Glencoe, New York, 1954.

PARTEN, MILDRED: *Surveys, Polls, and Samples: Practical Procedures*, Harper & Row, Publishers, Incorporated, New York, 1950.

PASLEY, VIRGINIA: *21 Stayed*, Farrar, Straus & Co., New York, 1955.

PEARLIN, LEONARD I.: "Sources of Resistance to Change in a Mental Hospital," *American Journal of Sociology*, 68:325–334, 1962.

PEARLIN, LEONARD I., AND MORRIS ROSENBERG: "Nurse-Patient Social Distance and the Structural Context of a Mental Hospital," *American Sociological Review*, 27:56–65, 1962.

PEARSON, KARL: *The Grammar of Science*, A. & C. Black, Ltd., London, 1900.

PODALSKY, EDWARD: "The Sociopathic Alcoholic," *Quarterly Journal of Studies on Alcohol*, 21:292–297, June, 1960.

PRESIDENT'S COMMISSION ON THE HEALTH NEEDS OF THE NATION: *Building America's Health*, Government Printing Office, Washington, D.C., 1953.

PROTHRO, E. TERRY: "Ethnocentrism and Anti-Negro Attitudes in the Deep South," *Journal of Abnormal and Social Psychology*, 47:104–108, January, 1952.

Public Health Reports, 79:539, 1957.

PYLE, ERNIE: *Brave Men*, Holt, Rinehart and Winston, Inc., New York, 1943.

QUEEN, STUART A., ROBERT W. HABERSTEIN, AND JOHN B. ADAMS: *The Family in Various Cultures*, J. B. Lippincott Company, Philadelphia, 1961.

RAO, P. KODANDRA: *Bi-lingualism for India*, W. O. Judge, Bengal, India, 1956.

RAPER, ARTHUR F.: *The Tragedy of Lynching*, The University of North Carolina Press, Chapel Hill, N.C., 1933.

REISS, IRA L.: *Pre-marital Sexual Standards in America*, The Free Press of Glencoe, New York, 1960.

REITZES, DELBERT C.: *Negroes and Medicine*, Harvard University Press, Cambridge, Mass., 1958.

REUSCH, JURGEN: "Social Technique, Social Status, and Social Change in Illness," in Clyde Kluckhohn and Henry A. Murray, with D. M. Schiender (eds.), *Personality in Nature, Society, and Culture*, 2d ed., Alfred A. Knopf, Inc., New York, 1953, pp. 123–136.

RIBBLE, MARGARET A.: *The Rights of Infants*, Columbia University Press, New York, 1943.

RIEMER, SVEND: "Social Planning and Social Organization," *American Journal of Sociology*, 52:508–516, 1947.

RIEMER, SVEND: "Urban Personality— Reconsidered," in Marvin B. Sussman (ed.), *Community Structure and Analysis*, Thomas Y. Crowell Company, New York, 1959, pp. 433–444.

RIESMAN, DAVID, WITH NATHAN GLAZER AND REUEL DENNEY: *The Lonely Crowd: A Study in the Changing American Character*, Yale University Press, New Haven, Conn., 1950.

RIESS, ALBERT J., JR.: "Rural-Urban Status Differences in Interpersonal Contacts," *American Journal of Sociology*, 65:182–195, 1959.

RIESSMAN, LEONARD, AND JOHN H. ROHRER: *Change and Dilemma in the Nursing Profession*, G. P. Putnam's Sons, New York, 1957.

RIVERS, W. H. R. (ED.): *Essays on the Depopulation of Melanesia*, Cambridge University Press, London, 1922.

RIVERS, W. H. R.: "On the Disappearance of Useful Arts," in *Festskrift Tillägnad Edward Westermarck*, Helsingfors, 1912, pp. 109–130; summarized in A. L. Kroeber, *Anthropology*, Harcourt, Brace & World, Inc., New York, 1949, p. 375.

ROBINSON, H. A., F. C. REDLICH, AND J. K. MYERS: "Social Structure and Psychiatric Treatment," *American Journal of Orthopsychiatry*, 24:307–316, 1954.

ROBINSON, KENNETH: "The Case for Britain's Health Service," *New York Times Magazine*, Nov. 18, 1962, pp. 42ff.

ROETHLISBERGER, F. J., AND WILLIAM J. DICKSON: *Management and the Worker*, Harvard University Press, Cambridge, Mass., 1939.

ROGOFF, NATALIE: *Recent Trends in Occupational Mobility*, The Free Press of Glencoe, New York, 1953.

ROSE, ARNOLD: *Union Solidarity: The Internal Cohesion of a Union*, The University of Minnesota Press, Minneapolis, 1952.

ROSE, ARNOLD: *Theory and Method in the Social Sciences*, The University of Minnesota Press, Minneapolis, 1954.

ROSEN, BERNARD: "The Reference Group Approach to the Parental Factor in Attitude and Behavior Formation," *Social Forces*, 34:137–144, 1955(*a*).

ROSEN, BERNARD: "Conflicting Group Membership: A Study of Parent– Peer Group Cross-pressure," *American Sociological Review*, 20:155–161, 1955(*b*).

ROSEN, BERNARD: "The Achievement Syndrome: A Psychocultural Dimension of Social Stratification,"

American Sociological Review, 21:203–211, 1956.

ROY, DONALD: "Efficiency and 'The Fix'; Informal Intergroup Relations in a Piecework Machine Shop," *American Journal of Sociology*, 60:225–266, 1955.

RUSSELL, CHARLES H.: "Nursing Education Today . . . on a Liberal Background," *American Journal of Nursing*, 60:1485–1487, 1960.

RYAN, BRYCE F.: *Caste in Modern Ceylon*, Rutgers University Press, New Brunswick, N.J., 1953.

SAHLINS, MARSHALL D.: "Land Use and the Extended Family in Moala, Fiji," *American Anthropologist*, 59:449–462, 1957.

SALOUTOS, THEODORE: *They Remember America: The Story of the Repatriated Greek Americans*, University of California Press, Berkeley, Calif., 1956.

SANDOZ, MARI: *The Buffalo Hunters*, Hastings House, Publishers, Inc., New York, 1954.

SAUNDERS, LYLE: "The Changing Role of Nurses," *American Journal of Nursing*, 54:1094–1098, 1954(a).

SAUNDERS, LYLE: *Cultural Difference and Medical Care*, Russell Sage Foundation, New York, 1954(b).

SCHACHTER, STANLEY: "Deviation, Rejection, and Communication," *Journal of Abnormal and Social Psychology*, 46:190–207, 1951.

SCHEIN, EDGAR H.: "Interpersonal Communication, Group Solidarity and Social Influence," *Sociometry*, 23:148–161, 1960.

SCHINDLER, JOHN A.: *How to Live 365 Days a Year*, Prentice-Hall, Inc., Englewood Cliffs, N.J., 1954.

SCHNEIDER, HAROLD K.: "Pakot Resistance to Change," in William R. Bascom and Melville J. Herskovitz (eds.), *Continuity and Change in African Cultures*, The University of Chicago Press, Chicago, 1959, pp. 144–167.

SCHNEIDER, LOUIS, AND SVERRE LYSGAARD: "The Deferred Gratification Pattern: A Preliminary Study," *American Sociological Review*, 18:142–194, 1953.

SCHULER, EDGAR A., AND V. J. PARENTON: "A Recent Epidemic of Hysteria in a Louisiana High School," *Journal of Social Psychology*, 17:221–235, 1943.

SCHUR, EDWIN M.: *Narcotic Addiction in Britain and America: The Impact of Public Policy*, Indiana University Press, Bloomington, Ind., 1962.

SCOTT, J. C., JR.: "Membership and Participation in Voluntary Associations," *American Sociological Review*, 22:315–326, 1957.

SEARS, ROBERT R., ELEANOR E. MACOBY, AND HARRY LEVIN: *Patterns of Child Rearing*, Harper & Row, Publishers, Incorporated, New York, 1957.

SELLTIZ, CLAIRE, MARIE JAHODA, MORTON DEUTSCH, AND STUART A. COOK: *Research Methods in Social Relations*, Holt, Rinehart and Winston, Inc., New York, 1959.

SELYE, HANS: *The Stress of Life*, McGraw-Hill, New York, 1956.

SEWELL, WILLIAM H.: "Infant Training and the Personality of the Child," *American Journal of Sociology*, 58:150–159, 1952.

SHARP, LAURISTON: "Steel Axes for Stone Age Australians," in Edward H. Spicer (ed.), *Human Problems in Technological Change*, Russell Sage Foundation, New York, 1952, pp. 69–90.

SHAW, CLIFFORD R., AND M. E. MOORE: *The Natural History of a Delinquent Career*, The University of Chicago Press, Chicago, 1931.

SHAW, CLIFFORD R., H. D. MC KAY, AND G. F. MC DONALD: *Brothers in Crime*, The University of Chicago Press, Chicago, 1938.

SHELDON, WILLIAM H.: *Varieties of Delinquent Youth*, Harper & Row, Publishers, Incorporated, New York, 1949.

SHELDON, WILLIAM H., AND S. S. STEVENS: *The Varieties of Temperament*, Harper & Row, Publishers, Incorporated, New York, 1942.

SHERIF, MUZAFER A.: "A Study of Some Social Factors in Perception," *Archives of Psychology*, No. 187, 1935.

SHERIF, MUZAFER: "Superordinate Goals in the Reduction of Intergroup Conflict," *American Journal of Sociology*, 63:349–356, 1958.

SHERIF, MUZAFER, AND CAROLYN SHERIF: *Groups in Harmony and Tension*, Harper & Row, Publishers, Incorporated, New York, 1953.

SHERMAN, MANDELL, AND THOMAS R. HENRY: *Hollow Folk*, Thomas Y. Crowell Company, New York, 1933.

SHILS, EDWARD A.: "Primary Groups in the American Army," in Robert K. Merton and Paul Lazarsfeld (eds.), *Continuities in Social Research: Studies in the Scope and Method of the American Soldier*, The Free Press of Glencoe, New York, 1950.

SHILS, EDWARD A., AND MORRIS JANOWITZ: "Cohesion and Disintegration in the Wehrmacht in World War II," *Public Opinion Quarterly*, 12:280–315, 1948.

SHUEY, AUDREY M.: *The Testing of Negro Intelligence*, J. P. Bell Company, Lynchburg, Va., 1958.

SHUVAL, JUDITH L.: "Class and Ethnic Correlates of Casual Neighboring," *American Sociological Review*, 21:453–458, 1956.

SHUVAL, JUDITH L.: "Perceived Role Components of Nursing in Israel," *American Sociological Review*, 28:37–46, 1963.

SILVERMAN, MILTON: "The High Cost of Chiseling," *Saturday Evening Post*, 230:36ff., June 14, 1958.

SIMMEL, GEORGE: *Conflict*, tr. by Reinhard Bendix, The Free Press of Glencoe, New York, 1955.

SINGH, J. A. L., AND ROBERT M. ZINGG: *Wolf-Children and Feral Men*, Harper & Row, Publishers, Incorporated, New York, 1942.

SJOBERG, GIDEON: "Are Social Classes in America Becoming More Rigid?" *American Sociological Review*, 16:775–783, 1951.

SMITH, HARVEY L.: *The Sociological Study of Hospitals*, unpublished Ph.D. dissertation, Department of Sociology, University of Chicago, 1949.

SMITH, HARVEY L.: "Psychiatry: A Social Institution in Process," *Social Forces*, 33:310–317, 1955.

SMITH, HARVEY L.: "Two Lines of Authority—Are One Too Many," *Modern Hospital*, 84(3):59–64, 1955; reprinted in E. Gartly Jaco, *Patients, Physicians and Illness*, The Free Press of Glencoe, New York, 1958, pp. 468–477.

SMUTZ, ROBERT W.: *Women and Work in America*, Columbia University Press, New York, 1959.

SOROKIN, PITIRIM: *Contemporary Sociological Theories*, Harper & Row, Publishers, Incorporated, New York, 1928.

SOROKIN, PITIRIM A., AND CARLE C. ZIMMERMAN: *Principles of Rural-Urban Sociology*, Holt, Rinehart and Winston, Inc., New York, 1929.

SPIRO, MELFORD E.: "Culture and Personality: The Natural History of a False Dichotomy," *Psychiatry*, 14:19–46, 1951.

SPITZ, RENÉ: "Hospitalism," in *The Psychoanalytic Study of the Child*, vol. 1, International Universities Press, Inc., New York, 1945, pp. 53–74.

SPOCK, BENJAMIN: *The Pocket Book of Child Care*, Pocket Books, Inc., New York, 1945, 1957.

STARKEY, MARION L.: *The Devil in Massachusetts*, Alfred A. Knopf, Inc., New York, 1949.

STEIN, MAURICE R.: *The Eclipse of Community*, Princeton University Press, Princeton, N.J., 1960.

STEINBECK, JOHN: *The Moon Is Down*, The Viking Press, Inc., New York, 1942.

STERN, BERNARD J.: *Society and Medical Progress*, Princeton University Press, Princeton, N.J., 1941.

STERN, BERNARD J.: "The Specialist and the General Practitioner," in *American Medical Practice in the Perspectives of a Century*, The Commonwealth Fund, 1945, New York, pp. 45–61.

STERN, BERNARD J.: "Resistance to the Adoption of Technological Inventions," in U.S. National Resources Committee, *Technological Trends and National Policy*, 1937, pp. 39–66.

STERN, BERNARD J.: "Socio-economic Aspects of Heart Disease," *Journal of Educational Sociology*, 24:450–462, April, 1951.

STEVENS, ALDEN: "Make Dope Legal," *Harper's Magazine*, 205:40–47, November, 1952.

STEWART, CHARLES T., JR.: "The Rural-Urban Dichotomy: Concepts and Uses," *American Journal of Sociology*, 64:152–158, 1958.

STOETZEL, JEAN: Cited in Alva Myrdal and Viola Klein, *Women's Two Roles: Home and Work*, Routledge & Kegan Paul, Ltd., London, 1956.

STOLZ, LOIS KEEK: "Effects of Maternal Employment upon Children: Evidence from Research," *Child Development*, 31:749–782, 1960.

STONE, CAROL: "Some Family Characteristics of Socially Active and Inactive Teenagers," *Family Life Coordinator*, 8:53–57, 1960.

STONEQUIST, EVERETT H.: *The Marginal Man*, Charles Scribner's Sons, New York, 1937.

STOUFFER, SAMUEL A., ET AL.: *Studies in the Social Psychology of World War II*, vol. 2, *The American Soldier: Combat and Aftermath*, Princeton University Press, Princeton, N.J., 1949.

STOUFFER, SAMUEL A.: *Communism, Conformity and Civil Liberties*, Doubleday & Company, Inc., Garden City, N.Y., 1955.

STRAUSS, ANSELM L.: "The Literature on Panic," *Journal of Abnormal and Social Psychology*, 39:317–328, 1944.

STRODTBECK, F. L., AND A. PAUL HARE: "Bibliography of Small Group Research," *Sociometry*, 17:107–178, May, 1954.

STUCKERT, ROBERT P.: "African Ancestry of the White American Population," *Ohio Journal of Science*, 58:155–160, 1958.

SUMNER, WILLIAM GRAHAM: *Folkways*, 1906; 3d ed., Ginn and Company, Boston, 1940.

SYME, LEONARD: "Personality Characteristics and Alcoholics: A Critique of Current Studies," *Quarterly Journal of Studies on Alcohol*, 18:288–302, 1957.

TANNENBAUM, JUDITH: "The Neighborhood: A Socio-psychological Analysis," *Journal of Land Economy*, 24:358–369, 1948.

TERMAN, LEWIS M.: *Psychological Factors in Marital Happiness*, McGraw-Hill Book Company, New York, 1938

THOMAS, W. I.: *The Unadjusted Girl*, Little, Brown, and Company, Boston, 1923.

THOMAS, W. I., AND FLORIAN ZNANIECKI: *The Polish Peasant in Europe and America*, Alfred A. Knopf, Inc., New York, 1927.

THOMPSON, WARREN S.: *Danger Spots in World Population*, Alfred A. Knopf, Inc., New York, 1929.

THORWALD, JURGEN: *Science and Secrets of Early Medicine*, tr. by Richard and Clara Winston, Harcourt, Brace & World, Inc., New York, 1963.

Time, Aug. 11, 1961, pp. 20–21, "What's Wrong?"

TUDDENHAM, READ D.: "The Influence of a Distorted Group Norm upon Judgments of Adults and Children," *Journal of Psychology*, 52:231–239, 1961.

TUMIN, MELVIN J.: "Some Unapplauded Consequences of Social Mobility," *Social Forces*, 36:21–37, 1957.

TURNER, RALPH H.: "Role-taking, Role Standpoint, and Reference Group Behavior," *American Journal of Sociology*, 61:316–338, 1956.

TURNER, RALPH H., AND SAMUEL J. SURACE: "Zoot-suiters and Mexicans: Symbols in Crowd Behavior," *American Journal of Sociology*, 62:14–20, 1956.

TYLOR, EDWARD: *Primitive Culture: Researches into the Development of Mythology, Philosophy, Religion, Language, Art and Custom*, vol. 1, John Murray (Publishers), Ltd., London, 1871.

UNITED NATIONS: *The Future Growth of World Population*, New York, 1958.

UNNI, K. P.: "Polyandry in Malabar," *Sociological Bulletin* (India), 7:62–79, 1958.

USEEM, JOHN: "South Sea Island Strike: Labor-Management Relations in the Carolina Islands, Micronesia, in Edward H. Spicer (ed.), *Human Problems in Technological Change*, Russell Sage Foundation, New York, 1952, pp. 149–164.

VAN DER KROEF, JUSTUS M.: "The Changing Class Structure in Indonesia," *American Sociological Review*, 21:138–148, 1956.

VAUGHN, JAMES: "An Experimental Study of Competition," *Journal of Applied Psychology*, 20:1–15, 1936.

VELLA, CHARLES G.: "Italian Catholicism," *Catholic World*, 179:367–372, 1954.

VERNON, RAYMOND: *Metropolis 1985: An Interpretation of the Findings of the New York Metropolitan Study*, Harvard University Press, Cambridge, Mass., 1960.

VON FELSINGER, JOHN M., LOUIS LASAGNA, AND HENRY K. BEECHER: "Drug-induced Mood Changes in Man: Personality and Reactions to Drugs," *Journal of the American Medical Association*, 157:1113–1119, 1955.

VON HENTIG, HANS: "Redhead and Outlaws," *Journal of Criminal Law and Criminology*, 38:1–6, May–June, 1947.

WADA, GEORGE, AND JAMES C. DAVIES: "Riots and Rioters," *Western Political Quarterly*, 10:864–874, 1957.

WAKEFIELD, DAN: "The Careful Conversion of the Nouveau Riche," *Esquire*, November, 1961, pp. 105ff.

WALLACE, A. F. C.: "The Modal Personality Structure of the Tuscarora Indians as Revealed by the Rorschach Test," *Bureau of American Ethnology*, Bulletin no. 150, 1952(*a*).

WALLACE, A. F. C.: "Individual Differences and Cultural Uniformities," *American Sociological Review*, 17:747–750, 1952(*b*).

WALLING, WILLIAM E.: "The Race War in the North," *Independent*, 65: 529–531, 1908. Quoted in Ralph H. Turner and Lewis M. Killian, *Collective Behavior*, Prentice-Hall, Inc., Englewood Cliffs, N.J., 1957, pp. 155–157.

WARNER, W. L.: "Murngin Warfare," *Oceania*, 1:457–494, 1931.

WARNER, W. LLOYD, AND PAUL S. LUNT: *The Social Life of a Modern Community*, Yale University Press, New Haven, Conn., 1941.

WARNER, W. LLOYD, AND PAUL S. LUNT: *The Status System of a Modern Community*, Yale University Press, New Haven, Conn., 1942.

WARNER, W. LLOYD, AND JAMES C. ABEGGLEN: *Big Business Leaders in America*, Harper & Row, Publishers, Incorporated, New York, 1955.

WARRINER, CHARLES K.: "the Nature and Functions of Official Morality," *American Journal of Sociology*, 54:165–168, 1958.

WEINBERG, S. KIRSON: *Society and Personality Disorder*, Prentice-Hall, Inc., Englewood Cliffs, N.J., 1952.

WELLMAN, PAUL L.: *The Trampling Herd*, Carrick and Evans, New York, 1939.

WEST, JAMES: *Plainville, U.S.A.*, Columbia University Press, New York, 1945.

WESTIE, FRANK R.: "Social Distance Scales: A Tool for the Study of Stratification," *Sociology and Social Research*, 43:251–258, 1959.

WHELPTON, PASCAL K., AND CLYDE V. KISER: "Social and Psychological Factors Affecting Fertility," *Milbank Memorial Fund Quarterly*, 21:221–280, 1943.

WHYTE, WILLIAM H., JR.: "The Wives of Management," and "The Corporation and the Wife," *Fortune*, October, 1951, pp. 86–88ff.; and November, 1951, pp. 109–111ff.

WHYTE, WILLIAM H., JR.: "Urban Sprawl," in EDITORS OF *Fortune*, *The Exploding Metropolis*, Doubleday & Company, Inc., Garden City, N.Y., 1958, pp. 115–139.

WILDER, RUSSELL M.: "Experimental Induction of Psychoneuroses through Restriction of Intake of Thiamine," in Milbank Memorial Fund, *Biology of Mental Health and Disease*, Harper & Row, Publishers, Incorporated, New York, 1952, pp. 531–538.

WILLIAMS, ROGER J.: *Biochemical Individuality*, John Wiley & Sons, Inc., New York, 1956.

WILSON, BRYAN: "The Pentacostalist Minister: Role Conflicts and Status Contradictions," *American Journal of Sociology*, 54:503–504, 1959.

WILSON, GALE E.: "Christian Science and Longevity," *Journal of Forensic Medicine*, 1:43–60, 1956.

WILSON, ROBERT N.: "Teamwork in the Operating Room," *Human Organization*, 12:9–14, Winter, 1954.

WILSON, ROBERT N.: "The Social Structure of a General Hospital," *Annals of the American Academy of Political and Social Science*, 346:67–76, 1963.

WINSLOW, CHARLES N.: "The Social Behavior of Cats," *Journal of Comparative Psychology*, 37:297–326, 1944.

WIRTH, LOUIS: *The Ghetto,* The University of Chicago Press, Chicago, 1928.

WISSLER, CLARK: "Depression and Revolt," *Natural History,* 41:108–112, 1938.

WOLF, ELEANOR P.: "The Invasion-Succession Sequence as a Self-fulfilling Prophesy," *Journal of Social Issues,* 13:7–20, 1957.

WOLFE, DONALD M.: "Power and Authority in the Family," in Dorwin Cartwright (ed.), *Studies in Social Power,* Institute for Social Research, University of Michigan, Ann Arbor, Mich., 1959.

WOMEN'S BUREAU: *Who Are the Working Mothers?* U.S. Department of Labor, Leaflet no. 37, 1961.

WORSLEY, PETER: *The Trumpet Shall Sound: A Study of "Cargo" Cults in Melanesia,* MacGibbon & Kee, London, 1957.

WRIGHT, CHARLES R., AND HERBERT H. HYMAN: "Voluntary Association Memberships," *American Sociological Review,* 23:284–294, 1958.

YANG, C. K.: *The Chinese Family in the Communist Revolution,* The Technology Press of the Massachusetts Institute of Technology, Cambridge, Mass., 1959.

YERACARIS, CONSTANTINE A.: "Social Factors Associated with the Acceptance of Medical Innovations: A Pilot Study," *Journal of Health and Human Behavior,* 3:193–198, 1962.

YOUNG, LEONTINE: *Out of Wedlock,* McGraw-Hill Book Company, New York, 1954.

ZILBOORG, GREGORY: *Mind, Medicine, and Man,* Harcourt, Brace & World, Inc., New York, 1943.

ZORBAUGH, HARVEY: *The Gold Coast and the Slum,* The University of Chicago Press, Chicago, 1929.

Name Index

Subject Index